VOLUME 1

VINYL POLYMERIZATION

PART I

KINETICS AND MECHANISMS OF POLYMERIZATION

(*In Three Volumes*)

Volume 1: Vinyl Polymerization (In Two Parts)

Volume 2: Ring-Opening Polymerization

Volume 3: Condensation Polymerization

VOLUME 1

VINYL POLYMERIZATION

PART I

EDITED BY

George E. Ham

GEIGY RESEARCH
GEIGY CHEMICAL CORPORATION
ARDSLEY, NEW YORK

1967

MARCEL DEKKER, INC., New York

MARCEL DEKKER, INC.
95 Madison Avenue, New York, New York 10016

LIBRARY OF CONGRESS CATALOG CARD NUMBER 66-29483

PRINTED IN THE UNITED STATES OF AMERICA

Introduction to the Series

An explanation is perhaps in order for the apparent emphasis on kinetic studies which suffuses polymer science. The novice will benefit and the veteran, though he may rush to say none is necessary, will, I believe, profit from a re-examination of motivations.

First, and the fact must be faced, kinetic studies, with their interrelations and insights into mechanistic effects, have many of the aesthetic aspects of a "pure" science. Some of the most able work in the field has been motivated by a selfless dedication which is almost clerical in nature.

Second, in spite of the ascendancy of the empiricist and the statistician, the fundamental insight provided by these studies affords an essential basis for any sound commercial venture in polymers. There are numerous examples of polymer developments which have foundered or been needlessly delayed or impeded by the failure to conduct adequate kinetic studies.

Third, there is perhaps no other area which offers so many directly pertinent instructional possibilities to the budding polymer researcher. Many of the most able polymer scientists, whose present activities embrace the whole of polymer studies, conducted their first research on polymer kinetics.

Thus, we come to it—a field which is all things to all scientists. It is like the universe—the more we explore, the more we find unexplored.

George E. Ham

Contributors to Volume 1, Part I

John M. Barton, *Polymer Branch, Nonmetallic Materials Division, Air Force Materials Laboratory, Wright–Patterson Air Force Base, Ohio*

Maurice H. George, *Department of Chemistry, University of Queensland, Brisbane, Queensland, Australia*

William E. Gibbs, *Polymer Branch, Nonmetallic Materials Division, Air Force Materials Laboratory, Wright–Patterson Air Force Base, Ohio*

George E. Ham, *Geigy Research, Geigy Chemical Corporation, Ardsley, New York*

A. D. Jenkins, *The Chemical Laboratory, University of Sussex, Sussex, England*

R. M. Joshi, *Thermodynamics Research Center, Department of Chemistry, Texas A & M University, College Station, Texas*

Martin K. Lindemann, *Mobil Chemical Company, Metuchen, New Jersey*

Evaristo Peggion, *Centro di Chimica Macromolecolare del C.N.R., Istituto di Chimica organica, Università di Padova, Padova, Italy*

Rolf C. Schulz, *Institute of Organic Chemistry, Universität Mainz, Mainz, West Germany*

Gianpietro Talamini, *Società Edison, Azienda chimica and Istituto di Chimica fisica, Università di Padova, Padova, Italy*

B. J. Zwolinski, *Thermodynamics Research Center, Department of Chemistry, Texas A & M University, College Station, Texas*

Contributors to Volume1, Part II

W. Frank Fowler, Jr., *Research Laboratories, Eastman Kodak Company, Rochester, New York*

Arthur F. Helin, *Gulf Research and Development Company, Merriam, Kansas*

Gerald J. Mantell, *Gulf Research and Development Company, Merriam, Kansas*

Maurice Morton, *Institute of Rubber Research, University of Akron, Akron, Ohio*

Wayne E. Smith, *Gulf Research and Development Company, Merriam, Kansas*

Harry K. Stryker, *Gulf Research and Development Company, Merriam, Kansas*

Yoneho Tabata, *Department of Nuclear Engineering, Faculty of Engineering, University of Tokyo, Tokyo, Japan*

John W. Vanderhoff, *Plastics Department, Research Laboratory, Dow Chemical Company, Midland, Michigan*

Z. Zlámal, *Research Institute of Macromolecular Chemistry, Brno, Czechoslovakia*

Contents

CHAPTER 1

General Aspects
of Free-Radical Polymerization

George E. Ham

Geigy Chemical Corp., Ardsley, New York

1-1. FACTORS INFLUENCING REACTIVITY OF
RADICALS AND MONOMERS

A thorough understanding of the polymerization of vinyl monomers by radical mechanisms must rest upon an intimate acquaintance with the nature of free radicals. For the purposes of our discussion a free radical is defined as an organic fragment possessing an odd or unshared electron. Thus, an ethyl radical may be represented as

$$
\begin{array}{c}
\text{H}\quad\text{H} \\
\text{H}:\text{C}:\text{C}\cdot \\
\text{H}\quad\text{H}
\end{array}
\tag{1-1}
$$

Whereas the usual bond angles of 109° 22′ prevail about the first carbon, the second carbon, containing the unpaired electron, has all its substituents in a coplanar configuration. Such radicals are highly reactive with most organic molecules. In the absence of substrates the radicals destroy themselves by disproportionation to ethane and ethylene or, to a minor extent, by combination to butane.

Until 1900 the elusive nature of radicals prevented their detection by chemists. Gomberg (1) at that time, however, discovered that treatment of solutions of triphenylmethyl chloride with zinc dust yielded a substance that reacted readily with air, iodine, and various compounds. He could only conclude that he had synthesized the "radical" $\phi_3\text{C}\cdot$. Gomberg found that the radical existed in equilibrium with hexaphenylethane:

$$\phi_3\text{C}:\text{C}\phi_3 \rightleftharpoons 2\phi_3\text{C}\cdot$$

Subsequently derivatives, particularly the nitro type, were produced, which exist almost entirely in the radical form.

Such resonance-stabilized radicals are poor initiators of polymerization of vinyl monomers. Conversely, unstabilized radicals, such as ethyl radicals, are very effective initiators. However, the resonance-stabilized radicals, including, for instance, diphenylpicrylhydrazyl, are effective scavengers of radicals and have been used for counting radicals produced in polymerization by noting the disappearance of characteristic colors owing to, for instance, the dislocated nature of the unpaired electron (2).

1-2. NATURE OF FREE-RADICAL POLYMERIZATION

We are now prepared to consider the nature of free-radical polymerization. It is appropriate to consider the reaction in three stages: initiation, propagation, and termination. Although self-initiation of some monomers, such as styrene and methyl methacrylate, appears to be possible, the addition of free-radical-producing catalysts, such as benzoyl peroxide and azodiisobutyronitrile, is far more practical and conducive to reproducible results. In the latter case initiation of polymerization is preceded by the following reaction:

$$
\begin{array}{c}
\quad\text{CH}_3\qquad\quad\text{CH}_3\qquad\qquad\quad\text{CH}_3 \\
\quad| \qquad\qquad | \qquad\qquad\qquad | \\
\text{CH}_3\text{C}-\text{N}=\text{N}-\text{C}-\text{CH}_3 \longrightarrow 2\text{CH}_3-\text{C}\cdot + \text{N}_2 \\
\quad| \qquad\qquad | \qquad\qquad\qquad | \\
\quad\text{CN}\qquad\qquad\text{CN}\qquad\qquad\qquad\text{CN}
\end{array}
\tag{1-2}
$$

The reactive dimethylcyanocarbinyl radical readily adds a large variety of monomers (including easily oxidized types, such as dimethylaminoethyl methacrylate, which react with benzoyl peroxide to yield amine oxides):

$$\underset{\underset{CN}{|}}{\overset{\overset{CH_3}{|}}{CH_3C}}\cdot + CH_2 = \overset{\overset{R}{|}}{CH} \longrightarrow \underset{\underset{CN}{|}}{\overset{\overset{CH_3}{|}}{CH_3C}}-CH_2-\overset{\overset{R}{|}}{CH}\cdot \quad \text{(initiation)} \qquad (1\text{-}3)$$

It is seen that the free radical has been merely transferred to the new chain ending with a net gain in resonance stabilization in the creation of a radical from the monomer. Once this process has been accomplished, a condition prevails that is capable of virtually unlimited repetition. Of course, the availability of monomer being limited, chain termination will eventually occur. In the meantime we are dealing with the propagation step that gives polymers their special character:

$$CH_3-\underset{\underset{CN}{|}}{\overset{\overset{CH_3}{|}}{C}}-CH_2\overset{\overset{R}{|}}{CH}\cdot + CH_2 = \overset{\overset{R}{|}}{CH} \longrightarrow CH_3-\underset{\underset{CN}{|}}{\overset{\overset{CH_3}{|}}{C}}-CH_2-\overset{\overset{R}{|}}{CH}-CH_2-\overset{\overset{R}{|}}{CH}\cdot \quad \text{(propagation)}$$

$$\text{...etc.} \qquad (1\text{-}4)$$

Indeed, from a strictly practical standpoint more valuable information can be obtained from an exhaustive study of the propagation step in polymerization and copolymerization than from one of initiation and "pure" termination.

The next step of interest kinetically is the "pure" termination step. The polymer radicals formed in reaction (1–4) may be terminated by coupling or disproportionation:

$$2CH_3\underset{\underset{CN}{|}}{\overset{\overset{CH_3}{|}}{C}}-CH_2-\overset{\overset{R}{|}}{CH}-CH_2\overset{\overset{R}{|}}{CH}\cdot$$

$$\longrightarrow CH_3\underset{\underset{CN}{|}}{\overset{\overset{CH_3}{|}}{C}}-CH_2-\overset{\overset{R}{|}}{CH}-CH_2\overset{\overset{R}{|}}{CH}-\overset{\overset{R}{|}}{CH}-CH_2-\overset{\overset{R}{|}}{CH}-CH_2-\underset{\underset{CN}{|}}{\overset{\overset{CH_3}{|}}{C}}-CH_3$$

$$(1\text{-}5)$$

$$\longrightarrow CH_3\underset{\underset{CN}{|}}{\overset{\overset{CH_3}{|}}{C}}-CH_2-\overset{\overset{R}{|}}{CH}-CH = \overset{\overset{R}{|}}{CH} \quad \overset{\overset{R}{|}}{CH_2}-CH_2-\overset{\overset{R}{|}}{CH}-CH_2\underset{\underset{CN}{|}}{\overset{\overset{CH_3}{|}}{C}}-CH_3$$

Of far more practical value is "termination" by chain transfer. Most monomers of potential commercial utility, if allowed to polymerize in the absence of chain-transfer agents, are converted to polymers of sufficiently high molecular weight, sometimes in the millions, to be intractable in the melt or in solution and are of little value. An exception is cast sheet, such as polymethyl methacrylate, for which no postforming other than heat-shaping is usually required. Most commercial polymers must be of controlled molecular weight, so that extrusion to film, sheeting, or fibers, molding, bottle-blowing, or vacuum-devolatilizing in an extruder is possible without degradation owing to excessive heat. Most commercial polymers require the addition of various agents, such as stabilizers, plasticizers, slip and anti-block additives; so compoundability is a necessity. Even polyacrylonitrile, which cannot be melted, must, to be extrudable, be of controlled molecular weight to yield spinning solutions of sufficient concentration without excessive viscosity.

Accordingly, extensive use is made of the ability of polymer radicals to undergo chain transfer, effecting chain termination and reinitiation of polymer growth. An added agent is required, which contains a readily extracted hydrogen or halogen atom. Thus, the reaction of chain transfer may be formulated as follows:

$$
\begin{aligned}
& \underset{\displaystyle\overset{|}{R}}{-CH}-\underset{\displaystyle\overset{|}{R}}{CH}-CH_2-\underset{\displaystyle\overset{|}{R}}{CH\cdot} + R'H \longrightarrow -\underset{\displaystyle\overset{|}{R}}{CHCH}-CH_2-\underset{\displaystyle\overset{|}{R}}{CH_2} + R'\cdot \\
& R'\cdot + CH_2 = \underset{\displaystyle\overset{|}{R}}{CH} \longrightarrow R'-CH_2-\underset{\displaystyle\overset{|}{R}}{CH\cdot}
\end{aligned}
$$

(1-6)

...etc.

An order of selectivity is shown by certain chain-transfer agents toward monomers of distinctive types. This selectivity is related to resonance stabilization and polarity factors, which will be discussed later.

Finally, polymer radicals may transfer intermolecularly or intramolecularly with existing polymers at active sites:

$$(1-7)$$

Such a reaction generally yields long-chain branching, when occurring intermolecularly, or short-chain branching when occurring intramolecularly.

$$-CH_2-\overset{\underset{|}{R}}{CH}-CH_2-\overset{\underset{|}{R-CH}}{\overset{H}{\underset{\diagdown}{C}}}{\overset{\diagup}{\underset{\diagdown}{CH_2}}}{\overset{CH_2}{\underset{|}{CHR}}} \longrightarrow -CH_2-\overset{\underset{|}{R}}{CH}-CH_2-\overset{\underset{|}{R}}{C}-CH_2-\overset{\underset{|}{R}}{CH}-CH_2-CH_2-R$$

$$\downarrow CH_2=CHR$$

$$(1\text{-}8)$$

$$-CH_2-\overset{\underset{|}{R}}{CH}-CH_2-\overset{\underset{|}{\underset{CHR}{\underset{|}{CH_2}}}}{\overset{R}{\underset{|}{C}}}-CH_2-\overset{\underset{|}{R}}{CH}-CH_2-CH_2-R$$

Beyond a few carbon atoms the influence of remote monomer units in a polymer radical on the radical reactivity is not generally felt. Accordingly, one may learn a great deal about the reactivity of a polyethylene radical, for instance, from knowledge acquired about an ethyl radical. James and MacCallum (3) have compared the rates of the addition to ethyl radicals of various vinyl monomers with illuminating results. They have shown that styrene reacts far more readily than vinyl acetate or heptene-1 with an ethyl radical because of the lower energy of activation for the addition of the former (see Fig. 1-1 and Table 1-1).

The absence of any significant difference in the pre-exponential factor is evidence that steric factors for the three compounds in the addition reaction are similar. A low energy of activation for addition is believed to be associated with a gain in resonance stabilization in the radical adduct compound with the monomer and with the contributions made to the stability of the transition state by ionic forms. The reactivity of styrene is thought to be due primarily to the first of these two factors. In their study ethyl radicals were

TABLE 1-1

Addition of the Ethyl Radical to Vinyl Monomers[a]

	$E_1 - \frac{1}{2}E_2$, kcal/mole	$13 + \log(A_1/A_2^{1/2})$
Styrene	4.0 ± 0.6	4.9 ± 0.3
Vinyl acetate	6.8 ± 0.4	5.3 ± 0.3
Heptene-1	7.0 ± 0.2	5.2 ± 0.1

[a] Reproduced by permission of the Chemical Society.

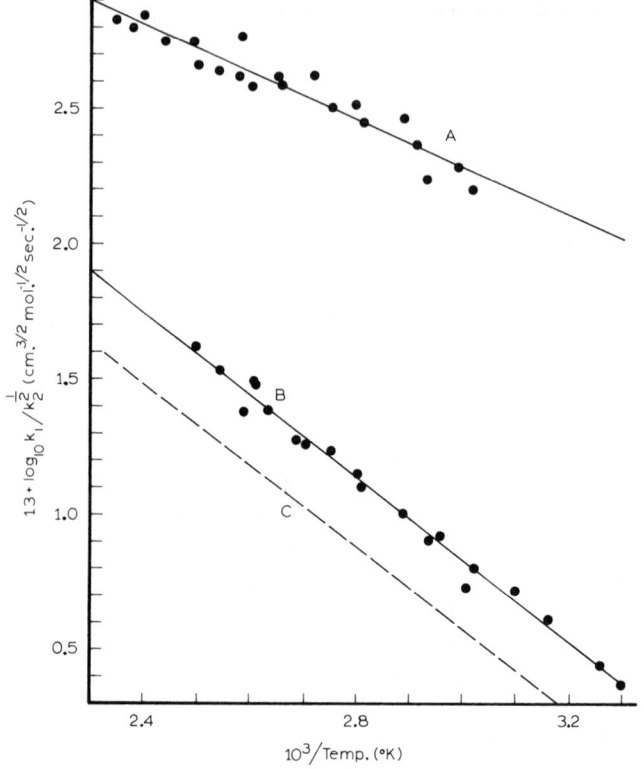

Fig. 1-1. Addition of the ethyl radical to vinyl monomers. A, styrene; B, vinyl acetate; C, heptene-1.

generated by photolysis of diethyl ketone. The two competing reactions were examined:

$$C_2H_5\cdot + CH_2 = CHX \longrightarrow C_2H_5-CH_2-\overset{\overset{\displaystyle X}{\displaystyle |}}{C}H\cdot \qquad k_1 \qquad (1\text{-}9)$$

$$2C_2H_5\cdot \longrightarrow C_4H_{10} \qquad\qquad\qquad k_2 \qquad (1\text{-}10)$$

Their comparisons were based on the ratio $k_1/k_2^{1/2}$, which they showed to be equal to

$$k_1/k_2^{1/2} = [R_{CO}-(R_{C_2H_6} + R_{C_4H_{10}})]/[B](R_{C_4H_{10}})^{1/2} \qquad (1\text{-}11)$$

where R_Y is the rate of formation of product Y in moles per second per cubic centimeter of illuminated volume and [B] is the concentration of appropriate monomer.

Conversely, polymerization and copolymerization studies offer unusual opportunities for comparing radical reactivity and monomer reactivity among various polymer radicals and monomers, respectively. Mayo (4) has tabulated second-order rate constants for the additions of radicals to monomers at 60°C for a series of common monomers (Table 1-2). Thus, for styrene additions to styrene radical the rate of polymerization in moles per liter per second is

$$-d[M]/dt = 145[M\cdot][M] \qquad (1\text{-}12)$$

In pure styrene, which is 8.4 molar, each polymer radical adds 1200 monomer units per second. It is seen from the table that with the given radicals styrene is 50 to 100 times as reactive as vinyl acetate. On the other hand, with the given monomers vinyl acetate radical is about 1000 times as reactive as styrene radical.

The general rule may be formulated, that monomers of low resonance stabilization yield polymer radical adducts of low resonance stabilization and high reactivity with monomers in general and that monomers of high resonance stabilization yield radical adducts of high resonance stabilization and low reactivity with monomers in general.

Accordingly, the results of studies with simple radicals such as ethyl radicals, although still sketchy, are in harmony with those of polymerization and copolymerization studies.

TABLE 1-2

Second-Order Rate Constants for Additions of Radicals to Monomers at 60°C[a]

	Radicals			
Monomers	$R{-}CH_2{-}\underset{H}{\overset{\phi}{C}}\cdot$	$R{-}CH_2{-}\underset{CH_3}{\overset{COOCH_3}{C}}\cdot$	$R{-}CH_2{-}\underset{H}{\overset{COOCH_3}{C}}\cdot$	$R{-}CH_2{-}\underset{H}{\overset{O{\overset{\parallel}{C}}CH_3}{C}}\cdot$
Styrene	145	1520	11,500	$\approx 200,000$
Methyl methacrylate	278	705		$\approx 140,000$
Methyl acrylate	194		2,090	11,500
Vinyl acetate	3	35	230	2,300

[a] Reproduced from *J. Chem. Educ.* (4) by permission of the American Chemical Society.

1-3. Q–e SCHEME

Discrepancies in Table 1-2 are known to be due to polar factors (5–7). Alfrey and Price (7) in 1947 formulated the empirical relationship

$$r_1 = (Q_1/Q_2)\exp[-e_1(e_1 - e_2)] \qquad (1\text{-}13)$$

$$r_2 = (Q_2/Q_1)\exp[-e_2(e_2 - e_1)] \qquad (1\text{-}14)$$

where $r_1 = k_{11}/k_{12}$ and $r_2 = k_{22}/k_{21}$, the binary reactivity ratios of propagation rate constants, Q_1 and Q_2 are quantities related to the resonance stabilization of monomers M_1 and M_2, respectively, and e_1 and e_2 are quantities related to polarity. One may question the generality of the form of the Alfrey–Price equation, but there no longer appears any reasonable doubt concerning the fact that monomer reactivity may be expressed in terms of two factors, one related to resonance stabilization and the other tó polarity. From Table 1-2 the high second-order rate constant for the addition of styrene to a methyl acrylate radical relative to methyl acrylate monomer (factor of 5) is a direct reflection of the large difference in e (polarity) values (-0.8 for styrene and $+0.6$ for methyl acrylate). By way of contrast, a factor of only 2 exists in the relative addition rates of styrene and methyl methacrylate added to a methyl methacrylate radical—still a reflection of polarity difference, but smaller (-0.8 for styrene and $+0.4$ for methyl methacrylate).

In further consideration of homopolymerization it appears that an interpretation of the observed second-order rate constants in terms of resonance stabilization and polarity phenomena is possible. It is believed that among the four monomers listed in Table 1-2 polarity factors may be neglected and polymerization behavior may be almost entirely ascribed to resonance stabilization phenomena. Thus, the gain in resonance stabilization from monomer to radical adduct progressively increases as the Q value of the monomer (and radical adduct) decreases. Thus, vinyl acetate possesses a much higher propagation rate constant than styrene, since there is a much greater proportionate gain in resonance stabilization from monomer to radical adduct. The relation between Q and propagation rate constants is shown in Table 1-3.

It is conceivable that steric inhibition of resonance with the carbon-carbon double bond may occur in vinyl acetate monomer and other "unconjugated" monomers, with the result that quite low values of Q, characteristic of the monomer, occur. However, on formation of the radical adduct ending in the vinyl acetate moiety, a coplanar configuration occurs. Such a relief of strain (and lengthening of C—O bond distance) in the molecule could lead to a net gain in resonance stabilization and furnish the driving force for the

TABLE 1-3

Monomer	Resonance stabilization Q	Propagation rate
Styrene	1.0	145
Methyl methacrylate	0.74	705
Methyl acrylate	0.42	2090
Vinyl acetate	0.02	2300

facile addition of vinyl acetate to its own radical. Similar effects must occur in vinyl chloride.

In the case of ethylene polymerization steric inhibition of resonance in the monomer is more difficult to see. However, the rapid polymerization of ethylene at elevated pressures could hardly be due to polar factors. Certainly, the radical adduct of ethylene would exhibit less crowding of hydrogens about the terminal carbon under attack. In ethylene the carbon-hydrogen distance is 1.087 A, compared with 1.095 A for ethane (which would approximate the C—H bond distance in the radical adduct). Therefore, the carbon containing the free radical would be more available for attack, and less steric inhibition of resonance in the radical adduct would result. Accordingly, a net gain in resonance stabilization would occur between the monomer and the radical adduct.

In the case of homopolymerization of highly polar monomers, such as acrylonitrile and vinylidene cyanide, it is highly likely that the propagation rate constants are much lower than those anticipated on the basis of resonance stabilization, because of polar factors causing a reduction in attraction between radical and adding monomer. Indeed, there is no reported instance of the homopolymerization of vinylidene cyanide by radical mechanisms. On the other hand, anionic polymerization, in the presence of water, alkalis, etc., is rapid. Vinylidene cyanide readily forms alternating copolymers by radical mechanisms, however, when desirable spacer units are available. The rapid observed polymerization of acrylonitrile in bulk or aqueous suspension appears to be primarily due to the inhibition of the termination step by the immobility of polymer radicals after their precipitation as very stiff and semicrystalline chains (8). Both acrylonitrile (9) and vinylidene cyanide (10) exhibit pronounced penultimate-unit effects on the competitive addition of the same monomer and other monomers to chain radicals. This reduced tendency of the highly polar monomers to add is further evidence of repulsion due to polar factors.

The comparatively low propagation rate constants of styrene and methyl methacrylate appear to arise from the very slight increase in contribution to resonance stabilization from monomer to radical adduct. A high degree of stabilization exists in both monomer and adduct. That the propagation occurs at all may arise from the greater steric inhibition of resonance in the monomer compared with that in the coplanar radical.

1-4. KINETIC SCHEME OF FREE-RADICAL POLYMERIZATION

A most excellent review of free-radical polymerization has been compiled by Flory (*11a*). His nomenclature will be employed in the outline that follows.

As discussed earlier, a free radical must be generated in some manner for propagation of a vinyl polymer to occur by the stated mechanism. Although this phenomenon can be made to occur by a thermal process, it is most convenient to add a compound capable of dissociation into active free radicals, such as benzoyl peroxide or azodiisobutyronitrile. Thus, in the general case an initiator (I) yields two radicals (R·):

$$I \xrightarrow{k_d} 2R\cdot \tag{1-15}$$

These radicals are usually (not necessarily) more reactive than the polymeric radicals produced. Accordingly, monomer is readily added to the initiating radical:

$$R\cdot + M \xrightarrow{k_i} RM\cdot \tag{1-16}$$

This reaction is a highly productive one, since initiator concentrations are generally in the range of 0.01 to 0.1% of monomer present. However, as much as 40% of the initiator radicals may be destroyed in certain cases by other reactions, to be discussed later. Radical efficiencies approaching 1 usually are realized.

Chain propagation then occurs; it represents a continuation of the process, except that any rate effects arising from the initiator residue rapidly vanish with increasing monomer units:

$$RM\cdot + M \xrightarrow{k_p} RMM\cdot \ \ldots, \text{etc.} \tag{1-17}$$

As long as monomer is available at the radical site the reaction (3) will be repeated, until the unlikely approach of two similar radicals results in a fertile collision. Such a termination must result in the re-establishment of a covalent bond. Otherwise, chain propagation will be reinitiated (unless the new radical is highly stabilized by resonance).

Chain termination, as described before, can occur by radical combination,

$$R(M)_m\cdot + R(M)_n\cdot \xrightarrow{k_{tc}} R(M)_m(M)_n R \tag{1-18}$$

or by disproportionation,

$$R(M)_m\cdot + R(M)_n\cdot \xrightarrow{k_{td}} R(M)_m H + [R(M)_n - H] \tag{1-19}$$

Although the two termination reactions are quite different and can substantially influence molecular weight (particularly when both processes occur in varying degrees), both processes lead to radical destruction and the same kinetic effect. Accordingly,

$$k_t = k_{tc} + k_{td} \tag{1-20}$$

It is fortunate for a simplified kinetic treatment that k_p and k_t are independent of the molecular weight of the growing chain. That this is true is in harmony with the concept of a flexible, growing chain, free to move at random and to undergo collision with monomers moving at random and unhampered in diffusion. Furthermore, the sequential propagation reactions are essentially identical, at least beyond 3 to 5 monomer units. We shall deal later with complications introduced by increases in viscosity with conversion or with polymer separation. For the present we shall limit our treatment to homogeneous systems at relatively low conversions. It follows, then, that the disappearance of monomer may be represented as

$$-d[\mathrm{M}]/dt = k_i[\mathrm{R}\cdot][\mathrm{M}] + k_p[\mathrm{M}\cdot][\mathrm{M}] \tag{1-21}$$

where M· is now a polymer radical of any length. Since the polymer approaches high molecular weight in 1 to 10 sec and the remaining species are almost entirely monomer, it is clear that the disappearance of monomer is essentially uninfluenced by the initiating rate $k_i[\mathrm{R}\cdot][\mathrm{M}]$, so

$$-d[\mathrm{M}]/dt = k_p[\mathrm{M}\cdot][\mathrm{M}] \tag{1-22}$$

It is also true that the rate of change of *radical* concentration is a function of the difference between their rate of formation and rate of destruction (by termination):

$$d[\mathrm{M}\cdot]/dt = k_i\mathrm{R}\cdot[\mathrm{M}] - 2k_t[\mathrm{M}\cdot]^2 \tag{1-23}$$

Radicals by virtue of their great reactivity simply do not last long, as shown above, compared with the over-all process of converting monomer to polymer. Therefore we may make a steady-state assumption that the rate of change of radical concentration, $d[\mathrm{M}\cdot]/dt$, relative to the rates of formation and destruction is vanishingly small. Hence,

$$k_i[\mathrm{R}\cdot][\mathrm{M}] = 2k_t[\mathrm{M}\cdot]^2 \tag{1-24}$$

Furthermore, the rate of change of initiating radical concentration is a function of its rate of appearance minus its rate of disappearance,

$$d[\mathrm{R}\cdot]/dt = 2f k_d[\mathrm{I}] - k_i[\mathrm{R}\cdot][\mathrm{M}] \tag{1-25}$$

and in turn is equal to 0, if we invoke the steady-state assumption. In the equation f is the fraction of initiator radicals successfully reacting with monomer. We may accordingly write:

$$-d[M]/dt = k_p[M](k_d f[I]/k_t)^{1/2} \qquad (1\text{-}26)$$

If R_p is the rate of polymerization and R_i is the rate of chain initiation, we may shorten Eq. (1-26) to

$$R_p = k_p[M](R_i/2k_t)^{1/2} \qquad (1\text{-}27)$$

1.5. RELATION OF POLYMERIZATION RATE TO INITIATOR AND MONOMER CONCENTRATIONS

An extensive study of various monomer-initiator combinations has abundantly confirmed the relationship between the rate of polymerization and the square root of the initiator concentration (*11*). Figure 1-2 shows excellent agreement with Eq. (1-26) for styrene and methyl methacrylate. The straight lines, although drawn with the theoretical slope of 0.5, fit the experimental data very well over a wide initiator concentration range. In the case of styrene at low benzoyl peroxide levels (Fig. 1-2, curve B) deviation is due to a significant amount of thermal polymerization.

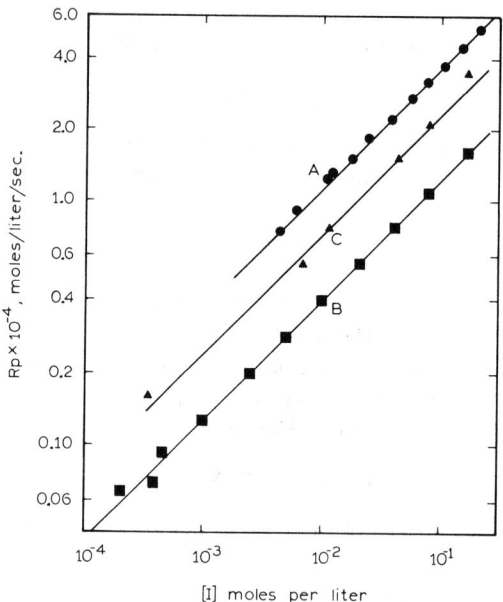

Fig. 1-2. Initial polymerization rate versus initiator concentration: A, methyl methacrylate with azobisisobutyronitrile at 50°C; B, styrene with benzoyl peroxide at 60°C; C, methyl methacrylate with benzoyl peroxide at 50°C. [After Mayo (*4*).]

TABLE 1-4

Polymerization of Methyl Methacrylate in Benzene with Azodiisobutyronitrile [Arnett (13)][a]

[M], moles/liter	[I] × 10³, moles/liter	Initial rate R_p × 10⁴, moles/liter/sec	$R_p/[I]^{1/2}[M]$ × 10⁴
9.04 (undiluted)	0.235	1.93	14.0
8.63	0.206	1.70	13.7
7.19	0.255	1.65	14.4
6.13	0.228	1.29	14.0
4.96	0.313	1.22	13.9
4.75	0.192	0.937	14.3
4.22	0.230	0.867	13.6
4.17	0.581	1.30	13.0
3.26	0.245	0.715	14.0
2.07	0.211	0.415	13.8

[a] Reproduced by permission of American Chemical Society.

In Fig. 1-2 the excellent agreement of the experimental data with straight lines of slope 0.5 confirms the bimolecular mechanism of polymer radical termination processes, whether by combination or disproportionation, as discussed above. Photopolymerization studies have supplied additional evidence (12).

Table 1-4 shows data on the polymerization of methyl methacrylate in the presence of azodiisobutyronitrile at 77°C, after Arnett (13). The constancy of the quantity $R_p/I^{1/2}[M]$ is evidence that the efficiency f of propagation of primary radicals is not dependent on monomer concentration.

The polymerization of methyl methacrylate in the presence of constant benzoyl peroxide concentration, however, shows a small decrease in f with increase in solvent (14), and the polymerization of styrene with constant benzoyl peroxide concentration shows a distinct decrease in f with dilution (15). The most likely (although not universally accepted) explanation of these effects is that a "cage effect" exists, in which primary radicals cannot all diffuse away from each other before being destroyed by bimolecular combination. This effect would obviously become more pronounced as the likelihood of radical meeting monomer was diminished by dilution.

1-6. BEHAVIOR OF INITIATORS

The question of the efficiency f with which initiators decompose into catalyst fragments that result in polymer chains is of some importance. There is reason to believe that this efficiency approaches unity, since the polymerization rate is often proportional to the monomer concentration. Studies by Arnett and Peterson (16) of the radioactive content of polymer produced with ^{14}C-labelled azodiisobutyronitrile compared with catalyst consumed in the reaction have led to values of initiator efficiency in the polymerization of various monomers. That induced decomposition was neglected appears to be justified in the case of this catalyst. Efficiencies of initiation increasing from 0.6 to 1.0 were obtained in going from methyl methacrylate to vinyl acetate, styrene, vinyl chloride, and acrylonitrile.

Johnson et al. (17) showed by a molecular-weight technique that for benzoyl peroxide in styrene and methyl methacrylate initiator efficiencies of 0.6 to 1.0 were also obtained. Their data on azodiisobutyronitrile and methyl methacrylate agreed with those reported by Arnett and Peterson (16).

1-7. SIGNIFICANCE OF k_p^2/k_t

The parameter k_p^2/k_t is particularly significant because it can be readily determined from a knowledge of fairly easily determined quantities by several methods and gives a measure of the relative importance of propagation and termination reactions. The parameter arises from Eq. (1-26):

$$f k_d k_p^2/k_t = R_p^2[I][M]^2 \qquad (1\text{-}28)$$

It follows that

$$k_p^2/k_t = 2R_p^2/R_i[M]^2 \qquad (1\text{-}29)$$

R_i may be calculated, for example, from a determination of efficiency f and rate of decomposition of the catalyst. Table 1-5 from Flory (11b) summarizes values of k_p^2/k_t obtained by various means.

1-8. KINETICS OF CONVERSION OF MONOMER TO POLYMER

If the efficiency of catalyst decomposition f is independent of monomer concentration and the initiator concentration [I] does not change appreciably during polymerization, then the transformation of monomer to polymer should be first order. Examples are the polymerization of styrene in toluene solution in the presence of benzoyl peroxide catalyst, as determined by Schulz and Husemann (18) and the polymerization of d-sec-butyl α-chloroacrylate and vinyl-l-β-phenylbutyrate in dioxane solution initiated by benzoyl peroxide (19) (see Fig. 1-3).

In the case of the polymerization of pure monomer or monomer containing very little solvent the results are distinctly different from those cited above. Data obtained by Schulz and Harborth (20), for instance, illustrate behavior quite dissimilar from that in first-order kinetics; the polymerization curves are shown in Fig. 1-4. In their studies methyl methacrylate was polymerized

TABLE 1-5

Comparison of Values of k_p^2/k_t

Monomer	Initiator[a]	Method of assigning initiation rate[b]	Temp., °C	$(k_p^2/k_t) \times 10^3$ liter/mole/sec[c]
Styrene	Bz_2O_2	MW	27	0.105
Styrene	Azo.	Init.	30	0.125
Styrene	Azo.	Inhib.	30	0.115
Styrene	Bz_2O_2	MW	50	0.39
Styrene	Bz_2O_2	MW	60	1.19
Styrene	Azo.	MW	60	1.18
Styrene	Bz_2O_2	Init.	60	0.95 (1.58)
Styrene	Azo.	Init.	60	0.76 (0.95)
Styrene	Azo.	Inhib.	60	0.74
Vinyl acetate	Azo.	Init.	25	30.4
Vinyl acetate	Azo.	Inhib.	25	34.8
Vinyl acetate	Photo.	Inhib.	25	31.3
Vinyl acetate	Azo.	Init.	50	125
Vinyl acetate	Azo.	Inhib.	50	119

[a] Azo = azobisisobutyronitrile, Bz_2O_2 = benzoyl peroxide, Photo. = direct photochemical initiation.

[b] Determinations based on the rate of decomposition of the initiator assuming $f = 1$ are indicated by Init. Those from the inhibition method are indicated by Inhib., and those from analysis of molecular weights by MW.

[c] Values given in parentheses have been calculated by means of $f = 0.60$ and 0.80 for styrene–Bz_2O_2 and for styrene–azo, respectively.

in mass and at various concentrations in benzene with benzoyl peroxide as catalyst in a dilatometer. The dilatometer was employed to follow the polymerization by observation of the decrease in volume of the polymerizate, which is due to the higher density of polymer than of monomer. At monomer concentrations up to approximately 40% the curves showing polymerization as a function of time show independence of the initial concentration of monomer in benzene and, consequently, the process is first order in nature. When the monomer concentration is increased to higher value, a great acceleration of rate of polymerization is encountered at 15 to 40% conversion to polymer. The acceleration occurs at a higher conversion when the monomer is more dilute, say at 60% monomer, whereas in undiluted monomer it occurs at conversions as low as 15%. Moreover, the molecular weight of the polymer that is formed under the conditions leading to autoacceleration is found to increase sharply. This rapid increase in polymerization rate often leads to a substantial increase in the temperature of the polymerization,

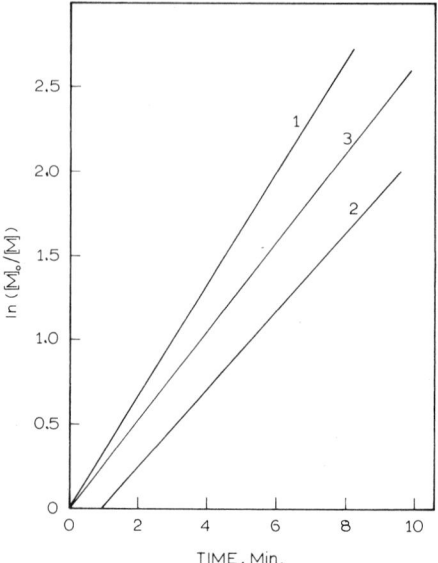

Fig. 1-3. Polymerization of vinyl–*l*–*β*–phenylbutyrate initiated by benzoyl peroxide in dioxane at 60°C: $[M]_0$ and $[M]$ represent concentrations of monomer initially and at time t, respectively. In experiments 1, 2, and 3 $[M]_0$ = 2.4, 7.28, and 5.97 g of monomer per 100 cm³ of dioxane, respectively. [Results of Marvel et al. (*19*).]

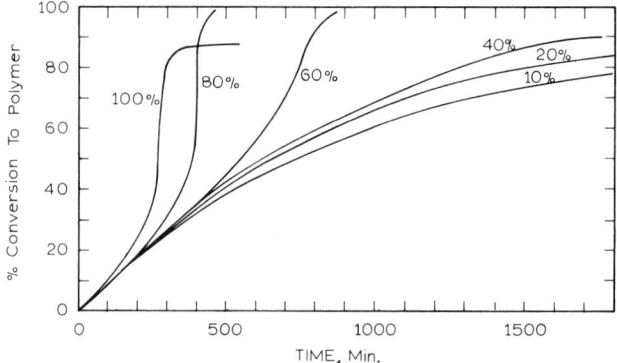

Fig. 1-4. The polymerization of methyl methacrylate at 50°C in the presence of benzoyl peroxide at stated concentrations of monomer in benzene. [Schulz and Harborth (*20*).]

since the dissipation of the heat of polymerization becomes quite inefficient with the viscosity increase. The effect cannot be eliminated, however, by keeping the temperature uniform throughout the reaction (21,22).

The behavior is by no means limited to the polymerization of methyl methacrylate. The homologous acrylates and methacrylates exhibit a tendency to autoacceleration, as do acrylic and methacrylic acids and acrylonitrile. In the case of methyl acrylate autoacceleration occurs at less than 1% conversion. It is often accompanied by an explosion, as the conversion of monomer to polymer approaches higher levels, unless special precautions are taken to dissipate the heat generated. To a lesser degree styrene and vinyl acetate exhibit autoacceleration too.

It is now generally believed that this phenomenon can be explained by a large reduction in the termination rate constants in relation to the propagation rate constants. There is no basis for believing that the decomposition rate constant or the efficiency constant is increased. Autoacceleration is not altered by changes in initiator. This phenomenon has been the subject of numerous studies over the years. The most important contributions have been made by Norrish and Smith (22), Trommsdorff et al. (23,24), and Schulz and Harborth (20). These researchers have determined that the autoacceleration in the polymerization of methyl methacrylate and the increase in the molecular weight of the polymer produced are most satisfactorily explained by a decrease in the rate of termination of growing free radicals. This decrease in k_t is believed to arise from the high viscosity of the monomer-polymer mixture when the concentration rises to the levels mentioned earlier. Since we have already established that chain termination occurs by the combination of two free radicals, it is reasonable to expect that, as the polymer molecules become more and more immobilized through entanglements, the collective diffusion of more than a few segments, such as at the radical site, is greatly hampered. The termination of the free radicals by combination will be greatly impeded. In fact, the rate of termination will become controlled by the rate of diffusion of these growing chains. Furthermore, all evidence indicates that the radical reactivity itself is not affected. A diminution in reactivity must be ascribed to the decrease in the availability of radicals for reaction with one another. These collective effects, arising from the great increase in viscosity, will cause the concentration of radicals to increase.

It is not believed that the propagation reaction is influenced by the viscosity of the medium. The monomer molecules are small enough to diffuse more readily through the reaction medium than the polymer molecules, because they do not have long entangling tails to carry with them. Moreover, that fraction of fertile collisions between radical and monomer that results in reaction is only about 10^{-9}. Accordingly, maintenance of the concentration of monomer at suitable equilibrium level in the environment of the radical is less subject to diffusion processes. By contrast, chain termination through the combination of two polymer radicals is a fast reaction (about 10^{-4} fertile collisions).

An increase in viscosity, then, would have a much greater effect on the radical concentration than on the monomer concentration.

Further inspection of Fig. 1-4 indicates that in the case of pure monomer acceleration ends abruptly short of complete conversion to polymer and that the extent of conversion as the curve levels off is about 90%. In the case of pure methyl methacrylate or monomer/solvent ratios that are very high the polymerizing mixture approaches a glass at temperatures less than 90°C. At this point the monomer molecules as well as polymer molecules are no longer free to diffuse through the medium. Accordingly, polymerization ceases substantially short of completion under conditions in which the polymerization is taking place below the glass-transition temperature of the polymer.

Obviously, the size of the polymer molecule being produced plays an important part in the autoacceleration phenomenon. There is little question that the high propagation and low termination rate constants in monomers such as methyl acrylate, compared to those of other common monomers, accounts for both the high degree of polymerization and the decrease in the termination constant at very low conversions.

The measurements of the absolute values of the individual rate constants have furnished further proof of the validity of this explanation, and the termination constant has been found to decrease by about 100 times during the autoacceleration phenomenon, whereas k_p does not appear to change. The autoacceleration effect, although first demonstrated and carefully studied with respect to homogeneous systems, has significant implications for the polymerization of monomers that yield insoluble polymers. Accordingly, the polymerization of acrylonitrile, which leads to separation of insoluble polyacrylonitrile at an early stage, demonstrates autoacceleration to a large extent. It is believed that this result arises from occlusion of radicals in the separated polymer, whereas monomer is still relatively free to diffuse to the radical site of reaction. However, under certain conditions even the diffusion of monomer can be restricted or eliminated, leading to termination of polymerization.

The addition of polymethyl methacrylate and other polymers to the monomer also results in a large increase in the initial polymerization rate for methyl methacrylate and is further evidence for the explanation of auto-acceleration given above (23–25). Moreover, the addition of chain-transfer agents, such as mercaptans, results in the elimination of autoacceleration. The suppression or elimination of autoacceleration by chain-transfer agents undoubtedly arises from the reduction of molecular weight of the polymer formed, so that the diffusion of polymer radicals through the polymer medium is less inhibited. Furthermore, the radicals themselves are of short or average length and can diffuse more readily.

1-9. DISTINCTIVE FEATURES OF FREE-RADICAL POLYMERIZATION

It is instructive to compare free-radical and condensation polymerizations. In the course of free-radical polymerization at any instant the reaction mixture consists of a mixture of unreacted monomer and high-molecular-weight polymer. It is true that a very small proportion of polymer is undergoing rapid increase in molecular weight by the propagation mechanism described earlier. However, the mixture may in its essential physical features be described as a combination of monomer and high-molecular-weight polymer. Moreover, the so-called high-molecular-weight polymer does not undergo further growth in the normal course of events. Thus, a molecule of polymethyl methacrylate, once formed, does not progressively increase in molecular weight.

Condensation polymerization of ethylene glycol and terephthalic acid or hexamethylenediamine and adipic acid, on the other hand, is distinguished by a stepwise progression of simple reactants—to dimers, trimers, tetramers, etc.—until high-molecular-weight polymer is obtained. Thus, the number-average degree of polymerization is simply $1/(1 - p)$, where p is the extent of reaction. Thus, at 99% conversion to polymer the number-average degree of polymerization is only 100. Very little of the polymer is of a high degree of polymerization, such as 1000. By contrast, at this conversion virtually all of a typical vinyl polymer would be of very high molecular weight.

Once we have promulgated the rule, however, we must immediately break it. Vinyl polymers, particularly those with "susceptible" structures and derived from high-energy radicals, have an obtuse way of undergoing chain transfer of growing radical with completed polymer with a net gain in molecular weight. This reaction is much more prevalent at higher temperatures, at which covalent bonds are weaker and hydrogen atoms are more susceptible to being attacked by the growing radicals. Thus, polyethylene undergoes extensive branching at the higher temperatures, at which it is normally produced (150 to 250°C) (27). Polyvinyl acetate even at lower temperatures (70°C and up) of polymerization becomes highly branched (28). Although all the hydrogens in polyvinyl acetate can, presumably, participate in the transfer reaction, indications from molecular-weight determinations, made before and after hydrolysis and followed by reacetylation, suggest that hydrogens on the acetate function are favored:

$$
\begin{array}{c}
\text{O} \qquad\qquad \text{H--C--OCCH}_3 \\
\text{OCCH}_3 \quad \text{CH}_2\ \text{O} \\
-\text{CH}_2-\text{CH}\cdot\ +\ \text{H--C--OCCH}_3 \longrightarrow -\text{CH}_2-\text{CH}_2\ +\ \text{H--C--OCCH}_2\cdot \\
\text{CH}_2
\end{array}
\qquad (1\text{-}30)
$$

The resulting polymer radical can then attack vinyl acetate monomer and lead to long-chain branching.

Vinyl benzoate also undergoes chain transfer with polymer during polymerization (*29*), presumably by the following mechanism:

$$ (1\text{-}31) $$

The fate of the generated polymer radical is open to some question. Since it is allylic in nature and thus stabilized, two such radicals might couple or disproportionate:

$$ (1\text{-}32) \qquad\qquad (1\text{-}33) $$

A competing reaction with the "normal" growing free radical is similar to that for polymer.

$$
\text{R}\cdot\ +\ \text{(benzoate with CH=CH}_2\text{)} \longrightarrow \text{R--(ring)--CH=CH}_2
\qquad (1\text{-}34)
$$

Since this radical is stabilized by resonance, it is not disposed to propagate by adding more monomer in the normal way, so reactions of coupling or disproportionation, as described above, may occur. The net result is that polymerization is very slow but the polymer produced is highly branched.

In the polymerization of vinyl chloride high-molecular-weight polymer is readily produced by normal propagation, but there is some evidence that chain transfer with polymer may occur (30). Whether abstraction of chlorine or tertiary hydrogen is predominant is not known:

$$
\begin{array}{c}
\text{Cl}-\overset{\mid}{\underset{\mid}{\text{C}}}-\text{H} \qquad\qquad\qquad \text{Cl}-\overset{\mid}{\underset{\mid}{\text{C}}}-\text{H} \\
\overset{\mid}{\underset{\mid}{\text{C}}}-\text{Cl} \quad \overset{\mid}{\underset{\mid}{\text{CH}_2}} \qquad\qquad\qquad \overset{\mid}{\underset{\mid}{\text{CH}_2}} \\
-\text{CH}_2-\overset{\cdot}{\text{CH}} + \text{Cl}-\overset{\mid}{\underset{\mid}{\text{C}}}-\text{H} \longrightarrow -\text{CH}_2\text{CHCl}_2 + \text{H}\overset{\cdot}{\text{C}} \\
\overset{\mid}{\underset{\mid}{\text{CH}_2}} \qquad\qquad\qquad\qquad \overset{\mid}{\underset{\mid}{\text{CH}_2}}
\end{array}
\qquad (1\text{-}35)
$$

$$
\begin{array}{c}
\text{H}-\overset{\cdot}{\underset{\mid}{\text{C}}}-\text{Cl} \qquad\qquad\qquad \text{Cl}-\overset{\mid}{\underset{\mid}{\text{C}}}-\text{H} \\
\overset{\mid}{\underset{\mid}{\text{CH}_2}} \qquad\qquad\qquad\qquad \overset{\mid}{\underset{\mid}{\text{CH}_2}} \\
\text{H}-\overset{\mid}{\underset{\mid}{\text{C}}}-\text{Cl} \longrightarrow -\text{CH}_2\text{CH}_2\text{Cl} + \text{Cl}\,\overset{\cdot}{\text{C}} \\
\overset{\mid}{\underset{\mid}{\text{CH}_2}} \qquad\qquad\qquad\qquad \overset{\mid}{\underset{\mid}{\text{CH}_2}}
\end{array}
\qquad (1\text{-}36)
$$

It is less surprising that unconjugated monomers exhibit chain transfer with polymer (because of the high-energy radicals involved) than that certain conjugated monomers (yielding low-energy radicals) also display this phenomenon. Thus, the acrylates, particularly methyl acrylate, exhibit varying inclinations to chain transfer with their polymers (31). This tendency is aided by the electron-withdrawing characteristics of the ester groups, which shift electrons away from the tertiary hydrogens in the polymer:

$$
\begin{array}{c}
\text{H}-\overset{\mid}{\underset{\mid}{\text{C}}}-\text{COOCH}_3 \qquad\qquad\qquad \text{H}-\overset{\mid}{\underset{\mid}{\text{C}}}-\text{COOCH}_3 \\
\overset{\mid}{\text{COOCH}_3} \quad \overset{\mid}{\underset{\mid}{\text{CH}_2}} \qquad\qquad\qquad\qquad \overset{\mid}{\underset{\mid}{\text{CH}_2}} \\
-\text{CH}_2\overset{\cdot}{\underset{\mid}{\text{C}}} \quad + \text{H}-\overset{\mid}{\underset{\mid}{\text{C}}}-\text{COOCH}_3 \longrightarrow -\text{CH}_2\text{CH}_2\text{COOCH}_3 + \cdot\text{C}-\text{COOCH}_3 \\
\overset{\mid}{\text{H}} \qquad \overset{\mid}{\underset{\mid}{\text{CH}_2}} \qquad\qquad\qquad\qquad\qquad \overset{\mid}{\underset{\mid}{\text{CH}_2}}
\end{array}
\qquad (1\text{-}37)
$$

The resulting polymer radical may then freely add acrylate monomer, yielding a branched structure.

The infusibility and insolubility of polyacrylonitrile (32) observed in the early days led to the rather widely held belief that this polymer was highly cross-linked. The discovery of solvents for polyacrylonitrile (*33*), such as dimethylformamide, dimethylacetamide, dimethyl sulfoxide, and N-methyl pyrrolidone, which yield gel-free solutions, removed the primary basis of this belief. Nevertheless, the high selectivity of polyacrylonitrile–solvent combinations and the infusibility of the polymer required explanation. It appears likely that hydrogen bonding of the following type is an important element in the phenomenon:

$$
\begin{array}{ccc}
\text{CN} & \text{CN} & \text{CN} \\
| & | & | \\
-\text{CH}_2\text{CCH}_2\text{CCH}_2\text{C}- \\
| & | & | \\
\text{H} & \text{H} & \text{H} \\
\cdot\cdot & \cdot\cdot & \cdot\cdot \\
\text{N} & \text{N} & \text{N} \\
||| & ||| & ||| \\
\text{C} & \text{C} & \text{C} \\
| & | & | \\
-\text{CH}_2\text{CCH}_2\text{CCH}_2\text{C}- \\
| & | & | \\
\text{H} & \text{H} & \text{H}
\end{array}
$$

The electron-withdrawing characteristics of the nitrile groups would drain the tertiary hydrogens of electrons. Thus, hydrogen-bonding possibilities with the electron-rich nitrile groups of adjacent chains would be enhanced. Of course, the observed characteristics can also be explained by dipole interaction of nitrile groups between chains.

It was desirable to obtain some information concerning possibilities of chain transfer of growing polyacrylonitrile radicals. Ham (*34*) polymerized acrylonitrile monomer in the presence of a model compound, isobutyronitrile, characteristic of a repeat moiety in polyacrylonitrile:

$$
\begin{array}{cc}
\quad\text{CN} & \quad\text{CN} \\
\quad| & \quad| \\
\text{CH}_3-\text{C}-\text{CH}_3 & -\text{CH}_2-\text{C}-\text{CH}_2- \\
\quad| & \quad| \\
\quad\text{H} & \quad\text{H}
\end{array}
$$

A very small chain-transfer constant resulted, indicating that the tertiary hydrogens in polyacrylonitrile are unlikely to undergo chain transfer.

1-10. THERMAL POLYMERIZATION OF VINYL MONOMERS

It is well established that thermal polymerization of vinyl monomers occurs by radical mechanisms. This fact is best demonstrated by the efficacy of known radical scavengers in inhibiting such reactions. Foord (*35*) has shown that benzoquinone effectively prolongs the induction period in the thermal polymerization of styrene. Thus, 0.01, 0.02, and 0.05 % benzoquinone yield induction periods at 90°C of approximately 350 min, 650 min, and 1300 min, respectively. In the absence of benzoquinone an induction period of 50 min was observed. Whether it arises from the time necessary for thermally generated radicals to "scavenge" traces of inhibitors or for the formation of some necessary radical intermediate from pure monomer has never been conclusively demonstrated. Once the induction period is over, the rate of polymerization of styrene, as measured by rise in relative viscosity, is the same in all cases.

Attempts to reproduce thermal polymerization rates have led to highly erratic results, particularly when monomer coming from different sources and subjected to different methods of purification is employed. The results reported from different laboratories have varied widely. These observations are undoubtedly due to variations of the nature and amount of inhibitors that are encountered as by-products or intermediates in monomer preparation or are accidentally incorporated. Perhaps the only monomer for which unequivocal results have been obtained in thermal polymerization by different workers is styrene (36,37). Induction periods may be minimized and reproducible rates obtained if monomer is carefully purified in the complete absence of oxygen.

Methyl methacrylate may be thermally polymerized in a reproducible manner, if the same scrupulous care is observed (38). An observed rate only 1 % of that of styrene has been obtained.

Numerous attempts at thermally polymerizing vinyl chloride (39), vinyl acetate (40), and methyl acrylate (41) have been unsuccessful.

From these meager data attempts have been made to construct a mechanism of thermal initiation consistent with the observed results. The initiating body would undoubtedly have to be derived entirely from the monomer itself, since the effects of impurities appear to be ruled out. Flory (42) has postulated a diradical of a tail-tail type,

$$2CH_2 = CHR \longrightarrow R - \overset{\overset{\displaystyle H}{|}}{\underset{|}{C}} - CH_2CH_2 - \overset{\overset{\displaystyle H}{|}}{\underset{|}{C}} - R \qquad (1\text{-}38)$$

on the basis that the energy required for the new bond, frequently quoted as 20 to 30 kcal, is of the same order as that required to open two double bonds (-36 kcal). Walling (43) has pointed out that in the case of styrene corrections must be made for the resonance energy of the aliphatic double bond (2×1.5 kcal) and the resonance energy of the resulting benzyl radicals ($\sim 2 \times 24.5$ kcal). Accordingly, a ΔH of -10 kcal, indicating an exothermic reaction, may be proposed.

However, diradicals of either the tail-tail or head-head type may be severely restricted as initiators because of the ease of cyclization in the early stages of polymerization. The situation is similar to the "cage effect" encountered with conventional initiators after cleavage, with the even more important limitation that the radical sites are unable to diffuse apart because of covalent linkages. It has been shown that under these conditions the chances that polymer of high molecular weight will be produced are infinitesimally small (44). The reaction rate characteristics would also be altered, since bimolecular termination would be eliminated.

Walling (43) has suggested that the following reaction leading to monoradicals is energetically feasible, although he does not appear to propose it as a source of initiation of thermal polymerization:

$$2CH_2 = CH\phi \longrightarrow CH_3\overset{\overset{\displaystyle H}{|}}{\underset{\underset{\displaystyle \phi}{|}}{C}}\cdot + CH_2{=}\dot{C}{-}\phi \qquad (1\text{-}39)$$

It is apparent that the theory about the state of initiation of thermal polymerization is as confused as ever. Therefore, it is reasonable to re-examine some of the more straightforward explanations, to see whether they may have been discarded for reasons no longer valid in the light of new information. A mechanism to consider is the formation of the head-tail diradical:

$$2CH_2 = CHR \longrightarrow \cdot CH_2{-}\overset{\overset{\displaystyle R}{|}}{CH}{-}CH_2{-}\overset{\overset{\displaystyle R}{|}}{CH}\cdot \qquad (1\text{-}40)$$

In the case of styrene, in spite of the formation of a primary radical together with a substituted benzyl radical, the energetics may be not very unfavorable. The known electron-donating tendencies of the phenyl group, exhibited in the negative polarity of the styryl radical, also could partially stabilize the primary radical. Moreover, resonance stabilization of the styryl radical moiety would aid its formation. If this structure were then significant as an initiator, one would expect propagation to occur almost exclusively at the primary radical site rather than at the resonance-stabilized styryl radical site. As shown in Table 1-2, such a reaction of a nonconjugated radical with styrene might be preferred by a factor of about 2000 to the reaction of a styryl radical. The mechanism would conform to observed rate behavior. Termination would be bimolecular, as in catalyzed polymerizations. In the absence of significant additions at both ends of the diradical cyclization would be unimportant and radical efficiency would be high. Of course, the over-all rate of thermal polymerization is quite low (0.1 % per hour at 60°C), so the concentration of active species could be very small.

1-11. COPOLYMERIZATION

Since World War I, which is the approximate birth date of the study of copolymerization, the kinetic theory has generally lagged far behind practice. About 1920 some polymers and copolymers of isoprene and 2,3-dimethyl-butadiene were studied as possible synthetic rubbers. The only monomers available in quantity, however, were styrene, vinyl chloride, and vinyl acetate. It is perhaps obvious that the availability of several monomers would immediately suggest copolymerization.

There is little doubt that most of the early work on copolymerization was done in laboratories of I. G. Farbenindustrie at Ludwigshafen. With the three monomers styrene, vinyl chloride, and vinyl acetate in varying proportions a large group of copolymers was made. Some of the more important properties of the copolymers were determined. Moreover, the various techniques of radical polymerization, such as mass, emulsion, solvent, nonsolvent, and solution polymerizations were studied. Later the acrylic monomers, specifically methyl methacrylate and ethyl acrylate, became available, and these led to a still broader study of copolymerization.

The first attempt to treat copolymerization kinetics in a systematic way was made by Wall (45) in 1941, about twenty years after the start of copolymerization studies and about ten years after the commercial introduction of copolymers. Wall reasoned that the relative rates of addition of monomers to growing radicals might be dependent only on the nature of the monomers being added and on their relative proportions. These assumptions led him to the following equation (expressed in current form):

$$n = rx \qquad (1\text{-}41)$$

where $x = M_1/M_2$, the ratio of monomers in the feed, and $n = m_1/m_2$, the ratio of added monomers in the resulting copolymer. The relative rate of addition, k_1/k_2, of two individual monomers M_1 and M_2 to the growing chain was given the value r. It is evident that the nature of this equation requires that the chain ending, whether m_1 or m_2, have no effect on the rate of addition of M_1 or M_2. This quite simple equation is found to hold for many free-radical copolymerizations and for most ionic copolymerizations even to the present day.

Chemists were not long in discovering numerous copolymer systems, particularly those prepared by a free-radical mechanism, to which the simple equation of Wall did not apply. The exceptions in general took the form of high reactivity of either monomer when present in low proportion in the mixture of monomers. Thus, the systems had a single composition, in which the ratio of monomers in the copolymer was the same as that in the feed. This composition was designated the "azeotropic" composition. In a very crude way in the beginning the effects were thought to be due to some type of interaction between the last unit added in the growing chain radical and the unlike monomer. In time this result was recognized as the outgrowth of polar interactions.

Almost simultaneously Mayo and Lewis (46), Alfrey and Goldfinger (47), and Wall (48) derived equations that took into account the effects of the last added unit on the rates of addition of the two individual monomers. They reasoned as follows. The four propagation steps inherent in binary copolymerization are

$$-M_1\cdot + M_1 \rightarrow -M_1M_1\cdot \qquad k_{11} \qquad (1\text{-}42)$$

$$-M_1\cdot + M_2 \rightarrow -M_1M_2\cdot \qquad k_{12} \qquad (1\text{-}43)$$

$$-M_2\cdot + M_1 \rightarrow -M_2M_1\cdot \qquad k_{21} \qquad (1\text{-}44)$$

$$-M_2\cdot + M_2 \rightarrow -M_2M_2\cdot \qquad k_{22} \qquad (1\text{-}45)$$

For each of these there is, of course, a characteristic propagation rate constant, k. The rate of each reaction may be represented as the product of a given rate constant and the radical and monomer concentrations:

$$k_{11}[M_1\cdot][M_1]$$

$$k_{12}[M_1\cdot][M_2]$$

$$k_{21}[M_2\cdot][M_1]$$

$$k_{22}[M_2\cdot][M_2]$$

Accordingly, the rate of disappearance of M_1 by incorporation in the copolymer is

$$-d[M_1]/dt = k_{11}[M_1\cdot][M_1] + k_{21}[M_2\cdot][M_1] \qquad (1\text{-}46)$$

The rate of disappearance of M_2 is

$$-d[M_2]/dt = k_{22}[M_2\cdot][M_2] + k_{12}[M_1\cdot][M_2] \qquad (1\text{-}47)$$

It is reasonable to assume that the rate of disappearance of a given radical, say $-M_1\cdot$, is equal to its rate of appearance. So one may write

$$k_{21}[M_2\cdot][M_1] = k_{12}[M_1\cdot][M_2] \qquad (1\text{-}48)$$

Substitution of the value of $M_1\cdot$ in Eq. (1-46) for that in Eq. (1-48) and dividing by Eq. (1-47) leads to

$$n = \frac{r_1 x + 1}{(r_2/x) + 1} \qquad (1\text{-}49)$$

where $r_1 = k_{11}/k_{12}$, $r_2 = k_{22}/k_{21}$, $x = M_1/M_2$, and $n = m_1/m_2$. This equation, although slightly more complicated in form than Wall's, has the ability

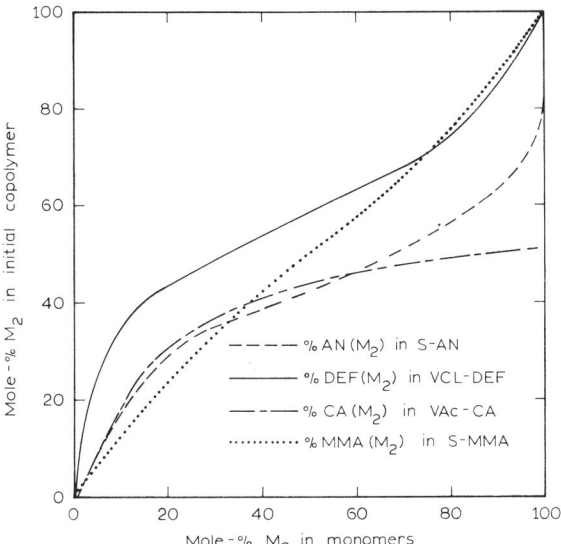

Fig. 1-5. DEF, diethyl fumarate; CA, crotonic acid.

to deal with azeotropic systems, as described earlier, through dealing with the effects of the last unit in a growing chain. Several typical copolymer systems are plotted in Fig. 1-5. A most complete summary of reactivity ratios for monomer pairs studied has recently been prepared (*48*).

Before we turn to the important subject of copolymerizations involving more than two monomers, we shall find it interesting to treat the often-encountered condition in which the addition of either monomer to a growing radical in a binary system is influenced, not only by the terminal unit, but also by the penultimate unit. In 1948 Merz and co-workers (*50*) proposed an equation that treated such a circumstance. It was observed that there were eight distinct reactions to be considered, as follows.

$$-M_1M_1\cdot + M_1 \longrightarrow -M_1M_1M_1\cdot \tag{1-50}$$

$$-M_1M_1\cdot + M_2 \longrightarrow -M_1M_1M_2\cdot \tag{1-51}$$

$$-M_2M_2\cdot + M_2 \longrightarrow -M_2M_2M_2\cdot \tag{1-52}$$

$$-M_2M_2\cdot + M_1 \longrightarrow -M_2M_2M_1\cdot \tag{1-53}$$

$$-M_2M_1\cdot + M_1 \longrightarrow -M_2M_1M_1\cdot \tag{1-54}$$

$$-M_2M_1\cdot + M_2 \longrightarrow -M_2M_1M_2\cdot \tag{1-55}$$

$$-M_1M_2\cdot + M_2 \longrightarrow -M_1M_2M_2\cdot \tag{1-56}$$

$$-M_1M_2\cdot + M_1 \longrightarrow -M_1M_2M_1\cdot \tag{1-57}$$

Employing these transformations and the corresponding expressions for the rate of individual reactions and certain steady-state assumptions, Merz and co-workers were able to arrive at the following equation:

$$n = \frac{1 + [r_1'x(r_1x + 1)]/(r_1'x + 1)}{1 + (r_2'/x)(r_2 + x)/(r_2' + x)} \qquad (1\text{-}58a)$$

where $r_1 = k_{111}/k_{112}$, $r_2 = k_{222}/k_{221}$, $r_1' = k_{211}/k_{212}$, and $r_2' = k_{122}/k_{121}$. The equation in published form contained an error, which may have accounted for its lack of application for several years. Furthermore, experimental data reported in their paper did not confirm experimentally that such an effect existed.

Later work by Fordyce and Ham (51), reported in 1951, indicated that the system styrene–fumaronitrile gave definite evidence that the reactivity of fumaronitrile for a growing chain ending in styrene was reduced as the concentration of fumaronitrile in the starting monomer mixture was increased. It was suggested that interpolymerized fumaronitrile repelled adding monomer. Later it was shown by Barb (52) that this observation was consistent with the conjecture proposed by Merz and co-workers, that the penultimate unit could have a significant effect on the addition of monomers to growing chains. In this case, in which fumaronitrile was incapable of adding to itself, Eq. (1-58a) reduces to

$$n - 1 = \frac{r_1'x(r_1x + 1)}{r_1'x + 1} \qquad (1\text{-}58b)$$

This equation was employed by Barb to interpret the data of Ham and Fordyce. As shown in Fig. 1-6, the agreement was relatively good. However, the retardation in the addition of fumaronitrile at high fumaronitrile concentrations was even more pronounced than that anticipated from the penultimate unit effect alone, so it was proposed by Ham (53) that these effects could be due to more remote units. Specifically, in the copolymerization of styrene and fumaronitrile it was not possible to produce copolymers containing more than 40 mole-% fumaronitrile. Such a circumstance suggests the structure

$$M_2M_1M_1M_2M_1M_2M_1M_1M_2M_1M_2M_1M_1$$

where the sequence $M_2M_1M_1$ alternates with M_2M_1. It is presumed that a possible structure, in which styrene would alternate with fumaronitrile, would require fumaronitrile units to be placed so close together that the polar interactions would lead to unstable compositions or prevent their formation altogether. The alternating structure shown above presumably would reduce the steric and polar interactions encountered.

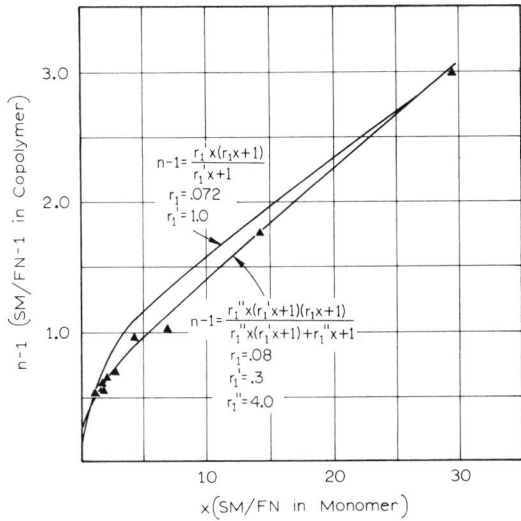

Fig. 1-6. Styrene–fumaronitrile copolymerization: ▲, experimental points.

The observation also suggests the following inequality:

$$k_{11211}/k_{11212} \neq k_{21211}/k_{21212} \qquad (1\text{-}59)$$

Ham proposed the following equation (see also Fig. 1-6) for the circumstances proscribed by this inequality and for those in which the polar monomer could not add to itself:

$$n - 1 = \left[\frac{r_1'' x(r_1' x + 1)}{r_1'' x + 1} \right] [r_1 x + 1] \Bigg/ \left[\frac{r_1'' x(r_1' x + 1)}{r_1'' x + 1} \right] + 1 \qquad (1\text{-}60)$$

where $r_1 = k_{111}/k_{112}$, $r_1' = k_{11211}/k_{11212}$, and $r_1'' = k_{21211}/k_{21212}$. Later this equation was rigorously proven by the use of Markov chains (*54*).

Accordingly, it is seen that a very substantial change in monomer reactivity ratios as a function of monomer concentration can occur, when sterically hindered or polar monomers are involved, and that these effects are discernible at substantial distances from a growing chain ending.

A. Multicomponent Polymerizations

The problem of approaching the polymerization of more than two monomers is quite similar to that of approaching binary copolymerizations. Similar steady-state assumptions are employed, and consideration of the rate of disappearance of monomers as a function of characteristic rate constants and monomer and radical concentrations is necessary. Accordingly, it was shown by Alfrey and Goldfinger (*55*) that in the terpolymerization of three monomers there are nine possible propagation reactions that must be considered:

$$-M_1\cdot + M_1 \longrightarrow -M_1M_1\cdot \tag{1-61}$$

$$-M_1\cdot + M_2 \longrightarrow -M_1M_2\cdot \tag{1-62}$$

$$-M_1\cdot + M_3 \longrightarrow -M_1M_3\cdot \tag{1-63}$$

$$-M_2\cdot + M_1 \longrightarrow -M_2M_1\cdot \tag{1-64}$$

$$-M_2\cdot + M_2 \longrightarrow -M_2M_2\cdot \tag{1-65}$$

$$-M_2\cdot + M_3 \longrightarrow -M_2M_3\cdot \tag{1-66}$$

$$-M_3\cdot + M_1 \longrightarrow -M_3M_1\cdot \tag{1-67}$$

$$-M_3\cdot + M_2 \longrightarrow -M_3M_2\cdot \tag{1-68}$$

$$-M_3\cdot + M_3 \longrightarrow -M_3M_3\cdot \tag{1-69}$$

Furthermore, the rate of consumption of monomer is readily shown to be

$$-dM_1/dt = k_{11}(M_1\cdot)(M_1) + k_{21}(M_1\cdot)(M_1) + k_{31}(M_3\cdot)(M_1) \tag{1-70}$$

$$-dM_2/dt = k_{12}(\dot{M}_1\cdot)(M_2) + k_{22}(M_1\cdot)(M_2) + k_{32}(M_3\cdot)(M_2) \tag{1-71}$$

$$-dM_3/dt = k_{13}(M_1\cdot)(M_3) + k_{23}(M_2\cdot)(M_3) + k_{33}(M_3\cdot)(M_3) \tag{1-72}$$

The requisite steady-state assumptions for the derivation of the equation of Alfrey and Goldfinger are as follows:

$$k_{12}(M_1\cdot)(M_2) + k_{13}(M_1\cdot)(M_3) + k_{21}(M_2\cdot)(M_1) + k_{31}(M_3\cdot)(M_1) \tag{1-73}$$

$$k_{21}(M_2\cdot)(M_1) + k_{23}(M_2\cdot)(M_3) = k_{12}(M_1\cdot)(M_2) + k_{32}(M_3\cdot)(M_2) \tag{1-74}$$

$$k_{31}(M_3\cdot)(M_1) + k_{32}(M_3\cdot)(M_2) = k_{13}(M_1\cdot)(M_3) + k_{23}(M_2\cdot)(M_3) \tag{1-75}$$

These steady-state assumptions merely indicate that the rate of appearance and the rate of disappearance of given radicals $M_1\cdot$, $M_2\cdot$, and $M_3\cdot$ are equal. Combinations of the equations led to the following relationships for terpolymerization:

$$dM_1:dM_2:dM_3::m_1:m_2:m_3$$

$$::M_1\left[\frac{M_1}{r_{31}r_{21}} + \frac{M_2}{r_{21}r_{32}} + \frac{M_3}{r_{31}r_{23}}\right]\left[M_1 + \frac{M_2}{r_{12}} + \frac{M_3}{r_{13}}\right]$$

$$:\ M_2\left[\frac{M_1}{r_{12}r_{31}} + \frac{M_2}{r_{12}r_{32}} + \frac{M_3}{r_{32}r_{13}}\right]\left[M_2 + \frac{M_1}{r_{21}} + \frac{M_3}{r_{23}}\right]$$

$$:\ M_3\left[\frac{M_1}{r_{13}r_{21}} + \frac{M_2}{r_{23}r_{12}} + \frac{M_3}{r_{13}r_{23}}\right]\left[M_3\frac{M_1}{r_{31}} + \frac{M_2}{r_{32}}\right] \tag{1-76}$$

where $r_{12} = k_{11}/k_{12}$, $r_{13} = k_{11}/k_{13}$, $r_{21} = k_{22}/k_{21}$, $r_{23} = k_{22}/k_{23}$, $r_{31} = k_{33}/k_{31}$, and $r_{32} = k_{33}/k_{32}$.

Alfrey and Goldfinger (56) also treated the circumstances in which one or two of the monomers were incapable of self-propagation. In these cases an additional terpolymerization experiment was necessary, to define requisite rate constants; however, the equations given above appear to have been too complicated for application, since the literature does not indicate that they have been subsequently employed. However, for the circumstance that M_2 and M_3 cannot add to themselves or to each other the following relationships can be derived:

$$\frac{m_1}{m_2} = 1 + \frac{r_{12}M_1}{M_2} + \frac{r_{12}M_3}{r_{13}M_2}, \qquad \frac{m_2}{m_3} = \frac{r_{13}M_2}{r_{12}M_3},$$

$$\frac{m_1}{m_3} = 1 + \frac{r_{13}M_1}{M_3} + \frac{r_{13}M_2}{r_{12}M_3}$$

Walling et al. (57) have applied this treatment to the determination of the competitive rates of addition of substituted α-methylstyrenes to the maleic anhydride radical. It may be shown from the treatment given above that

$$\frac{d[M_1]}{d[M_2]} = \frac{k_{31}[M_1]}{k_{32}[M_2]} \tag{1-77}$$

where M_1 and M_2 are substituted α-methylstyrenes and M_3 is maleic anhydride.

Table 1-6 shows the effects of nuclear substitution in α-methylstyrene on reactivity with the maleic anhydride radical.

With respect to the Alfrey–Goldfinder terpolymer equations it is significant that predictions of terpolymer composition may be based entirely upon

TABLE 1-6

Relative Reactivities of Substituted
α-Methylstyrenes with the Maleic Anhydride
Radical (Polymer)

Substituent	Relative reactivity
p-N(CH$_3$)$_2$	300
p-OCH$_3$	18.5 ± 4
p-CH$_3$	1.72 ± 0.12
None	1.00
p-F	0.72 ± 0.10
p-Cl	0.79 ± 0.02
p-Br	0.73 ± 0.15
m-Br	0.96 ± 0.14
p-CN	0.96 ± 0.57

data obtained in binary systems. Walling and Briggs (58) and Fordyce et al. (59) have confirmed the Alfrey–Goldfinger terpolymer equations experimentally. The data are shown in Tables 1–7 and 1–8.

Fordyce, Chapin, and Ham have also substituted into the Alfrey–Goldfinger terpolymer equations the Alfrey–Price Q–e relationship to obtain the following equations:

$$\frac{d[M_1]}{d[M_2]} = \frac{\begin{array}{c}[M_1]^2Q_1^2\exp(-e_1^2) + [M_1][M_2]Q_1Q_2\exp(-e_1e_2) \\ + \cdots + [M_1][M_n]Q_1Q_n\exp(-e_1e_n)\end{array}}{\begin{array}{c}[M_2]^2Q_2^2\exp(-e_n^2) + [M_1][M_2]Q_1Q_2\exp(-e_1e_2) \\ + \cdots + [M_2][M_n]Q_2Q_n\exp(-e_2e_n)\end{array}} \quad (1\text{-}78)$$

TABLE 1-7

Three- and Four-Component Polymerizations of Monomers at 60°C[a]

Expt. no.	Feed Content, mole-%	Monomers[a]	Time, hr	Yield, wt-%	Polymer Found, mole-%	Calcd., mole-%
1	31.24	S	16	18.2	43.4	44.3
	31.12	M			39.4	41.2
	37.64	V			17.2	14.5
2	35.10	M	12	18.1	50.8	54.3
	28.24	A			28.3	29.7
	36.66	V			20.9	16.0
3	34.03	S	8	16.5	52.8	52.4
	34.49	A			36.7	40.5
	31.48	V			10.5	7.1
4	35.92	S	3.5	13.6	44.7	43.6
	36.03	M			26.1	29.2
	28.05	A			29.2	26.2
5	53.23	S	5.75	15.4	52.6	52.9
	26.51	M			20.2	23.2
	20.26	A			27.2	23.9
6	28.32	S	4.5	18.4	38.4	41.4
	28.24	M			23.0	22.7
	43.44	A			38.6	35.9
7	27.76	S	5.75	17.2	36.4	36.8
	52.06	M			40.6	43.8
	20.18	A			23.0	19.4
8	25.21	S	8.5	18.9	40.7	41.0
	25.48	M			25.5	27.3
	25.40	A			25.8	24.8
	23.91	V			8.0	6.9

[a] Styrene (S), Methyl Methacrylate (M), Acrylonitrile (A), and Vinylidene Chloride (V).

TABLE 1-8

Predictions of Multicomponent Polymer Composition

Monomer	Initial monomer compn., wt-%	Predicted polymer compn., wt-%	Polymer compn. by anal., wt-%
Styrene	32.0	65.7	67.1
Acrylonitrile	48.8	33.7	32.5
Vinyl chloride	19.2	0.6	0.4
Styrene	30.2	70.5	70.4
Acrylonitrile	15.4	26.4	26.2
Vinyl chloride	54.4	3.1	3.4
Styrene	60	75.5	76.1
Methyl acrylate	20	23.4	22.8
Vinyl chloride	20	1.1	1.1

$$\frac{d[M_1]}{d[M_n]} = \frac{\begin{aligned}[M_1]^2 Q_1^2 \exp\left(-e_1^2\right) + [M_1][M_2]Q_1 Q_2 \exp\left(-e_1 e_2\right) \\ + \cdots + [M_1][M_n]Q_1 Q_n \exp\left(-e_1 e_n\right)\end{aligned}}{\begin{aligned}[M_n]^2 Q_n^2 \exp\left(-e_n^2\right) + [M_1][M_n]Q_1 Q_n \exp\left(-e_1 e_n\right) \\ + \cdots + [M_n][M_{n-1}]Q_n Q_{n-1} \exp\left(-e_n e_{n-1}\right)\end{aligned}} \tag{1-79}$$

In this form the terpolymer equation is more amenable for application to many systems. Recently this expression received considerable attention in approaching problems of the general relationships of monomer reactivity in copolymerizations and in the study of such effects as alternation and clustering.

B. General Relationships among Monomers in Copolymerization

Although the effects due to polarity, steric factors, and resonance stabilization were appreciated by early workers in the field, it remained for Alfrey and Price (60) to present relationships that for the first time quantified these factors in predicting monomer reactivity ratios in copolymerization. Specifically, the Alfrey–Price Q–e scheme proposed that reactivity ratios were a function of two fundamental parameters: Q, representing the resonance stabilization of monomer and its corresponding radical adduct in copolymerization, and e, representing the polarity of monomer and radical adduct in copolymerization. Accordingly,

$$k_{11}/k_{12} = (Q_1/Q_2)\exp\left[-e_1(e_1 - e_2)\right] \qquad (1\text{-}80)$$

$$k_{22}/k_{21} = (Q_2/Q_1)\exp\left[-e_2(e_2 - e_1)\right] \qquad (1\text{-}81)$$

Although the $Q-e$ scheme is generally regarded as an empirical relationship and does not adequately predict the copolymerization of many monomers with precision, it is the first successful tool for assessing the reactivity of untried combinations of monomers in binary and multicomponent polymerizations (61). Moreover, this treatment has the most desirable effect of allowing for the first time the elucidation of polar factors: specifically, the extent of positivity or negativity of monomers in their reactivity behavior. The resonance stabilization of monomers and radicals also was assessed. Furthermore, certain specific substituent groups, such as methyl and chlorine groups, were found to have fairly reproducible additive effects when applied to monomers and their derivatives. In spite of the fact that the equations have been subjected to numerous theoretical analyses none of these approaches has yielded results inconsistent with them. Theoretical proof of the equations, however, remains as elusive as ever. Indeed, the fundamental problem of applying the same criterion (i.e., resonance stabilization) to monomers of very high and very low resonance stability appears to be at present an insurmountable obstacle to the universal application of the $Q-e$ scheme.

The inherent deficiencies of the $Q-e$ scheme have led to a new approach, made by Ham (62), to the general problem of monomer reactivity in copolymerization. This approach endeavored to build a scheme of monomer reactivity resting on the simple premise that in terpolymerization and multicomponent polymerization the probability of producing sequences in one direction was equal to the probability of producing the same sequences in the reverse direction. Although this hypothesis has no direct mathematical basis, it has a definite appeal in that it would eliminate the requirement for characteristic terpolymer chains, for example, which owe their sequence distribution to the direction in which they were formed.

It is inherent in the Alfrey–Goldfinger terpolymer equation that such a circumstance is treated; however, it would be most disconcerting to many polymer chemists to find that their efforts to produce uniform terpolymers were hampered by the circumstance that the entire character of the polymer chain could be influenced by the direction of propagation. Indeed, such a circumstance might lead to the expectation that so-called uniform terpolymers could be fractionated to yield two species, each characteristic of the direction of propagation. Such a prospect is neither appealing nor, more important, in harmony with nature's well-known inclination to more simplified situations. Accordingly, a premise such as the one to be described in Eq. (1-84) has considerable appeal, since only one species might be expected in terpolymerization or multicomponent polymerizations. The problem, of course, does not arise in binary copolymerization, since one encounters there a trivial case $(P_{12}P_{21} = P_{21}P_{12})$. However, when one expresses the conventional Alfrey–Goldfinger terpolymer equation in terms of probabilities, one arrives at two relationships:

$$\frac{d[M_1]}{d[M_2]} = \frac{P_{21}P_{31} + P_{32}P_{21} + P_{23}P_{31}}{P_{12}P_{32} + P_{31}P_{12} + P_{13}P_{32}} \tag{1-82}$$

$$\frac{d[M_1]}{d[M_3]} = \frac{P_{21}P_{31} + P_{32}P_{21} + P_{23}P_{31}}{P_{13}P_{23} + P_{21}P_{13} + P_{12}P_{23}} \tag{1-83}$$

The numerators of both equations are the same and presumably give the various ways of producing M_1 sequences in a polymer chain. Correspondingly, the denominators indicate means of producing M_2 and M_3 sequences. We turn now to the equation

$$P_{12}P_{23}P_{31} = P_{13}P_{32}P_{21} \tag{1-84}$$

This relationship may be regarded as having the following significance. The over-all probability of initiating M_2, M_3, and M_1 sequences preceded by M_1, M_2, and M_3, respectively, is equal to the probability of terminating the same sequences with M_1, M_2, and M_3 units, respectively. As shown in Table 1-9, the relationship holds moderately well for many ternary and related binary systems.

Of considerable importance is the finding that relationship (1-84), applied to the Alfrey–Goldfinger terpolymerization equation, results in a simplified expression. Specifically, the equality $P_{21}P_{12}(P_{32} + P_{31}) = P_{12}P_{21}(P_{31} + P_{32})$ is added to both sides of the equation. One obtains the relationship

$$\frac{P_{21}}{P_{12}} = \frac{P_{21}P_{31} + P_{23}P_{31} + P_{32}P_{21}}{P_{12}P_{32} + P_{31}P_{12} + P_{13}P_{32}} \tag{1-85}$$

One can see from the conventional terpolymer equation that

$$\frac{d[M_1]}{d[M_2]} = \frac{P_{21}}{P_{12}} = \frac{P_{21}P_{31} + P_{23}P_{31} + P_{32}P_{21}}{P_{12}P_{32} + P_{31}P_{12} + P_{13}P_{32}} \tag{1-86}$$

TABLE 1-9

Product Probabilities of Various Monomer Combinations

Monomers[a]	$P_{12}P_{23}P_{31} = P_{13}P_{32}P_{21}$ [b]
St, MM, AN	0.053 = 0.0454
St, MA, VCl	0.00504 = 0.00435
	0.0157 = 0.00284[c]
St, MM, VCl$_2$	0.042 = 0.023
MM, AN, VCl$_2$	0.0262 = 0.0467
St, MM, VP	0.051 = 0.0562
St, MM, MA	0.0348 = 0.046
St, AN, AA	0.0491 = 0.0199
	0.0164 = 0.085[d]
St, MA, AN	0.050 = 0.0122
MM, MA, VCl	0.00782 = 0.0055
	0.0131 = 0.00315[c]
AN, MA, VCl	0.0168 = 0.0167
VAc, VBz, NVP	0.0451 = 0.0461
VCl, VAc, VCr	0.0162 = 0.0222

[a] AA = acrylic acid, AN = acrylonitrile, MA = methyl acrylate, MM = methyl methacrylate, NVP = N-vinyl-pyrrolidone, St = styrene, VAc = vinyl acetate, VBz = vinyl benzoate, VCl = vinyl chloride, VCl$_2$ = vinylidene chloride, VCr = vinylene carbonate, VP = 2-vinylpyridine.

[b] Calculated for terpolymerization of equimolar mixtures.

[c] MA–VCl by Marvel and Schwen; others by Doak.

[d] AN–AA from Ito and Suzuki; St–AA from Chapin, Ham, and Mills; both instead of unpublished data by Young.

In a similar way one may add $P_{13}P_{31}(P_{23} + P_{21})$ to both sides of Eq. (1-84) and obtain the following relationship:

$$\frac{d[M_1]}{d[M_3]} = \frac{P_{31}}{P_{13}} = \frac{P_{21}P_{31} + P_{23}P_{31} + P_{32}P_{21}}{P_{13}P_{23} + P_{12}P_{23} + P_{21}P_{13}} \tag{1-87}$$

There are many advantages to the simplified expressions so obtained:

$$\frac{d[M_1]}{d[M_2]} = \frac{P_{21}}{P_{12}} \tag{1-88}$$

$$\frac{d[M_1]}{d[M_3]} = \frac{P_{31}}{P_{13}} \tag{1-89}$$

These expressions allow prediction of terpolymer composition in a far simpler manner than previously possible. It is of particular significance that the ratio $d[M_1]/d[M_2]$ is not dependent on additions to radical M_3· and, furthermore, that the ratio $d[M_1]/d[M_3]$ is not dependent on additions to radical $[M_2\cdot]$. Accordingly, reactivity ratios involving such additions may be neglected for the purpose of determining the appropriate ratios.

Of course, one will find immediately the analogy between the simple binary copolymerization relationship

$$d[M_1]/d[M_2] = P_{21}/P_{12} \qquad (1\text{-}90)$$

and that for the new terpolymer relationship. However, in the case of the terpolymer relationship the probabilities represent possibilities of the addition of M_1, M_2, and M_3 to radicals, whereas in the binary case only additions of M_1 and M_2 monomers to radicals are involved.

It was deemed desirable to check the validity of the new simplified terpolymer equations with actual reported data. The equations were applied to the data reported by Walling and Briggs (58) for the system styrene–methyl methacrylate–acrylonitrile–vinylidene chloride. Agreement between calculated and reported results from the simplified equations was quite good, as shown in Table 1-10. Adjustments in the value of r_{31} led to improved values for ratios of $[M_1]/[M_3]$ and suggest that the application of these equations offers opportunities to arrive at more precise reactivity ratios when the value are either very large or very small.

C. Calculation of Reactivity Parameters for Monomers

Of even more significance is the fact that the new relationships

$$P_{12}P_{23}P_{31} = P_{13}P_{32}P_{21} = \mathscr{P} \qquad (1\text{-}91)$$

where $\mathscr{P}$ is a characteristic constant, suggest that, when the copolymerization

TABLE 1-10

Application of the Simplified Equations to Terpolymerization

			Polymer compn., $[M_1]/[M_2]$ ratio		
Monomer compn., mole-%				Calcd. from simplified	Calcd. from Alfrey–Goldfinger
SM	MMA	AN	Found	eq.	eq.
35.92	36.03	28.05	1.70	1.44	1.49
53.23	26.51	20.26	2.60	2.26	2.27
28.32	28.24	43.44	1.67	1.76	1.82
27.76	52.06	20.18	0.898	0.84	0.84

behavior of systems M_1-M_2 and M_2-M_3 is known, one may predict the copolymerization behavior of system M_1-M_3. Such a possibility rests upon the demonstration that the product probabilities involved are constant and characteristic of some unique parameters associated with the monomers employed (63).

As a first approach the $\mathscr{P}$ values were determined for a large variety of ternary systems, and it was found that, when the three monomers involved are conjugated, the value for $\mathscr{P}$, assuming equimolar proportions of each monomer, is approximately 0.037. When one or two of the three monomers, however, are unconjugated and the remainder is conjugated, then it is found to be about 0.006. Accordingly, when the only assumption involved is that one knows whether a novel monomer is conjugated or unconjugated, one may calculate the binary copolymerization reactivity ratios for the untried pair from the following relationships obtained by substitution into Eq. (1-91):

$$\frac{r_{13}}{r_{13} + r_{12}r_{13} + r_{12}} \cdot \frac{r_{21}}{r_{21} + r_{21}r_{23} + r_{23}} \cdot \frac{r_{32}}{r_{32} + r_{32}r_{31} + r_{31}}$$

$$= \frac{r_{12}}{r_{12} + r_{12}r_{13} + r_{13}} \cdot \frac{r_{31}}{r_{31} + r_{31}r_{32} + r_{32}} \cdot \frac{r_{23}}{r_{23} + r_{23}r_{21} + r_{21}} = 0.037$$

$$(1\text{-}92)$$

$$\text{Same} = 0.006 \qquad\qquad\qquad (1\text{-}93)$$

Hence, the value for $\mathscr{P}$ is known, and so is that for all but two of the reactivity ratios. The solution of the simultaneous equations leads to the determination of the untried reactivity ratios.

It was soon recognized that the limitation of the value of $\mathscr{P}$ to either 0.006 or 0.037 represented too great a simplification of the results, although it was certainly true that there was a definite line of demarcation between systems of three conjugated monomers and systems containing one or two unconjugated monomers. There was a substantial range of values of $\mathscr{P}$ in each of these categories. It appeared probable that the individual values of $\mathscr{P}$ were in some definite manner related to the reactivity characteristics of the individual monomers comprising $\mathscr{P}$. Specifically, it was proposed that there existed for each monomer a p that could be regarded as a probability that the monomer would attack a different radical in the presence of two unlike monomers. Obviously; one of the three monomers would be competing for its own radical. It was furthermore suggested that $\mathscr{P}$ should be the product of these probabilities p, which were characteristic of individual monomers.

Accordingly, by taking available experimental information on binary copolymerizations it was possible to calculate p's for various common monomers, specifically for styrene (x), acrylonitrile (y), methyl methacrylate

(z), and methyl acrylate (w). It was possible to formulate four equations, each in three unknowns:

$$xyz = 0.049$$

$$yzw = 0.0279$$

$$xzw = 0.0417$$

$$xyw = 0.031$$

These equations were solved for the four unknowns and the following values obtained:

x (styrene)	$= 0.434$
y (acrylonitrile)	$= 0.291$
z (methyl methacrylate)	$= 0.390$
w (methyl acrylate)	$= 0.248$

In a similar way values for styrene, methyl methacrylate, acrylonitrile, and butadiene were obtained from the corresponding systems of three monomers and the individual reactivity parameters determined:

Styrene	0.531
Methyl methacrylate	0.313
Acrylonitrile	0.295
Butadiene	0.284

Once the validity of this approach has been established, it is obvious that one might determine the reactivity of the parameter in copolymerization for a new monomer in a more direct fashion: simply by application of

$$p_1 = \mathscr{P}/p_2 p_3 \tag{1-94}$$

Fortunately, this equation was found to be applicable to systems of two conjugated monomers and one unconjugated monomer. In the case of data on two unconjugated monomers and one conjugated monomer it was found that the following equation applied:

$$p_1 = (\mathscr{P}/p_2 p_3)(0.006/0.037) \tag{1-95}$$

A moderate amount of information on copolymerizations of unconjugated monomers is available, so it was desirable to formulate an equation covering such systems. The following equation resulted:

$$p_1 = (\mathscr{P}/p_2 p_3)(0.006/0.037)^3 \tag{1-96}$$

TABLE 1-11

Monomer Reactivity Parameters

Monomer	p
α-Methylstyrene	0.52
Styrene	0.47
Methacrylic acid	0.39
Methyl methacrylate	0.39
Methyacrylonitrile	0.30
Butadiene	0.29
Acrylonitrile	0.28
Methyl acrylate	0.26
Vinylidene chloride	0.17
Vinyl chloride	0.054
N-Vinylpyrrolidone	0.053
Vinyl acetate	0.045
Vinyl benzoate	0.045
Vinylene carbonate	0.026

Table 1-11 gives in summary form the results of these calculations based on reported data. It is apparent that values of the reactivity parameter p range from as much as about 0.5 to as little as 0.025. For conjugated monomers, such as styrene and methyl methacrylate, the values of the reactivity parameter are bunched between about 0.25 and 0.5. For unconjugated monomers, such as vinyl chloride and vinyl acetate, the values are about 0.05. A definite anomaly appears in the case of vinylidene chloride, which has a value of 0.170. It is apparent that this result must follow from the somewhat conjugated nature of one of the chlorines in this monomer. It is interesting that the quite simple relationship $r_{13}r_{32}r_{21} = r_{12}r_{23}r_{31}$, which proceeds from this study, was not previously recognized, particularly since the Alfrey–Price scheme from which it may also be derived had been published in 1947. The relationship results from the incorporation of the equation

$$k_{ij} = P_i Q_j \exp\left(-e_i e_j\right) \tag{1-97}$$

into the expressions for the various reactivity ratios (63):

$$r_{13} = k_{11}/k_{13} = (Q_1/Q_3)\exp\left[-e_1(e_1 - e_3)\right] \tag{1-98}$$

$$r_{32} = k_{33}/k_{32} = (Q_3/Q_2)\exp\left[-e_3(e_3 - e_3)\right] \tag{1-99}$$

$$r_{21} = k_{22}/k_{21} = (Q_2/Q_1)\exp\left[-e_2(e_2 - e_1)\right] \tag{1-100}$$

Accordingly,

$$r_{13}r_{32}r_{21} = \exp\left(-e_1^2 + e_1 e_3 - e_3^2 + e_2 e_3 - e_2^2 + e_1 e_2\right) \tag{1-101}$$

Similarly, it is found that

$$r_{12}r_{23}r_{31} = \exp\left(-e_1^2 + e_1e_3 - e_3^2 + e_2e_3 - e_2^2 + e_1e_2\right) \quad \text{(1-102)}$$

Accordingly,

$$r_{13}r_{32}r_{21} = r_{12}r_{23}r_{31} \quad \text{(1-103)}$$

Furthermore, it will be noted that Eqs. (1-92) and (1-93) are special cases of

$$P_{12}P_{23}P_{31} = P_{13}P_{32}P_{21} = \mathscr{P} \quad \text{(1-91)}$$

for equimolar monomer concentrations. More generally, for all monomer concentrations it may be shown that the relationship is consistent with the Q–e scheme, because a common denominator is possessed:

$$\left(\frac{M_2r_{13}}{M_2r_{13} + M_1r_{12}r_{13} + M_3r_{12}}\right)\left(\frac{M_3r_{21}}{M_3r_{21} + M_2r_{23}r_{21} + M_1r_{23}}\right)$$

$$\times \left(\frac{M_1r_{32}}{M_1r_{32} + M_3r_{31}r_{32} + M_2r_{31}}\right) = \left(\frac{M_3r_{12}}{M_3r_{12} + M_1r_{13}r_{12} + M_2r_{13}}\right)$$

$$\times \left(\frac{M_2r_{31}}{M_2r_{31} + M_3r_{31}r_{32} + M_1r_{32}}\right)\left(\frac{M_1r_{23}}{M_1r_{23} + M_2r_{21}r_{23} + M_3r_{31}}\right) \quad \text{(1-104)}$$

It is obvious that demonstration of the validity of Eqs. (1-91) and (1-103) raises the possibility of the validity of

$$P_{12}P_{23}P_{34}P_{41} = P_{14}P_{43}P_{32}P_{21} \quad \text{(1-105)}$$

where, of course, each probability includes possibilities of the addition of any of four monomers to each radical. These may be as shown in the following example:

$$P_{12} = \frac{k_{12}[M_1\cdot][M_2]}{k_{12}[M_1\cdot][M_2] + k_{11}[M_1\cdot][M_1] + k_{13}[M_1\cdot][M_3] + k_{14}[M_1\cdot][M_4]} \quad \text{(1-106)}$$

$$= \frac{M_2/r_{12}}{(M_2/r_{12}) + M_1 + (M_3/r_{13}) + (M_4/r_{14})} \quad \text{(1-107)}$$

This premise was applied to the system styrene–methyl methacrylate–acrylonitrile–vinylidene chloride. Assuming equimolar concentrations, one obtains from Eq. (1-105)

$$\left(\frac{r_{13}r_{14}}{r_{13}r_{14} + r_{12}r_{13}r_{14} + r_{12}r_{14} + r_{12}r_{13}}\right)$$

$$\times \left(\frac{r_{21}r_{24}}{r_{21}r_{24} + r_{21}r_{23}r_{24} + r_{23}r_{24} + r_{21}r_{23}}\right)$$

$$\times \left(\frac{r_{31}r_{32}}{r_{31}r_{32} + r_{31}r_{32}r_{34} + r_{32}r_{34} + r_{31}r_{34}}\right)$$

$$\times \left(\frac{r_{42}r_{43}}{r_{42}r_{43} + r_{41}r_{42}r_{43} + r_{41}r_{43} + r_{41}r_{42}}\right)$$

$$= \left(\frac{r_{12}r_{13}}{r_{13}r_{14} + r_{12}r_{13}r_{14} + r_{12}r_{14} + r_{12}r_{13}}\right)$$

$$\times \left(\frac{r_{41}r_{42}}{r_{42}r_{43} + r_{41}r_{42}r_{43} + r_{41}r_{43} + r_{41}r_{42}}\right)$$

$$\times \left(\frac{r_{31}r_{34}}{r_{31}r_{32} + r_{31}r_{32}r_{34} + r_{32}r_{34} + r_{31}r_{34}}\right)$$

$$\times \left(\frac{r_{23}r_{24}}{r_{21}r_{24} + r_{21}r_{23}r_{24} + r_{23}r_{24} + r_{21}r_{23}}\right) \tag{1-108}$$

Substitution of the reactivity ratios $r_{12} = 0.52$, $r_{21} = 0.46$, $r_{23} = 1.35$, $r_{32} = 0.18$, $r_{34} = 0.91$, $r_{43} = 0.37$, $r_{13} = 0.41$, $r_{31} = 0.04$, $r_{14} = 1.85$, and $r_{41} = 0.085$ leads to

$$P_{12}P_{23}P_{34}P_{41} = P_{14}P_{43}P_{32}P_{21} \tag{1-105}$$

$$(0.326)(0.172)(0.0338)(0.60) = (0.0915)(0.138)(0.169)(0.505)$$

$$0.00114 = 0.00108$$

Then the following equation also is correct:

$$r_{14}r_{43}r_{32}r_{21} = r_{12}r_{23}r_{34}r_{41} \tag{1-109}$$

Then, of course, for any multicomponent polymerization the highly simplified Eqs. (1-110), (1-111), and (1-112) result in

$$m_1/m_2 = P_{21}/P_{12} \tag{1-110}$$

$$m_1/m_3 = P_{31}/P_{13} \tag{1-111}$$

$$m_i/m_j = P_{ji}/P_{ij} \tag{1-112}$$

TABLE 1-12

Monomer	Compn., mole-%	Polymer composition, mole-%		
		Found	Calcd. from Walling–Briggs equations	Calcd. from simplified equations
Acrylonitrile	25.4	25.8	24.8	23.2
Methyl methacrylate	25.5	25.5	27.3	27.8
Styrene	25.2	40.7	41.0	42.7
Vinylidene chloride	23.9	8.0	6.9	6.1

Applying these results to the data, reported by Walling and Briggs (58), on styrene–methyl methacrylate–acrylonitrile–vinylidene chloride, one obtains the encouraging agreement shown in Table 1-12 (63).

The Q–e scheme, and indeed that of any other system which endeavors to determine unique reactivity parameters for monomers, has the advantage of allowing one to determine characteristic values for a given monomer by copolymerization of this monomer with two or three reference monomers. Once these parameters are determined, substitution into suitable equations, such as those for the Q–e scheme, allows the direct calculation of the copolymerization reactivity ratios for an untried pair. In this way for a novel monomer it is only necessary to make determinations of reactivity ratios with two or three other monomers to obtain parameters suitable for prediction of the copolymerization behavior of this monomer with any of the hundreds of other monomers for which similar parameters may be determined. Most approaches to this subject have emphasized the value of the Q–e scheme as a labor-saving technique. It is far more pertinent to regard it as a means of unifying concepts about monomer reactivity by showing over-all characteristics of monomers that lend themselves to copolymerization.

The underlying assumption of the Q–e scheme is that the rate constant k_{ij} for the reaction of given monomer j with radical i is given by the following relationship: $k_{ij} = P_i Q_j \exp\left(-e_i e_j\right)$. In this case P_i is a constant characteristic of the nature of radical i, Q_j is the reactivity of the monomer j, and e_i and e_j are the polarities of radical and monomer, respectively. It is important to note that the same polarity factor e is employed in this treatment for monomer and corresponding radical. When this equation is expressed in the form of a reactivity ratio of monomers j and k with a given free radical i, the radical reactivity constant P_i cancels out, and one obtains

$$\frac{k_{ij}}{k_{ik}} = \left(\frac{Q_j}{Q_k}\right) \exp\left[-e_i(e_j - e_k)\right] \qquad (1\text{-}113)$$

Accordingly, in binary copolymerization r_1 and r_2 may be expressed as follows:

$$r_1 = \left(\frac{k_{11}}{k_{12}}\right) = \left(\frac{Q_1}{Q_2}\right) \exp\left[-e_1(e_1 - e_2)\right] \qquad (1\text{-}114)$$

$$r_2 = \left(\frac{k_{22}}{k_{21}}\right) = \left(\frac{Q_2}{Q_1}\right) \exp\left[-e_2(e_2 - e_1)\right] \qquad (1\text{-}115)$$

An earlier book, *Copolymerization* (64), stated that the introduction of an additional chlorine atom into vinyl chloride, methyl acrylate, or butadiene caused a similar shift in log Q and in e ($\Delta \log Q = +0.7$, $\Delta e = +0.4$).

Similarly, the introduction of a methyl group into acrylonitrile and methyl acrylate caused approximately the same shift ($\Delta \log Q = +0.4$, $\Delta e = -0.35$). At this point these results should be regarded as interesting but not necessarily conclusive. It remains to be rigorously demonstrated that the contribution of functional groups to monomer reactivity is additive in nature.

In addition to the obvious conclusions about the Q–e scheme, that conjugated monomers tend to have high Q values and that e values are measures of the electron-donating or electron-withdrawing character of substituents, there are several other general observations that have been made. It has been observed by Alfrey and Young (65) that in the case of ring-substituted styrenes the Q values obtained are very similar to those of styrene. Principally, the effect of substituents is to alter e values. Correlations of the e values with the Hammett σ values are obtained and, since Q values do not differ substantially, it is concluded that the reactivity ratios themselves are correlatable with Hammett σ values.

The presence in the two *ortho* positions of styrene of large groups may force the vinyl group out of coplanarity with the benzene ring and lead to steric inhibition of resonance. Accordingly, pentachlorostyrene has a Q value that is only about 20% of that of styrene.

Several other important effects have been recognized. Sulfide, sulfone, and sulfonate groups have been studied in some detail. Price and Zomlefer (66) have found that methyl vinyl sulfide has a high Q value and negative e value, whereas methyl vinyl sulfone appears to have a positive e value and a low Q value. They have stated that the electron-donating character of the sulfide group and the electron-withdrawing character of the sulfone group, indicated by this evidence, is in harmony with other chemical behavior.

These data are perhaps the best existing evidence that sulfur—oxygen bond should be regarded as a semipolar bond rather than as a normal unsaturated covalent bond.

An obvious limitation of the Q–e scheme, although one probably necessary for its general applicability, is the assignment of similar polarity values to radical and monomer. Wall (67) has suggested that the following equations might apply, in which three parameters are proposed: Q, e, and e^*. In this case e refers to the polarity of the monomer and e^* to its radical adduct. Wall's expressions are:

$$r_1 = (Q_1/Q_2) \exp\left[-e_1^*(e_2 - e_1)\right] \tag{1-116}$$

$$r_2 = (Q_2/Q_1) \exp\left[-e_2^*(e_2 - e_1)\right] \tag{1-117}$$

Some success has been encountered in the extension of the Q–e scheme to chain-transfer reactions. Fuhrman and Mesrobian (68) have done most of the work in this area. Essentially, the treatment is that of regarding the chain-transfer solvent as a monomer and otherwise proceeding as in the case of two monomers. A corresponding equation, similar in form to the Alfrey–Price relationship, is obtained, where C is the chain-transfer constant:

$$C = \frac{k_{tr}}{k_{11}} = \frac{Q_{tr}}{Q_{11}} \exp\left[-e_1(e_{tr} - e_1)\right] \tag{1-118}$$

It is interesting to note that this treatment does not deal with the reactivity and polarity of the solvent radical (S·). Application of this equation to chain-transfer experiments involving carbon tetrabromide with various monomers gave a desirable amount of agreement. The results are shown in Table 1-13.

TABLE 1-13

Observed and Calculated Chain-Transfer Constants for
Carbon Tetrabromide |after Fuhrman and Mesrobian (68)|†

Monomer	Chain-transfer constant C obsd.	Chain-transfer constant C calcd.
p-Chlorostyrene	5.2	3.1
Methacrylonitrile	0.07	0.14
Methyl acrylate	0.41	0.40
Methyl methacrylate	0.27	$(0.27)^a$
Styrene	2.2	$(2.2)^a$
Vinyl acetate	39	89

† By permission of the American Chemical Society.
^{a} Values in parentheses used as bases for Q_{tr} and e_{tr}.

TABLE 1-14

Substrate	α	β
Acrylonitrile	−3.1	5.3
n-Butyl mercaptan	−4.8	6.05
Carbon tetrabromide	−4.3	5.25
Chloroform	−1.4	0.9
Methyl acrylate	−3.0	5.2
Methyl methacrylate	−1.4	4.9
Styrene	0	4.8
Vinyl chloride	−1.4	3.65

A somewhat different approach has been employed by Bamford and Jenkins (69), which proposes a relationship between the rate constant k for the reaction between any radical and any substrate in terms of the rate constant for a specific reaction, that is, hydrogen abstraction between the radical $R\cdot_i$ and toluene $k_{i,T}$, a standard substrate. Of the other parameters σ represents the polarity of the radical $R\cdot_i$ and α and β are characteristic of the substrate. Several values reported by Bamford and Jenkins are given in Table 1-14.

Significantly, in free-radical polymerization the application of this treatment yields the result that the value of α for a monomer and σ for a radical are closely related. Bamford and Jenkins suggest that α is equal to $-\mu^2\sigma$, where $\mu^2 = 5.3$. Such a result leads to the conclusion that the polarities for monomer and radical adduct should be approximately equal.

D. Approaches to Theoretical Treatment of Monomer Reactivity

It is recognized that the Q–e equation is essentially an empirical relationship, since results obtained from it, although of definite significance in the prediction of monomer reactivity in copolymerization, are based upon a rather crude electrostatic model of polar effects. More recent attempts have been made at formulating a rigorous theoretical basis of predicting monomer reactivity in copolymerization. Some of these studies have the effect of suggesting possible theoretical bases of some of the effects expressed in the Q and e parameters of various monomers. The activation energies of the various radical–monomer additions have been calculated by Evans et al. (70). In this procedure two intersecting potential-energy surfaces (one for the initial state and the other for the final state) have been constructed, and an estimate has been made of the resonance energy in the region of intersection of the surfaces. The conclusion is reached that high monomer reactivity correlates with a substantial gain in resonance stabilization on addition of monomer to radical. Further, the suggestion that the Q value of a monomer can be regarded as the quantity $\exp[(R_A - R_M)/RT]$, where R_M and R_A are the resonance energies of monomer and radical adduct, respectively.

In another approach Hayashi et al. have determined the π conjugation energy in radical–monomer systems by using an LCAO molecular orbital technique (71,72). Results led to reactivity ratios that agreed well with reported values. The π localization energies of several vinyl compounds have been determined by Fueno et al. (73), and correlations with methyl affinities were shown. These workers suggest that there is a relationship between P and Q and the localization energies of radical and monomer. Furthermore, their work suggests that the $e_i e_j$ product is probably related to the stabilization energy in the transition state between monomer and radical adduct.

Recent work by Levinson (74) has furthered the approach of Hayashi. In this new approach resonance and polar factors are included. Parallels are drawn between the e value and the electron affinity of a monomer and between the Q value and the localization energy. The MO treatment in general requires only two parameters for each type of atom, in contrast to the Q–e scheme, which requires two parameters for each monomer.

1-12. CHAIN TRANSFER IN POLYMERIZATION

The phenomenon of molecular-weight reduction in radical polymerization caused by the presence of solvent has been known for many years. In 1937 Flory (75) suggested that this phenomenon might be explained by radical mechanisms in which the reactions were as follows:

$$R(M)_n\cdot + SX \rightarrow R(M)_n X + S\cdot \tag{1-119}$$

$$S\cdot + M \rightarrow M\cdot \tag{1-120}$$

where M is a vinyl monomer, SX is a solvent molecule, and X is a radical-extractable group. It is seen that the product of the reaction is dead polymer and a new radical. If the new radical is active enough, a new chain is initiated by the addition of more monomer. If the rate of addition of monomer to the new solvent radical is rapid enough, no change in over-all rate of polymerization will be observed. Generally speaking, the addition of chain-transfer agents tends to reduce the rate of polymerization. There is no well-documented instance in which the rate of polymerization has been increased by the presence of the chain-transfer agent (except for redox effects arising from catalyst–telogen interaction).

It is reasonable to expect that the rate of polymerization in the absence of the chain-transfer agent is a maximum toward which chain-transfer polymerization might approach. Conceivably, the first monomer unit or the first two might be added at an enhanced rate, but thereafter the rate of addition would be only a function of the monomer radical and not of the solvent radical.

Of course, the molecular weight of polymer produced in the presence of chain-transfer agents is always lower than that in the absence of such agents. Subsequent work confirmed Flory's hypothesis. In particular, work by Breitenbach and Maschin (76) indicated that in the polymerization of styrene in the presence of carbon tetrachloride polymers that contained four chlorine atoms per molecule were obtained. Moreover, studies of vinyl acetate polymerization in benzene solution showed a distinct relationship between the degree of polymerization and chain transfer (77). In 1943 three different groups of workers endeavored to treat chain transfer quantitatively (78–80). In particular, Mayo studied the polymerization of styrene in the presence of carbon tetrachloride. Employing these and the data of other investigators, he showed that there existed a chain transfer constant C_s, which was defined as a ratio of the rate of transfer to the rate of propagation and was related to the degree of polymerization in the presence and absence of solvent as follows:

$$1/\bar{P} = C_s[S]/[M] + 1/\bar{P}_0 \qquad (1\text{-}121)$$

where $\bar{P}$ and $\bar{P}_0$ are the degrees of polymerization in the presence and absence of chain transfer agent, respectively, and $[S]$ and $[M]$ are the concentrations of chain-transfer agent and monomer, respectively. In a plot of $1/\bar{P}$ versus $[S]/[M]$ the slope is, of course, the chain-transfer constant C_s. To yield polymers of value in this study, the polymerization in the presence of the chain-transfer agent must be interrupted at conversions sufficiently low for the ratio of solvent to monomer to be, for practical purposes, unchanged. Obviously, as the value of C_s increases, the degree of polymerization for a specific system will decrease. Generally speaking, Eq. (1-121) is satisfactory for use on monomers when the chain-transfer constant is smaller than about 5.

In the case of more active chain-transfer agents a more profitable relationship to use is the following:

$$C_s = (d \log[S])/(d \log[M]) \qquad (1\text{-}122)$$

In this case C_s is obtained from the observed relative rates of disappearance of chain-transfer agent and monomer (81). The theory of chain-transfer processes has been extended by Alfrey and Hardy (82) to systems containing more than one monomer.

Obviously, monomer can act as chain-transfer agent in polymerization. Table 1-15 shows the chain-transfer constants for three common monomers.

TABLE 1-15

Chain-Transfer Constants for Certain Monomers

Monomer	$C_m \times 10^5$	Temp., °C	Ref.
Styrene	6.0	60	17
Methyl methacrylate	0.7	60	83
Vinyl acetate	21	60	84

A. Factors Influencing Chain Transfer

Generally speaking, the usual variables such as temperature, pressure, and concentration of reactants might be expected to influence chain transfer in radical polymerization. The value of C_s, however, which is the ratio of the rate of the chain-transfer reaction to the propagation reaction, might be expected to be substantially less sensitive to temperature, since the rates of both reactions presumably would increase with an increase in temperature. In the case of the less efficient chain-transfer agents temperature can have a great effect. This result follows from the fact that, although the propagation rate constant increases, the rate constant for chain transfer increases much more rapidly. In the case of very reactive chain-transfer agents, such as mercaptans, the reverse is true; that is, the rate of increase of chain transfer with temperature is far less in the case of mercaptans than the rate of increase of the propagation reaction for most monomers. The consequence is that the chain-transfer constant can actually decrease for very reactive chain-transfer agents as the temperature is increased.

Of course, as pointed out above, the ratio of solvent to monomer has a profound effect on the chain-transfer reaction. Walling and Pellon (85) have found, however, in pressure studies on liquid monomers and telogens that in the polymerization of styrene in the presence of carbon tetrachloride there is no significant pressure effect on the chain-transfer reaction. In the case of gaseous olefins, such as ethylene, it is significant that the average length of chains in the presence of telogens can be increased by an increase in pressure. This, however, is a concentration effect rather than a pressure effect alone.

As in the case of monomers, those factors which influence the ability of a chain-transfer agent to react with a growing radical are resonance, polarity, and steric factors. The stability of the resulting telogen radical can be increased by resonance. Polarity effects are also important. Generally speaking, the chain-transfer agents that react most readily are those that yield conjugated structures in which the odd electron is in conjugation with unsaturated linkages. This phenomenon may be shown by the order of increasing stability of resulting radicals on hydrogen abstraction:

$$\text{Ph}\dot{\text{C}}\text{H}_2 \; < \; \text{Ph}_2\dot{\text{C}} \; < \; \text{Ph}_3\dot{\text{C}} \; < \; \text{PhC}_6\text{H}_4\dot{\text{C}}\text{Ph}_2$$

In the case of alkyl radicals the order of reactivity is as follows:

$$\text{R}_3\text{C} \cdot \; < \; \text{R}_2\text{CH} \cdot \; < \; \text{RCH}_2 \cdot$$

Various efforts have been made to give the order of reactivity of various radicals. A summary of the specific exchange reaction $R \cdot + XY \rightarrow RX + Y \cdot$ leads to the following result:

$$H \cdot \; > \; \text{CH}_3 \cdot \; > \; \text{Ph} \cdot \; > \; \text{RCH}_2 \cdot \; > \; \text{R}_2\text{CH} \cdot \; > \; \text{CCl}_3 \cdot \; > \; \text{R}_3\text{C} \cdot \; > \; \text{CBr}_3 \cdot$$

$$> \; \text{R}\dot{\text{C}}\text{HCOR} \; > \; \text{R}\dot{\text{C}}\text{HCN} \; > \; \text{R}\dot{\text{C}}\text{HCOOR} \; >$$

$$\text{CH}_2{=}\text{CHCH}_2 \cdot \; > \; \text{PhCH}_2 \cdot \; > \; \text{Ph}_2\text{CH} \cdot \; > \; \text{Cl} \cdot \; > \; \text{Br} \cdot \; > \; \text{Ph}_3\text{C} \cdot \; > \; \text{I} \cdot$$

Of course, the more stable the radical, the lower its reactivity in the initiation of a new chain.

B. Degradative Chain Transfer

A class of chain transfer agents that warrants special consideration is that exhibited by certain compounds such as allyl derivatives. Propagation of any of the common monomers that normally result in high-molecular-weight products in the presence of allyl compounds leads to chain transfer with the allyl compound and a consequent removal of the hydrogen from the $-\text{CH}_2 \cdot$ group. The resulting allyl radical is quite stable (that is, its tendency to add more monomer is quite low) and termination by some other means is likely to occur. Gaylord (86) investigated the order of reactivity of several allyl monomers and has determined the fraction of effective chain transfer. In another study Lewis and Mayo (87) showed that polymers containing only one to three monomer units may be obtained on the polymerization of allylic monomers in the presence of chloroform and carbon tetrachloride.

Table 1-16, based on data by Kharasch and co-workers (88,89), compares various vinyl compounds in their reactivity toward trichloromethyl radicals derived from bromotrichloromethane.

Tables 1-17 and 1-18 summarize chain-transfer constants of various compounds with styrene and methyl methacrylate radicals (90). Table 1-19 shows a comparison of chain-transfer constants for various vinyl monomers with selected chain-transfer agents (90).

C. Calculation of Reactivity Parameters for Chain-Transfer Agents

Since chain transfer may be regarded as a special case of copolymerization, in which the resulting telogen radical is incapable of adding unreacted telogen, it seems reasonable to apply the principle of chain reversibility (91)

TABLE 1-16

Olefin	Relative reactivity[a]
Styrene	>100
Butadiene	18
Cyclopentadiene	4.5
Cyclohexadiene	4.0
Indene	3.0
Methallyl chloride	1.6
β-Methylstyrene	1.1
Octene-1	1.0
Cyclopentene	0.8
Vinyl acetate	0.8
Allylbenzene	0.7
Allyl chloride	0.5
Cyclohexene	0.2

[a] Octene-1 is here regarded as unity.

to this phenomenon. As in the earlier approach involving three monomers a three-component system was constructed. This system, however, was composed of two monomers and a chain-transfer agent. It was suggested that the probability that the copolymer sequences of the following type would be terminated by telogen and the new radical-initiating copolymerization was equal to the probability of the reversed reaction:

$$p_{x1}p_{11}^{m-1}p_{12}p_{22}^{n-1}p_{23}p_{31} = p_{13}p_{32}p_{22}^{n-1}p_{21}p_{11}^{m-1}p_{1x} \qquad (1\text{-}123)$$

$$p_{12}p_{23}p_{31} = p_{13}p_{32}p_{21}$$

where 1 and 2 are monomers and 3 is a telogen, m and n are the number of 1 and 2 units in given sequences, respectively, and x is either 1 or 2 but only one of them in a given equation. In this case p_{12}, for instance, is the probability that monomer 2 will add to radical 1 in the presence of monomers 1 and 3, and p_{31} is the probability that monomer 1 will add to telogen radical 3 in the presence of monomers 2 and 3. It may be shown that, in this case much as in the combinations of three monomers, the following relationship holds for equimolar proportions of reactants:

$$\frac{r_{13}}{r_{13} + r_{13}r_{12} + r_{12}} \frac{r_{21}}{r_{21} + r_{21}r_{23} + r_{23}} \frac{1}{(k_{32}/k_{31}) + 1}$$

$$= \frac{r_{12}}{r_{12} + r_{12}r_{13} + r_{13}} \frac{k_{32}/k_{31}}{k_{32}/k_{31} + 1} \frac{r_{23}}{r_{23} + r_{23}r_{21} + r_{21}} = \mathscr{P} \qquad (1\text{-}124)$$

where $\mathscr{P}$ is a characteristic probability product.

TABLE 1-17

Chain-Transfer Constants for Radicals from Styrene

Molecule	Temp., °C	$C \times 10^4$
n-Butyl chloride	60	0.04
Isobutyl chloride	60	1.4
sec-Butyl chloride	60	1.2[a]
n-Butyl bromide	60	0.06
n-Butyl iodide	60	1.85
n-Amyl chloride	60	0.49
Methallyl chloride	60	24.0
Methylene dichloride	60	0.15
Methylene dichloride	80	9.5
Methylene dichloride	100	11.8
Methylene dibromide	60[b]	110
Methylene diiodide	60[b]	710
Ethylene dichloride	80	9.8
Bis(chloroethyl)formal	80	6
1,4-dichlorobutene-2	80	51
Styrene dibromide	60[b]	1950
Stilbene dibromide	60[b]	.3020
Chlorobenzene	80	1.5
o-Dichlorobenzene	80	3.4
p-Xylylene dibromide	60[b]	150
Benzyl chloride	60	1.56
Benzal chloride	60	50
Benzotrichloride	60	57.5
Benzyl methyl ether	68	6
p-Chlorobenzyl methyl ether	68	4
p-Bromobenzyl methyl ether	68	6
p-Cyanobenzyl methyl ether	68	20
Chloroform	60	0.5
Carbon tetrachloride	60	92
Carbon tetrachloride	100	185
Carbon tetrabromide	60	13600
Chloracetic acid	68	200
Bromoacetic acid	68	300
Iodoacetic acid	68	8000
Trichloracetic acid	60	66
Chloroacetyl chloride	60[a]	3300
Acetyl bromide	60[a]	8600[a]
Methyl chloroacetate	60	0.3
Ethyl dichloroacetate	60	1.3
Ethyl trichloroacetate	60	65
Diethyl dichloromalonate	60	30

TABLE 1-17 (Continued)

Molecule	Temp., °C	$C \times 10^4$
Diethyl bromomalonate	60	700
Diethyl dibromomalonate	60	12000
Diethyl malonate	60	0.47
Propionic acid	60	0.05
Phenylacetic acid	60	6.0
Acetic anhydride	60	0.7
Butyraldehyde	60	5.7
Acetone	80	4.1
Methyl ethyl ketone	80	5.0
Cyclohexanone	80	7.9
Benzoin	60	40
Dibenzoylmethane	60	7
Isopropyl alcohol	100	1.7
Butanol	10	0.06
tert-Butyl alcohol	100	0.55
Allyl alcohol	10	1.5
Propargyl alcohol	10	7.0
Hydroquinone	10	3.6
Acetoxime	10	2.2
Acetonitrile	10	0.44
2-Methylpropionitrile	100	2.7
n-Butylamine	60	0.5
Aniline	60	2.0
Piperidine	60	1.0
Pyridine	60	0.6
1,4-Dioxane	60	0^a
Benzene	60^b	0.018
Toluene	60^b	0.125
Ethylbenzene	60^b	0.67
Isopropylbenzene	60^b	0.82
tert-Butylbenzene	60^b	0.06
Diphenylmethane	60^b	2.3
Triphenylmethane	60^b	3.5
Fluorene	60^b	75
Pentaphenylethane	60^b	20000
Cyclohexane	60^b	0.024
Decalin	60^b	0.4
n-Heptane	60^b	0.42

[a] Value uncertain.

[b] Thermal polymerization; all others initiated by benzoyl peroxide.

TABLE 1-18

Chain-Transfer Constants for Radicals from
Methyl Methacrylate

Molecule	Temp., °C	$C \times 10^4$
n-Butyl chloride	80	1.2
Benzyl chloride	60	4.2
Chlorobenzene	80	0.2
Methylene chloride	80	0.22
Ethylene chloride	80	0.76
Propylene chloride	80	0.68
Chloroform	80	1.4
1,1,1-Trichloroethane	80	0.6
sym-Tetrachloroethane	80	0.2
Carbon tetrachloride	80	2.4
Carbon tetrabromide	60	2700
Acetic acid	80	0.24
Ethyl acetate	80	0.24
Isobutyric acid	80	0.9
Acetone	80	0.23
Methyl ethyl ketone	80	0.7
Methyl isobutyl ketone	80	0.7
Diethyl ketone	80	1.8
Isopropyl alcohol	80	1.9
n-Butyl alcohol	80	0.25
Isobutyl alcohol	80	0.25
sec-Butyl alcohol	80	0.85
tert-Butyl alcohol	80	0.10
Dioxane	80	0.22
Benzene	80	0.075
Toluene	80	0.53
Ethylbenzene	80	1.35
Isopropyl benzene	80	1.9
tert-Butyl benzene	80	0.26
Cyclohexane	80	0.1
Methylcyclohexane	80	0.2
Isopropyl mercaptan	60	3800
n-Butyl mercaptan	60	6600
tert-Butyl marcaptan	60	1800
n-Amyl mercaptan	100	8000
Thiophenol	60	27000
2-Hydroxyethyl mercaptan	60	1800
Carbethoxymethyl mercaptan	60	6300

TABLE 1-19

Comparison of Chain-Transfer Constants ($C \times 10^4$) for Vinyl Monomers and Selected Transfer Agents

Transfer agent	Styrene	Methyl methacrylate[a]	Acrylonitrile[b]	Ethyl acrylate[c]	Methyl Acrylate[d]	Vinyl Acetate[e]
Cyclohexane	0.024[f]	0.010	2.06	0.61	1.2	6.6
Benzene	0.018[f]	0.075	2.5	0.27	0.45	3.0
Toluene	0.125[f]	0.525	5.8	1.84	2.7	21.0
Chlorobenzene	1.5[g]	0.20	0.79		0.52	8.35
Acetone	4.1[g]	0.225	1.13	0.27	1.1	11.7
Chloroform	0.5[f]	1.4	5·6	1.57	2.5	112.5
Carbon tetrachloride	92[h]	2.4	0.85	1.13	1.25	
Dimethylaniline[i]	53	430	1040	380[j]		2700[k]
Carbon tetrabromide[l]	22000	2700	900[m]		4100	>390000
n-Butyl mercaptan[n]	220000	6700			16000	4800

[a] At 80°C.
[b] At 60°C.
[c] PhMe, CHCl₃, and CCl₄ at 70°C; others at 60°C.
[d] At 80°C.
[e] At 60°C.
[f] At 60°C.
[g] At 80°C.

[h] At 60°C.
[i] At 50°C.
[j] At 50°C, value for butyl acrylate.
[k] At 50°C, value for vinyl chloride.
[l] At 60°C.
[m] At 100°C, value for methacrylonitrile.
[n] At 60°C.

Of the various reactivity ratios only k_{32}/k_{31} is not readily obtained. However, since both sides of Eq. (1-124) possess a common denominator,

$$\frac{k_{32}}{k_{31}} = \frac{r_{13}r_{21}}{r_{12}r_{23}} \tag{1-125}$$

it is possible to predict telogen activity in homopolymerizations. The only necessary information is that on the reactivity ratios of the binary monomer pair and the chain-transfer constant C_s of the specific chain-transfer agent with each monomer. Substituting in Eq. (1-124) yields a characteristic $\mathscr{P}$. Since characteristic copolymerization reactivity parameters p are available from studies of monomer systems, the reactivity parameter p for the telogen may be calculated from the $\mathscr{P}$ value just determined by the following equation:

$$p_1 = 3\mathscr{P}/2p_2p_3 \tag{1-126}$$

The factor 3/2 must be included, since there are only two possible reactions of telogen radicals as against three for monomers. It is obvious that after

TABLE 1-20

Reactivities of Various Monomers Relative to Styrene with Various Telogen Radicals

Telogen radical	Monomer	Monomer reactivity relative to styrene as 1
n-Butyl mercaptan	Methyl methacrylate	0.027
n-Butyl mercaptan	Methyl acrylate	0.018
Ethyl thioglycolate	Methyl methacrylate	0.010
Carbon tetrabromide	Methyl methacrylate	0.109
Carbon tetrabromide	Methyl acrylate	0.045
Carbon tetrachloride	Methyl methacrylate	0.023

the reactivity parameter p for telogen has been determined, the $\mathscr{P}$ for any new system, including a new monomer of known p, may be calculated from Eq. (1-124). Substituting in Eq. (1-124) yielded C_s the chain-transfer constant of n-butyl mercaptan with methyl acrylate, for which the reactivity parameter p was known. In this way the reciprocal of C_s was found to be 0.782, which compares well with the experimental value, 0.625. Similarly, the reactivity parameter p of carbon tetrabromide was found to be 0.219 from styrene–methyl methacrylate–carbon tetrabromide, in good agreement with a value of 0.210, obtained from styrene–methyl acrylate–carbon tetrabromide. These values are slightly less than the parameter calculated for methyl acrylate. It is interesting that a similar conclusion was obtained by Fuhrman and Mesrobian (68) from $Q–e$ calculations. They also concluded that the reactivity of carbon tetrabromide was slightly less than that of methyl acrylate.

Table 1-20 shows how one may employ Eq. (1-125) in determining the relative reactivity of monomers with telogen radicals.

REFERENCES

1. M. Gomberg, *Ber.*, **33**, 3150 (1900).
2. P. D. Bartlett and H. Kwart, *J. Am. Chem. Soc.*, **72**, 1051 (1950).
3. D. G. L. James and D. MacCallum, *Proc. Chem. Soc.*, **1961**, 259.
4. F. R. Mayo, *J. Chem. Educ.*, **36**(4), 157 (1959).
5. F. M. Lewis, F. R. Mayo, and W. F. Hulse, *J. Am. Chem. Soc.*, **67**, 1701 (1945).
6. C. C. Price, *J. Polymer Sci.*, **1**, 83 (1946).
7. T. Alfrey, Jr., and C. C. Price, *J. Polymer Sci.*, **2**, 101 (1947).
8. W. N. Thomas, *Advan. Polymer Sci.*, **2**, 401 (1961).
9. G. E. Ham, *J. Polymer Sci.*, **14**, 87 (1954).
10. G. E. Ham, *J. Polymer Sci.*, **24**, 349 (1957).
11a. P. J. Flory, *Principles of Polymer Chemistry*, Cornell Univ. Press, Ithaca, New York, 1953, p. 5.
11b. Ibid., p. 122.
12. G. M. Burnett and H. W. Melville, *Proc. Roy. Soc.* (*London*), **A189**, 456, 494 (1947).

13. L. M. Arnett, *J. Am. Chem. Soc.*, **74**, 2027 (1952).

14. G. V. Schulz and G. Harborth, *Makromol. Chem.*, **1**, 106 (1947).

15. F. R. Mayo, R. A. Gregg, and M. S. Matheson, *J. Am. Chem. Soc.*, **73**, 1691 (1951).

16. L. M. Arnett and J. H. Peterson, *J. Am. Chem. Soc.*, **74**, 2031 (1952).

17. D. H. Johnson and A. V. Tabolsky, *J. Am. Chem. Soc.*, **74**, 938 (1952); D. Baysal and A. V. Tabolsky, *J. Polymer Sci.*, **8**, 529 (1952).

18. G. V. Schulz and E. Husemann, *Z. Physik. Chem. Leipzig* **B39**, 246 (1938).

19. C. S. Marvel, J. Dec, and H. G. Cooke, *J. Am. Chem. Soc.*, **62**, 3499 (1940).

20. G. V. Schulz and G. Harborth, *Makromol. Chem.*, **1**, 106 (1947).

21. G. V. Schulz and G. Harborth, *Makromol. Chem.*, **1**, 106 (1947).

22. R. G. W. Norrish and R. R. Smith, *Nature*, **150**, 336 (1942).

23. E. Trommsdorff, *Coll. on High Polymers* (Freiburg, 1944.)

24. E. Trommsdorff, H. Köhle, and P. Lagally, *Makromol. Chem.*, **1**, 169 (1948).

25. Z. A. Rogovin and L. A. Tsaplina, *J. Appl. Chem. USSR (English Transl.)*, **20**, 875 (1947).

26. M. S. Matheson, E. E. Auer, E. B. Bevilacqua, and E. J. Hart, *J. Am. Chem. Soc.*, **73**, 5395 (1951).

27. H. D. Anspon and G. E. Ham, in *Manufacture of Plastics* (W. M. Smith, ed.), Reinhold, New York, 1964, p. 84.

28. O. L. Wheeler, S. L. Ernst, and R. N. Crozier, *J. Polymer Sci.*, **8**, 409 (1952).

29. G. E. Ham and E. L. Ringwald, *J. Polymer Sci.*, **8**, 91 (1952).

30. W. I. Bengough and R. G. W. Norrish, *Proc. Roy. Soc. (London)*, **A216**, 515 (1953).

31. T. G. Fox and S. Gratch, *Ann. N.Y. Acad. Sci.*, **57**, 367 (1953).

32. G. E. Ham, *Textile Res. J.*, **24**, 597 (1954).

33. G. E. Ham, *Ind. Eng. Chem.*, **46**, 390 (1954).

34. G. E. Ham, *J. Polymer Sci.*, **21**, 337 (1956).

35. S. G. Foord, *J. Chem. Soc.*, **1940**, 48.

36. G. V. Schulz, A. Dinglinger, and E. Husemann, *Z. Physik. Chem. Leipzig*, **B43**, 385 (1939).

37. C. Walling, E. R. Briggs, and F. R. Mayo, *J. Am. Chem. Soc.*, **68**, 1145 (1946).

38. C. Walling and E. R. Briggs, *J. Am. Chem. Soc.*, **68**, 1141 (1946).

39. J. W. Breitenbach and W. Thury, *Experientia*, **3**, 281 (1947).

40. C. Cuthbertson, G. Gee, and E. K. Rideal, *Nature*, **140**, 889 (1937).

41. J. W. Breitenbach and R. Raff, *Ber.*, **69**, 1107 (1936).

42. P. J. Flory, *J. Am. Chem. Soc.*, **59**, 241 (1937).

43. C. Walling, *Free Radicals in Solution*, Wiley, New York, 1957, pp. 182–183.

44. B. H. Zimm and J. K. Bragg, *J. Polymer Sci.*, **9**, 476 (1952).

45. F. T. Wall, *J. Am. Chem. Soc.*, **63**, 1862 (1941).

46. F. R. Mayo and F. M. Lewis, *J. Am. Chem. Soc.*, **66**, 1594 (1944).

47. T. Alfrey, Jr., and G. Goldfinger, *J. Chem. Phys.*, **12**, 205 (1944).

48. F. T. Wall, *J. Am. Chem. Soc.*, **66**, 2050 (1944).

49. H. Mark, B. Immergut, E. H. Immergut, L. J. Young, and K. I. Benyon, in *Copolymerization* (G. E. Ham, ed.), Wiley (Interscience), New York, 1964, App. A.

50. E. Merz, T. Alfrey, Jr., and G. Goldfinger, *J. Polymer Sci.*, **1**, 75 (1946).

51. R. G. Fordyce and G. E. Ham, *J. Am. Chem. Soc.*, **73**, 1186 (1951).

52. W. G. Barb, *J. Polymer Sci.*, **11**, 117 (1953).

53. G. E. Ham, *J. Polymer Sci.*, **45**, 177 (1960).

54. G. E. Ham, *J. Polymer Sci.*, **A2**, 3633 (1964).

55. T. Alfrey, Jr., and G. Goldfinger, *J. Chem. Phys.*, **12**, 322 (1944).

56. T. Alfrey, Jr., and G. Goldfinger, *J. Chem. Phys.*, **14**, 115 (1946).

57. C. Walling, D. Seymour, and K. Wolfstirn, *J. Am. Chem. Soc.*, **70**, 1544 (1948).

58. C. Walling and E. R. Briggs, *J. Am. Chem. Soc.*, **67**, 1774 (1945).

59. R. G. Fordyce, E. C. Chapin, and G. E. Ham, *J. Am. Chem. Soc.*, **70**, 2489 (1948).

60. T. Alfrey, Jr., and C. C. Price, *J. Polymer Sci.*, **2**, 101 (1947).

61. L. J. Young, in *Copolymerization* (G. E. Ham, ed.), Wiley, New York, 1964, App. B.

62. G. E. Ham, *J. Polymer Sci.*, **A2**, 2735 (1964).

63. G. E. Ham, *J. Polymer Sci.*, **A2**, 4181 (1964).

64. T. Alfrey, Jr., J. J. Bohrer, and H. Mark, *Copolymerization, High Polymer Series VIII*, Wiley (Interscience), New York, 1952.

65. T. Alfrey, Jr., and L. J. Young, in *Copolymerization* (G. E. Ham, ed.), Wiley, New York, 1964, Chap. II.

66. C. C. Price and J. Zomlefer, *J. Am. Chem. Soc.*, **72**, 14 (1950).

67. L. A. Wall, *J. Polymer Sci.*, **2**, 542 (1947).

68. N. Fuhrman and R. B. Mesrobian, *J. Am. Chem. Soc.*, **76**, 3281 (1954).

69. C. H. Bamford and A. D. Jenkins, *J. Polymer Sci.*, **53**, 149 (1961).

70. M. G. Evans, J. Gergely, and E. C. Seaman, *J. Polymer Sci.*, **3**, 866 (1948).

71. K. Hayashi, T. Yonezawa, C. Nagata, S. Okamura, and K. Fukui, *J. Polymer Sci.*, **14**, 312 (1954).

72. K. Hayashi, T. Yonezawa, C. Nagata, S. Okamura, and K. Fukui, *J. Polymer Sci.*, **20**, 537 (1956).

73. T. Fueno, T. Tsuruta, and J. Furukawa, *J. Polymer Sci.*, **40**, 487, 499 (1959).

74. G. S. Levinson, *J. Polymer Sci.*, **60**, 43 (1962).

75. P. J. Flory, *J. Am. Chem. Soc.*, **59**, 241 (1937).

76. J. W. Breitenbach and A. Maschin, *Z. Physik. Chem. Leipzig*, **A187**, 175 (1940).

77. S. Kamenskaya and S. S. Medvedev, *Acta Physicochim. (USSR)*, **13**, 565 (1940).

78. H. M. Hibbert, R. H. Harman, A. V. Tobolsky, and H. Eyring, *Ann. N.Y. Acad. Sci.*, **44**, 371 (1943).

79. F. R. Mayo, *J. Am. Chem. Soc.*, **65**, 2324 (1943).

80. S. S. Medvedev, O. Koritskaya, and E. Alekseeva, *Zh. Fiz. Khim.*, **17**, 391 (1943).

81. R. A. Gregg, D. M. Alderman, and F. R. Mayo, *J. Am. Chem. Soc.*, **70**, 3740 (1948).

82. T. Alfrey, Jr., and V. Hardy, *J. Polymer Sci.*, **3**, 505 (1948).

83. J. L. O'Brien and F. Gornick, *J. Am. Chem. Soc.*, **77**, 4757 (1953).

84. S. R. Palit and S. K. Das, *Proc. Roy. Soc. (London)*, **A226**, 82 (1954).

85. C. Walling and J. Pellon, *J. Am. Chem. Soc.*, **79**, 4776 (1957).

86. N. G. Gaylord, *J. Polymer Sci.*, **22**, 71 (1956).

87. F. M. Lewis and F. R. Mayo, *J. Am. Chem. Soc.*, **76**, 457 (1954).

88. M. S. Kharasch and C. F. Fuchs, *J. Org. Chem.*, **13**, 97 (1948).

89. M. S. Kharasch and M. Sage, *J. Org. Chem.*, **14**, 537 (1949); M. S. Kharasch and —. Friedlander, *J. Org. Chem.*, **14**, 290 (1949).

90. R. B. Fox and D. E. Field, Telomerization—A Review of the Literature, *NRL Rept. 5190*, Nov. 1958.

91. G. E. Ham, *J. Polymer Sci.*, **B3**, 459 (1965).

CHAPTER 2

The Mechanism of Cyclopolymerization of Nonconjugated Diolefins

William E. Gibbs
John M. Barton

Polymer Branch, Nonmetallic Materials Division
Air Force Materials Laboratory
Wright-Patterson Air Force Base, Ohio

2-1. INTRODUCTION

The polymerization of nonconjugated diolefins until rather recently had been regarded as yielding only cross-linked, insoluble polymers. However, in 1951 Butler and Ingley (*1*) found that diallyl quaternary ammonium salts, polymerized in aqueous solution, formed soluble, gel-free polymers, which were later reported (*2*) to have little or no residual unsaturation. To account for the formation of saturated, soluble, gel-free polymers Butler and Angelo (*2*) proposed for this system a novel chain propagation reaction, in which both diolefin double bonds are consumed:

$$\xrightarrow{\text{monomer}} \left[-CH_2-CH \underset{CH_2}{\overset{CH_2}{\underset{\underset{R}{\diagdown}\,\overset{}{N}\,\underset{R}{\diagup}}{\overset{\diagup\quad\diagdown}{\bigoplus}}}} CH-CH_2-CH \underset{CH_2}{\overset{CH_2}{\underset{\underset{R}{\diagdown}\,\overset{}{N}\,\underset{R}{\diagup}}{\overset{\diagup\quad\diagdown}{\bigoplus}}}} CH-CH_2-CH \underset{CH_2}{\overset{CH_2}{\underset{\underset{R}{\diagdown}\,\overset{}{N}\,\underset{R}{\diagup}}{\overset{\diagup\quad\diagdown}{\bigoplus}}}} CH- \right]_n$$

The first step is a normal intermolecular propagation reaction. The second reaction, however, is an intramolecular cyclization reaction, between the radical and the double bond present in the same recurring unit, forming a cyclized radical. The cyclized radical then propagates with monomer, and the sequence repeats itself. Butler and Angelo (2) termed this propagation sequence "alternating intra-intermolecular chain propagation." More recently the term cyclopolymerization has found general use.

The term cyclopolymerization, or alternating intra-intermolecular propagation, was originally restricted to the polymerization of nonconjugated diolefins having double bonds in the terminal positions and capable of short-range cyclization reactions. Recently it was extended to monomers with other types of reactive functions, which can undergo short-range cyclization; examples are dialdehydes, diisocyanates, diepoxides, and monomers with nonconjugated carbon-carbon triple bonds. It can include the polymerization of cyclic monomers, such as norbornadiene, 1,4-dimethylene cyclohexane, and others, which involve a transannular cyclization reaction as a part of the propagation reaction. Other novel types may also be cited. Recently the copolymerization of cyclizing monomers (cyclo-co-polymerization) has begun to be investigated. The feature common to all these systems is that the propagation reaction in each case involves a major contribution from an intramolecular, short-range cyclization reaction.

In the short period of time since the discovery of cyclopolymerization no broad foundation of theoretical and experimental information has been developed. Many interesting and important features of this area are still indefinite and insufficiently studied. Further research is required. For that reason it will be necessary to restrict the scope of this discussion primarily to the free-radical cyclopolymerization of nonconjugated diolefins. At present only for these systems is there sufficient experimental information on kinetics, etc., to allow a reasonable test of the proposed mechanisms. The basic features, however, of many of the other systems, indicated above, can often be described in a general fashion by the kinetics presented here. Moreover, most of the other information presented here can be applied almost equally well to all cyclopolymerization systems.

It should be noted that this survey of the field is not intended to be comprehensive, and significant numbers of published works are mentioned only briefly, if at all. Of particular interest have been those works in which information pertinent to the kinetics and mechanism of polymerization is given.

A recent review of the current status of the field has been completed by Butler (3).

2-2. CYCLOPOLYMERIZATION

The nonconjugated diolefins are a broad class of monomers, which include at one extreme the monomers under discussion in this chapter. Their polymers may be generally characterized as soluble, essentially linear and having high proportions of cyclized units. At the other extreme are the cross-linking monomers, such as the m- and p-divinyl benzenes, which form polymers that are insoluble and highly cross-linked and have moderate to high extents of residual unsaturation. In general there is a close relationship between both these types of monomers, and for that reason reference will be made in this section and the following to work conducted on cross-linking systems.

From at least the work of Staudinger and Heuer (4) until the time of Butler's discovery it had been generally observed that polymerization and copolymerization of nonconjugated diolefins gave only cross-linked, insoluble products. Although certain diolefins were found more effective and practical cross-linkers than others, relatively little was done on quantitatively describing the cross-linking process until the early 1940's. Then Flory (5–8) and Stockmayer (9,10), and later Walling (11), attempted to describe quantitatively the basic features of gelation for multifunctional condensation monomers, vulcanization reactions, and the polymerization and copolymerization of nonconjugated diolefins. They showed that in a monodisperse system gelation should occur when there is one cross-linked unit per primary molecule. In a randomly polydisperse system gelation should occur when there is one cross-linked unit per weight-average primary molecule. A cross-linked unit is a doubly reacted, nonconjugated diolefin. The primary chains are the chains that would be present if all cross-links were severed.

For the polymerization and copolymerization of divinyl and monovinyl monomers they considered that, if the double bonds in both monomers were of equal reactivity, the entire process could be described statistically on the basis of the degree of conversion of double bonds in the system and the primary chain length. With this approach they succeeded in deriving expressions relating the concentration of divinyl and monovinyl monomers, the degree of conversion of double bonds, and the primary chain length to the critical condition for gelation. Experimental work was then undertaken to test the theory.

Walling (11) copolymerized methyl methacrylate with ethylene dimethacrylate, and vinyl acetate with divinyl adipate, and found that the gel points (degrees of reaction at the gel points) were always higher than predicted. The difference between the predicted and observed gel points depended on the relative amounts of monovinyl and divinyl monomer (lower concentrations, <0.05 mole-% of divinyl monomer, tending to better agreement with theory) and upon the total concentration of monomers in the system (higher concentrations giving better agreement with theory). The theoretical predictions were most in error at higher concentrations of divinyl monomer or at lower over-all monomer concentrations, or both.

In an effort to reconcile theory and experiment the theory was re-examined (11) and assumptions made in the statistical analysis and concerning the physical and chemical nature of the system were critically inspected. Since the observed gel-point conversion occurred later than predicted, the primary weight-average molecular weight might be lower than expected (perhaps because of more rapid chain transfer of the radical from the divinyl monomer) or the reactivity of the monovinyl monomer might be greater than the divinyl compound, or the reactions that were more prone to diffusion control (i.e., chain termination) might depart from expectation as the viscosity of the system increased. The importance of cyclization reactions was reconsidered. The theories had omitted cyclization, because it was not expected to play an important role in the over-all picture and the inclusion of cyclization would have seriously complicated the mathematics.

Gel-point investigations in the polycondensation field showed a similar situation. In all systems investigated the gel point occurred later than predicted by theory. The similarity in direction of disagreement with theory for both polyaddition and polycondensation suggested that the lack of agreement was due to the basic theory and not to some specific departures in the chemistry of the reactions themselves.

In an elegant manner Stockmayer and Weil (12) pointed out the reason for disagreement of most polycondensation systems. They reasoned that a primary factor in the delay of gelation was the formation of cyclic structures. This removed end groups from the system in a manner not accounted for in the theory. The cyclization reaction, being unimolecular, should be unaffected by dilution of the system, whereas the true chain propagation, being intermolecular, should decrease as diluent is added. However, even in the bulk system with no diluent some cyclization could still occur. The only point at which this cyclization would be totally repressed would be at "infinite concentration." Stockmayer and Weil therefore conducted a series of stoichiometric polycondensations of adipic acid with pentaerythritol at varying concentrations in an inert diluent and measured the gel point as a function of monomer concentration. They plotted their results as gel point versus reciprocal monomer concentration and extrapolated to *infinite concentration*. At this point they obtained the theoretically predicted gel point (0.578 ± 0.005 found, 0.577 predicted). This work effectively demonstrated that the prime reason for disagreement between theory and experiment, at least in polycondensation, was the failure to include cyclization in the theoretical development.

Among the first reports of work in the polyaddition area directed toward an investigation of the gel theory was that of Holt et al. (*13–15*). Their work will be discussed here, because it was directed toward an investigation of cross-linking theory, but the early work of Butler and Ingley (*1*), who first observed that completely soluble polymers could be prepared from diallyl monomers, preceded it chronologically. In a series of three papers Simpson, Holt, and Zetie reported the polymerization of twelve diallyl esters and two di-β-methallyl esters of a series of dibasic acids. Their main interest, however, was cross-linking systems and, although they obtained much valuable information, they did not pursue systems in which the degree of cyclization might be expected to be higher (systems forming smaller rings).

The availability of a large variety of dibasic acids allowed a systematic variation of monomer structure, in which the reactivity of the allylic groups would remain relatively unchanged. They studied one member of the series, diallyl-*o*-phthalate, in detail (see Table 2-1). Cross-links that developed during polymerization of these monomers could be severed by saponification. The resulting polyalcohols were soluble and could be characterized.

TABLE 2-1

Bulk Polymerization of Diallyl Esters at 80°C (*15*)

Monomer	Convsn. (estmd.), %	No. of reacted DB per chain[a]	Unsaturation of polymer, % of units[b]	Ring size
Diallyl carbonate	20	20.4	74.2	8
	10		78.6	
oxalate	16.5	20.0	78.8	9
	20.0	20.0	79.6	
malonate	21.0	20.0	79.4	10
suberate	23.0	20.4	73.0	11
	23.0		74.4	
glutarate	23.0		79.2	12
adipate	23.0	19.3	78.4	13
azelate	23.0		82.6	16
sebacate	21.0	19.6	80.6	17
o-diphenate	23.0	15.3	58.0	
phthalate	22.2	19.8	52.0	
	23.5	21.5	51.6	
isophthalate	23.3	20.0	84.4	
terephthalate	23.6		98.0	
	23.6		82.0	
Di-β-methallyl-*o*-phthalate	22.5		59.4	
Di-β-methallyl carbonate	23.0		72.6	

[a] DB = double bonds.

[b] Unsaturated groups, expressed as percentage of recurring units in polymer.

Holt and Simpson (*15*) reported the effects of temperature and monomer concentration on the formation of cyclized units for diallyl-*o*-phthalate, as shown in Table 2-2. Their results with diallyl-*o*-phthalate, shown in Table 2-3, are fairly representative of the other monomers in the variation in polymer unsaturation with percentage of conversion. They summarized their findings on diallyl-*o*-phthalate as follows (*15*): "The extent of intramolecular reaction is: (a) independent of the rate of polymerization at both constant and varying temperature; (b) inversely dependent on monomer concentration; (c) almost independent of conversion up to the gel point."

They further observed (*15*) that the relationship between rate of polymer formation and initiator concentration gave neither a square-root nor a first-power dependency of initiator concentration and ascribed this fact to reinitiation by the degraded allylic radicals.

TABLE 2-2

Polymerization of Diallyl-*o*-Phthalate (*15*)

Temp., °C	Monomer concn.,[a] moles/liter at 80°C	Benzoyl peroxide, % of monomer	Polymer unsaturation,[b] % of units
60	4.34 (bulk)	2	53.4
80	4.34 (bulk)	2	52.0
100	4.34 (bulk)	1	50.8
80	4.34	1	52.0
80	3.20	2	50.6
80	2.11	4	42.8
80	1.25	4	32.0

[a] Solvent, when used, was dibutyl phthalate.
[b] Compared at $\approx 20\%$ conversion.

Simpson et al. (*13*) drew attention to the fact that, as the size of the smallest ring that could be formed grew larger (as the allyl groups became more and more separated), the tendency was to reduce the number of cyclized groups. Haward (*16*) attempted the calculation of the proportion of cyclized groups and the ratio of cyclization to linear polymerization by means of a mathematical model, in which the extent of reaction was based on the distance between reactive groups. Using the available bond angles and distances in the diallyl-*o*-phthalate molecule and the method of Wall (*17*), Haward calculated the separation in space between the initial radical formed from the diolefin and the double bond in the same monomer unit. He then calculated the average separation of this radical and the double bond in an unreacted monomer.

TABLE 2-3

Variation in Unsaturation of Poly(diallyl-*o*-Phthalate) with Extent of Polymerization (*15*)

At 60°C		At 80°C			
2% Bz_2O_2		1% Bz_2O_2		2% Bz_2O_2	
% convsn.	% unsatn.	% convsn.	% unsatn.	% convsn.	% unsatn.
3.15	57.6	6.7	56.0	4.5	58.6
8.75	52.4	15.6	53.2	11.1	56.0
16.75	53.0	22.2	52.0	19.9	55.6
23.3	53.4			21.5	51.6

The criterion for reaction was Kuhn's (18), in which reaction would occur when the atomic center of one of the reactive groups was within a small volume element dr of the atomic center of the other reactive group. The calculations for diallyl-o-phthalate gave a value of cyclized units (31 %), somewhat lower than the observed value (41 %). According to Simpson and Holt (15) there was no good correlation between the proportion of cyclized groups from their monomers and the mean separation based on the model of Haward.

The work of Holt et al. (13–15) was strong basis for considering that the lack of agreement between the theory of gelation and experiment was intramolecular cyclization. However, the possibility that the other factors mentioned above—unequal reactivity of monovinyl and divinyl monomer, decrease in primary degree of polymerization, and diffusion control—were responsible still existed. Gordon (19) and Gordon and Roe (20–23) in a series of papers considered each of these aspects in detail. Their conclusion was that intramolecular cyclization was the primary factor and that the other factors were either negligible or of secondary importance.

Others have considered the problem of cyclization with a view to modifying the theory proposed by Flory and Stockmayer. Jacobson and Stockmayer (24) have considered the statistics of ring formation for difunctional monomers. Harris (25) has considered the case of an f functional monomer. Kilb (26) has proposed an approximate manner in which to modify the theory so as to take most real systems into account. Experimental work by Price et al. (27), Price (28), and Zimm et al. (29) has attempted to verify this new approach with polyester, polyalkoxysilane, and divinyl benzene–styrene systems, respectively.

Starting in the latter 1940's Butler et al. (30–32) initiated work in preparing high-capacity ion-exchange resins by the polymerization of multifunctional quaternary ammonium salts. The earliest systems reported were triallyl benzyl ammonium bromide, tetraallyl ammonium bromide, triallyl butyl ammonium bromide, and certain copolymers of these monomers. They gave the expected cross-linked products. In 1951, however, Butler and Ingley (1) noted that the polymerization of monomers with two allyl groups gave water-soluble, non-cross-linked products. In 1957 Butler and Angelo (2) showed that dimethyl and diethyl diallyl ammonium bromide, when polymerized with t-butyl peroxide at 60 to 70°C, gave soluble polymers whose $\overline{DP}$ was estimated to be 25 to 50 units. Quantitative hydrogenation of these polymers indicated that about 20 % of the units were unsaturated. In this work the authors proposed the alternating inter-intramolecular propagation mechanism in which chains of recurring methylene-spaced piperidine rings were formed as described in the first section of this chapter:

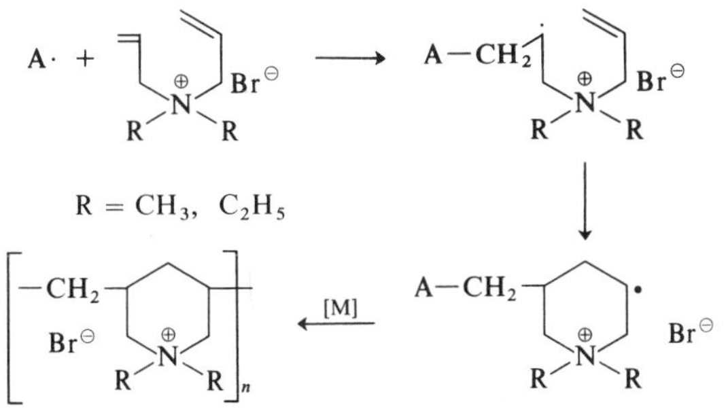

Butler et al. (*33*) obtained soluble polydiallyl ammonium bromide, which after careful purification exhibited no residual unsaturation. The polymer was converted to the benzoyl derivative and then degraded, as shown below, in order to confirm the cyclic nature of the repeating units:

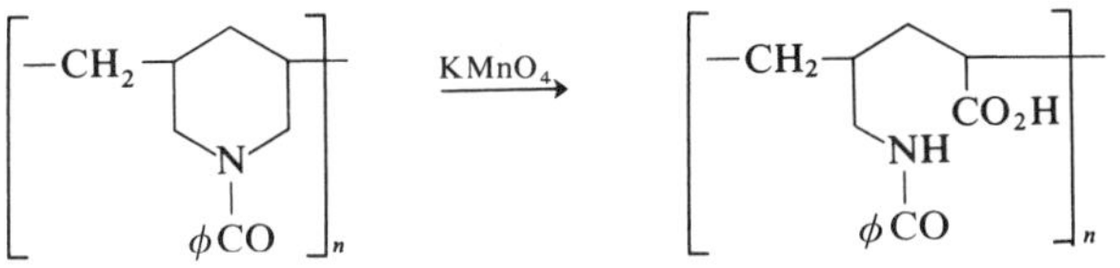

The proposed piperidine ring structure for polydimethyl diallyl ammonium bromide was finally confirmed by degradation by means of Hofmann exhaustive methylation:

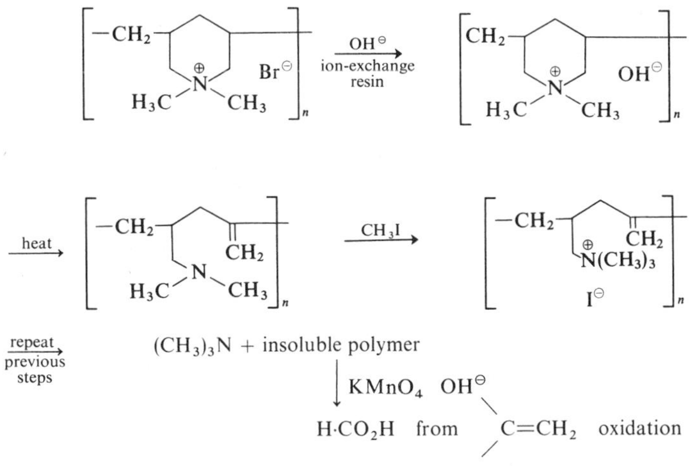

Marvel and Vest (*34*) extended Butler's discovery to the formation of cyclohexane rings in the free-radical polymerization of 2,6-dimethylene pimelic acid and its methyl and ethyl esters. The polymers were soluble in benzene and chloroform and showed no infrared absorption at 6.1 μ for $-CH=CH_2$. After partial dehydrogenation with KClO both the polymeric acid and the methyl ester showed ultraviolet absorption characteristic of *meta*-substituted aromatic rings.

Marvel and Stille (*35*) found that catalysts of the Ziegler–Natta type could also initiate cyclopolymerization. 1,7-Heptadiene, polymerized with $TiCl_4/Al$-i-Bu_3, gave a benzene-soluble polymer, $[\eta] = 0.4$, containing 4 to 10% unsaturated units. Partial dehydrogenation with $KClO_4$ gave a polymer with, again, the spectral characteristics of *meta*-substituted aromatic rings. Under similar conditions 2,5-dimethyl-1,5-hexadiene gave a soluble cyclo-polymer, $[\eta] = 0.1$ and 3 to 13% unsaturation, for which a dimethyl cyclo-pentane repeating unit was proposed. It was observed that 2,5-dimethyl hexene-1 would not polymerize beyond a pentamer under similar conditions; this suggested that the cyclic propagation promotes the polymerization of the diene.

Jones (*36*) reported cyclopolymerization systems involving anionic (diacrylmethane/Na) (*36*) and cationic (allocimene/BF_3OEt_2) (*37*) initiation, in which six-membered carbocycles were formed. The diacryl methane polymerization system used by Jones was later found by Marvel et al. (*38,39*) to yield a copolymer of this monomer and methyl vinyl ketone.

Free-radical cyclopolymerization was extended to many different sym-metrical and unsymmetrical dienes to form soluble polymers with five-, six-, and seven-membered cyclic repeating units. Acrylic anhydride, poly-merized in bulk (*40*) or in benzene solution (*40,41*), gave soluble polymer with negligible residual unsaturation. α,α'-Dimethylene pimelamide, α,α'-dimethylene pimelonitrile and dimethyl α,α'-dimethylene pimelate (*42*) gave soluble polymer with negligible residual unsaturation. Unsaturated esters of maleic and fumaric acid (*43*) gave partially soluble polymers with 40 to 80% residual unsaturation.

Gibbs and Murray (*44*) have described the kinetics of polymerization of methacrylic anhydride in dimethyl formamide solution. The rate expression was found to be $R_p = k[M]^{3/2}[A_2]^{1/2}$. The over-all activation energy was found to be 23.0 kcal/mole for methacrylic anhydride and 24.8 kcal/mole for methacrylic acid. At monomer concentrations of less than about 20 wt-% the intrinsic viscosity of the polyanhydride was constant, independent of conversion. At higher monomer concentration, 35% and more, gel was formed even at relatively low conversions.

Marvel and Garrison (*45*) studied the polymerization of α,ω dienes capable of forming rings of 7 to 21 carbon atoms using catalysts of the Ziegler–Natta type. They measured the residual unsaturation of the polymers and found that the relative ease of ring formation was 7 > 8-9 < 10 < 11-15 > 17, 21, where the numbers represent the number of ring atoms.

TABLE 2-4

Polymerization of α,ω Hydrocarbon Dienes (44),
$$CH_2=CH-(CH_2)\underset{N-3}{\overline{\hspace{2em}}}CH=CH_2$$

No. of ring atoms	Av. f_c in over-all polymer[a]
5[b]	0.93
6[b]	0.93
7	0.25
8	0.09
9	0.06
10	0.10
11	0.11
12	0.11
14	0.15
15	0.15
17	0.04
21	0.08

[a] f_c = estimated fraction of cyclized units in the soluble polymer formed at initial monomer concentration ≤ 0.20 mole/liter.
[b] Marvel and Stille (35).

The results are summarized in Table 2-4.

In a similar study, using the monomers

$$CH_2=\underset{\phi}{\underset{|}{C}}H(CH_2)_n\underset{\phi}{\underset{|}{C}}H=CH_2, \qquad n = 2, 3, 4$$

Marvel and Gall (46) reported that the order of ease of cyclopolymerization with ring size was $6 > 5 \approx 7$. These workers used various cationic, anionic, free-radical, and Ziegler–Natta initiators and obtained soluble polymers in all cases. The results are summarized in Table 2-5. The polymerization of 2,6-diphenyl-1,6-heptadiene, when initiated by free-radical, cationic, anionic, or Ziegler–Natta catalysts, was found by Marvel and Gall (46) and independently by Field (47) to form soluble cyclopolymers showing only low degrees of residual unsaturation.

Monomers reported to be capable of forming cyclopolymers with heterocyclic repeating units include diallylphosphine oxides and diallyl phosphonium halides (48,49) besides diallyl silanes (50–54).

Gibbs and Van Deusen (55) found that cyclopolymerization could also occur in the solid state. Linear soluble polymer was obtained by gamma

TABLE 2-5

Results[a] of Marvel and Gall (46) on the Polymerization of $CH_2=CH(\phi)(CH_2)_n(\phi)CH=CH_2$

				Initiator			
n	N	BF_3	$TiCl_4$	ϕ-Li	Cumene hydroperoxide	Thermal	Al-i-Bu$_3$ + TiCl$_4$
2	5	83 (5–10)	No data	No data	2 (5)	No data	58 (3–5)
3	6	67 (3–5)	52 (5–10)	85 (5–10)	56 (3)	54 (3)	56 (5–10)
4	7	6 (0)	47 (2–5)	No data	No data	No data	75 (0)

[a] The results are expressed as y(u), where y is percentage of yield and u is percentage of residual unsaturation.

irradiation of the crystalline monomer diallylmelamine at room temperature, followed by postirradiation reaction at temperatures below the melting point, and also by continued in-source polymerization.

Stille (56) found that 1,6-heptadiyne would cyclopolymerize. A Ziegler–Natta type of catalyst yielded a high-molecular-weight cyclopolymer with conjugated unsaturation. Reduction of the polymer with palladized charcoal formed aromatic structures:

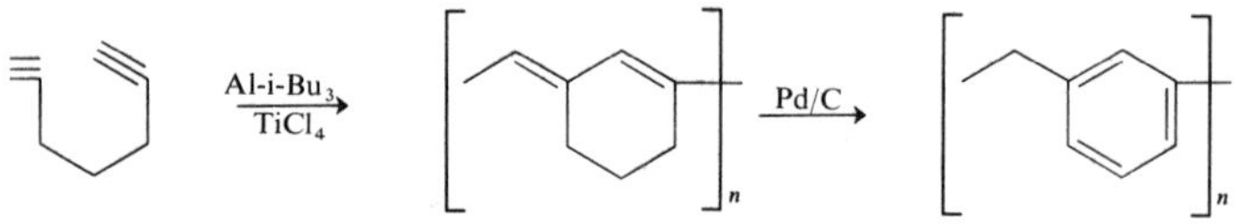

An extensive series of papers by Matsoyan and co-workers describe the free-radical-initiated polymerization of divinyl acetals and ketals, such as the cyclopolymerization of various aliphatic (57–60) and aromatic (61–63) divinyl acetals and aliphatic divinyl ketals (64). In general, soluble, linear polymers with low degrees of residual unsaturation were obtained; the cyclic structure was supported by the infrared absorption spectra, which showed characteristics of dioxane rings. Certain aliphatic and aromatic divinyl acetals were found to cyclopolymerize under cationic initiation conditions (65). Matsoyan and Morlyan also obtained high-molecular-weight soluble cyclopolymers from vinyl ethynyl carbinols (66–71).

The cyclopolymerization of 1,4-dienes is a special case, because the cyclization of the monomer radical or ion to a four-membered ring is sterically inhibited. The dimer radical or ion can, however, cyclize more readily, and this may be followed by secondary cyclization to form a bicyclic structure:

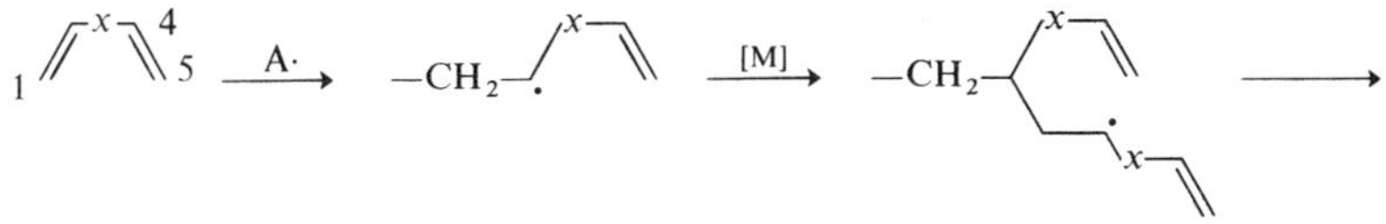

where $x = CH_2$, O, CO, etc.

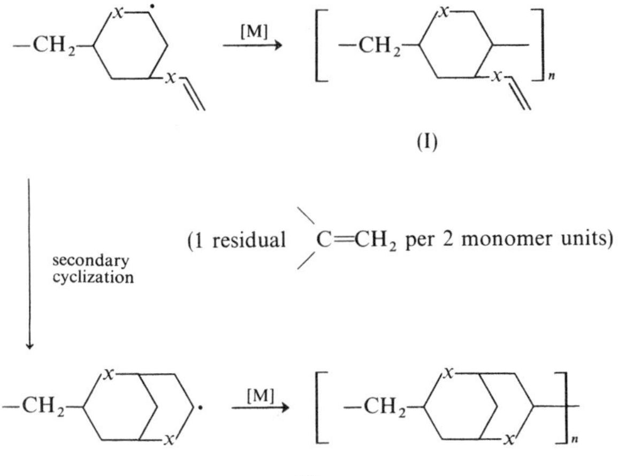

(I)

secondary cyclization

(1 residual $\diagup C=CH_2$ per 2 monomer units)

(II)

Although six-membered rings would be expected, a priori, bulky substituents at positions 1 or 5 of the monomer could lead to five-membered rings by ring closure at position 4 in the dimer.

Matsoyan and Avetyan (72) report the cyclopolymerization of some methyl-substituted 1,4-diene-3-one monomers. Using radical initiation in solution, they obtained soluble polymers with 25% residual unsaturation. In the absence of cross-linking the low residual unsaturation could be ascribed to secondary cyclization of the type outlined above (although the authors do not appear to have considered this).

Aso and Ushio (73) studied the polymerization of divinyl ether and found that cationic catalysts led to a gel with no residual unsaturation, but radical initiation formed a benzene-soluble polymer of fairly high molecular weight ($[\eta] = 0.2$ to 0.5) with a residual unsaturation of 1 vinyl group per 5 monomer units. The authors concluded that cyclic structures were present but did not investigate the detailed structure. In view of the low residual unsaturation it appears very likely that bicyclic units of type (II) were present.

The formation of bicyclic and tricyclic units in the polymer chain has been observed in the polymerization of triallyl and tetraallyl monomers. Trifan and Hoglen (74) prepared soluble, un-cross-linked, and highly saturated polymers from ethyl triallyl ammonium bromide (I) and tetraallyl ammonium bromide (II). These polymers were obtained in aqueous solution by initiation with t-butyl peroxide at 60°C. Monomer (I) at concentrations of 17 to 100 wt-% gave soluble polymer with a residual unsaturation corresponding to about 0.01 to 0.30 double bonds per monomer unit. Similarly, monomer (II) in the same concentration range gave soluble polymer with residual unsaturation of 0.01 to 0.69 double bonds per monomer unit. These low degrees of unsaturation, together with the absence of cross-linking or extensive branching, point to the occurrence of recurring intramolecular propagation reactions, producing bicyclic and tricyclic units:

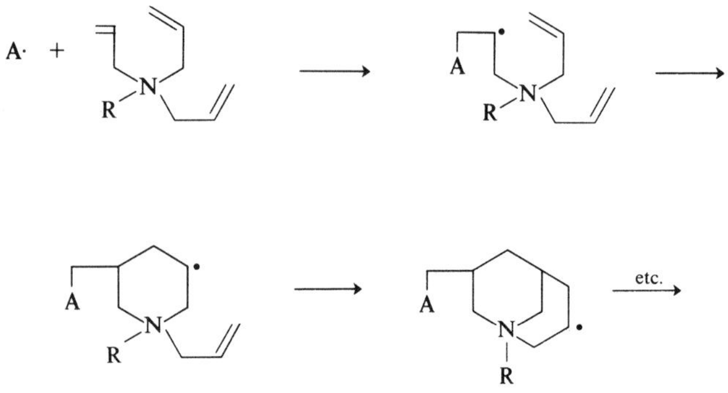

The same workers (74) also obtained soluble polymers showing characteristics of bicyclic structures by the action of a Ziegler initiator on triallylmethylsilane and on 3-vinyl-1,5-hexadiene.

Similarly, Matsoyan et al. (75) found that free-radical initiation of the trivinyl ether monomers $(CH_2=CH-O)_3X$, where X = CH, PO, N^+, gave soluble polymers ($[\eta] = 0.1$ to 0.2) and residual unsaturation of ≈ 0.05 double bonds per monomer unit. The high saturation values were explained by the formation of bicyclic structures.

Guselnikov et al. (76) obtained soluble polymers from triallylsilanes by gamma irradiation of the monomers in solution. The low residual unsaturation of the polymers, 0.13 to 0.20 double bonds per monomer unit, was again interpreted in terms of the formation of monocyclic and bicyclic repeating units.

Matsoyan et al. (77) found that, when divinyl ethanol or divinyl butyral were copolymerized with vinyl acetate in bulk at 60°C by free-radical initiation, soluble copolymers were formed that had the same composition as the monomer feed. The cyclic propagation of the divinyl acetal, forming 1,3-dioxane rings, was supported by the very low residual unsaturation of the copolymers. Soluble, fusible copolymers also were prepared from divinyl acetals and styrene (78,79).

Hwa and Miller (*80*) studied the free-radical copolymerization of methacrylic anhydride with a variety of monovinyl monomers. They obtained both soluble and cross-linked polymers, depending on the reaction conditions and the comonomer used. They found that the conditions favoring the formation of soluble copolymers were low reactivity in the comonomer, high dilution, excess concentration of either monomer in the monomer charge, and low conversion. All these conditions apparently favor the intramolecular cyclization of the methacrylic anhydride radicals. The investigators showed that, when the rate of cyclization of the diene radical was very much greater than its rates of intermolecular propagation (giving a pendent double bond), this type of copolymerization could, in theory, be described by the classical binary copolymer composition equation. They derived reactivity ratios for the copolymerization of methacrylic anhydride with benzyl vinyl sulfide, 2-chloroethyl vinyl ether, allyl urea, and allyl chloroacetate, by the usual method of compositional analysis of copolymers prepared at low degrees of conversion.

Gibbs (*81*) has published an account of the kinetics of polymerization of symmetrical nonconjugated diolefins, including rate expressions and composition relationships.

Roovers and Smets (*82*) investigated the free-radical homopolymerization of vinyl-*trans*-cinnamate and its copolymerization with vinyl acetate, vinyl pyrrolidone, methacrylonitrile, and styrene. Earlier Van Paesschen et al. (*83*) had shown that vinyl-*trans*-cinnamate did undergo cyclopolymerization with the formation of γ-lactone rings and the leaving of a small residual unsaturation. Roovers and Smets determined the ratio of rate constants governing intermolecular and intramolecular (cyclic) propagation, and they also derived the appropriate reactivity ratios for the copolymerization. These results will be discussed later.

Gibbs and McHenry (*84*) have considered the general composition relationships for copolymerization of symmetrical nonconjugated diolefins with monoolefins.

Radical copolymerization of 1,5-hexadiene and sulfur dioxide leads to a novel 2:1 alternating cyclopolymer (*85*):

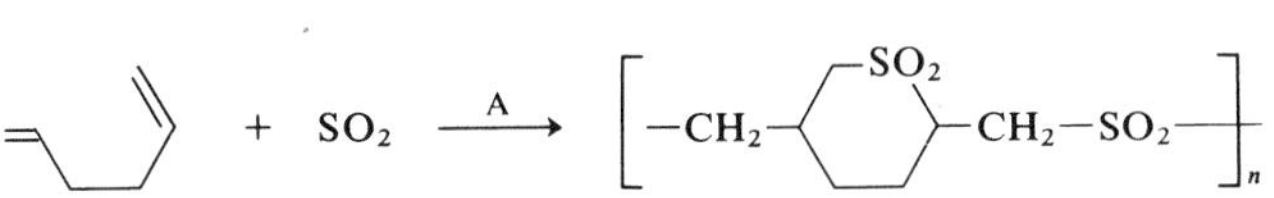

Alternating 2:1 cyclopolymers were obtained from certain 1,4 dienes and certain monoolefins (*86,87*), such as divinyl ether and maleic anhydride, with radical initiation (*86*):

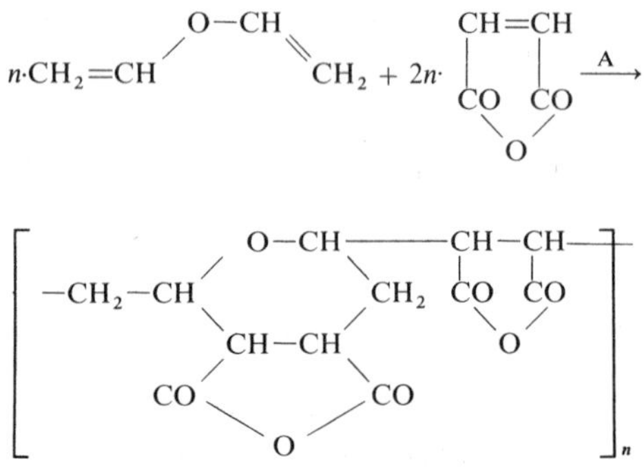

Random cyclopolymers of this type, in which both monomers combine to form the cyclic repeating unit, are formed from certain 1,4 dienes and reactive monoolefins such as acrylonitrile (87,88).

The examples illustrate the strong driving force toward the formation of six-membered rings.

Another type of cyclopolymerization that should be mentioned has been termed "transannular polymerization." Here a difunctional cyclic monomer gives a polymer with a bicyclic repeating unit. For instance, the cationic polymerization of 1,4-dimethylene cyclohexane proceeds, as follows, to give a soluble polymer with not more than one double bond per 25 monomer units (89):

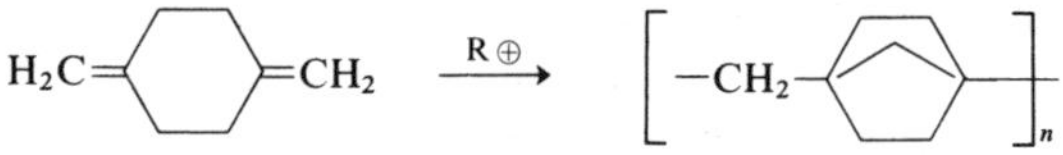

Other monomers that have given cyclopolymers or copolymers by trans-annular ring closure include 1,5-cyclooctadiene (90,91), norbornadiene (92), and 4-vinyl cyclohexane (93).

Zutty (94) reports the copolymerization of norbornadiene with vinyl chloride, vinylidene chloride, acrylonitrile, ethyl acrylate, and methyl methacrylate:

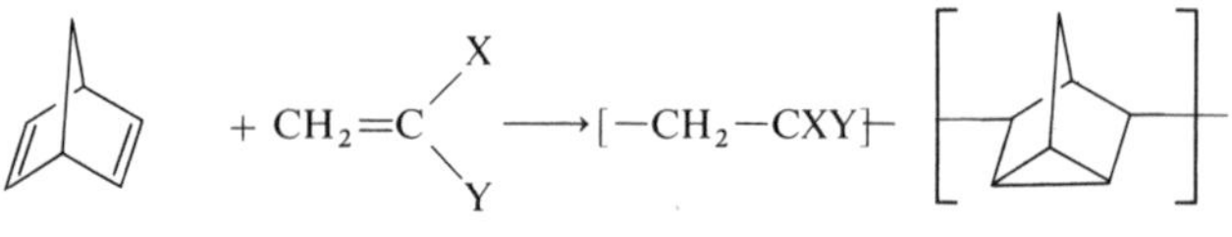

The norbornadiene was essentially completely cyclized in the copolymer. Zutty determined the Q and e values by using r values obtained from the vinyl binary copolymer equation, in which $Q = 0.08$ and $e = -1.0$.

A rather different type of cyclopolymerization may be defined, in which the intramolecular step involves aromatic substitution rather than addition to a reactive group. An example of this is the cationic polymerization of diisopropenyl benzenes, which gives linear polyindane structures through intramolecular cyclization of the dimer (95,96):

Certain catalyst systems give a soluble, high-molecular-weight polyindane with quantitative ring closure (96).

The phenomenon of cyclopolymerization has now been extended to difunctional monomers with reactive groups other than alkene or alkyne, such as certain dialdehydes (97–99), diepoxides (100), and diisocyanates (101).

Relatively little work on the stereochemical aspects of cyclopolymerization has been reported, but there is evidence that the cyclopolymerization process involves some control of the stereoregularity of the polymer.

Crawshaw and Butler (40) polymerized acrylic anhydride in benzene solution with benzoyl peroxide as initiator at 65°C. The polymer was soluble in dimethyl sulfoxide and dimethyl formamide and showed only a small residual unsaturation. The cyclopolymer was hydrolyzed to polyacrylic acid,

which showed a substantially greater degree of crystallinity by x-ray diffraction measurements than normal free-radical-polymerized acrylic acid, indicating that the cyclopolymerization process had imposed some degree of stereoregularity on the parent polyacrylic anhydride.

Tiers and Bovey (102) analyzed the NMR spectra of polymethyl methacrylate samples and assigned three observed α-methyl proton peaks to syndiotactic (dld or ldl), isotactic (ddd or lll) and heterotactic (dll, ddl, ldd or lld) configurations, respectively. These may be denoted the s, i, and h configurations.

Miller et al. (103) obtained soluble cyclopolymers from methacrylic anhydride by free-radical initiation in benzene or dimethyl formamide at different temperatures. After conversion to polymethyl methacrylate by hydrolysis and esterification with diazomethane the NMR spectra of the polymers were obtained. The proportions of the three types of structure were determined and the following observations made:

1. The isotactic character decreases markedly with decreasing temperature, and there is a much stronger tendency to form isotactic structures than in the normal free-radical polymerization of methyl methacrylate.

2. Both the heterotactic and the syndiotactic character increase with decreasing temperature, and usually $h > s$.

The polymerization at 80°C yielded polymethyl methacrylate having a configuration almost identical with that obtained by Tiers and Bovey (102) from methyl methacrylate at 25°C by anionic polymerization with n-butyl-lithium.

At lower temperatures the thermodynamically more stable configuration would be expected to predominate. In this sense the most stable configuration is that which reduces ring strain and steric hindrance of neighboring groups to a minimum; this appears to be the heterotactic form.

Butler (104) has discussed some conformational aspects of cyclopolymerization.

Hwa (105) polymerized methacrylic anhydride in toluene solution at −50°C, using ultraviolet irradiation. The polymer was soluble in dimethyl sulfoxide and dimethyl formamide and showed only very weak infrared absorption for $-CH=CH_2$. The polymer was converted to polymethyl methacrylate in the same manner as that used by Butler et al. (103). From the NMR spectrum of the polymer Hwa found that $h = s \gtrsim 49\%$ and $i \lesssim 0.02$. The polymers appear to be a random run of syndiotactic and heterotactic blocks of various lengths, and there are no isotactic sequences of more than two units.

Further confirmation of the unusual configuration of polymethyl methacrylate derived from cyclopolymerized methacrylic anhydride was obtained by Hwa and Ries (106), who studied the polymethyl methacrylate of Hwa (105). Pressure–area isotherms were obtained for monolayers of the polymer in benzene on water at 25°C. Different isotherms were obtained from conventional isotactic, syndiotactic, and atactic polymers and from the polymer derived from methacrylic anhydride. The isotherm of the latter polymer extrapolates to a lower specific area at zero pressure than do those of the other polymers.

Mercier and Smets (107,108) investigated the free-radical polymerization of acrylic anhydride and found that the syndiotactic and isotactic forms of the anhydride units could be detected by their different carbonyl absorption bands in the infrared spectra. The structural assignments of the two types was made by comparing the spectra with those of pure meso and racemic

α,α'-dimethylglutaric anhydride. On this basis it presumably would not be possible to differentiate between the syndiotactic and heterotactic forms. Polymerization of acrylic anhydride in cyclohexanone at 35°C led to a preponderance of the syndiotactic (racemic) structure. Heat or the presence of traces of acrylic acid causes the syndiotactic form to isomerize to the isotactic (*meso*) form. The direct formation of the isotactic polymer is facilitated by polymerization in the polar solvent dimethyl formamide. The tendency of the isotactic form to be favored at higher temperatures shows a direct parallel with the polymerization of methacrylic anhydride (*103*).

2-3. KINETICS OF CYCLOPOLYMERIZATION AND CYCLOCOPOLYMERIZATION

As indicated in the preceding section, cyclopolymerization has become a more general phenomenon than it used to be and covers a wide variety of monomers. Some of the monomers form very high proportions of five-, six-, or seven-membered recurring rings in the backbone with a minimal participation from inter-intermolecular propagation and subsequent branching and cross-linking reactions. Others, capable of forming only larger rings, form some proportion of cyclic structures, but the participation of other reactions becomes significant. In still other cases, such as that of the 1,4 diolefins, the cyclization reaction can occur only upon the addition of another monomer unit. The mechanism and kinetics of these diverse systems may be quite complex. In this section emphasis will be placed upon the general kinetics of cyclopolymerization and cyclocopolymerization of the most studied types of diolefins, leading to the development of expressions for rates of polymerization and copolymer composition and other desirable relationships. The results of experimental work in this area will be considered later.

Although cyclopolymerizations and copolymerizations have been conducted with free-radical and ionic initiator systems, consideration will be given here only to free-radical initiation. The lack of sufficient detailed information at this time precludes a detailed discussion of the mechanism of ionic cyclopolymerization.

A. Cyclopolymerization

The kinetics of cyclopolymerization (*81*) may appear similar in many respects to the kinetics of vinyl polymerization. The chief distinguishing feature is the unusual chain propagation reaction. As a result of it cyclopolymerization of a single monomer more or less involves the participation of at least two types of growing radical: the radical from the initial reaction of a radical on a diolefinic monomer and the cyclized radical. The expressions for rates of polymerization, therefore, are more complex than those of vinyl polymerization and resemble the rate expressions for binary vinyl *co*polymerization. Further, in the absence of information on the mode of chain termination several rate expressions are possible. A large proportion of work in cyclopolymerization has involved allylic monomers that generally terminate by a degradative chain-transfer mechanism (*109*). Therefore, monoradical and biradical termination reactions must both be considered. This leads to further variation in expressions describing the polymerization.

Besides describing the rates of polymerization, a major objective of the work on kinetics has been to develop expressions for the determination of the important k_c/k_{11} ratio, the ratio of rate constants for cyclization and linear propagation. It is this ratio, together with monomer concentration, that determines the cyclic nature of the polymer; it is therefore of prime significance in the subject at hand.

1. SIMPLE CYCLOPOLYMERIZATION

The reaction scheme operable in the cyclopolymerization of a symmetrical monomer that contains two identical double bonds and undergoes complete cyclization may be described as follows.

Initiator decomposition:

$$A_2 \xrightarrow{k_d} 2A\cdot$$

Chain initiation:

$$A\cdot + M_1 \xrightarrow{k_I} M_1\cdot$$

Chain propagation: (a)

$$M_1\cdot \xrightarrow{k_c} M_2\cdot$$

(b)

$$M_2\cdot + M_1 \xrightarrow{k_{21}} M_1\cdot$$

Chain termination: (a)

$$2M_2\cdot \xrightarrow{k_{22}} \text{inactive products}$$

(b)

$$2M_1\cdot \xrightarrow{k_{11}} \text{inactive products}$$

(c)

$$M_1\cdot + M_2\cdot \xrightarrow{k_{12}} \text{inactive products}$$

Here A_2 is a thermally dissociating initiator, $A\cdot$ is an initiator fragment, M_1 is either double bond of a previously unreacted, symmetrical monomer, $M_1\cdot$ is the initial radical derived from the attack of a radical on M_1, and $M_2\cdot$ is the radical produced when $M_1\cdot$ cyclizes. The units of $[M_1]$ are moles of monomer double bonds per liter.

Under conditions that the kinetic chain length is sufficiently large for only a negligible amount of double bonds to be consumed by reactions other than propagation, the rate of disappearance of double bonds in the system may be written as

$$-d[\text{DB}]/dt = k_c[M_1\cdot] + k_{21}[M_2\cdot][M_1] \tag{2-1}$$

As in vinyl *co*polymerization, the relative concentrations of $M_1\cdot$ and $M_2\cdot$ are determined, not by the specific mechanisms of the initiation and termination reactions, but by the rate at which an active chain end of one type is converted into an active chain end of the other type. An $M_1\cdot$ chain end is converted into an $M_2\cdot$ chain end by the cyclization reaction; an $M_2\cdot$ chain end is converted to an $M_1\cdot$ chain end by reaction with M_1. The rate of change of $M_1\cdot$ with time is given by

$$d[M_1\cdot]/dt = k_{21}[M_2\cdot][M_1] - k_c[M_1\cdot] \tag{2-2}$$

If it is assumed that a stationary state is established (that is, that the rate of change of $[M_1\cdot]$ with time is very much smaller than either the rate of formation or disappearance of $M_1\cdot$), then

$$k_{21}[M_2\cdot][M_1] = k_c[M_1\cdot] \tag{2-3}$$

Hence

$$[M_1\cdot] = k_{21}[M_2\cdot][M_1]/k_c \tag{2-4}$$

Substitution of this expression for $[M_2\cdot]$ in Eq. (2-1) leads to

$$-d[DB]/dt = 2k_{21}[M_2\cdot][M_1] \tag{2-5}$$

In the case in which $k_c \gg k_{21}[M_1]$ it might be expected that chain termination would be due primarily to interaction of pairs of $M_2\cdot$ radicals. Equating the rate of formation and the rate of disappearance of chain radicals, we have

$$k_I[A\cdot][M_1] = 2k^{22}[M_2\cdot]^2$$
$$[M_2\cdot] = (k_I[A\cdot][M_1]/2k^{22})^{1/2} \tag{2-6}$$

Writing for the stationary state of $[A\cdot]$ radicals, we get

$$d[A\cdot]/dt = 2fk_d[A_2] - k_I[A\cdot][M_1] = 0$$
$$[A\cdot] = 2fk_d[A_2]/k_I[M_1] \tag{2-7}$$

Substitution of this expression for $A\cdot$ in Eq. (2-6) and substitution of the result for $M_2\cdot$ in Eq. (2-5) yields, for the over-all rate of disappearance of double bonds,

$$-d[DB]/dt = 2k_{21}[M_1](fk_d[A_2]/k^{22})^{1/2} \tag{2-8}$$

For cross-termination, the reaction of $M_1\cdot$ with $M_2\cdot$, the over-all rate expression becomes

$$-d[DB]/dt = 2(k_c k_{21} fk_d[A_2][M_1]/k^{12})^{1/2} \tag{2-9}$$

For $M_1\cdot + M_1\cdot$ termination the expression is:

$$-d[DB]/dt = 2k_c(fk_d[A_2]/k^{11})^{1/2} \tag{2-10}$$

For simple cyclopolymerization, which involves degradative chain transfer as the important means of chain termination, the scheme given above is modified by substitution of the following for the biradical termination reactions:

$$M_1\cdot \xrightarrow{k_{t_1}} M_1*$$

$$M_2\cdot + M_1 \xrightarrow{k_t} M_2 + M_1*$$

where the asterisk indicates a stabilized radical, whose propagation rate is essentially zero.

Applying the stationary-state principles gives

$$[M_1\cdot] = 2fk_d[A_2]/k_{t_1} \tag{2-11}$$

$$[M_2\cdot] = 2fk_d[A_2]/k_t[M_1] \tag{2-12}$$

The over-all expressions for disappearance of double bonds in allylic polymerization often cannot neglect the loss of double bonds by the initiation and termination reactions, because kinetic chain lengths are generally low. If, however, the kinetic chain length is about 20 or more, the error introduced by omission of these reactions may be low enough to be neglected. On this assumption the rate of disappearance of double bonds may be written

$$-d[DB]/dt = 4k_c fk_d[A_2]/k_{t_1} \tag{2-13}$$

$$-d[DB]/dt = 4k_{21} fk_d[A_2]/k_t \tag{2-14}$$

for $M_1\cdot$ and $M_2\cdot + M_1$ termination, respectively.

If the loss of double bonds by the initiation reaction is taken into account, then

$$-d[DB]/dt = k_1[A\cdot][M_1] + k_c[M_1\cdot] + k_{21}[M_2\cdot][M_1] \tag{2-15}$$

since

$$[A\cdot] = 2f k_d[A_2]/k_I[M_1] \tag{2-7}$$

$$-d[DB]/dt = 2fk_d[A_2] + k_c[M_1\cdot] + k_{21}[M_2\cdot][M_1] \tag{2-16}$$

For $M_1\cdot$ and $M_2\cdot + M_1$ termination the rate expressions respectively become

$$-d[DB]/dt = 2f k_d[A_2][1 + 2k_{21}/k_{t_1}] \tag{2-17}$$

$$-d[DB]/dt = 2f k_d[A_2][1 + 2k_{21}/k_t] \tag{2-18}$$

These expressions are combined in Table 2-6.

The foregoing expressions for the biradical terminating systems and the ones to follow are derived on the basis that the total termination reaction

TABLE 2-6

Rate Expressions for Simple Cyclopolymerization

Termination reaction	$-d[\mathrm{DB}]/dt$
$M_2\cdot + M_2\cdot$	$2k_{21}[M_1](fk_d[A_2]/k^{22})^{1/2}$
$M_2\cdot + M_1\cdot$	$2(k_ck_{21}fk_d[A_2][M_1]/k^{12})^{1/2}$
$M_1\cdot + M_1\cdot$	$2k_c(fk_d[A_2]/k^{11})^{1/2}$
$M_2\cdot + M_1$	
Including loss of double bonds by	
initiation reactions	$2fk_d[A_2](1 + 2k_{21}/k_{t_1})$
Not including it	$4k_{21}fk_d[A_2]/k_t$
M_1 (intramolecular)	
Including loss of double bonds by	
initiation reactions	$2fk_d[A_2](1 + 2k_c/k_{t_1})$
Not including it	$4k_cfk_d[A_2]/k_{t1}$

for a given system can be described by one or another of the following: $M_2\cdot + M_2\cdot$, $M_2\cdot + M_1\cdot$, or $M_1\cdot + M_1\cdot$. Although this may not be strictly true of all systems, it may be reasonably argued that the most important termination reaction for symmetrical nonconjugated diolefins is $M_2\cdot + M_2\cdot$. For nonsymmetrical monomers other effects may be important. The argument for $M_2\cdot + M_2\cdot$ termination considers the rate constant to be expected for $M_2\cdot + M_2\cdot$, relative to the other types of termination, and the relative concentrations of $M_2\cdot$ and $M_1\cdot$.

The noncyclized radical has a relatively long pendent group on the β carbon. The cyclic radical, on the other hand, does not have this steric interference to reaction. The relative effect of the β carbon substituent in the acrylate series may be determined by a comparison of k_p and k_t values for methyl acrylate and butyl acrylate (110):

Absolute Rate Constants for Methyl and Butyl Acrylate (110)

	k_p at 30°C, liter/mole/sec	k_t at 30°C, liter/mole/sec × 10^{-6}
Methyl acrylate	720	2.2
Butyl acrylate	14	0.009

The k_p values for the two monomers reflect a factor of 50 difference in their rate of radical attack on monomer. This must be due almost entirely to steric hindrance, because the activation energies for the two monomers should be very close to the same value (110). The effect of the bulky sub-stituent is even more pronounced in the termination rate constants. Here, the difference amounts to a factor of about 220. This would be expected, since both radicals have the bulky group and the effect is perturbed.

On this basis it would be predicted than k^{11} should be lower than k^{22} by a factor of about 200, owing to steric hindrance to termination. The value of the cross-termination rate constant k^{12} would be predicted to be lower than k^{22} by a factor of about 50. On the basis of the rate constant, then, termination by pairs of cyclized radicals would be significantly preferred.

The values of $[M_1\cdot]$ and $[M_2\cdot]$ can also affect the nature of the termination reaction, if the differences between them are large enough to overshadow the rate constants. The values of $[M_1\cdot]$ and $[M_2\cdot]$ are determined by

$$k_{21}[M_2\cdot][M_1] \approx k_c[M_1\cdot]$$

In general, $k_{21} \approx k_c$, and $[M_1\cdot]/[M_2\cdot]$ varies approximately as $[M_1]$. The usual variation for $[M_1]$ is about one order of magnitude, from 1 to 10 molar. Therefore, $[M_2\cdot]$ and $[M_1\cdot]$ are within about one order of magnitude of each other. This would not be sufficient to alter the effects of the rate con-stants, noted above, on the termination rate by any of the three mechanisms.

Therefore, for the symmetrical nonconjugated diolefins, considering both the values of the individual termination rate constants and the radical concentrations, the favored mechanism of termination should be $M_2\cdot + M_2\cdot$.

For nonsymmetrical monomers other effects may become quite important. In particular, polar effects leading to a high preference for cross-termination may be found (111). These effects are well known in vinyl copolymerization, in which monomers of different polarities cross-terminate almost exclusively. Cross-termination accounts for 90% or more of the total termination in the copolymerization of styrene and methyl methacrylate. In the case of nonsymmetrical diolefins undergoing biradical termination, therefore, $M_2\cdot + M_1\cdot$ termination may predominate, if the double bonds are of different polarities.

2. GENERAL CYCLOPOLYMERIZATION

The preceding section discussed the most simple case of cyclopolymeriza-tion. In this section a more general case will be considered, in which poly-merization does not lead to completely cyclized structures, and the rates of certain competing reactions are significant. These competing reactions are the direct propagation of a noncyclized radical with another monomer, the attack of radicals on the pendent unsaturated groups, and the propaga-tion of radicals derived from the pendent unsaturated groups. The approach used here does not take into account the possible physical effects on the rate that may be due to formation of network polymers.

The following reactions will be considered:

$$M_1\cdot \longrightarrow M_2\cdot \qquad \text{cyclization}$$

$$M_1\cdot + M_1 \longrightarrow M_1\cdot \qquad \text{linear propagation}$$

$$M_1\cdot + M_3 \longrightarrow M_3\cdot \qquad \text{cross-linking}$$

$$M_2\cdot + M_1 \longrightarrow M_1\cdot \qquad \text{propagation}$$

$$M_2\cdot + M_3 \longrightarrow M_3\cdot \qquad \text{cross-linking}$$

$$M_3\cdot + M_1 \longrightarrow M_1\cdot \qquad \text{pendent-radical propagation}$$

$$M_3\cdot + M_3 \longrightarrow M_3\cdot \qquad \text{cross-linking}$$

The termination reactions include all possible combinations of $M_1\cdot$, $M_2\cdot$, and $M_3\cdot$ radicals in biradical termination and also the degradative chain-transfer reactions possible with these radicals and monomers.

The rate of loss of double bonds may be written

$$-d[DB]/dt = (k_c + k_{11}[M_1] + k_{13}[M_3])[M_1\cdot] + (k_{21}[M_1] + k_{23}[M_3])[M_2\cdot]$$
$$+ (k_{31}[M_1] + k_{33}[M_3])[M_3\cdot] \qquad (2\text{-}19)$$

The rate of change of radical concentrations may be described as

$$d[M_1\cdot]/dt = k_{21}[M_2\cdot][M_1] + k_{31}[M_3\cdot][M_1] - k_c[M_1\cdot] - k_{13}[M_1\cdot][M_3]$$
$$(2\text{-}20)$$

$$d[M_2\cdot]/dt = k_c[M_1\cdot] - k_{21}[M_2\cdot][M_1] - k_{23}[M_2\cdot][M_3] \qquad (2\text{-}21)$$

$$d[M_3\cdot]/dt = k_{13}[M_1\cdot][M_3] + k_{23}[M_2\cdot][M_3] - k_{31}[M_3\cdot][M_1] \qquad (2\text{-}22)$$

From these equations and by means of the stationary-state assumption used earlier the following expressions for $M_1\cdot$ and $M_3\cdot$ may be found:

$$[M_1\cdot] = (k_{21}[M_1] + k_{23}[M_3])[M_2\cdot]/k_c \qquad (2\text{-}23)$$

$$[M_3\cdot] = [(k_{13}k_{21}[M_1] + k_{13}k_{23}[M_3])/k_c + k_{23}]([M_3][M_2\cdot]/k_{31}[M_1]) \qquad (2\text{-}24)$$

The substitution of these expressions for $M_1\cdot$ and $M_3\cdot$ in Eq. (2-19) and expansion and simplification lead to

$$-d[DB]/dt =$$

$$\left([M_1] + \frac{k_{23}}{k_{21}}[M_3]k_{21}\right)[M_2\cdot]\left(2 + \frac{k_{11}}{k_c}[M_1] + \frac{k_{13}}{k_c}[M_3] + \frac{k_{13}}{k_c}\frac{[M_3]}{[M_1]}\right)$$

$$\times \left([M_1] + \frac{k_{33}}{k_{31}}[M_3] + \frac{k_c}{k_{13}}\frac{k_{23}}{k_{21}}\frac{[M_1] + k_{33}[M_3]/k_{31}}{[M_1] + k_{23}[M_3]/k_{21}}\right) \qquad (2\text{-}25)$$

TABLE 2-7

Rate Expressions for Complex Cyclopolymerizations

Termination reaction	Substitute for $[M_2\cdot]$ in Eq. (2-25)
$M_2\cdot + M_2\cdot$	$(f k_d[A_2]/k^{22})^{1/2}$
$M_2\cdot + M_1\cdot$	$[(f k_d[A_2]k_c)/k^{12}(k_{21}[M_1] + k_{23}[M_3])]^{1/2}$
$M_1\cdot + M_1\cdot$	$[k_c(f k_d[A_2]/2k^{11})^{1/2}]/(k_{21}[M_1] + k_{23}[M_3])$
$M_2\cdot + M_1$	$f k_d[A_2]/k_t[M_1]$
$M_1\cdot + M_1$	$k_c f k_d[A_2]/k_{t_1}[M_1](k_{21}[M_1] + k_{23}[M_3])$
$M_2\cdot$ (intramolecular)	$f k_d[A_2]/k_{t_2}$
$M_1\cdot$ (intramolecular)	$k_c f k_d[A_2]/k_{t_1}(k_{21}[M_1] + k_{23}[M_3])$

This equation, which contains a single radical concentration term, may now be solved, depending upon the selection of a termination reaction. Of the biradical termination reactions the most likely is the $M_2\cdot + M_2\cdot$ reaction.

From Eq. (2-7):

$$[M_2\cdot] = (f k_d[A_2]/k^{22})^{1/2} \qquad (2\text{-}7)$$

Therefore:

$$-d[DB]/dt = k_{21}([M_1] + \beta_3[M_3])(f k_d[A_2]/k^{22})^{1/2}\left\{2 + \frac{[M_1]}{\alpha_c} + \frac{[M_3]}{\alpha'_c}\right.$$

$$\left. + \frac{[M_3]}{\alpha'_c[M_1]}\left[[M_1] + \frac{[M_3]}{\gamma_1} + \left(\frac{\beta_3}{\alpha'_c}\frac{[M_1] + [M_3]/\gamma_1}{[M_1] + \beta_3[M_3]}\right)\right]\right\} \qquad (2\text{-}26)$$

where $\alpha_c = k_c/k_{11}$, $\alpha'_c = k_c/k_{13}$, $\beta_3 = k_{23}/k_{21}$, and $\gamma_1 = k_{31}/k_{33}$.

In a similar manner expressions for other types of termination reaction may be derived. Table 2-7 gives the expressions for substitution in Eq. (2-25) for several other termination reactions, including degradative chain transfer.

3. APPROXIMATIONS TO THE GENERAL CASE

The equations developed for complex cyclopolymerization, although interesting and useful from a general point of view, are not sufficiently simple to allow ready use. Approximate relations have been derived (81), which assume that certain of the competing reactions are not significant in determining the over-all characteristics of the polymerization.

One of the most useful approximate equations results from the assumption that the rate of radical attack on pendent double bonds is slow, owing to the relatively low concentration of these groups compared with monomer double bonds. Thus, the reactions of radicals with M_3 and the subsequent products of these reactions are not considered. The rate of disappearance of double bonds is given by

$$-d[DB]/dt = k_c[M_1\cdot] + k_{11}[M_1\cdot][M_1] + k_{21}[M_2\cdot][M_1] \qquad (2\text{-}27)$$

The stationary-state equation is still

$$k_{21}[M_2\cdot][M_1] = k_c[M_1\cdot] \qquad (2\text{-}3)$$

Hence,

$$-d[DB]/dt = (2k_c + k_{11}[M_1])[M_1\cdot] \qquad (2\text{-}28)$$

or

$$-d[DB]/dt = (2 + k_{11}[M_1]/k_c)k_{21}[M_1][M_2\cdot] \qquad (2\text{-}29)$$

In a way similar to that used earlier in the complex cyclopolymerization case, expressions for $-d[DB]/dt$ may be derived for each type of chain termination. For $M_2\cdot + M_2\cdot$ termination the rate expression can be shown to be

$$-d[DB]/dt = (2k_c + k_{11}[M_1])(k_{21}[M_1]/k_c)(fk_d[A_2]/k^{22})^{1/2} \qquad (2\text{-}30)$$

Table 2-8 lists the rate expressions for several termination reactions.

Besides describing the dependence of rate on monomer concentration, initiator concentration, temperature, etc., the expressions in Table 2-8 can yield information on the mechanism of termination or, alternatively, on k_c/k_{11}, if the termination mechanism is known or can be assumed (81). As pointed out in Section 2-3-A-1, a consideration of the structure and the relative concentrations of $M_1\cdot$ and $M_2\cdot$ leads to the prediction that most symmetrical diolefins will terminate by interaction of pairs of $M_2\cdot$ radicals. Nonsymmetrical diolefins are likely to terminate by $M_2\cdot + M_2\cdot$ or $M_2\cdot + M_1\cdot$, depending upon the presence of polar effects. No prediction was made for the degradative chain-transfer termination reactions.

According to the expressions in Table 2-8, if one plots the rate divided by $[M_1]$ raised to a power of 0, 1/2, or 1 against $[M_1]$, a straight line should be

TABLE 2-8
Rate Expressions for Cyclopolymerization

Termination reaction	$-d[DB]/dt$
$M_2\cdot + M_2\cdot$	$(2k_c + k_{11}[M_1])(k_{21}[M_1]/k_c)(fk_d[A_2]/k^{22})^{1/2}$
$M_2\cdot + M_1\cdot$	$(2k_c + k_{11}[M_1])(k_d k_{21}[M_1][A_2]/k^{12}k_c)^{1/2}$
$M_1\cdot + M_1\cdot$	$(2k_c + k_{11}[M_1])(fk_d[A_2]/k^{11})^{1/2}$
$M_2\cdot + M_1$	$(2k_c + k_{11}[M_1])(2fk_d[A_2]k_{21}/k_tk_c)$
$M_1\cdot + M_1$	$(2k_c + k_{11}[M_1])(2fk_d[A_2]/k_{t_1}[M_1])$

obtained with a slope-to-intercept ratio of $k_{11}/2k_c$, if the termination reaction is $M_1\cdot + M_1\cdot$, $M_1\cdot + M_2\cdot$, or $M_2\cdot + M_2\cdot$, respectively. Thus, if k_c/k_{11} is known, the three plots can be made, and the one yielding a linear relationship and a k_c/k_{11} value close to that determined independently strongly suggests a specific termination reaction. Alternatively, if the termination is known, e.g. $M_2\cdot + M_2\cdot$, a plot of $-d[DB]/dt/[M_1]$ versus $[M_1]$ should yield a straight line whose slope-to-intercept ratio is the desired $k_{11}/2k_c$ value. In general, distinctions can be made between the three plots on the basis of linearity, the k_c/k_{11} value, or the predicted mechanism of termination.

In those cases in which degradative chain transfer occurs and termination involves only one radical (109) other dependencies of rate on $[M_1]$ should be found. In those cases in which the $k_{11}[M_1\cdot][M_1]$ reaction is taken into account and termination is $M_2\cdot + M_1$ the rate varies linearly with $[M_1]$ when the ratio of $k_c/k_{11}[M_1]$ is small. As this ratio increases, the dependence on $[M_1]$ drops to zero. When termination is $M_1\cdot + M_1$, then $-d[DB]/dt$ varies as the reciprocal of $[M_1]$, if $2k_c/k_{11}[M_1]$ is not large, and it tends toward a zero dependence as $k_c/k_{11}[M_1]$ becomes larger. The more general situation for the $M_2\cdot + M_1$ case is, then, that $-d[DB]/dt$ should vary linearly with $[M_1]$. When plotted in this fashion the ratio of slope to intercept should be $k_{11}/2k_c$. For $M_1\cdot + M_1$ termination the ratio times $[M_1]$ should be plotted against $[M_1]$ to give the same slope-to-intercept ratio.

4. POLYMERIZATION OF 1,4 DIOLEFINS

The kinetics of 1,4 diolefin polymerization differs in principle from the cases treated earlier, since, owing to steric considerations, the initial radical from the diolefin cannot cyclize,

$$A\cdot + CH_2{=}CH{\diagdown}{\diagup}CH{=}CH_2 \longrightarrow A{-}CH_2{-}\dot{C}H{\diagdown}{\diagup}CH{=}CH_2$$
$$\qquad\qquad R \qquad\qquad\qquad\qquad\qquad R$$

$$(M_1) \qquad\qquad\qquad\qquad\qquad (M_1\cdot)$$

but must wait for the addition of another monomer unit:

$$A{-}CH_2{-}\dot{C}H{\diagdown}{\diagup}CH{=}CH_2 \xrightarrow{(CH_2=CH)_2R} A{-}CH_2{-}CH{\diagup}^{CH_2{-}\dot{C}H{-}R{-}CH{=}CH_2}_{R{-}CH{=}CH_2} \longrightarrow$$
$$\qquad\qquad R$$

$$(M_1\cdot) \qquad\qquad\qquad\qquad\qquad (M_x\cdot)$$

$$A{-}CH_2{-}CH{\diagup}^{CH_2{-}CH{-}R{-}CH{=}CH_2}_{R{-}{-}\dot{C}H}{\diagdown}CH_2$$

$$(M_c\cdot)$$

This radical may then undergo a second cyclization, to yield a bicyclic unit:

$$(\text{M}_c'\cdot)$$

Neglecting cross-linking, long-range cyclization (rings of more than six members), and branching reactions, it is possible to derive expressions for the rate of polymerization and the composition of the polymer. Under these conditions the propagation reactions of interest are

$$\text{M}_\alpha\cdot + \text{M}_1 \xrightarrow{k_{\alpha 1}} \text{M}_\alpha\cdot$$

$$\text{M}_\alpha\cdot \xrightarrow{k_c} \text{M}_c\cdot$$

$$\text{M}_c\cdot + \text{M}_1 \xrightarrow{k_{c1}} \text{M}_1\cdot$$

$$\text{M}_1\cdot + \text{M}_1 \xrightarrow{k_{11}} \text{M}\cdot$$

$$\text{M}_c\cdot \xrightarrow{k_c'} \text{M}_c'\cdot$$

$$\text{M}_c'\cdot + \text{M}_1 \xrightarrow{k_{c1}'} \text{M}_1\cdot$$

$$-d[\text{M}_1]/dt = 2[\text{M}_1](k_{11}[\text{M}_1\cdot] + k_{\alpha 1}[\text{M}_\alpha\cdot] + k_{c1}[\text{M}_c\cdot] + k_{c1}'[\text{M}_c'\cdot]) \quad (2\text{-}31)$$

The coefficient 2 arises from the fact that the reaction of one monomer double bond removes two monomer double bonds from the system. The following are assumed at the stationary state:

$$d[\text{M}_1\cdot]/dt = k_{c1}[\text{M}_c\cdot][\text{M}_1] + k_{c1}'[\text{M}_c'\cdot][\text{M}_1] - k_{11}[\text{M}_1\cdot][\text{M}_1] = 0 \quad (2\text{-}32)$$

$$d[\text{M}_\alpha\cdot]/dt = k_{11}[\text{M}_1\cdot][\text{M}_1] - k_c[\text{M}_\alpha\cdot] = 0 \quad (2\text{-}33)$$

$$d[\text{M}_c\cdot]/dt = k_c[\text{M}_\alpha\cdot] - k_{c1}[\text{M}_c\cdot][\text{M}_1] - k_c'[\text{M}_c\cdot] = 0 \quad (2\text{-}34)$$

$$d[\text{M}_c\cdot]/dt = k_c'[\text{M}_c\cdot] - k_{c1}'[\text{M}_c'\cdot][\text{M}_1] = 0 \quad (2\text{-}35)$$

Solution of Eqs. (2-32) to (2-35) for $\text{M}_c\cdot$, $\text{M}_{c1}\cdot$, and $\text{M}_\alpha\cdot$ in terms of $\text{M}_1\cdot$, substitution of the result into (2-31), and simplification lead to

$$-d[\text{M}_1]/dt = 2k_{11}[\text{M}_1\cdot][\text{M}_1](2 + k_{\alpha 1}[\text{M}_1]/k_c) \quad (2\text{-}36)$$

For $\text{M}_1\cdot + \text{M}_1\cdot$ termination

$$-d[\text{M}_1]/dt = 2k_{11}[\text{M}_1](fk_d[\text{A}_2]/k^{11})^{1/2}(2 + k_{\alpha 1}[\text{M}_1]/k_c) \quad (2\text{-}37)$$

For $\text{M}_c\cdot + \text{M}_c\cdot$ termination

$$-d[\text{M}_1]/dt = 2(k_{c1}[\text{M}_1] + k_c')(fk_d[\text{A}_2]/k^{cc})^{1/2}(2 + k_{\alpha 1}[\text{M}_1]/k_c) \quad (2\text{-}38)$$

The composition relationships in terms of the concentration of diolefin residues relative to monocyclic and bicyclic rings may be obtained as follows:

$$d[m_c]/dt = k_c[M_\alpha\cdot] - k_c'[M_c\cdot] \qquad (2\text{-}38A)$$

$$d[m_c']/dt = k_c[M_c\cdot] \qquad (2\text{-}38B)$$

$$d([m_c] + [m_c'])/dt = k_c[M_\alpha\cdot] \qquad (2\text{-}38C)$$

From Eq. (2-33):

$$d([m_c] + [m_c'])/dt = k_{11}[M_1\cdot][M_1] \qquad (2\text{-}38D)$$

From Eq. (2-36):

$$d[m_1]/dt = k_{11}[M_1\cdot][M_1](2 + k_{\alpha 1}[M_1]/k_c) \qquad (2\text{-}39)$$

where the lower-case symbols denote formation of the unit in the polymer.

The coefficient 2 is dropped from Eq. (2-39), because now we are considering the rate of placement of diolefin residues in the chain, and each reaction of M_1 incorporates one diolefin residue. Dividing Eq. (2-39) by Eq. (2-38D) we obtain

$$\frac{d[m_1]}{d([m_c] + [m_c'])} = 2 + k_{\alpha 1}[M_1]/k_c \qquad (2\text{-}40)$$

At low conversions:

$$\frac{d[m_1]}{d([m_c] + [m_c'])} \approx \frac{[m_1]}{[m_c] + [m_c']} \qquad (2\text{-}41)$$

The expression resulting from a consideration of the formation of pendent unsaturated groups (M_3) is

$$d[M_3]/dt = (k_{c1}[M_c\cdot] + k_{\alpha 1}[M_\alpha\cdot])[M_1]$$

$$= k_{11}[M_1\cdot][M_1][k_{c1}[M_1]/(k_c' + k_{c1}[M_1]) + k_{\alpha 1}[M_1]/k_c]$$

$$\frac{d[m_1]}{d[M_3]} = \frac{2 + k_{\alpha 1}[M_1]/k_c}{k_{c1}[M_1]/(k_c' + k_{c1}[M_1]) + k_{\alpha 1}[M_1]/k_c} \qquad (2\text{-}42)$$

If $k_c' \ll k_{c1}[M_1]$,

$$\frac{d[m_1]}{d[M_3]} = \frac{2k_c + k_{\alpha 1}[M_1]}{k_c + k_{\alpha 1}[M_1]} \qquad (2\text{-}43)$$

Both Eqs. (2-42) and (2-43) reduce to the expected values of 2 when $k_c \gg k_{\alpha 1}[M_1]$. Under these conditions one half of the diolefin residues contain a pendent double bond.

5. MONOMERS WITH NON-EQUIVALENT DOUBLE-BONDS

Thus far the discussion has been limited to monomers of a symmetrical nature with double bonds equivalent in reactivity. However, a significant amount of work has been reported on monomers, such as allyl methacrylate and others in which the monomer double bonds significantly differ in reactivity; still others have been reported, in which the monomer double bonds are different but more nearly of the same reactivity, such as allyl methallyl, etc.

When the two double bonds are different but both reactive enough to undergo all the initiation, propagation, and cyclization reactions, the kinetic picture becomes very complicated; any rate expressions derived will be too complex for use. In kinetic studies the practice that has been followed is to use only monomers containing double bonds that differ significantly in reactivity. In such case it is often possible to neglect any initiation reaction involving the less reactive double bond. Moreover, the assumption is usually made that the attack of any radical on monomer always involves the more reactive double bond. The less reactive double bond may become involved in the cyclization reaction or may persist as a pendent unsaturated group, but otherwise it plays no important role. These assumptions lead to a rather simple rate expression (82), equivalent to the expressions outlined in Section 2-3, through the considerations mentioned there.

If, however, these conditions are not met, a much more complex situation develops. If all the reactions involving each double bond and the radicals generated from each double bond were taken into account, there would be 2 initiation, 2 cyclization, 12 propagation, 12 cross-linking, and 21 termination reactions involving 6 types of radical and 4 types of double bond. If the propagation and termination of the radicals generated from the pendent double bonds are ignored, there are 2 initiation, 2 cyclization, 8 propagation, 8 cross-linking, and 10 termination reactions remaining. If besides neglecting pendent radical propagation, one neglects attack of any radicals on the pendent double bonds, there are 2 initiation, 2 cyclization, 8 propagation, and 10 termination reactions, involving 4 types of radical and 2 types of double bond.

6. THE k_c/k_{11} RATIO

In the study of cyclopolymerization considerable attention has been directed toward the microstructure of the polymer and the influence of reaction conditions upon microstructure. From the kinetics of cyclopolymerization a very useful derivation yields expressions, at least for most of the simple systems, for the ratio of rate constants for cyclization to linear propagation. It is this important parameter which, along with monomer concentration, governs the microstructure of the polymer from a given monomer.

If the rate of placing diolefin residues in the chain is

$$d[m_1]/dt = (k_{11}[M_1\cdot] + k_{21}[M_2\cdot])[M_1] \qquad (2\text{-}44)$$

$$[M_2\cdot] = k_c[M_1\cdot]/k_{21}[M_1], \qquad \text{from equation (2-3)}$$

then

$$-d[m_1]/dt = (k_c + k_{11}[M_1])[M_1\cdot] \qquad (2\text{-}45)$$

The rate at which pendent unsaturated groups (M_3) are formed in the chain is the rate of linear propagation, because every propagation of a noncyclized radical with monomer produces a pendent unsaturated group:

$$d[M_3]/dt = k_{11}[M_1\cdot][M_1] \qquad (2\text{-}46)$$

Dividing Eq. (2-45) by (2-46) leads to

$$-d[m_1]/d[M_3] = 1 + k_c/k_{11}[M_1] \qquad (2\text{-}47)$$

At low conversions this differential form may be approximated by the concentration of diolefin residues $[m_1]$ and pendent double bonds $[M_3]$ in the polymer:

$$[m_1]/[M_3] = 1 + k_c/k_{11}[M_1] \qquad (2\text{-}47A)$$

Therefore, a plot of $[m_1]/[M_3]$ versus $1/[M_1]$ should yield a straight line of slope k_c/k_{11} and an intercept of 1.

Smets and co-workers (82,108) had earlier utilized a different equation, which was based upon the same type of reasoning, to determine k_c/k_{11} for acrylic anhydride and vinyl-*trans*-cinnamate. Their approach was to consider the rates of linear propagation (given as $R_v = 2k_p[M\cdot][M]$) and cyclization ($R_c = k_c[M\cdot]$) to obtain

$$1/f_c = 1 + 2(k_p/k_c)[M] \qquad (2\text{-}48)$$

where $f_c = R_c/(R_v + R_c)$ and $[M]$ is the diolefin concentration.

Gibbs (81) has pointed out that appropriate plots of the data on double-bond disappearance with time can also lead to values for k_c/k_{11}, providing some information is available on the mechanism of termination.

As will be noted in the following sections, additional information on k_c/k_{11} may be obtained from studies of cyclocopolymerization.

7. TEMPERATURE EFFECTS

In the case of vinyl polymerization the total apparent activation energy may be easily determined by differentiation of the logarithmic rate expression with respect to $1/RT$. For typical vinyl polymerization with biradical termination the total activation energy is given by (112)

$$E_T = E_d/2 + E_p - E_t/2 \qquad (2\text{-}49)$$

where the subscripts T, d, p, and t refer to the total apparent activation energy and the activation energies for the individual initiator decomposition, propagation, and termination reactions, respectively.

For allylic polymerization the expression is (44)

$$E_T = E_d + E_p - E_t \qquad (2\text{-}50)$$

providing that the kinetic chain length is reasonably high.

In cyclopolymerization the effect of temperature on rate is obtained from a similar differentiation of the rate expression with respect to temperature.

For the case of simple cyclopolymerization with termination by pairs of $M_2\cdot$ radicals

$$E_T = E_d/2 + E^{21} - E^{22}/2 \qquad (2\text{-}51)$$

Similarly,

$$E_T = E_d/2 + E_c - E^{11}/2, \qquad \text{for } M_1\cdot + M_1\cdot \text{ termination} \qquad (2\text{-}52)$$

$$E_T = E_d/2 + E_{21}/2 + E_c/2 - E^{12}/2, \qquad \text{for cross-termination} \qquad (2\text{-}53)$$

The rate expressions for the general case are too complicated to give useful relationships for the total activation energy. However, the approximate forms can be used, as follows.

For $M_2\cdot + M_2\cdot$ termination:

$$-d[\text{DB}]/dt = (2k_c + k_{11}[M_1])(k_{21}[M_1]/k_c)(fk_d[A_2]/k_{22})^{1/2} \qquad (2\text{-}54)$$

If $E_c \approx E_{11}$,

$$E_T = E_d/2 + E_{11(c)} + E_{21} - E_c - E_{22}/2 \qquad (2\text{-}55)$$

For $M_2\cdot + M_1\cdot$ termination (also where $E_c \approx E_{11}$):

$$E_T = E_d/2 + E_{11(c)} + E_{21}/2 - E_c/2 - E_{12}/2 \qquad (2\text{-}56)$$

For $M_1\cdot + M_1\cdot$ termination (also where $E_c \approx E_{11}$):

$$E_T = E_d/2 + E_{11(c)} - E_{11}/2 \qquad (2\text{-}57)$$

For cases in which degradative chain transfer occurs, in the simple case

$$E_T = E_d + E_{21} - E_t, \qquad \text{for } M_2\cdot + M_1 \text{ termination} \qquad (2\text{-}58)$$

$$E_T = E_d + E_c - E_{t1}, \qquad \text{for } M_1\cdot \text{ intramolecular termination} \qquad (2\text{-}59)$$

In the approximations to the general case the relations are

$$E_T = E_d + E_{11(c)} + E_{21} - E_c - E_t, \qquad \text{for } M_2\cdot + M_1 \text{ termination} \qquad (2\text{-}60)$$

$$E_T = E_d + E_{11(c)} - E_t, \qquad \text{for } M_1\cdot + M_1 \text{ termination} \qquad (2\text{-}61)$$

The other interesting equation is the variation in k_c/k_{11} with temperature:

If

$$R' = [m_1]/[M_3] = 1 + k_c/k_{11}[M_1]$$

Then

$$-\frac{d \ln R'}{d(1/RT)} = E_c - E_{11} \qquad (2\text{-}62)$$

B. Copolymerization

Cyclocopolymerization has been an area of activity, not only from the point of view of obtaining new polymeric materials, but also as a means of gaining further information on the nature and reactivity of the radicals and monomers involved in cyclopolymerization. Although a variety of co-polymers have been prepared, only a limited amount of fundamental information has been obtained. This is due to the difficulties in obtaining pure copolymers and determining composition, to difficulties in interpreta-tion of the composition data for obtaining reactivity ratios, and to the relative newness of the field.

The relationship for the composition of copolymers from pairs of vinyl monomers is usually written

$$\frac{d[M_1]}{d[M_2]} = \frac{[M_1]}{[M_2]} \frac{r_1[M_1] + [M_2]}{r_2[M_2] + [M_1]} \qquad (2\text{-}63)$$

where $r_1 = k_{11}/k_{12}$ and $r_2 = k_{22}/k_{21}$. At low conversions $d[M_1]/d[M_2] \simeq [m_1]/[m_2]$, where the lower-case symbols refer to the concentration of M_1 and M_2 residues in the polymer.

1. SIMPLE CYCLOCOPOLYMERIZATION

Simple cyclocopolymerization, as given earlier, refers to polymerization with quantitative cyclization, that is, $k_c \gg k_{11}[M_1]$. Every $M_1\cdot$ formed cyclizes to $M_2\cdot$. Therefore, the propagation reactions taking place in the copolymer-ization of such a monomer with a vinyl monomer are (where M_4 is the monovinyl comonomer and $M_4\cdot$ its radical):

$$M_1\cdot \xrightarrow{\ k_c\ } M_2\cdot$$

$$M_2\cdot + M_1 \xrightarrow{\ k_{21}\ } M_1\cdot$$

$$M_2\cdot + M_4 \xrightarrow{\ k_{24}\ } M_4\cdot$$

$$M_4\cdot + M_1 \xrightarrow{\ k_{41}\ } M_1\cdot \qquad (2\text{-}64)$$

$$M_4\cdot + M_4 \xrightarrow{\ k_{44}\ } M_4\cdot$$

The equations describing the disappearance of monomers and change in radical concentrations are:

$$-d[M_1]/dt = 2(k_{21}[M_2\cdot] + k_{41}[M_4\cdot])[M_1] \tag{2-65}$$

$$-d[M_4]/dt = (k_{24}[M_2\cdot] + k_{44}[M_4\cdot])[M_4] \tag{2-66}$$

$$d[M_1\cdot]/dt = (k_{41}[M_4\cdot] + k_{21}[M_2\cdot])[M_1] - k_c[M_1\cdot] \tag{2-67}$$

$$d[M_4\cdot]/dt = k_{24}[M_2\cdot][M_4] - k_{41}[M_4\cdot][M_1] \tag{2-68}$$

$$d[M_2\cdot]/dt = k_c[M_1\cdot] - k_{21}[M_2\cdot][M_1] - k_{24}[M_2\cdot][M_4] = 0 \tag{2-69}$$

Using the previous stationary-state assumptions to obtain solution for $M_4\cdot$ in terms of $M_2\cdot$ in Eqs. (2-69) and (2-70), substitution for $M_4\cdot$ in Eqs. (2-67) and (2-68), dividing Eq. (2-67) by Eq. (2-68), and simplification lead, for low-conversion copolymer, to

$$\frac{d[m_1]}{d[m_4]} = \frac{[M_1]}{[M_4]} \frac{r_2[M_1] + [M_4]}{r_4[M_4] + [M_1]} \tag{2-70}$$

where $r_2 = k_{21}/k_{24}$ and $r_4 = k_{44}/k_{41}$. This, as expected, has the same form as the binary vinyl copolymerization equation.

2. GENERAL CYCLOCOPOLYMERIZATION (84)

Often the copolymerization of nonconjugated diolefins with vinyl monomers leads to polymer containing higher degrees of residual unsaturation or branched and cross-linked units, or both, than are present in the homocyclopolymer. The competition of M_4 for $M_1\cdot$ may be higher than the rate of cyclization. It is possible to derive the more general composition relationships relating the concentration of m_1, m_4, and M_3 units in the polymer to the concentration of M_1 and M_4 in the monomer feed, taking into account the formation of pendent unsaturation, reactions of radicals with pendent unsaturation, etc., in the manner outlined in Section 2-3-A-2.

The general kinetics of polymerization of nonconjugated diolefin has been discussed in Section 2-3-A-2. The kinetics of copolymerization involving such monomers may be obtained by the additional consideration of reactions involving the monovinyl comonomer and its radical. That part of the general scheme of interest here may be given as follows.

Chain propagation:

$$M_1\cdot \xrightarrow{k_c} M_2\cdot$$

$$M_1\cdot + M_1 \xrightarrow{k_{11}} M_1\cdot$$

$$M_1\cdot + M_4 \xrightarrow{k_{14}} M_4\cdot$$

$$M_2\cdot + M_1 \xrightarrow{k_{21}} M_1\cdot$$

$$M_2\cdot + M_4 \xrightarrow{k_{24}} M_4\cdot \qquad (2\text{-}71)$$

$$M_3\cdot + M_1 \xrightarrow{k_{31}} M_1\cdot$$

$$M_3\cdot + M_4 \xrightarrow{k_{34}} M_4\cdot$$

$$M_4\cdot + M_1 \xrightarrow{k_{41}} M_1\cdot$$

$$M_4\cdot + M_4 \xrightarrow{k_{44}} M_4\cdot$$

Cross-linking:

$$M_1\cdot + M_3 \xrightarrow{k_{13}} M_3\cdot$$

$$M_2\cdot + M_3 \xrightarrow{k_{23}} M_3\cdot$$

$$M_3\cdot + M_3 \xrightarrow{k_{33}} M_3\cdot \qquad (2\text{-}72)$$

$$M_4\cdot + M_3 \xrightarrow{k_{43}} M_3\cdot$$

From these equations the rate of change of each monomer concentration is

$$-d[M_1]/dt = 2(k_{11}[M_1\cdot] + k_{21}[M_2\cdot] + k_{31}[M_3\cdot] + k_{41}[M_4\cdot])[M_1] \qquad (2\text{-}73)$$

$$-d[M_3]/dt = (k_{23}[M_2\cdot] + k_{33}[M_3\cdot] + k_{43}[M_4\cdot])[M_3]$$
$$- (k_{11}[M_1] + k_{14}[M_4])[M_1\cdot] \qquad (2\text{-}74)$$

$$-d[M_4]/dt = (k_{14}[M_1\cdot] + k_{24}[M_2\cdot] + k_{34}[M_3\cdot] + k_{44}[M_4\cdot])[M_4] \qquad (2\text{-}75)$$

The coefficient 2 in Eq. (2-73) arises from the fact, mentioned earlier, that the reaction of one of the diolefin double bonds removes two monomer double bonds from the system, the second, unreacted, double bond becoming the site of an intramolecular cyclization reaction or a pendent double bond, depending upon the fate of the $M_1\cdot$ radical.

The rate of change of each radical concentration is given by

$$d[M_1\cdot]/dt = (k_{11}[M_1\cdot] + k_{21}[M_2\cdot] + k_{31}[M_3\cdot] + k_{41}[M_4\cdot])[M_1]$$
$$- (k_c + k_{11}[M_1] + k_{13}[M_3] + k_{14}[M_4])[M_1\cdot] \qquad (2\text{-}76)$$

$$d[M_2\cdot]/dt = k_c[M_1\cdot] - (k_{21}[M_1] + k_{23}[M_3] + k_{24}[M_4])[M_2\cdot] \qquad (2\text{-}77)$$

$$d[M_3\cdot]/dt = (k_{13}[M_1\cdot] + k_{23}[M_2\cdot] + k_{33}[M_3\cdot] + k_{43}[M_4\cdot])[M_3]$$
$$- (k_{31}[M_1] + k_{33}[M_3] + k_{34}[M_4])[M_3\cdot] \qquad (2\text{-}78)$$

$$d[M_4\cdot]/dt = (k_{14}[M_1\cdot] + k_{24}[M_2\cdot] + k_{34}[M_3\cdot] + k_{44}[M_4\cdot])[M_4]$$
$$- (k_{41}[M_1] + k_{43}[M_3] + k_{44}[M_4])[M_4\cdot] \qquad (2\text{-}79)$$

By invoking the usual steady-state assumption Eqs. (2-76) to (2-79) may be taken as approximately equal to zero. On collecting like terms they may then be written

$$-(k_c + k_{13}[M_3] + k_{14}[M_4])[M_1\cdot] + k_{21}[M_2\cdot][M_1]$$
$$+ k_{31}[M_3\cdot][M_1] = -k_{41}[M_4\cdot][M_1] \qquad (2\text{-}76A)$$

$$k_c[M_1] - (k_{21}[M_1] + k_{23}[M_3] + k_{24}[M_4])[M_2\cdot] = 0 \qquad (2\text{-}77A)$$

$$k_{13}[M_1\cdot][M_3] + k_{23}[M_2\cdot][M_3] - (k_{31}[M_1] + k_{34}[M_4])[M_3\cdot]$$
$$= -k_{43}[M_4\cdot][M_3] \qquad (2\text{-}78A)$$

$$k_{14}[M_1\cdot][M_4] + k_{24}[M_2\cdot][M_4] + k_{34}[M_3\cdot][M_4]$$
$$= (k_{41}[M_1] + k_{43}[M_3])[M_4\cdot] \qquad (2\text{-}79A)$$

These four equations represent a set of linear, dependent, homogeneous equations in four unknowns: the respective radical concentrations. If Eq. (2-76A) is solved for the right-hand side of Eq. (2-73), we have

$$(k_{11}[M_1\cdot] + k_{21}[M_2\cdot] + k_{31}[M_3\cdot] + k_{41}[M_4\cdot])[M_1]$$
$$= (k_c + k_{11}[M_1] + k_{13}[M_3] + k_{14}[M_4])[M_1\cdot]$$

If this is then substituted for the right-hand side of Eq. (2.73), we have

$$-d[M_1]/dt = 2(k_c + k_{11}[M_1] + k_{13}[M_3] + k_{14}[M_4])[M_1\cdot] \quad (2\text{-}73A)$$

Similarly, Eqs. (2-74) and (2-78A) and (2-75) and (2-79A) yield Eqs. (2-74A) and (2-75A):

$$-d[M_3]/dt = (k_{31}[M_1] + k_{33}[M_3] + k_{34}[M_4])[M_3\cdot]$$
$$- (k_{11}[M_1] + k_{13}[M_3] + k_{14}[M_4])[M_1] \qquad (2\text{-}74A)$$

$$-d[M_4]/dt = (k_{41}[M_1] + k_{43}[M_3] + k_{44}[M_4])[M_4\cdot] \qquad (2\text{-}75A)$$

The relative rate of change of $[M_1]$ and $[M_3]$ and $[M_1]$ and $[M_4]$ in the system is given by

$$\frac{d[M_1]}{d[M_3]} = \frac{2(k_c + k_{11}[M_1] + k_{13}[M_3] + k_{14}[M_4])[M_1\cdot]}{(k_{31}[M_1] + k_{33}[M_3] + k_{34}[M_4])[M_3\cdot]} \qquad (2\text{-}80)$$
$$- k_{11}[M_1] + k_{13}[M_3] + k_{14}[M_4])[M_1\cdot]$$

$$\frac{d[M_1]}{d[M_4]} = \frac{2(k_c + k_{11}[M_1] + k_{13}[M_3] + k_{14}[M_4])[M_1\cdot]}{(k_{41}[M_1] + k_{43}[M_3] + k_{44}[M_4])[M_4\cdot]} \qquad (2\text{-}81)$$

These equations as written describe the loss of M_1 double bonds compared with the loss of M_3 double bonds and M_4 monomer in the system. They may be modified to reflect the relative rate of formation of M_1, M_3, and M_4 types of structure in the copolymer. For this purpose the coefficient 2 must be dropped from the equations, since the reaction of one M_1 double bond results in the incorporation of an entire diolefin residue into the chain. This M_1 type of unit (diolefin residue) may be cyclized or noncyclized.

The next step will be to obtain expressions for $M_1\cdot$ and $M_3\cdot$ in terms of $M_4\cdot$, so that the radical concentrations may be cancelled from the equations. Walling and Briggs (113) have used determinants to attain a similar end for the treatment of the n-component vinyl copolymerization system, and this method will be used here. The determinant expressions for $M_1\cdot$ and $M_3\cdot$ in terms of $M_4\cdot$, based on Eqs. (2-76A), (2-77A), and (2-78A) are

$$[M_1\cdot] = \frac{\begin{vmatrix} -k_{41}[M_4\cdot][M_1] & k_{21}[M_1] & k_{31}[M_1] \\ 0 & -(k_{21}[M_1] + k_{23}[M_3] + k_{24}[M_4]) & 0 \\ -k_{43}[M_4\cdot][M_3] & k_{23}[M_3] & -(k_{31}[M_1] + k_{34}[M_4]) \end{vmatrix}}{\begin{vmatrix} -(k_c + k_{13}[M_3] + k_{14}[M_4]) & k_{21}[M_1] & k_{32}[M_1] \\ k_c & -(k_{21}[M_1] + k_{23}[M_3] + k_{24}[M_4]) & 0 \\ k_{13}[M_3] & k_{23}[M_3] & -(k_{31}[M_1] + k_{34}[M_4]) \end{vmatrix}}$$

$$(2\text{-}82)$$

$$[M_3\cdot] = \frac{\begin{vmatrix} -(k_c + k_{13}[M_3] + k_{14}[M_4]) & k_{21}[M_1] & -k_{41}[M_4\cdot][M_1] \\ k_c & -(k_{21}[M_1] + k_{23}[M_3] + k_{24}[M_4]) & 0 \\ k_{13}[M_3] & k_{23}[M_3] & -k_{43}[M_4\cdot][M_3] \end{vmatrix}}{D_4}$$

$$(2\text{-}83)$$

where D_4 is the denominator of the $M_1\cdot$ expression.

It is convenient at this point to introduce the relative reactivity ratios. Since the comparisons to be used here are the rate constants for the homopolymerization reactions, that is k_{11}, k_{33}, and k_{44}, and since the comparison for the cyclized ($M_2\cdot$) radical reactions will be k_{21}, the numerator and denominator of the determinant will be divided by the product of these parameters (*114*). Making this change and solving the determinant expression for $M_1\cdot$ yields

$$[M_1\cdot] = \frac{k_{44}[M_1][M_4\cdot]}{D_4'k_{11}}(\gamma_1\delta_1[M_1] + \gamma_1\delta_3[M_3] + \gamma_4\delta_1[M_4])$$
$$\times ([M_1] + \beta_3[M_3] + \beta_4[M_4]) \quad (2\text{-}84)$$

In a similar manner the expression for $M_3\cdot$ may be shown to be

$$[M_3\cdot] = \frac{-k_{44}[M_3][M_4\cdot]}{D_4'k_{33}}[\alpha_c(\beta_3\delta_1[M_1] + \beta_3\delta_3[M_3] + \beta_4\delta_3[M_4])$$
$$+ ([M_1] + \beta_3[M_3] + \beta_4[M_4])(\alpha_3\delta_1[M_1] + \alpha_3\delta_3[M_3] + \alpha_4\delta_3[M_4])] \quad (2\text{-}85)$$

where $\alpha_c = k_c/k_{11}$, $\alpha_3 = k_{13}/k_{11}$, $\alpha_4 = k_{14}/k_{11}$, $\beta_3 = k_{23}/k_{21}$, $\beta_4 = k_{24}/k_{21}$, $\gamma_1 = k_{31}/k_{33}$, $\delta_1 = k_{41}/k_{44}$, and $\delta_3 = k_{43}/k_{44}$.

D_4', the denominator of the $M_1\cdot$ and $M_3\cdot$ determinants divided by the product of the rate constants, is given by

$$D_4' = \frac{[M_4]}{-k_{44}}[(\alpha_4\gamma_1[M_1] + \alpha_3\gamma_4[M_3] + \alpha_4\gamma_4[M_4])$$

$$([M_1] + \beta_3[M_3] + \beta_4[M_4]) + \alpha_c(\beta_4\gamma_1[M_1] + \beta_3\gamma_4[M_3] + \beta_4\gamma_4[M_4])] \quad (2\text{-}86)$$

Substituting Eq. (2-86) in Eqs. (2-84) and (2-85) and substituting the resulting expressions for $M_1\cdot$ and $M_3\cdot$ in Eqs. (2-80) and (2-81), respectively, and carrying out the indicated divisions by k_{11}, k_{33}, and k_{44} lead to the desired relationships. These may be summarized as follows:

$$d[m_1]:d[M_3]:d[m_4]::\quad (2\text{-}87)$$

$$[M_1](\alpha_c + [M_1] + \alpha_3[M_3] + \alpha_4[M_4])A\cdot B:$$
$$-[M_3](\gamma_1[M_1] + [M_3] + \gamma_4[M_4])[\alpha_c(\beta_3\delta_1[M_1] + \beta_3\delta_3[M_3]$$
$$+ \beta_4\delta_3[M_4] + B\cdot C] - [M_1]([M_1] + \alpha_3[M_3] + \alpha_4[M_4])A\cdot B:\quad (2\text{-}88)$$
$$[M_4](\delta_1[M_1] + \delta_3[M_3] + [M_4])(\alpha_4\gamma_1[M_1] + \alpha_3\gamma_4[M_3] + \alpha_4\gamma_4[M_4])\cdot B$$
$$+ \alpha_c(\beta_4\gamma_1[M_1] + \beta_3\gamma_4[M_3] + \beta_4\gamma_4[M_4]) \quad (2\text{-}89)$$

where $A = \gamma_1\delta_1[M_1] + \gamma_1\delta_3[M_3] + \gamma_4\delta_1[M_4]$

$B = [M_1] + \beta_3[M_3] + \beta_4[M_4]$

$C = \alpha_3\delta_1[M_1] + \alpha_3\delta_3[M_3] + \alpha_4\delta_3[M_4]$

These expressions represent the most general composition relationships available for the copolymerization of symmetrical nonconjugated diolefins and vinyl monomers. They more quantitatively account for the formation of cyclized and noncyclized diolefin units and consider the reactions of pendent double bonds with growing radicals.

3. APPROXIMATIONS TO THE GENERAL CASE

The more general case considered in the preceding section is too complicated to allow use for experimental determination of the relative reactivity ratios with any reasonable degree of accuracy and convenience. Approximations to the more general case have been derived, which consider one or more of the reactions listed therein of vanishing importance under specific conditions. They will be discussed in this section.

One of the most useful assumptions to consider is that in the early stages of reaction the copolymer formed is a small fraction of the total reacting system. Thus, pendent double bonds formed by the k_{11} and k_{14} reactions constitute a very small proportion of all double bonds available for reaction. Under these conditions it may be assumed that the rate of reaction of radicals with M_3 is slow, owing to the low concentration of M_3, and may be ignored. The subsequent reactions of $M_3\cdot$ with monomer or M_3 are also not considered. The kinetics for homocyclopolymerization under these same conditions has been discussed in Section 2-3-A-3.

Roovers and Smets (82) first published the development of a copolymer composition relationship for the condition in which reactions of M_3 were not significant. The applicable propagation reactions are

$$M_1\cdot + M_1 \xrightarrow{k_{11}} M_1\cdot$$

$$M_1\cdot + M_4 \xrightarrow{k_{14}} M_4\cdot$$

$$M_1\cdot \xrightarrow{k_c} M_2\cdot$$

$$M_2\cdot + M_1 \xrightarrow{k_{21}} M_1\cdot$$

$$M_2\cdot + M_4 \xrightarrow{k_{24}} M_4\cdot$$

$$M_4\cdot + M_1 \xrightarrow{k_{41}} M_1\cdot$$

$$M_4\cdot + M_4 \xrightarrow{k_{44}} M_4\cdot$$

Roovers and Smets described the rate of disappearance of monomers:

$$-d[M_1]/dt = 2(k_{11}[M_1\cdot] + k_{21}[M_2\cdot] + k_{41}[M_4\cdot])[M_1] \qquad (2\text{-}90)$$

$$-d[M_4]/dt = (k_{14}[M_1\cdot] + k_{24}[M_2\cdot] + k_{44}[M_4\cdot])[M_4] \qquad (2\text{-}91)$$

From the usual stationary-state relationships expressions for $[M_2\cdot]$ and

$[M_4\cdot]$ may be obtained:

$$[M_2\cdot] = k_c[M_1\cdot]/(k_{21}[M_1] + k_{24}[M_4])$$

$$[M_4\cdot] = \frac{[M_1\cdot][M_4]}{k_{41}[M_1]}k_{14} + \frac{k_{24}k_c}{k_{21}[M_1] + k_{24}[M_4]}$$

The relative rate of disappearance of $[M_1]$ to $[M_4]$ may then be shown to be equal to

$$\frac{d[m_1]}{d[m_4]} = \frac{[M_1]}{[M_4]}\frac{r_1[M_1] + [M_4] + K_c}{r_4[M_4] + [M_1] + K'_c(r_4[M_4] + [M_1])/(r_2[M_1] + [M_4])} \quad (2\text{-}92)$$

where $r_1 = k_{11}/k_{14}, r_2 = k_{21}/k_{24}, r_4 = k_{44}/k_{41}, K_c = k_c/k_{11}$, and $K'_c = k_c/k_{14}$ in the terminology used here. When K_c and K'_c become large compared with $r_1[M_1] + [M_4]$ and $r_4[M_4] + [M_1]$, respectively, Eq. (2-92) reduces to Eq. (2-72).

Gibbs and McHenry (84) also considered the approximation in which reactions of radicals with M_3 were slow, as an adjunct to the development of the general case. The relation given is

$$d[m_1]:d[M_3]:d[m_4]::$$

$$[M_1]([M_1] + \alpha_c + \alpha_4[M_4]):$$

$$-[M_1]([M_1] + \alpha_4[M_4]): \quad (2\text{-}93)$$

$$[M_4]([M_1] + [M_4]/\delta_1)[\alpha_4 + \alpha_c/([M_1]/\beta_4 + [M_4])]$$

The relationship for $d[m_1]/d[m_4]$ may be rearranged for comparison with the expression of Roovers and Smets (82):

$$\frac{d[m_1]}{d[m_4]} = \frac{[M_1]}{[M_4]}$$

$$\times \frac{[M_1] + \alpha_c + \alpha_4[M_4]}{\alpha_4([M_1] + [M_4]/\delta_1) + \alpha_c([M_1] + [M_4]/\delta_1)/([M_4] + [M_1]/\beta_4)} \quad (2\text{-}94)$$

where, as before, $\alpha_c = k_c/k_{11}, \alpha_4 = k_{14}/k_{11}, \delta_1 = k_{41}/k_{44}$, and $\beta_4 = k_{24}/k_{21}$. When α_c becomes large compared with $[M_1] + \alpha_4[M_4]$ and $\alpha_4([M_1] + [M_4]/\delta_1)$, Eq. (2-94) reduces to Eq. (2-72).

Roovers and Smets (82) also derived equations for $d[m_1]/d[m_c]$ and $d[m_4]/d[m_c]$, where $[m_c]$ is the concentration of cyclized units in the polymer:

$$\frac{d[m_1]}{d[m_c]} = 1 + \frac{[M_1]}{K_c} + \frac{[M_4]}{K_c} \quad (2\text{-}95)$$

$$\frac{d[m_4]}{d[m_c]} = [M_4]\left(1 + r_4\frac{[M_4]}{[M_1]}\right)\left(\frac{1}{K'_c} + \frac{1}{r_2[M_1] + [M_4]}\right) \quad (2\text{-}96)$$

In the case in which the degree of cyclization of the diolefin is unaffected by the presence of the comonomer ($k_{14} \to 0$), Eq. (2-96) may be further simplified to

$$\frac{d[m_1]}{d[m_4]} = \frac{[M_1]}{[M_4]} \frac{r_2[M_1] + [M_4]}{r_4[M_4] + [M_1]} \left(1 + \frac{[M_1]}{K_c}\right) \tag{2-97}$$

$$\frac{d[m_1]}{d[m_c]} = 1 + \frac{[M_1]}{K_c} \tag{2-98}$$

$$\frac{d[m_4]}{d[m_c]} = \frac{[M_4]}{[M_1]} \frac{r_4[M_4] + [M_1]}{r_2[M_1] + [M_4]} \tag{2-99}$$

Roovers and Smets further pointed out, by setting

$$\frac{d[m_1]}{d[m_4]} = \rho, \qquad \frac{[M_1]}{[M_4]} = R, \qquad \text{and} \qquad \frac{d[m_c]}{d[m_4]} = \Delta \tag{2-100}$$

that the equations given above may be put in a form for graphical determination of r_2 and r_4:

$$\frac{1}{R} \left(\frac{\rho}{1 + [M_1]/K_c} - 1\right) = r_2 - r_4 \left(\frac{\rho}{R^2(1 + [M_1]/K_c}\right) \tag{2-101}$$

$$\frac{\Delta - 1}{R} = r_2 - r_4 \left(\frac{\Delta}{R^2}\right) \tag{2-102}$$

They used these equations for the interpretation of results from the copolymerization of vinyl-*trans*-cinnamate with vinyl acetate, N-vinyl pyrolidone, methacrylonitrile, and styrene to determine relative reactivity ratios (82). The results of this work will be discussed in a later section.

4. CYCLOCOPOLYMERIZATION OF 1,4 DIOLEFINS

The copolymerization of 1,4 diolefins, such as divinyl ether, sulfide and sulfone, 1,4-pentadiene, etc., with monovinyl monomers is an interesting situation. As described earlier (Section 2-3-A-4), the initial radical formed from the diolefin cannot cyclize, because a four-membered ring would have to form if it did. However, upon the addition of another monomer unit, either M_1 or M_4, cyclization can proceed with the formation of a six-membered ring:

The propagation reactions are

$$M_1\cdot + M_1 \xrightarrow{k_{11}} M_1\cdot$$

$$M_1\cdot + M_4 \xrightarrow{k_{14}} M_\beta\cdot$$

$$M_\beta\cdot \xrightarrow{k_c} M_c\cdot$$

$$M_\beta\cdot + M_1 \xrightarrow{k_{\beta 1}} M_1\cdot$$

$$M_\beta\cdot + M_4 \xrightarrow{k_{\beta 4}} M_4\cdot$$

$$M_c\cdot + M_1 \xrightarrow{k_{c1}} M_1\cdot$$

$$M_c\cdot + M_4 \xrightarrow{k_{c4}} M_4\cdot$$

$$M_4\cdot + M_1 \xrightarrow{k_{41}} M_1\cdot$$

$$M_4\cdot + M_4 \xrightarrow{k_{44}} M_4$$

The assumptions implicit in the selection of these reactions for determining copolymer composition are that, if $M_1\cdot$ reacts with M_1, the resulting radical does not cyclize, and that the disappearance of any pendent unsaturation by reaction with radicals is not significant. The rate of disappearance of $[M_1]$ may be written from the equations given above:

$$-d[M_1]/dt = 2(k_{11}[M_1\cdot] + k_{\beta 1}[M_\beta\cdot] + k_{c1}[M_c\cdot] + k_{41}[M_4\cdot])[M_1] \quad (2\text{-}103)$$

For the disappearance of $[M_4]$:

$$-d[M_4]/dt = (k_{14}[M_1\cdot] + k_{\beta 4}[M_\beta\cdot] + k_{c4}[M_c\cdot] + k_{44}[M_4\cdot])[M_4] \quad (2\text{-}104)$$

The rates of change of radical concentrations are:

$$d[M_1\cdot]/dt = -k_{14}[M_1\cdot][M_4] + (k_{\beta 1}[M_\beta\cdot] + k_{c1}[M_c\cdot] + k_{41}[M_4\cdot])[M_1]$$

$$d[M_4\cdot]/dt = [M_4](k_{\beta 4}[M_\beta\cdot] + k_{c4}[M_c\cdot]) - k_{41}[M_4\cdot][M_1]$$

$$d[M_c\cdot]/dt = k_c[M_\beta\cdot] - (k_{c1}[M_c\cdot] + k_{c4}[M_c\cdot])[M_4]$$

From these equations and by assuming a stationary state expressions for $M_1\cdot$, $M_\beta\cdot$, and $M_4\cdot$ may be found in terms of $M_c\cdot$:

$$[M_1\cdot] = ([M_c\cdot]/k_{14}[M_4]k_c)(k_{c1}[M_1] + k_{c4}[M_4])(k_{\beta 1}[M_1] + k_{\beta 4}[M_4] + k_c)$$

$$[M_4\cdot] = ([M_c\cdot]/k_{41}[M_1]k_c)[k_{c4}[M_4]k_c + k_{\beta 4}[M_4](k_{c1}[M_1] + k_{c4}[M_4])]$$

$$[M_\beta\cdot] = ([M_c\cdot]/k_c)(k_{c1}[M_1] + k_{c4}[M_4])$$

Substitution of these expressions for $M_1\cdot$, $M_4\cdot$, and $M_\beta\cdot$ in the equations given above for $-d[M_1]/dt$ and $-d[M_4]/dt$ and dividing $-d[M_1]/dt$ by $-d[M_4]/dt$ and simplification yield

$$\frac{d[m_1]}{d[m_4]}$$

$$\times \frac{(1 + r_1[M_1]/[M_4])[1/[M_4] + a(1 + [M_1]/r_\beta[M_4])]}{a[([M_1]/r_\beta[M_4]) + r_4[M_4]/[M_1] + 2] + (1/[M_4])}$$

$$\times (1 + r_4[M_4]/[M_1])/(1 + r_c[M_1]/[M_4]) \quad (2\text{-}105)$$

where $r_1 = k_{11}/k_{14}$, $r_\beta = k_{\beta4}/k_{\beta1}$, $r_4 = k_{44}/k_{41}$, $r_c = k_{c1}/k_{c4}$, and $a = k_c/k_{\beta4}$.

In a similar fashion an expression for the ratio of M_1 residues to cyclic units in the chain may be obtained:

$$d[m_1]/d[m_c] = [(r_1[M_1]/[M_4]) + 1][([M_1]/r_\beta a) + ([M_4]/a) + 1] \quad (2\text{-}106)$$

If $k_c \gg k_{\beta4}$, almost all the units cyclize. The composition expression for this case is

$$\frac{d[m_1]}{d[m_4]} = \frac{(1 + r_1[M_1]/[M_4])(1 + r_c[M_1]/[M_4])}{r_c[M_1]/[M_4] + r_4[M_4]/[M_1] + 2} \quad (2\text{-}107)$$

This expression has been used by Barton et al. (88) for determining relative reactivity ratios for the copolymerization of divinyl ether and 1,4-pentadiene with acrylonitrile. The results will be discussed later.

5. COPOLYMERIZATION OF NON-CYCLIZING DIOLEFINS

An extension of the general case is the situation in which a diolefin incapable of cyclizing (115), such as an m- or p-divinyl benzene, is copolymerized with a monovinyl monomer. In this case $k_c = 0$, and no cyclic radicals are formed.

The propagation reactions of concern are

$$M_1\cdot + M_1 \xrightarrow{k_{11}} M_1\cdot$$

$$M_1\cdot + M_4 \xrightarrow{k_{14}} M_4\cdot$$

$$M_4\cdot + M_1 \xrightarrow{k_{41}} M_1\cdot$$

$$M_4\cdot + M_4 \xrightarrow{k_{44}} M_4\cdot$$

$$M_3\cdot + M_1 \xrightarrow{k_{31}} M_1\cdot$$

$$M_3\cdot + M_4 \xrightarrow{k_{34}} M_4\cdot$$

The cross-linking reactions are

$$M_1 \cdot + M_3 \xrightarrow{k_{13}} M_3 \cdot$$

$$M_4 \cdot + M_3 \xrightarrow{k_{43}} \dot{M}_3 \cdot$$

$$M_3 \cdot + M_3 \xrightarrow{k_{33}} M_3 \cdot$$

The rate of formation of M_3 is given by

$$k_{11}[M_1 \cdot][M_1] + k_{14}[M_1 \cdot][M_4]$$

The rates of formation of m_1 and m_4 elements in the polymer are given by

$$d[m_1]/dt = (k_{11}[M_1 \cdot] + k_{31}[M_3 \cdot] + k_{41}[M_4 \cdot])[M_1] \qquad (2\text{-}108)$$

$$d[m_4]/dt = (k_{14}[M_1 \cdot] + k_{34}[M_3 \cdot] + k_{44}[M_4 \cdot])[M_4] \qquad (2\text{-}109)$$

The over-all rate of formation of M_3 units in the chain is

$$d[M_3]/dt = (k_{11}[M_1] + k_{13}[M_3] + k_{14}[M_4])[M_1 \cdot]$$
$$- (k_{13}[M_1 \cdot] + k_{33}[M_3 \cdot] + k_{43}[M_4 \cdot])[M_3] \qquad (2\text{-}110)$$

The stationary-state equations are:

$$(k_{31}[M_3 \cdot] + k_{41}[M_4 \cdot])[M_1] = (k_{13}[M_3] + k_{14}[M_4])[M_1 \cdot]$$

$$(k_{13}[M_1 \cdot] + k_{43}[M_4 \cdot])[M_3] = (k_{31}[M_1] + k_{34}[M_4])(M_3 \cdot]$$

$$(k_{14}[M_1 \cdot] + k_{34}[M_3 \cdot])[M_4] = (k_{41}[M_1] + k_{43}[M_3])[M_4 \cdot]$$

This series of linear, dependent, homogeneous equations can be solved for any one radical concentration in terms of the other two by means of determinants in a manner analogous to that used in Section 2-3-B-2.

The resulting expression for $d[m_1]/d[m_4]$ is

$$\frac{d[m_1]}{d[m_4]}$$

$$= \frac{[M_1]([M_1] + \alpha_3[M_3] + \alpha_4[M_4])(\delta_1\gamma_1[M_1] + \gamma_4\delta_1[M_4] + \gamma_1\delta_3[M_3])}{[M_4](\delta_1[M_1] + \delta_3[M_3] + [M_4])(\alpha_4[M_4] + \alpha_3\gamma_4[M_3] + \alpha_4\gamma_4[M_4])}$$

$$(2\text{-}111)$$

where $\alpha_3 = k_{13}/k_{11}$, $\alpha_4 = k_{14}/k_{11}$, $\gamma_1 = k_{31}/k_{33}$, $\gamma_4 = k_{34}/k_{33}$, $\delta_1 = k_{41}/k_{44}$, and $\delta_3 = k_{43}/k_{44}$.

If the reactions of radicals with M_3 and subsequent reactions of $M_3\cdot$ are ignored, the expression obtained is

$$\frac{d[m_1]}{d[m_4]} = \frac{[M_1]}{[M_4]} \frac{r_1[M_1] + [M_4]}{r_4[M_4] + [M_1]} \qquad (2\text{-}112)$$

where $r_1 = k_{11}/k_{14}$ ($= 1/\alpha_4$), $r_4 = k_{44}/k_{41}$ ($= 1/\delta_1$), and $[M_1]$ is the molar concentration of diolefin double bonds.

Equation (2-112) has been found empirically by Wiley and Sale (116) and was used to describe copolymer compositions in a wide variety of noncyclizing diolefin copolymerizations.

2-4. THE CYCLOPOLYMERIZATION PROCESS

A. Results of Experimental Investigations

On the basis of the information presented in Section 2-2 it appears that the mechanism originally proposed by Butler and Angelo (2) for the polymerization of diallyl ammonium halides generally describes the polymerization and copolymerization of a wide variety of nonconjugated diolefins and other related difunctional monomers. In most cases in which cyclic units of nearly favored size can form the propagation process consists essentially of alternating intermolecular-intramolecular reaction sequences. In most of these cases the direct reaction of the noncyclized radical with monomer, with the attendant consequences of pendent double-bond formation, cross-linking, etc., accounts for a far smaller number of propagation reactions. In this section we shall consider the results of the investigations reported in Section 2-2 in additional detail, in an effort to define more quantitatively the effect of reaction variables and monomer structure on the nature of the cyclopolymerization process. The effect of reaction variables will be discussed in context with the general kinetics outlined in Section 2-3. The effect of monomer structure will be compared and discussed in context with results available on this subject from model compounds and studies conducted in the polycondensation area. In the concluding part of this section we shall consider the mechanisms proposed for cyclopolymerization and the pertinent theoretical questions involved.

1. RATES OF POLYMERIZATION

As the basis for discussion of the results of rate studies the equations in Table 3-8 will be used. These equations were derived for cases in which cyclization need not be quantitative and formation of pendent double bonds is taken into account (81). These expressions reduce to the equations describing simple cyclopolymerization (Table 2-6) when the $k_c/k_{11}[M_1]$ ratio is high. The use of these relationships does not restrict the discussion and interpretation of results only to those cases in which $k_c/k_{11}[M_1]$ is high.

Cases in which the dependence of rate on $[M_1]$ has been measured and reported are methacrylic anhydride in dimethyl formamide (44), acrylic anhydride in cyclohexanone (108), vinyl-*trans*-cinnamate in benzene and dioxane (82), methacrylic anhydride in cyclohexanone (108a), and divinyl acetal in benzene (117). The initiator was azobisisobutyronitrile (AIBN) in all cases.

Gibbs and Murray (44) report for methacrylic anhydride a dependence of rate on the 3/2 power of the monomer concentration. These data converted to $[M_1] = 2[M]$ may be plotted according to the relations discussed in Section 2-3-A-3, as shown in Fig. 2-1. The plot of rate versus $[M_1]$ is non-linear and the extrapolated value of the intercept and the slope of the low $[M_1]$ part of the curve leads to a k_c/k_{11} value of 0.13 moles/liter. The plot of rate/ $[M_1]^{1/2}$ versus $[M_1]$ is linear; $k_c/k_{11} = 0.70$ moles/liter. The plot of rate/$[M_1]$ versus $[M_1]$ is also linear; k_c/k_{11} is 11.4 moles/liter. The latter value is more in agreement with expectation (based upon the extensive cyclization in this case) and with the range in values obtained from copolymerization studies, to be discussed shortly. The only relationship leading to a linear plot and a value for k_c/k_{11} in agreement with independent measurements is that derived on the basis of $M_2\cdot + M_2\cdot$ termination.

Smets et al. (108a) report a study of methacrylic anhydride polymerization in cyclohexanone, in which the variation in polymerization rate with

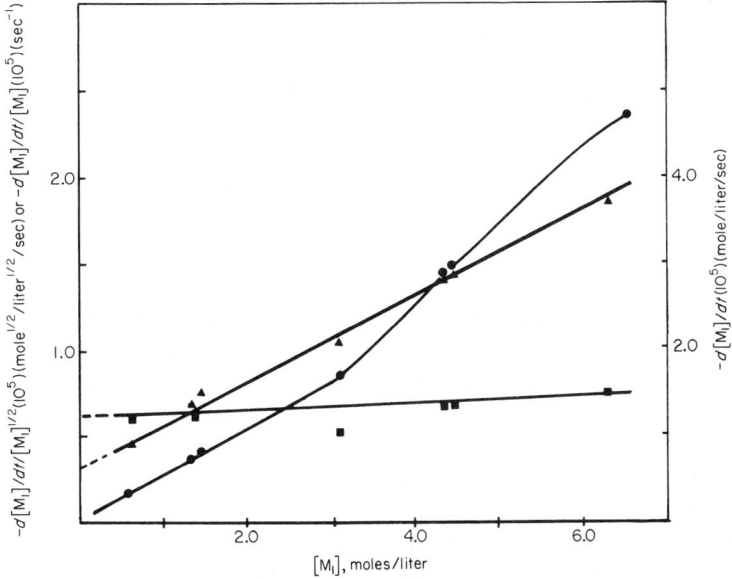

Fig. 2-1. $-d[DB]/dt/[M_1]^a$ versus $[M_1]$ for methacrylic anhydride in dimethylformamide at 40°C, initiated by azobisisobutyronitrile: ●, ▲, or ■ are $a = 0$, 1/2, or 1, respectively (44).

monomer concentration increased somewhat with increasing monomer concentration. Their data plotted according to the procedures given above for the various termination reactions gave values for k_c/k_{11} of 1.0 and 12 moles/liter for $M_2\cdot + M_1\cdot$ and $M_2\cdot + M_2\cdot$ termination, respectively. Both plots were linear. The highest value of k_c/k_{11}, for $M_2\cdot + M_2\cdot$, termination is lower than the value of 50 moles/liter found from residual-unsaturation measurements. However, at high values of k_c/k_{11} (>25 moles/liter), both the rate and residual-unsaturation methods become less accurate, and the difference is probably outside experimental error. It is interesting to note that the value of k_c/k_{11} calculated from the data of Smets et al. (108a) agrees well with the value determined from the data of Gibbs and Murray (44).

Mercier and Smets (108) found a complicated variation in rate for acrylic anhydride polymerization. For polymerizations conducted in cyclohexanone at monomer concentrations of 0.76 moles/liter (the lowest studied) and 4.5 moles/liter the rate was found to be *independent* of monomer concentration. Above 4.5 moles/liter the rate varies linearly with monomer concentration. Mercier and Smets (108) noted that the polymerization proceeded heterogeneously and believed this the source of the unusual behavior. They observed that microgel particles are formed even at low conversions and measured the concentration of "trapped" radicals and their variation with time and conversion.

Their results may be explained qualitatively, if it is assumed, as indicated by these workers, that cyclohexanone is a much poorer swelling agent than monomer. The independence of rate on monomer at lower initial monomer concentration is due to the early formation of discrete microgel particles, which imbibe monomer and serve as the locus of further polymerization. As this monomer is consumed by free radicals in the particle, further monomer is absorbed, so that a sensibly constant ratio of monomer to polymer in the particle is maintained. This situation persists, until sufficient monomer is charged initially to preclude the formation of the discrete microgel particles. At this and higher monomer concentrations presumably the polymerization occurs in the medium at large. This is perhaps only one of several possible explanations, and insufficient information is on hand to substantiate it. Crawshaw and Butler (40) and Jones (41) have reported that acrylic anhydride polymerized homogeneously both in benzene solution and in bulk, giving soluble polymers. It is interesting that the linear portion of the curve, above $[M] = 4.5$ moles/liter, is consistent with an $M_2\cdot + M_2\cdot$ termination, where k_c/k_{11} is large.

Roovers and Smets (82) determined the relation between rate and monomer concentration for vinyl-*trans*-cinnamate in benzene and dioxane. In these cases the rates were found proportional to monomer concentration at monomer concentrations up to about 3.0 moles/liter. Above 3.0 moles/liter

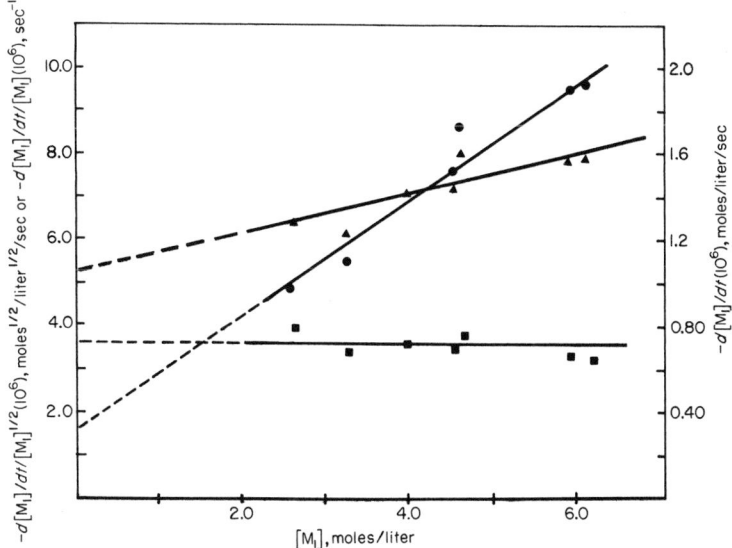

Fig. 2-2. Rate/$[M_1]^a$ versus $[M_1]$ for vinyl-*trans*-cinnamate in benzene at 70°C initiated by azobisisobutyronitrile: ●, ▲ or ■ are $a = 0$, $1/2$, or 1, respectively (*82*).

in both benzene and dioxane the effect of monomer concentration decreased. The data obtained at initial monomer levels below 3.0 moles/liter, plotted according to the discussion above, is shown in Fig. 2-2. There is considerable scatter, but each plot can be represented as linear up to $[M_1] = 6.0$ moles/liter. The value of k_c/k_{11} obtained from rate versus $[M_1]$, $M_1\cdot + M_1\cdot$ termination, is 0.55 mole/liter; from rate/$[M_1]^{1/2}$ versus $[M_1]$, $M_2\cdot + M_1\cdot$ termination, it is 6.3 moles/liter; and for rate/$[M_1]$ versus $[M_1]$, $M_2\cdot + M_2\cdot$ termination, it is infinite, since the slope is zero. Actually, a line with a small negative slope best fits the last data. The values of k_c/k_{11} reported by Roovers and Smets from unsaturation measurements and copolymerization are 13 and 11 moles/liter, respectively. This suggests that cross-termination occurs in vinyl-*trans*-cinnamate polymerization, because the value of k_c/k_{11} for $M_2\cdot + M_1\cdot$ termination is quite close to that reported from the other methods. The scatter of data, however, cannot rule out $M_2\cdot + M_2\cdot$ termination.

Minoura and Mitoh (*117*) investigated the dependence of rate on monomer concentration for divinyl acetal. Their experimental rate expression was complicated but could be represented by $R_p = K[M]^a[A_2]^{3/4}$, where a varied from 1.5 to 2.0. The reaction proceeded under homogeneous conditions. Minoura and Mitoh (*117*) derived a rate expression based upon all three types of termination, occurring simultaneously, and a sufficiently low $\overline{DP}_n$ for the initiation and termination reactions to be factors determining the stationary-state relationships between the various radicals. This approach yielded a complex rate expression in which the dependence of rate on monomer and initiator varied between 1 and 2 and between 1/2 and 1, respectively, and which on that basis fit the experimental results. Measurements of $\underline{DP}_n$ made by osmometry, however, yielded values of about 100. At this high DP_n it is doubtful that the stationary-state considerations used are valid. For every initiation and termination reaction the end of the growing chain changes from $M_1\cdot$ to $M_2\cdot$ and back again some two hundred times. The data on rate as a function of monomer concentration, however, plotted according to the methods given above, do not yield values of k_c/k_{11}, in accord with the value reported from unsaturation (130 moles/liter) for any of the three termination reactions. Values obtained range from about zero to 0.4 to 2 moles/liter for $M_1\cdot + M_1\cdot$, $M_2\cdot + M_1\cdot$, and $M_2\cdot + M_2\cdot$ termination, respectively.

The cases of simple cyclopolymerization and the expressions, when the $k_{11}[M_1\cdot][M_1]$ reaction is taken into account, listed in Tables 3-6 and 3-8, respectively, predict a square-root dependence on initiator concentration for all cases in which termination occurs by pairs of radicals. All cases in which degradative chain transfer occur require a first-order dependence on initiator concentration.

Studies of the dependence of rate on initiator concentration have been conducted with diallyl phthalate (bulk) (15), diallyl dimethyl silane (bulk) (52), methacrylic anhydride in dimethyl formamide (44), acrylic anhydride in bulk, cyclohexanone, and dimethyl formamide (108), vinyl-trans-cinnamate in benzene (82), divinyl formal in benzene (117), dimethyl-α,α'-dimethylene pimelate in toluene (118), and methacrylic anhydride in cyclohexanone (108a). In addition, the radiation-induced polymerization of acrylic anhydride has been reported (119).

Holt and Simpson (15) report that the rate of diallyl phthalate polymerization was not quite proportional to the first power of the benzoyl peroxide concentration and suggested that some reinitiation by the "degraded" radicals is responsible. Mikulasova and Hrivik (52) report that the rates of polymerization of both allyltrimethyl silane and diallyl dimethyl silane are proportional to the first power of the t-butyl peroxide concentration.

Gibbs and Murray (44) report that the polymerization of methacrylic anhydride with AIBN obeys a square-root law. Data on polymerization of dimethyl-α,α'-dimethylene pimelate in toluene initiated with AIBN also show a square-root dependence (119).

Smets et al. (108a) report dependencies of rate on AIBN concentration of 0.58 to 0.66 for methacrylic anhydride in cyclohexanone and attribute this to the viscous nature of the reaction system.

Roovers and Smets (*82*) found a dependence on $[AIBN]^{0.58}$ for the rate of polymerization of vinyl-*trans*-cinnamate in benzene at a monomer concentration of 1.72 moles/liter. At higher monomer concentrations (3.85 and 5.95 moles/liter) and in bulk, however, the dependence increased to $[AIBN]^{0.93}$. Mercier and Smets (*108*) report that acrylic anhydride in both cyclohexane and dimethyl formamide shows dependencies greater than 0.50. This depended upon the monomer concentration and the solvent but varied from $[AIBN]^{0.67}$ in bulk to $[AIBN]^{0.75}$ at 1.5 moles of monomer per liter in cyclohexanone to $[AIBN]^{0.83}$ at 6.0 moles of monomer per liter in cyclohexanone to a maximum of $[AIBN]^{1.0}$ at 1.8 moles of monomer per liter in dimethyl formamide. The workers attributed this behavior to the heterogeneous nature of the polymerizing system, as indicated earlier. Minoura and Mitoh (*117*) found a dependence upon $[AIBN]^{0.75}$ in the polymerization of divinyl acetal, as indicated earlier.

Okada et al. (*119*) reported that the rate of radiation-induced bulk (liquid) polymerization of acrylic anhydride at 13°C varied as the radiation dose rate to the 0.55 power. The value of the exponent is in reasonable agreement with a free-radical mechanism.

The diversity of results obtained for the dependence of rate on monomer and initiator concentration appears to be due more to problems of microgel formation, which distort the results, than to a failure of the proposed kinetics to describe the normal situation. However, the results are limited. Generally, in the cases in which homogeneous polymerization has occurred the results indicate agreement with expectation. The variation in rate with monomer concentration for methacrylic anhydride in dimethyl formamide and vinyl-*trans*-cinnamate in benzene are consistent with an expected mode of termination and the values of k_c/k_{11} from other work. Acrylic anhydride in cyclohexanone and vinyl-*trans*-cinnamate at high monomer concentrations are apparently heterogeneous polymerizations. The reason for the divergence of divinyl formal in benzene is not clear.

Results of the dependence of rate on initiator concentration also tend to confirm the proposed kinetics. Systems involving degradative chain transfer show about first-order dependencies. Homogeneous polymerizations of systems expected to show square-root dependencies generally show values of about 0.5. Systems tending toward microgel show higher dependencies, in accord with a "trapped radical" mechanism.

2. MEASUREMENTS OF RESIDUAL UNSATURATION

As indicated in Section 2-3-A-6, measurements of the degree of residual unsaturation in cyclopolymers as a function of monomer concentration can yield values for k_c/k_{11}. A great number of unsaturation measurements have been reported on specific cyclopolymers, but the data are usually insufficient for calculating k_c/k_{11}. These have been noted in Section 2-2 and will be referred to later in comparing the effect of monomer structure on degree of cyclization.

Holt and Simpson (15), using bromimetry and iodine–monochloride methods, analyzed their entire series of diallyl polymers, some fourteen in all, as indicated in Section 2-2. Only in the case of diallyl phthalate, however, are data given for the variation in unsaturation with monomer concentration (see Table 2-2). Gibbs (81) has plotted these data according to Eq. (2-47) and obtained for k_c/k_{11} a value of 4.25 moles/liter. The plot was linear; as expected, however, the intercept was slightly higher than expected (1.25 versus 1.0).

From measurements of residual unsaturation as a function of extent of reaction, as shown in Table 2-3 (15) the apparent extent of cyclization increases as polymerization proceeds. The increase in proportion of cyclized units is somewhat smaller than the reduction in monomer concentration. However, considering that the monomer units cyclize in somewhat less than one half the time, in this case of diallyl-o-phthalate (15) the increase is about in accord with the decrease in total double bonds in the system.

Mercier and Smets (108) in their study of acrylic anhydride measured residual unsaturation by infrared spectrometry and bromimetry and obtained $k_c/k_{11} = 5.9$ moles/liter. Okada et al. (119) polymerized acrylic anhydride in toluene by ionizing radiation and measured unsaturation by bromimetry. The value of k_c/k_{11} reported was 11.1 moles/liter. It was further noted by these workers that the degrees of cyclization in the bulk (solid) and toluene solution polymers were the same at $-78°C$. Roovers and Smets (82) report $k_c/k_{11} = 13.0$ moles/liter from infrared, ultraviolet, and bromimetry measurements of poly(vinyl-trans-cinnamate). Minoura and Mitoh (117) report that $k_c/k_{11} = 130$ for divinyl acetal from infrared measurements. Linear plots were obtained in all these cases.

Smets et al. (108a) determined residual unsaturation by bromimetry and infrared spectrometry for polymethacrylic anhydride prepared in cyclohexanone. They obtained a k_c/k_{11} of ≈ 50 moles/liter.

Aso (120) suggests a value of k_c/k_{11} for ethylene dimethacrylate of 3 moles/ liter on the basis of residual unsaturation, the fit of the data to his relationship at higher monomer concentrations, and analogy of this system to the work of Simpson et al. (13).

The degree of cyclization from unsaturation measurements follows the predicted relationships with monomer concentration, no ambiguities being reported. In all cases reported the plots have been linear and have the expected intercept within experimental error. Even in cases such as that of acrylic anhydride (108), in which anomalies due to microgel formation were observed, as noted earlier, the variation of residual unsaturation with monomer concentration is consistent with expectation. This suggests that the factors affecting the variation in rate with monomer and initiator concentration, at least in this system, are not effective in governing relative rates of the k_{11} and k_c reactions.

3. MEASUREMENT OF INTRINSIC VISCOSITY VERSUS CONVERSION

Intrinsic viscosity is a convenient means of testing for branching and cross-linking processes, which may occur during cyclopolymerization. The viscosity-average molecular weight is very sensitive to the higher-molecular-weight species, and the cross-linking and branching reactions occur preferentially among the larger species.

Gibbs and Murray (44) reported the variation in $[\eta]$ for polymethacrylic anhydrides prepared in dimethyl formamide as a function of conversion at three initial monomer levels. At 1.10 moles/liter the intrinsic viscosity remained unchanged within experimental error up to 20.7% conversion. At monomer concentrations of 2.2 moles/liter and more gelled polymer was obtained. Minoura and Mitoh (117) report that polydivinyl acetal prepared in benzene slowly increases in $[\eta]$ with conversion. Soluble polymer was obtained at concentrations as high as 4.49 moles of monomer per liter. They attributed the increase to moderately slow branching or cross-linking reactions, or both.

4. TEMPERATURE EFFECTS

Data on the temperature coefficients of the rate of cyclopolymerization are difficult to interpret, as indicated by the complexity of expressions for total activation energies obtained in Section 2-3-A-7 and given in Table 2-9. Measurements of the total activation energy for a few systems have been made. These are listed in Table 2-10.

TABLE 2-9

Activation Energy Expressions for Cyclopolymerization[a]

Termination reaction	Total activation energy E_T, cal/mole	
	Simple	Including $k_{11}[M_1\cdot][M_1]$
Biradical termination		
Monovinyl	$E_d/2 + E_p - E_t/2$	
$M_2\cdot + M_2\cdot$	$E_d/2 + E_{21} - E^{22}/2$	$E_d/2 + E_{11(c)} + E_{21} - E_c - E^{22}/2$
$M_2\cdot + M_1\cdot$	$E_d/2 + E_{21}/2 + E_c/2 - E^{12}/2$	$E_d/2 + E_{11(c)} + E_{21}/2 - E_c/2 - E^{12}/2$
$M_1\cdot + M_1\cdot$	$E_d/2 + E_c - E^{11}/2$	$E_d/2 + E_{11(c)} - E^{11}/2$
Monoradical termination		
Monoallylic	$E_d + E_p - E_t$	
$M_2\cdot + M_1$	$E_d + E_{21} - E_t$	$E_d + E_{11(c)} + E_{21} - E_c - E_t$
$M_1\cdot$ (intramolecular)	$E_d + E_c - E'_t$	$E_d + E_{11(c)} - E'_t$

[a] See Section 2-3-A-7.

TABLE 2-10

Over-all Activation Energies in Cyclopolymerization

No.	System[a]	E_T, kcal/mole	E'_T,[b] kcal/mole	Ref.
1	Methacrylic anhydride–AIBN–DMF	23.0	8.0	44
2	Methacrylic acid–AIBN–DMF	24.8	9.8	44
3	Diallyl dimethyl silane–t-butyl peroxide	49.7	12.6	52
4	Allyl trimethyl silane–t-butyl peroxide	34.5	3.7[c]	52
5	Divinyl formal–AIBN–benzene	27.7	12.7	117

[a] AIBN = azobisisobutyronitrile, DMF = dimethyl formamide.

[b] For Nos. 3 and 4 $E'_T = E_T - E_d$; for all others $E'_T = E_T - E_d/2$; that is, in all cases the total activation energy less the contribution of the initiator.

[c] From measurement of $\overline{DP}_n$ with temperature. Owing, apparently, to inapplicability of Eq. (2-50) to this case because of low $\overline{DP}$'s, the value of $E_T - E_d$ was negative when calculated in the normal manner (44).

Methacrylic anhydride (44) shows a somewhat lower E_T value than does methacrylic acid, and this is reflected in a lower E'_T value for the diolefin. The lower E'_T value interpreted on the basis of the simple cyclopolymerization scheme with termination by $M_2\cdot + M_2\cdot$ indicates that $E_{21} - E^{22}/2$ for the diolefin is lower than $E_p - E_t/2$ for methacrylic acid. Thus, either $E^{22} > E_t$ or $E_{21} < E_p$, or both. However, the differences are not large (1.8 kcal/mole) in either direction.

A very curious situation is observed in the case of the allyl silanes (52). The total activation energy less the contribution of initiator is considerably higher for the diolefin than for the monoolefin. On the basis of simple cyclopolymerization with termination by $M_2\cdot + M_1$ this would mean that E_{21} is some 9 kcal/mole higher than the E_p for the monoolefin. Mikulasova and Hrivik (52) originally simply divided the total activation energy for the diolefin by the number of double bonds and concluded that the activation energy required for the reaction of the second double bond was lower than for the first, on the basis that the value so obtained, ≈25 kcal/mole, was lower than E_T for the monoolefin, which is ≈35 kcal/mole. Unfortunately, this erroneous conclusion has been carried over into the more current literature as proof that the second double bond reacts the more easily. As illustrated above and in Section 2-3-A-7, this is an entirely incorrect conclusion. These data actually indicate that the E_{21} or E_c (depending on whether one chooses $M_2\cdot + M_1$ or $M_1\cdot$ termination) is far greater than the E_p.

The results for the allyl silanes are puzzling at present. These data suggest that E_{21} or E_c, depending upon the termination reaction, is *much* greater than E_p for a monoolefin of very similar structure. This conclusion is unacceptable on the basis of nearly all the other information contained in this chapter. A more reasonable result would be that $E_p \approx E_c$ with perhaps a variation of 1 to 2 kcals/mole in either direction.

The data for divinyl formal are listed in Table 2-10 but lack a suitable reference monomer for comparison. Perhaps a suitable model would be an alkyl vinyl ether, but data are not available on E_T for these systems. The relatively high values for E_T and E_T' may reflect the lack of resonance stabilization in this monomer.

As given in Eq. (2-62), the measurement of k_c/k_{11} with temperature leads to the difference in activation energy between the cyclization reaction and the k_{11} reaction. In all cases reported the proportion of cyclized units increases or remains constant with increasing temperature. No cases have been reported in which the proportion of cyclized units decreases with temperature. Mercier and Smets (108) report that $E_c - E_{11}$ is 2.4 kcal/mole for acrylic anhydride.

Okada et al. (119) report the effect of temperature on the radiation-induced polymerization of acrylic anhydride for bulk (solid), bulk (liquid), and toluene-solution polymerization over a broad temperature range. The value of $E_c - E_{11}$ depended upon the state of the system and was found to be zero, 4.7, and 2.3 kcal/mole for bulk (solid), bulk (liquid), and toluene-solution polymerization, respectively. The data are summarized in Table 2-11.

Roovers and Smets (82) report that $E_c - E_{11}$ is about zero for vinyl-*trans*-cinnamate. Minoura and Mitoh (117) report a value of $E_c - E_{11}$ of 2.6 kcal/mole for divinyl formal. Holt et al. (13–15) report that $E_c - E_{11}$ is zero for diallyl phthalate, but their data suggest a small positive difference of about 0.3 kcal/mole.

TABLE 2-11

Effect of Temperature on Cyclopolymerization of Acrylic Anhydride Initiated by Ionizing Radiation (118)

Temp., °C	Bulk		10% toluene solution	
	Convsn., %	Cyclized units, %	Convsn., %	Cyclized units, %
−78	2.39	37	4.00	41
−45	14.4	41	2.76	47
0	4.80	41	36.9	53
13	5.72	45		
22	15.1	51		
30			15.2	83
50			29.2	87

The differences between E_c and E_{11} are thus small but tend toward higher values for E_c than E_{11}. The placement of cyclized groups over-all is apparently a slightly higher activation energy process than the normal intermolecular propagation reaction.

5. COPOLYMERIZATION

The results obtained on relative reactivities from copolymerization studies, although as yet limited, provide some comparisons between the behavior of these radicals and monomers and their monovinyl counterparts. Table 2-12 lists the general data obtained for a variety of systems. In each case the diolefin is given as monomer 1. The monoolefins listed in Table 2-12 for comparison with the diolefins are those used in the original experiments.

TABLE 2-12

Relative Reactivity Ratios

Monomer 1	Monomer 4	$r_2\left(\dfrac{k_{21}}{k_{24}}\right)$	$r_4\left(\dfrac{k_{44}}{k_{41}}\right)$	Ref.
Methacrylic anhydride	Benzyl vinyl sulfide	0.8	0	
	2-Chloroethyl vinyl ether	6.1	0	
	Monoallyl urea	28	0	80
	Allyl chloroacetate	42	0	
Methyl methacrylate	Allyl chloroacetate	50	0	
Monoallyl urea	Lauryl methacrylate	−0.22	29.9	
N,N'-Diallyl urea	Lauryl methacrylate	−0.12	29.0, 14.5[a]	121
N,N-Diallyl urea	Lauryl methacrylate	0.014	54.8, 27.4[a]	
N-N-Diallyl melamine	Methyl methacrylate	−0.15	27.8	
	Vinyl acetate	0.20	1.44	122
	Styrene	−0.12	102.3	
Diallyl butyl phosphonate	Dodecyl methacrylate	0.09	18.7	123
Diallyl phenyl phosphine oxide	Dodecyl methacrylate	−0.011	10	124
Diallyl phthalate	Vinyl acetate	2.0	0.72	125a
	Vinyl chloride	0.2	5.0	125b
Divinyl ether	Acrylonitrile	0.012	0.47	88
Ethyl vinyl ether	Acrylonitrile	0.015	0.7	
1,4-Pentadiene	Acrylonitrile	0	0.56	88
1-Hexene	Acrylonitrile	0	12.2	
Norbornadiene	Vinyl chloride	0.35	0.74	
	Vinylidene chloride	0.08	1.41	
	Acrylonitrile	0.08	0.67	94
	Ethyl acrylate	0.01	3.05	
	Methyl methacrylate	0	10.0	

[a] For $[M_1] = [M]$.

TABLE 2-13

Relative Reactivity Ratios

System	k_c/k_{11}	k_c/k_{14}	k_{11}/k_{14}	k_{21}/k_{24}	k_{44}/k_{41}	Ref.
Vinyl-*trans*-cinnamate (M$_1$) with:	11					
Vinyl acetate		High		1.20	0.04	
N-Vinyl pyrrolidone		High		1.15	0.01	82
Methacrylonitrile		1	0.10	0.15	4	
Styrene			0.25^a		1.25^a	
Vinyl benzoate (M$_1$) with:						
Vinyl acetate			0.99		0.35	
N-Vinyl pyrrolidone			0.44		2.45	126
Acrylonitrile			0.05		5	
Vinyl acetate (M$_1$) with:						
N-Vinyl pyrrolidone			0.20		3.30	
Methacrylonitrile			0.01		12	126
Acrylonitrile			0.02		6	
Methacrylic anhydride (M$_1$) with:	10					127
Styrene		3.3	0.33	0.14	0.15	
Methacrylic anhydride (M$_1$) with:	48					108a
Styrene		5.0	0.26	0.26^b	0.12	127a
Methacrylonitrile		Very high	1.6	1.6^b	0.27	127a
Methacrylic acid (M$_1$) with:						
Styrene			0.70		0.15	126
Methacrylonitrile			1.63		0.59	
Methyl methacrylate (M$_1$) with:						
Styrene			0.48		0.46	126
Butyl methacrylate (M$_1$) with:						
Styrene			0.63		0.64	126
Methacrylonitrile (M$_1$) with:						
Styrene			0.16		0.30	126
Acrylic anhydride (M$_1$) with:	5.9					108
Styrene		0.25	0.1	0.1^b	0.17	
Methacrylonitrile		7.0	0.9	0.9^b	0.4	127a
Allyl chloride		Very high		11.5	0.01	
Acrylic acid (M$_1$) with:						
Styrene			0.25		0.15	126
Acrylonitrile (M$_1$) with:						
Styrene			0.07		0.37	126
Methacrylonitrile			0.32		2.68	
2-Hydroxyethyl acrylate (M$_1$) with:						
Allyl chloride			8.85		0.016	126

^{a} Involving only the cinnamate double bond or radical.

^{b} Taken equal to k_{11}/k_{14}.

The r_2 and r_4 values have been converted to the form indicated in Section 2-3A-13, that is, $[M_1] = 2[M]$. Values for acrylic and methacrylic anhydrides and vinyl-*trans*-cinnamate were obtained by using the relationships listed in Section 2-3B-3. The r_2 and r_4 values for the other monomers were obtained from the simple cyclopolymerization expression (2-12). The additional parameters found for vinyl-*trans*-cinnamate and acrylic and methacrylic anhydrides are given in Table 2-13.

The methacrylic anhydride, benzyl vinyl sulfide, 2-chloroethyl vinyl ether; monovinyl urea, and allyl chloroacetate systems (*80*) were selected so that r_4 would be very small, based on the copolymerization of similar monomers with methyl methacrylate. The values of r_2 obtained were compared with the appropriate values from methyl methacrylate. In general, values from methacrylic anhydride were similar to those from methyl methacrylate. This was interpreted as indicating that the cyclized radical and methyl methacrylate radical had similar reactivities (*80*).

Monoallyl urea was used as a reference point for the reactivity of the allylic double bond in the series including the N,N and N,N′ diallyl ureas (*121*). The N,N diallyl urea is capable of cyclizing to a six-membered ring. The N,N′ diallyl urea, however, can cyclize only to a larger, eight-membered, ring. In Section 2-3-B the composition equations were derived on the basis that $[M_1] = 2[M]$. If, however, the double bonds interact, so that in effect there is a single double bond system in the monomer, the relationship should be $[M_1] = [M]$. The composition of the copolymer from lauryl methacrylate and N,N′-diallyl urea lead to an r_4 value of 29.0, if $[M_1] = 2[M]$, which agrees with that found for the monoallyl system. This value is appropriate, because these two double bonds should have little tendency to interact. In the case of N,N-diallyl urea, however, if $[M_1] = 2[M]$, a high value of r_4 (54.8) is obtained. If $[M_1] = [M]$, the r_4 value is 27.4, which corresponds to the r_4 values for the monoallyl and N,N′ diallyl monomers. This was interpreted by the writers as being consistent with a mechanism by which the double bonds of N,N-diallyl urea function as a single double bond system.

In the copolymerization of vinyl-*trans*-cinnamate with vinyl acetate, N-vinyl pyrrolidone, methacrylonitrile, and styrene, and the copolymerization of methacrylic anhydride with styrene Roovers and Smets (*82*) and Gibbs and Murray (*127*) used the more appropriate relationships for obtaining relative reactivity ratios, which take into account the k_{11} reaction, and obtained values for k_c/k_{11}, k_c/k_{14}, and k_{11}/k_{14} in addition to values for k_{44}/k_{41} and k_{21}/k_{24}. These results are given in Table 2-13.

In copolymerization with vinyl acetate, N-vinyl pyrrolidone, and methacrylonitrile, vinyl-*trans*-cinnamate was found to react first through the vinyl double bond (*82*). This was followed by cyclization to a high extent with vinyl acetate and N-vinyl pyrrolidone (high values of k_c/k_{14} and k_c/k_{11})

or to a lesser extent with methacrylonitrile ($k_c/k_{14} = 1.0$). The k_c/k_{11} values obtained are in agreement with that obtained from residual unsaturation measurements. Copolymerization with styrene was found to involve the cinnamate double bond and leave relatively large proportions of pendent vinyl double bonds in the copolymer. In the case in which the vinyl double bond is first attacked vinyl-*trans*-cinnamate monomer might be expected to be similar in reactivity to vinyl benzoate or vinyl acetate. Relative reactivity data for these monomers are listed in Table 2-13. It appears that the diolefin is more reactive toward vinyl acetate or N-vinyl pyrrolidone radicals than is either vinyl benzoate or vinyl acetate monomer. It is somewhat less reactive than vinyl acetate monomer toward methacrylonitrile radicals. The k_{11}/k_{14} values for the vinyl-*trans*-cinnamate–methacrylonitrile and vinyl acetate–methacrylonitrile systems indicate a somewhat greater relative reactivity of the noncyclized radical for vinyl-*trans*-cinnamate monomer than vinyl acetate radical for its monomer.

The k_{21}/k_{24} values are more difficult to interpret, because relatively little data are available on the reactivity of radicals similar to a cyclized cinnamate radical:

$$\sim CH_2-CH--\overset{\overset{\displaystyle \phi}{|}}{C}H$$

The reactivity of simple cinnamate radicals is probably not a good comparison, because the cinnamate radical is likely to be

$$\phi-\overset{\cdot}{C}H-\overset{\overset{\displaystyle \{}{|}}{C}H-\overset{\overset{\displaystyle O}{||}}{C}-OR$$

owing to the somewhat greater degree of resonance stabilization of the radical on the carbon α to the phenyl group than of the radical on the carbon α to the ester.

The copolymerization of methacrylic anhydride with styrene in dimethyl formamide leads to copolymers with the compositions illustrated in Fig. 2-3. Figure 2-3 also gives an estimate of the sensitivity of the composition plot to the k_c/k_{11} value. The relative reactivity values were determined by means of Eq. (2-94) and are listed in Table 3-13. The k_c/k_{11} value obtained ($\gtrsim 10$ moles/liter) is in agreement with the value found from rate studies by assuming an $M_2 \cdot + M_2 \cdot$ termination reaction. The k_{11}/k_{14} values for methacrylic anhydride are lower than the corresponding values for methacrylic acid,

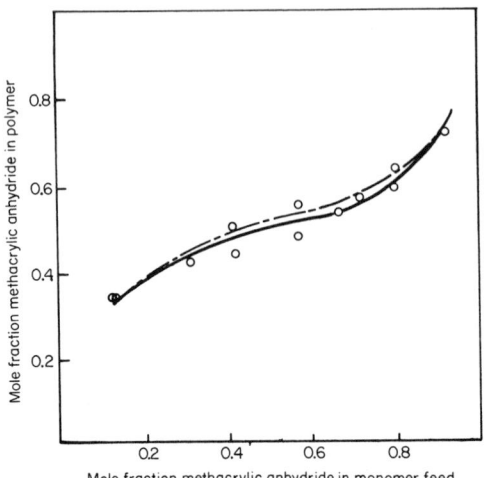

Fig. 2-3. Copolymerization of methacrylic anhydride with styrene in dimethyl formamide (*127*): ○ = experimental points; the solid line is drawn for Eq. (2-72), where $r_2 = 0.14$ and $r_4 = 0.15$, and for Eq. (2-97), where $\alpha_c = 20$, $\alpha_4 = 3$, $\beta_4 = 7$, and $\delta_1 = 7.0$; the dashed line is for Eq. (2-97), where $\alpha_c = 10$, $\alpha_4 = 3$, $\beta_4 = 7$, and $\delta_1 = 7.0$.

methyl methacrylate, or butyl methacrylate. The k_{44}/k_{41} value for methacrylic anhydride is about the same as that for methacrylic acid and lower than that for the methacrylate esters. These data indicate that the preference of the noncyclized radical for its own monomer is greater than for styrene monomer. The preference for its own monomer, however, is not as pronounced as for the other monomers listed. The reactivity of styrene radical for methacrylic anhydride monomer is greater, however, than the reactivity of styrene radical for methyl or butyl methacrylate and about the same as methacrylic acid.

The copolymerization of acrylic and methacrylic anhydrides with styrene, methacrylonitrile, and allyl chloride was found by Smets et al. (*127a*) to yield copolymers as described in Table 2-13, where the reactivities of the noncyclic, $M_1\cdot$, radical was found to be about equal to those of the cyclized radical, since the composition of the copolymer was almost unaffected by the total monomer concentration, providing that the same ratio of M_1 to M_4 was maintained.

The results from copolymerization of the 1,4 diolefins, divinyl ether, and 1,4-pentadiene show r_4 values for the diolefins greater than for the corresponding monoolefins. The extent of cyclization in these systems was quite high.

In all cases in which data are available the results from copolymerization work indicate that the relative reactivity of the diolefin is equal to or greater than that of the corresponding monoolefin. The methacrylic anhydride–styrene–methacrylic acid and N,N-diallyl urea–lauryl methacrylate–N-allyl urea systems are the only ones in which the reactivities of monoolefin and diolefin are essentially the same. This trend persists also in the 1,4 diolefins.

6. EFFECTS OF MONOMER STRUCTURE ON DEGREE OF CYCLIZATION

To define more clearly the effect of monomer structure on the tendency to form cyclic recurring units it is helpful to consider a representative selection of results from work in condensation and polycondensation systems. The condensation reactions have been well studied and provide a useful point from which to examine results from the cyclopolymerization field.

The classic studies of Spanagel and Carothers (*128*) and Carothers and Hill (*129*) provide the yields of cyclic monomeric and dimeric esters resulting from heating polyesters from various alkylene glycols and aliphatic dicarboxylic acids with transesterification catalysts. The variation in the yields of the cyclic products reflects the ease of formation of rings of different size in this series. The results are summarized in Fig. 2-4. The ease of formation of monomeric cyclic esters is strongly dependent upon ring size. The variation of degree of cyclization with N, the number of ring atoms in the cyclic monomer, is shown in the following series of N: 5, 6 ≫ 7, 8 < 10 > 13 < 15. A change in ring size from 5 or 6 to 7 or 8 results in a change in yield of the monomeric cyclic product from essentially 100% to essentially zero.

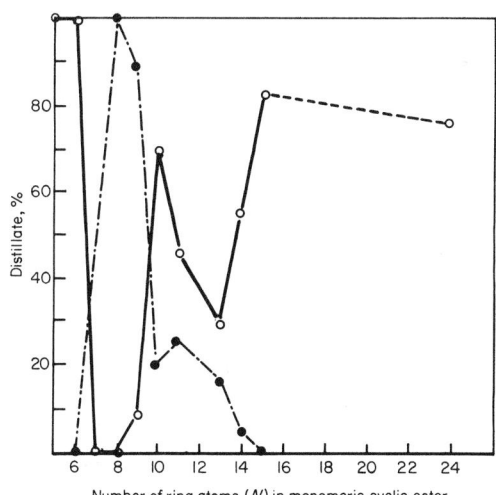

Fig. 2-4. Effect of ring size on yield of monomeric and dimeric cyclic esters (*128,129*)
$$[-(CH_2)_x-OOC(CH_2)_y-COO-]_n \xrightarrow[\text{SnC}]{270^\circ}.$$

Products: ◯—◯ = monomeric ester, ●---● = dimeric ester.

The corresponding change in the cyclization rate constant must be at least a few orders of magnitude. The results also show a maximum in the yields of cyclic dimers when the yields of cyclic monomers are small. Thus, the product is essentially cyclic dimer in the range $N = 7$ to 8 and predominantly cyclic dimer for $N = 9$. Smaller yields of cyclic dimer occur as N becomes larger than 9. The cyclic monomer-dimer competition in this series shows that rings of 14, 16, or 18 members are formed in preference to those of 7, 8, or 9 members.

Stoll and Rouve (*130*) and Stoll et al. (*131*) investigated the acid-catalyzed condensation of various aliphatic ω-hydroxy acids. The products of the reactions were monomeric and dimeric lactones and polyesters. The variation in rates of formation of the monomeric and dimeric lactones with ring size is shown in Fig. 2-5. An analogous trend in degree of cyclization with ring size is observed between the monomeric and dimeric esters of Carothers et al. (*128,129*) and this work.

For the monomeric lactones cyclization maxima are observed for $N = 5$ and $N = 18$ and a minimum for $N = 8$ to 10. Between $N = 5$ and $N = 8$ the cyclization constant falls by a factor of more than 10^4. Although the secondary maximum observed in the monomeric cyclic ester at $N = 10$ is not observed in the lactone series, the essential features common to both are evident: at $N = 5$ cyclization is at a maximum, and at $N = 8$ to 9 it is at a minimum. This is followed by an increase to a smaller maximum at

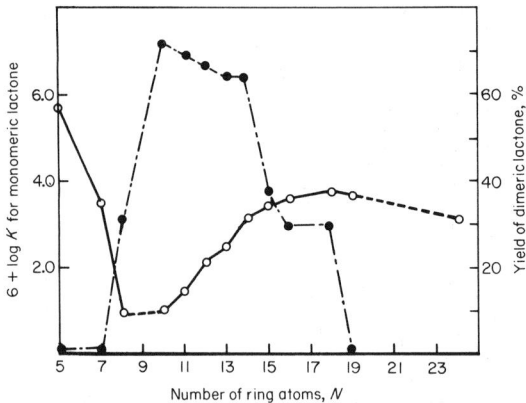

Fig. 2-5. Effect of ring size on rate of cyclization of ω-hydroxy acids (*130,131*)

$$HO\!-\!(CH_2)_{N-2}\!-\!CO_2H \rightarrow (CH_2)_{N-2}CO + H_2O.$$
$$\underset{\qquad\quad-O-\qquad}{\mid\qquad\qquad\mid}$$

Products: $\bigcirc\!-\!\bigcirc$ = monomeric lactone, $\bullet\!-\!-\!\bullet$ = dimeric lactone.

higher values of N. Both series show a strong dependence of ease of cyclization on ring size in the range $N = 5$ to 15.

The dimeric lactones also show behavior similar to the dimeric cyclic
esters. The dimeric species are formed preferentially when the monomeric
cycles have an unfavorable ring size. In the region $8 < N < 14$ to 15 the
dimeric lactone is obtained in yields of at least 70%.

The marked dependence of ease of cyclization on ring size for rings
consisting primarily of carbon atoms is generally explained on the basis of
the steric hindrance to ring closure and the possible deformation of valence
bond angles (*129*). In the 5-membered case the ring can be formed in a planar
arrangement with no distortion of valence angles. The 6-membered ring may
exist in the boat or chain form, either of which is essentially strainless. However, beginning with the 7- or 8-membered rings and continuing to about
12-membered systems, to bring the functional groups into close enough
contact to allow ring closure it is necessary to turn the substituent hydrogens
inward, toward the interior of the ring. This results in a very crowded condition, which greatly restricts the opportunity of the functional groups to
approach one another. The crowding is resisted by the repulsion between
hydrogens, making this configuration markedly less favorable. Allowing that
the crowding can be accomplished to the degree expected from modern
molecular models, the number of specific spatial arrangements available to
the ring atoms, which will allow close contact between the functional groups,
is very limited.

Salomon (*132*) has estimated that the minimum observed in cyclization
in the range $N = 8$ to 12 can be accounted for on the basis of a rather small
deformation of the carbon-carbon bond angles. Salomon estimates that a
deformation of some 6 to 7 degrees in the carbon-carbon bond angle would
lead to, in a 10-membered ring, an excess activation energy of 4 kcal/mole.
This would be sufficient to account for a minimum of this magnitude. This
proposal is supported by the results of Salomon (*132*) and Ziegler and
Hechelhammer (*133*) on the variation in the relative rates of ring closure of
imines and ketones at various temperatures, which indicates that the
minimum tends to become more shallow at higher temperatures.

Rings larger than about 12 members do not require the crowding of the
hydrogens into the interior of the ring to the degree required in the systems
with 8 to 12 members. This permits a larger number of arrangements of the
ring atoms, in which the functional groups may contact one another. With
this increase in probability of contact of functional groups, however, an
attendant rise is also noted in the probability of intermolecular reaction, to
the point that the intermolecular reaction becomes dominant as N becomes
larger than about 18. From that point on the probability of intramolecular
cyclization decreases as the intermolecular polymerization probability

increases. Jacobson and Stockmayer (24) have shown from statistical consideration that the probability of intramolecular reaction of two ends of a very long chain varies as the inverse 3/2 power of the number of chain atoms, while the probability of intermolecular reactions varies as the concentration of the functional ends and, hence, inversely proportionally to the first power of the number of chain atoms. As the functional groups become more separated, therefore, the intermolecular reaction is increasingly favored.

The substitution of carbonyl or ether oxygen for methylene groups in the ring will decrease the number of interfering hydrogens. The experimental results of Ziegler and Holl (134) show that the replacement of some of the methylenes in the chain with oxygen does increase the ease of formation of rings of 8 to 12 members.

Ziegler and Luttringhaus (135) have determined the relative rates of ring closure in a series of bromocatechol ethers:

where N varies between 6 and 14. They found that the 6-membered ring forms about two times faster than the 7-membered ring. The relative rate then decreases by smaller amounts, all within an order of magnitude, as N increases from 8 to 14 (136).

The available experimental data on the influence of monomer structure on the degree of cyclization in vinyl cyclopolymerization begin with the work of Holt and Simpson, mentioned earlier, (15), on the free-radical polymerization of diallyl esters of dibasic acids. These workers found that the proportion of cyclized units in the polymer depended on the number of ring atoms, as shown in Fig. 2-6.

In the aliphatic series a change in N from 8 to 17 is paralleled by a decrease in K, the estimated ratio of rate of cyclization to that of linear propagation, from about 4 to about 1.3 units, and K for $N = 11$ is higher than for $N = 10$ or 12. Within the series studied the minimal degree of cyclization, that for 16-membered rings, is within a factor of 2 of that for the maximal (8-membered rings).

In the aromatic series the o-phenylene compound displays a greater rate of cyclization than the aliphatic diester with the same size of aliphatic ring. In a comparison of the o, m, and p phenylene diesters the values for K are 5.5, 1.5, and 0.7, respectively, clearly displaying the effect of increasing steric strain.

It was also found that in the aliphatic series β-methyl substitution of the double bond has little effect on the magnitude of K.

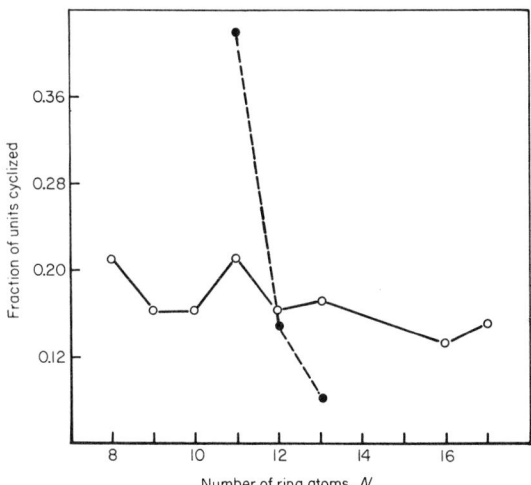

Fig. 2-6. Cyclization in the free-radical polymerization of diallyl esters (*15*): solid line, aliphatic series; dashed line, aromatic series.

The results of Holt and Simpson (*15*) on the cyclopolymerization of aliphatic diallyl esters may be compared with those of Carothers et al. (*128,129*) on the formation of monomeric cyclic aliphatic esters, since the rings formed have a rather similar structure in both cases. It is seen that the influence of ring size on relative rate of cyclization in the free-radical polymerization of the diallyl esters for rings of 8 to 17 members is very much less marked than in the case of intramolecular condensation of the ester.

Holt and Simpson's data (*15*) on the cyclopolymerization of aromatic diallyl esters have no strictly comparable model in the condensation field, and probably the work of Ziegler and Luttringhaus (*135*) on the formation of *ortho* phenylene cyclic ethers ($N = 6$ to 14) is the closest model system available. Both systems show a decreasing relative rate of cyclization for rings of 11 to 13 members, the maximal and minimal rates being within an order of magnitude of each other. However, in the diallyl esters the ring orientation is also changed from *ortho* to *meta* to *para*, whereas all of the condensed cyclic ethers are *ortho*-substituted.

Marvel and co-workers investigated the polymerization of α-ω dienes that are capable of giving carbocyclic rings in the chain. Marvel and Garrison (*45*) and Marvel and Stille (*35*) polymerized monomers of structure $CH_2{=}CH{-}(CH_2)_n{-}CH{=}CH_2$, where n was in the range 2 to 18. The polymerizations were initiated in bulk at room temperature with Al-i-Bu$_3$/TiCl$_4$. The unsaturation of the soluble fractions was measured by infrared spectrometry or bromimetry. The results are given in Fig. 2-7. The order of

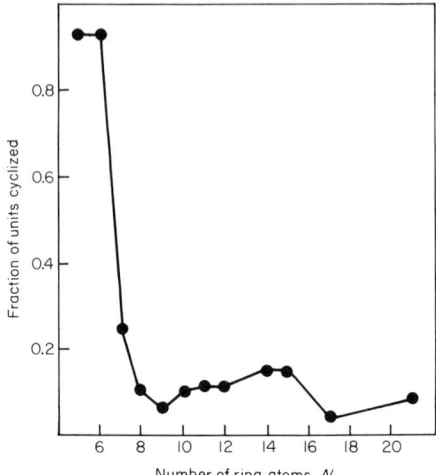

Fig. 2-7. Fraction of units cyclized in the soluble polymer from the Ziegler–Natta-initiated polymerization of various α-ω diolefins, (35,45).

ease of cyclization with ring size observed by Marvel and co-workers with the α-ω dienes is 5, 6 > 7 > 8 to 9 < 10 < 11 to 15 > 17, 21. The degree of cyclization falls sharply for rings of more than 6 atoms, and for rings of between 8 and 21 atoms the variations in degree of cyclization are relatively small. However, there is a secondary minimum at $N = 9$ and a secondary maximum at $N = 14$ to 15.

For the cyclopolymerization of α-ω dienes there is again no strictly comparable model in the cyclic condensation work, and the closest comparable system is that of cyclic lactones, reported by Stoll et al. (130,131). The trends in the variation of degree of cyclization with ring size are very similar between the two systems, but the variation in degree of cyclization is much more compressed in the diene cyclopolymerization.

Marvel and Stille (35) compared the Ziegler–Natta polymerization of 2,5-dimethyl-1,6-hexadiene (I) with that of 1,6-hexadiene (II) and 2,5-dimethylhexene-1 (III) under similar conditions. Poly (I) was completely soluble in benzene and had a residual unsaturation of 3 to 13%. The soluble portion of poly (II) had a residual unsaturation of 6 to 9%. There is probably no significant difference between these levels of cyclization, which suggests that any hindrance to cyclization presented by the bulky methyl groups is either not large or is offset by the increased inductive stabilization incurred by these in the cyclic ionic transition state. It was also found that (III) would not polymerize beyond an oily pentamer under conditions similar to those which produced a solid polymer in 100% conversion and at $[\eta] = 0.1$ from (I).

This suggests that the cyclic mechanism provides an additional driving force in the polymerization of diene (I).

The results of Marvel and Gall (46) on the polymerization of the monomers $CH_2=CH(\phi)(CH_2)_n(\phi)CH=CH_2$, where $n = 2, 3, 4$, are shown in Table 2-5. Cationic (BF_3) or Ziegler–Natta ($A-i-Bu_3/TiCl_4$) type of initiation gave soluble, 90 to 100% cyclized polymers. The workers report that in this series rings of 6 members are formed rather more readily than those of 5 or 7 members.

The soluble polymer extracted from methyl allyl fumarate (43) showed a degree of cyclization of 63%, and that from methyl-2-butenyl fumarate showed 43%. The higher degree of cyclization in the allyl monomer was attributed to the greater ease of formation of the expected 6-membered ring than of the expected 7-membered ring in the cyclopolymerization of the 2-butenyl monomer.

Marvel and Vest (34,42) report that the polymerization of dimethyl-α,α'-dimethylene adipate, giving recurring 5-membered cyclic units, occurs rather less readily than that of the corresponding pimelate derivative, giving recurring 6-membered units. The bulk or emulsion polymerization of the adipate gives insoluble gels containing no cyclic units. Emulsion polymerization of the pimelate ($N = 6$), however, gives a soluble cyclopolymer, whereas bulk polymerization gives soluble and insoluble fractions.

Although the cyclopolymerization of various diallyl monomers of structure $(CH_2=CH-CH_2)_2X$ is known, there has been no quantitative investigation into the effect of the group X on the ease of cyclization. The monomers in which $X =$ $\diagdown\!\!\!\!\diagup Si(CH_3)_2$, $\diagdown\!\!\!\!\diagup Si\phi_2$, $\diagdown\!\!\!\!\diagup\overset{\oplus}{N}H_2Cl^{\ominus}$, $\diagdown\!\!\!\!\diagup NH_2Br^{\ominus}$, and $\diagdown\!\!\!\!\diagup PO(\phi)$ are all reported to give soluble cyclopolymers with low degrees of residual unsaturation. Apparently, in none of these cases is there a sufficient variation in structure to affect the ease of cyclization significantly.

Investigations of the cyclopolymerization of unsymmetrical nonconjugated dienes have also been made, in which the two double bonds of the monomer are of unequal reactivity. The work of Barnett et al. (43) on the free-radical polymerization of unsaturated esters of maleic and fumaric acid has already been mentioned in connection with the effect of ring size on ease of cyclization. This work also reveals some effects resulting from the fact that the monomer double bonds have different structures and therefore different reactivities. The variation in degree of cyclization of the soluble fraction of the polymer with monomer structure is shown in Table 2-14. The investigators drew attention to the following points (cf. the table).

1. The degree of cyclization, IIa > Ia and IIc > Ic, which reflects the increased reactivity of fumarate compared to maleate double bonds toward the radical $-\dot{C}H-CH_2-$, derived from the terminal $-CH=CH_2$ group.

TABLE 2-14

Polymerization of Unsaturated Esters of Maleic and Fumaric Acid (43)

$$R_1 \diagdown \quad H \diagup$$
$$C=C$$
$$R_2 \diagup \quad \diagdown CO_2Me$$

Monomer No.	R_1	R_2	Type of structure	Cyclization in soluble fraction, %
Ia	—H	—CO$_2$CH$_2$CH=CH$_2$	Maleate (cis)	49
Ib	—H	—CH$_2$CH$_2$CH=CHCH$_3$	Maleate (cis)	60
Ic	—H	—CO$_2$CH$_2$CH$_2$CH=CH$_2$	Maleate (cis)	38
IIa	—CO$_2$CH$_2$CH=CH$_2$	—H	Fumarate (trans)	63
IIb	—CO$_2$CH$_2$CH=CHCH$_3$	—H	Fumarate (trans)	23
IIc	—CO$_2$CH$_2$CH$_2$CH=CH$_2$	—H	Fumarate (trans)	43

2. The maximal degree of cyclization is observed in monomer Ib. Both the double bonds in this monomer would be expected to be relatively unreactive to homopolymerization but more reactive to alternating copolymerization. The cyclopolymerization in this case is very similar to the alternating copolymerization of the two types of double bond.

3. The minimal degree of cyclization is found in monomer IIb, and this is consistent with the fact that fumarate double bonds show a greater homopolymerization tendency than do maleate double bonds.

A somewhat similar study of the polymerization of allyl and β-methallyl crotonates was made by Barnett and Butler (137).

Allyl crotonate: R = H
β-Methallyl crotonate: R = CH$_3$

Allyl crotonate was polymerized to about 10% conversion, and the soluble polymer was found to be 25 % cyclized. The soluble polymer from β-methallyl crotonate after polymerization to about 10% conversion was 31 % cyclized. The relatively low degree of cyclization in both polymers was assumed to be due to the great difference in reactivity between the double bonds of the monomers, which favored noncyclic propagation. The infrared absorption spectra of the soluble polymer fractions showed, in addition to bands at 1640 to 1655 cm^{-1}, characteristic of C=C stretching, and at 1725 to 1740 cm^{-1}, characteristic of the carbonyl group, a strong band at 1770 to 1772 cm^{-1}, characteristic of a 5-membered lactone:

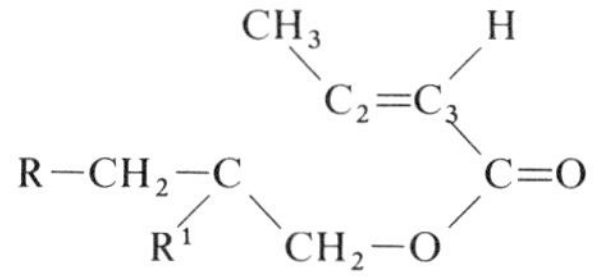

This unexpected 5-ring cyclization was attributed to the fact that there is less steric hindrance to ring closure at C_3 and this effect must exceed the resonance stabilization effect of the CH_3 group on the formation of a radical at C_2.

In an investigation of the free-radical solution polymerization of some 1,4-diene monomers Matsoyan and Avetyan (72) reported a similar type of steric control. Vinyl propenyl ketone gave polymer containing cyclopentanone rings, whereas 2-ethyl-4-methyl divinyl ketone gave polymer containing cyclohexanone rings:

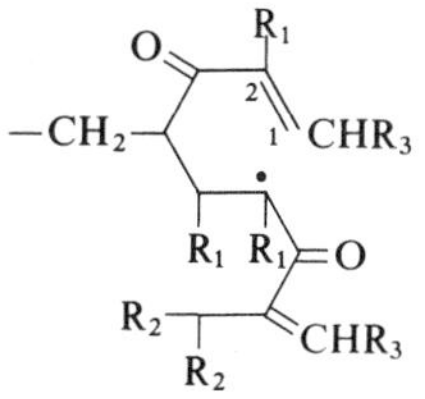

If $R_1 = R_2 = H$ and $R_3 = CH_3$, ring closes at 2
If $R_1 = CH_3$, $R_2 = C_2H_5$, and $R_3 = H$, ring closes at 1.

Arbuzova and Plotkina (138) obtained from the free-radical polymerization of diallyl maleate a soluble polymer with the characteristics of a 6-membered lactone and a residual unsaturation corresponding to one double bond per monomer unit. The proposed mechanism of polymerization was

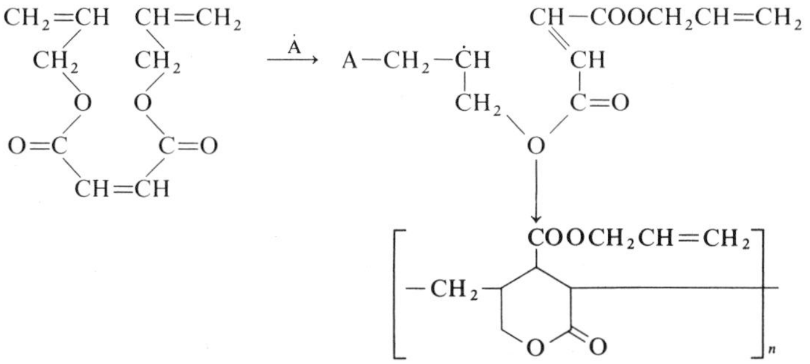

This may be explained in terms of two effects. First, ring closure at the terminal allyl double bond would form an 11-membered ring which, as we

have already seen in the work on cyclic lactone formation, is less readily formed than a ring of 6 members. Second, this may be another example of the "alternating copolymer" effect, since the allyl radical will be more reactive to a maleate double bond than it is to the terminal allyl double bond.

The following points arise from a comparison of the various systems discussed above.

All of the relevant available data for cyclopolymerization indicate much smaller differences in ease of cyclization with ring size than were found in the formation of cyclic esters and lactones through intramolecular condensation reactions. In general, the same arguments that have been invoked to explain the variation in ease of cyclization with ring size in the condensation reaction may be applied to the cyclopolymerization work. These arguments, elaborated earlier, are put in terms of the effects of steric hindrance (crowding of hydrogen atoms) and deformation of valence bond angles. Additional consideration will be given to this subject in the concluding part of this section.

If the data of Holt and Simpson (15) on the polymerization of aliphatic diallyl esters are compared with those of Marvel et al. (35,45) on the polymerization of the aliphatic dienes, it is seen that the aliphatic dienes show relatively larger variation in the degree of cyclization as the ring size is varied between 5 and 21 members. By contrast, the degree of cyclization of the diallyl esters changes relatively little in the range of $N = 8$ to 17. This is probably due to the effect of replacing methylene with carbonyl or ether groups, thereby reducing the number of sterically interfering hydrogen atoms, and to the larger rings studied by Holt and Simpson (15).

From the data of Holt and Simpson (15) on the cyclopolymerization of aromatic diallyl esters it is further seen that the degree of cyclization observed when a phenylene group is part of the ring is very markedly affected by whether the substitution is *ortho, meta,* or *para,* and the ease of cyclization decreases in that order. This may be ascribed to the increasing rigidity and size of the ring caused by introduction of the planar benzene ring.

β-Methyl substitution on the double bonds of diallyl esters (15), 1,5-hexadiene (35), and acrylic anhydride (108) appears to have no significant effect on the relative ease of cyclization in free-radical cyclopolymerization. Similarly, β-phenyl substitution in the aliphatic dienes has no significant effect on the relative degree of cyclization for cationic or Ziegler–Natta initiation (46). It appears that the steric hindrance to ring closure caused by the introduction of these substituents is offset by the increased stabilization of the intermediate radical or ion, caused by their inductive effect, or by the similarly increased interference with the linear propagation reaction.

In certain cases the introduction of a bulky substituent may force the formation of a 5-membered ring in place of a 6-membered ring. This has been observed for the β-methallyl crotonate (*137*) and for 2-ethyl-4-methyl-divinylketone (*72*).

The remaining effect of monomer structure on ease of cyclization to be discussed is that effect observed in nonsymmetrical monomers having double bonds of significantly differing reactivities. This is similar in many ways to the copolymerization of vinyl monomers, in which the monomers may have differing reactivities. The optimal situation for complete cyclization is that in which the double bonds present in the same monomer have a pronounced alternating tendency. If the radical from one double bond has a strong preference for the second double bond, the k_c/k_{11} ratio should be enhanced. On the other hand, if the radical from the more reactive double bond (which reacts with the attacking radical) has a low reactivity to the second double bond, intermolecular propagation will predominate. Examples of the former case are methyl methallyl maleate and diallyl maleate; of the latter, methyl methallyl fumarate.

B. Conclusions

Considerations of the detailed mechanism of cyclopolymerization to date have been primarily concerned with explaining why cyclization is favored over intermolecular propagation to the extent, at least in cases in which rings of favored size can be formed, that the polymers formed are highly cyclized. Electronic effects that could favor cyclization have been suggested. Butler (*3,86*) has proposed that the monomer double bonds interact to form a pseudocyclic structure:

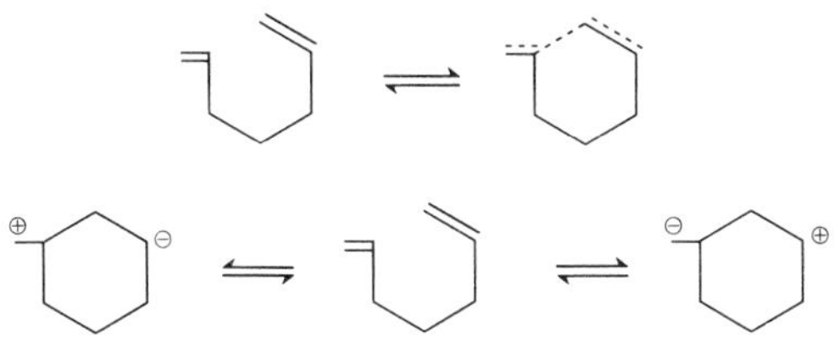

Marvel and Stille (*35*) and Butler (*3*) have suggested an interaction between the pendent double bond and the ion or radical in the noncyclized intermediate corresponding to $M_1\cdot$:

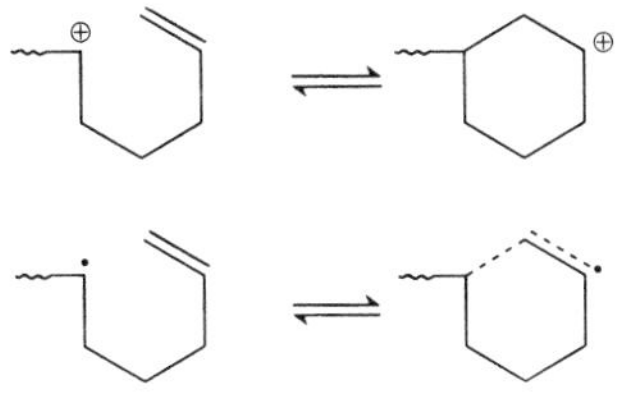

If such interactions as these do occur, they may be expected to make the cyclization reaction a lower activation energy process than intermolecular propagation and, hence, a favored path for reaction.

The experimental results available appear most consistent with the view that the double bonds in the monomer are noninteracting. Evidence in support of this view includes the fact that simple cyclopolymerization kinetics (Section 2-3-A-1) do not adequately describe the dependence of polymerization rate upon monomer concentration, whereas kinetics derived on the basis that the double bonds act independently, $[M_1] = 2[M]$, (Section 2-3-A-3) do appear to describe the dependence correctly and lead to values for k_c/k_{11} in good agreement with values from other methods. Dielectric-constant data and other data that would be useful in determining the absolute conformation of nonconjugated diolefins are not available. However, one spectroscopic study has appeared that is of interest. Wilcox et al. (139) reported that the electronic spectra of bicycloheptadiene (norbornadiene, bicyclo-(2,2,1)-hepta-2,5-diene) shows that the delocalization or resonance energy of this compound in the ground state is exactly zero; that is, there are no contributions from bonding interactions between the double bonds (140). Bicycloheptadiene is a monomer that gives exceptionally high yields of cyclized units in both homopolymerization and copolymerization, particularly in cationic systems (92). Furthermore, it has been found to undergo cyclization reactions of a similar nature when subjected to cationic or free-radical-initiated addition reactions (141–144). This will be further discussed shortly. The fact that this monomer, which is probably quite favorably structurally disposed to interaction, does not exhibit interaction in the ground state makes it appear unlikely that such interaction in the monomer is important in cyclopolymerization.

A resonance interaction is possible between the radical and the pendent double bond in the intermediate, noncyclized $M_1 \cdot$ radical. Bicycloheptadiene, which shows no interaction in the ground state, is described as possessing in the excited state interactions of the type (139,140)

where the bond order between carbons 1 and 2 and carbons 3 and 4 is 1.5 and between carbons 1 and 4 and carbons 2 and 3 it is 0.12.

A series of papers by Winstein and Shatavsky (141,143,144) and Schmerling et al. (142) describe the products resulting primarily from cationic addition reactions of bicycloheptadiene. The *extremely toxic dibromide mixtures* obtained in these reactions are only 17 to 24 unsaturated (142). The formation of the saturated dibromides has been described:

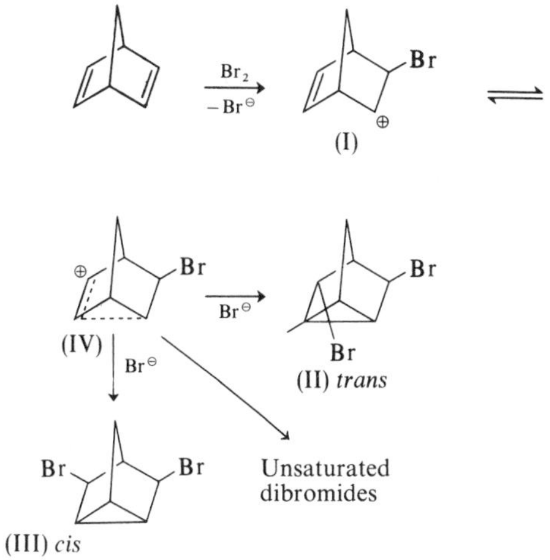

This is similar in over-all respects to the process proposed by Marvel and Stille (*35*) for the ionic polymerization of 1,6-heptadiene. No mention was made in the ionic reactions (*141–144*) of products resulting from the direct reaction of $Br^{\ominus}$ with (I). All unsaturated dibromides were visualized as being derived from (IV). Products from (I) would be analogous to noncyclic units from intermolecular propagation in polymerizing systems. Free-radical reactions were found to be less specific, however, and did yield such products.

Butler and co-workers (*3,145,146*) have observed the electronic spectra of several compounds expected to show interaction between nonconjugated double-bond systems: for example, methacrylic anhydride and allyl methacrylate as well as nonatriene and tetraene:

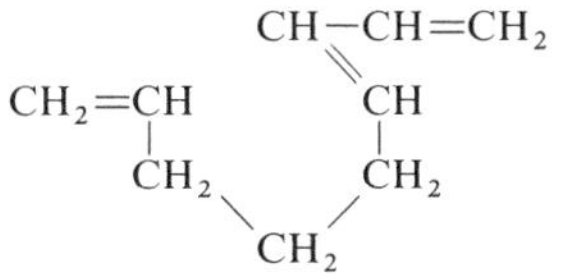

1,6,8-nonatriene 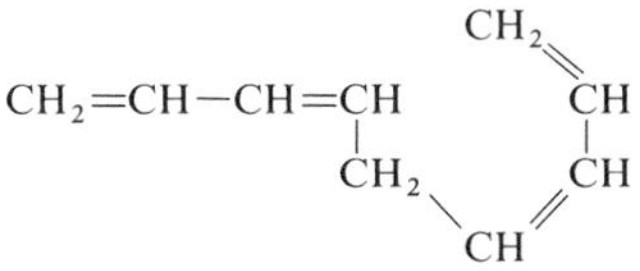   1,3,6,8-nonatetraene

Shifts from the calculated positions in the spectra were found amounting to 5 mμ or less for the dienes and up to 10 mμ for the tetraenes. These shifts were interpreted as evidence of interaction between double bonds in the excited state.

Results from the copolymerization studies summarized earlier led to the general observation that the double bonds of the diolefin are significantly more reactive than the double bond of a closely related monoolefin. This may also be interpreted as evidence of interaction in M_1·, since additional resonance stabilization would be absent in the monoolefin.

In both spectral and chemical evidence there is a reasonable basis for assuming that interaction can exist between the monomer double bonds in the excited state and between the ion or radical and the pendent double bond in intermediates similar to M_1·. The connection, however, between this information and cyclopolymerization, particularly free-radical-initiated cyclopolymerization, has yet to be firmly established.

Although the cationic addition reactions of bicycloheptadiene give no products analogous to noncyclized units, free-radical-initiated reactions do yield such compounds. This might indicate that free-radical reactions are less subject to these resonance effects. It has been observed that 1,6-heptadiene, a monomer that cyclopolymerizes ionically to nearly complete cyclopolymer ($N = 6$) in model reactions often prefers to form five-membered cyclic structures.

Brace (147) has observed that, whereas the free-radical-initiated reaction of iodoperfluoropropane with allyl ether gives a high yield of substituted six-membered ring compounds, similar reactions with 1,6-heptadiene yield only five-membered cyclic compounds with some noncyclic products. No cyclohexane derivatives were isolated. This was ascribed to the electronegative nature of the perfluoro group,

$$CF_3-CF_2-CF_2-CH_2-\overset{\cdot}{C}H \qquad \overset{CH_2}{\underset{CH_2}{\diagdown}}\overset{\diagup}{\underset{CH_2}{\diagup}}\overset{CH}{\underset{CH_2}{|}} \qquad \xrightarrow{R_fI}$$

$$CF_3-CF_2-CF_2-CH_2-\underset{\underset{CH_2\diagdown}{|}}{CH}\text{———}\underset{\underset{\diagup CH_2}{|}}{CH}-CH_2-I$$
$$\underset{CH_2}{}$$

and to steric hindrance in the transition state.

In our laboratory it has been observed that the addition of *n*-octyl mercaptan to 1,6-heptadiene, initiated by azobisisobutyronitrile, yields substituted cyclopentanes (148) as the only cyclic product:

$$C_8H_{17}SH + CH_2{=}CH \qquad \overset{CH_2}{\underset{CH_2\diagdown}{\underset{\diagup}{|}}}\overset{}{\underset{\diagup}{}}\overset{CH}{\underset{CH_2}{||}} \qquad \xrightarrow{A\cdot} C_8H_{17}S-CH_2-\underset{\underset{CH_2\diagdown}{|}}{CH}\text{———}\underset{\underset{\diagup CH_2}{|}}{CH}-CH_3$$

The primary products, however, are the noncyclic monoadduct, which leads to the noncyclic diadduct as reaction proceeds.

It appears, therefore, that if electronic interactions are present in these systems, they may be easily overcome, to such a point that the less stable five-membered rings can be formed.

The basis of postulating that electronic interaction, such as that described above, may take place and favor cyclization over intermolecular propagation is the belief that the formation of the pseudocyclic intermediates would lower the activation energy for the cyclization reaction. In view of this it is difficult to rationalize the general experimental results, which show that the activation energy for the intermolecular reaction is equal to, or less than, that for the cyclization reaction; that is, $E_{11} \lesssim E_c$. The value of $E_c - E_{11}$ is obtained directly from measurements of the k_c/k_{11} ratio as a function of temperature (Section 2-3-A-7 and Section 2-4-A-4). No cases have been reported in which $E_c < E_{11}$.

Since $E_c \gtrsim E_{11}$ and interaction between the radical and the pendent double bond might be expected, it may be that this interaction does not lead to a structure similar, in at least some key respects, to the transition state for the cyclization reaction. Thus, the interaction, if it is of this type, could actually be a barrier to cyclization.

Until a satisfactory explanation can be offered of the observed difference in activation energies (that is, $E_c \gtrsim E_{11}$), the use of electronic interaction, as indicated for bicycloheptadiene, to explain the preference for cyclization must be questioned.

It should be pointed out that the type of proposed interaction between the radical and the pendent double bond, although it represents a delocalization and stabilization of the intermediate radical or ion, should not be strictly compared to resonance effects in classical conjugated systems such as 1,3-butadiene and other conjugated dienes. In the case of cyclopolymerization the fate of the $M_1\cdot$ radical is strongly dependent upon monomer concentration. In a classical system such as the free-radical polymerization of 1,3-butadiene the nature of the polymer is governed essentially only by temperature. This is expected, because the structure of the classical resonance hybrid should be essentially independent of all but the more pronounced changes in the polarity, etc., of the system.

Even in the absence of electronic effects the nature of $M_1\cdot$ gives rise to other considerations, which make the cyclization reaction favored over linear propagation and also explain other characteristics of the cyclopolymerization reaction. These are considerations based upon the control that the pendent group can exercise on the course of reaction.

We have noted earlier that a pendent group on the β carbon of a monovinyl monomer has a significant effect on the absolute rate constants for propagation and termination. The k_p (30°C) and k_t (30°C) values for methyl acrylate and butyl acrylate are 720 versus 14 and 2.2×10^6 versus 9×10^3 liters/

mole/sec, respectively. The rate of intermolecular reaction of $M_1\cdot$ would be expected to be lower than that of a similar monomer with a noninterfering pendent group (that is, with less than four or five chain atoms in the pendent group). The very presence of the larger pendent group would tend to prevent intermolecular reaction from occurring at a rate that might be expected on the basis simply of the activation energy for the intermolecular propagation reaction. If the size of the pendent group is such that a conveniently sized cyclic structure can be formed by the cyclization reaction, the double bond will frequently be presented to the radical on the β carbon in a configuration favorable to reaction. On this basis the k_c/k_{11} values would be expected to be greater than unity for systems capable of facile cyclization. This type of steric interference would not entirely suppress the k_{11} reaction, and it would be expected that the k_c/k_{11} values would be moderate. This is in accord with the experimental values, which range generally from 5 to 20 moles/liter.

Other characteristics can also be predicted from this type of steric control. As the length of the pendent group containing the terminal double bond increases, two effects may be expected. First, the absolute value of k_c will fall, because the configurations of the pendent group that will lead to cyclization are fewer, and the radical will have less opportunity to encounter the double bond. Second, the bulkiness of the pendent group will increase and provide more shielding of the radical and prevent intermolecular propagation even more than before. The combined effect should be that the variation of k_c/k_{11} with ring size within a homologous series may be damped to some extent, compared with what would be predicted from a variation in k_c alone. Thus, k_c/k_{11} should vary somewhat less drastically with ring size than do the analogous ratios for the model compounds or polycondensation systems. This is in accord with experimental observation. The model based only on electronic interaction considerations would predict a change in k_c/k_{11} depending only upon the change in k_c.

This scheme would also predict that the rate of polymerization would be at a maximum when the ease of cyclization is greatest. Since $M_2\cdot$ will have less steric hindrance than $M_1\cdot$, then $k_{21} > k_{11}$. Therefore, at the point at which k_c/k_{11} is a maximum the formation of $M_2\cdot$ will be greatest and the rate will correspondingly be a maximum. This is also in accord with experiment.

The value of $E_c - E_{11}$ for the steric control model, to a first approximation, would be zero, since the double bonds are considered to be identical throughout, and the cyclization and intermolecular propagation activation energies would be the same. Thus, although E_c would not be expected to be greater than E_{11}, this mechanism would not require that E_c be lower than E_{11} for cyclization to be the favored reaction.

At present no single proposed mechanism explains all the characteristics of cyclopolymerization in an entirely satisfactory manner. The two extremes

—the one proposed, including strong electronic interactions in the non-cyclized radical (or monomer), and the other advocating a complete steric control—each answer many questions satisfactorily. Both are unable to account for all major characteristics. The former mechanism has its main weakness in the fact that the activation energy for cyclization experimentally is equal to or greater than that for linear propagation and that k_c/k_{11} values are typically moderate and not subject to wide variation within a homologous series. The steric-control mechanism suffers also from the fact that $E_c - E_{11}$ experimentally is most often greater than zero and that the reactivity of the diolefinic monomer is almost always greater than the reactivity of closely related monoolefins.

The most realistic mechanism based on the current available information might be that involving a major contribution from the steric-control hypothesis, since this gives reasonable answers to more of the important questions and is most easily reconciled with the existing information.

REFERENCES

1. G. B. Butler and F. L. Ingley, *J. Am. Chem. Soc.*, **73**, 894 (1951).
2. G. B. Butler and R. J. Angelo, *J. Am. Chem. Soc.*, **79**, 3128 (1957).
3. G. B. Butler, in *Encyclopedia of Plastics, Polymers and Resins*, in press.
4. H. Staudinger and W. Heuer, *Ber.*, **67**, 1164 (1935).
5. P. J. Flory, *J. Am. Chem. Soc.*, **63**, 3083 (1941).
6. P. J. Flory, *J. Am. Chem. Soc.*, **63**, 3091 (1941).
7. P. J. Flory, *J. Am. Chem. Soc.*, **63**, 3096 (1941).
8. P. J. Flory, *J. Phys. Chem.*, **46**, 132 (1942).
9. W. H. Stockmayer, *J. Chem. Phys.*, **11**, 45 (1943).
10. W. H. Stockmayer, *J. Chem. Phys.*, **12**, 125 (1944).
11. C. Walling, *J. Am. Chem. Soc.*, **67**, 441 (1945).
12. W. H. Stockmayer and L. L. Weil, in *Advancing Fronts in Chemistry* (S. B. Twiss, ed.), Reinhold, New York, 1945.
13. W. Simpson, T. Holt, and R. J. Zetie, *J. Polymer Sci.*, **10**, 489 (1953).
14. W. Simpson and T. Holt, *J. Polymer Sci.*, **18**, 335 (1955).
15. T. Holt and W. Simpson, *Proc. Roy. Soc. (London)*, **A238**, 154 (1956).
16. R. N. Haward, *J. Polymer Sci.*, **14**, 535 (1954).
17. F. T. Wall, *J. Chem. Phys.*, **11**, 67 (1943).
18. W. Kuhn, *Kolloid-Z.*, **68**, 2 (1934).
19. M. Gordon, *J. Chem. Phys.*, **22**, 610 (1954).
20. M. Gordon and R.-J. Roe, *J. Polymer Sci.*, **21**, 27 (1956).
21. M. Gordon and R.-J. Roe, *J. Polymer Sci.*, **21**, 39 (1956).
22. M. Gordon and R.-J. Roe, *J. Polymer Sci.*, **21**, 57 (1956).
23. M. Gordon and R.-J. Roe, *J. Polymer Sci.*, **21**, 75 (1956).
24. H. Jacobson and W. H. Stockmayer, *J. Chem. Phys.*, **18**, 1600 (1950).
25. F. E. Harris, *J. Chem. Phys.*, **23**, 1518 (1955).
26. R. W. Kilb, *J. Phys. Chem.*, **62**, 969 (1958).
27. F. P. Price, J. H. Gibbs, and B. H. Zimm, *J. Phys. Chem.*, **62**, 972 (1958).
28. F. P. Price, *J. Phys. Chem.*, **62**, 977 (1958).

29. B. H. Zimm, F. P. Price, and J. P. Bianchi, *J. Phys. Chem.*, **62**, 979 (1958).
30. G. B. Butler and R. L. Bunch, *J. Am. Chem. Soc.*, **71**, 3120 (1949).
31. G. B. Butler and R. L. Goette, *J. Am. Chem. Soc.*, **74**, 1939 (1952).
32. G. B. Butler and R. L. Goette, *J. Am. Chem. Soc.*, **76**, 2418 (1954).
33. G. B. Butler, A. Crawshaw, and W. L. Miller, *J. Am. Chem. Soc.*, **80**, 3615 (1958).
34. C. S. Marvel and R. D. Vest, *J. Am. Chem. Soc.*, **79**, 5771 (1957).
35. C. S. Marvel and J. K. Stille, *J. Am. Chem. Soc.*, **80**, 1740 (1958).
36. J. F. Jones, *J. Polymer Sci.*, **33**, 7 (1958).
37. J. F. Jones, *J. Polymer Sci.*, **33**, 513 (1958).
38. T. Otsu, J. E. Mulvaney, and C. S. Marvel, *J. Polymer Sci.*, **46**, 546 (1960).
39. W. DeWinter, C. S. Marvel, and A. Abdul-Karim, *J. Polymer Sci.*, **A1**, 3261 (1963).
40. A. Crawshaw and G. B. Butler, *J. Am. Chem. Soc.*, **80**, 5464 (1958).
41. J. F. Jones, *J. Polymer Sci.*, **33**, 15 (1958).
42. C. S. Marvel and R. D. Vest, *J. Am. Chem. Soc.*, **81**, 984 (1959).
43. M. D. Barnett, A. Crawshaw, and G. B. Butler, *J. Am. Chem. Soc.*, **81**, 5946 (1959).
44. W. E. Gibbs and J. T. Murray, *J. Polymer Sci.*, **58**, 1211 (1962).
45. C. S. Marvel and W. E. Garrison, *J. Am. Chem. Soc.*, **81**, 4737 (1959).
46. C. S. Marvel and E. J. Gall, *J. Org. Chem.*, **25**, 1784 (1960).
47. N. D. Field, *J. Org. Chem.*, **25**, 1006 (1960).
48. K. D. Berlin and G. B. Butler, *J. Am. Chem. Soc.*, **82**, 2712 (1960).
49. K. D. Berlin and G. B. Butler, *J. Org. Chem.*, **25**, 2006 (1960).
50. G. B. Butler and R. W. Stackman, *J. Org. Chem.*, **25**, 1643 (1960).
51. C. S. Marvel and R. G. Woolford, *J. Org. Chem.*, **25**, 1647 (1960).
52. D. Mikulasova and A. Hrivik, *Chem. Zvesti*, **11**, 641 (1957).
53. V. Ya. Bogomol'nyi, *Vysokomolekul. Soedin.*, **1**, 1469 (1959).
54. G. S. Kolesnikov, S. L. Davydova, and T. I. Ermolaeva, *Vysokomolekul. Soedin.*, **1**, 1493 (1959).
55. W. E. Gibbs and R. L. Van Deusen, *J. Polymer Sci.*, **54**, 51 (1961).
56. J. K. Stille, *J. Am. Chem. Soc.*, **83**, 1697 (1961).
57. S. G. Matsoyan and M. G. Avetyan, *Zh. Obshch. Khim.*, **30**, 697 (1960).
58. S. G. Matsoyan, M. G. Avetyan, and M. G. Voskanyan, *Vysokomolekul. Soedin.*, **2**, 314 (1960).
59. S. G. Matsoyan, M. A. Eliazyan, and E. Ts. Gevorkyan, *Vysokomolekul. Soedin.*, **4**, 1515 (1962).
60. S. G. Matsoyan and M. G. Voskanyan, *Izv. Akad. Nauk Arm. SSR, Ser. Tekhn. Nauk*, **16**, 151 (1963).
61. S. G. Matsoyan and L. M. Akopvan, *Vysokomolekul. Soedin.*, **3**, 1311 (1961).
62. S. G. Matsoyan and L. M. Akopvan, *Izv. Akad. Nauk Arm. SSR, Ser. Tekhn. Nauk*, **16**, 51 (1963).
63. S. G. Matsoyan, G. M. Pogosyan, and A. A. Saakyan, *Vysokomolekul. Soedin.*, **3**, 1963 (1961).
64. S. G. Matsoyan and A. A. Saakyan, *Vysokomolekul. Soedin.*, **3**, 1317 (1961).
65. S. G. Matsoyan, M. G. Voskanyan, and A. A. Saakyan, *Izv. Akad. Nauk Arm. SSR, Ser. Tekhn. Nauk*, **16**, 455 (1963).
66. S. G. Matsoyan, N. M. Morlyan, and A. A. Saakyan, *Izv. Akad. Nauk SSR, Ser. Tekhn. Nauk*, **15**, 405 (1962).
67. S. G. Matsoyan and N. M. Morlyan, *Izv. Akad. Nauk Arm. SSR, Ser. Tekhn. Nauk*, **16**, 347 (1963).
68. S. G. Matsoyan and N. M. Morlyan, *Izv. Akad. Nauk Arm. SSR, Ser. Tekhn. Nauk*, **16**, 571 (1963).
69. S. G. Matsoyan and N. M. Morlyan, *Vysokomolekul. Soedin.*, **6**, 945 (1964).

70. S. G. Matsoyan and N. M. Morlyan, *Izv. Akad. Nauk Arm. SSR, Ser. Tekhn. Nauk*, **17**, 319 (1964).

71. S. G. Matsoyan and N. M. Morlyan, *Izv. Akad. Nauk Arm. SSR, Ser. Tekhn. Nauk*, **17**, 329 (1964).

72. S. G. Matsoyan and M. G. Avetyan, *Zh. Obshch. Khim.*, **30**, 2431 (1960).

73. C. Aso and S. Ushio, *Kogyo Kagaku Zasshi.*, **65**, 2085 (1962).

74. D. S. Trifan and J. J. Hoglen, *J. Am. Chem. Soc.*, **83**, 2021 (1961).

75. S. G. Matsoyan, G. M. Pogosyan, and M. A. Eliazyan, *Vysokomolekul. Soedin.*, **5**, 777 (1963).

76. L. Ye. Gusel'nikov, N. S. Nametkin, L. S. Polak, and T. I. Chernysheva, *Izv. Akad. Nauk SSSR, Ser. Khim.*, **11**, 2072 (1964).

77. S. G. Matsoyan, M. G. Avetyan, and M. G. Voskanyan, *Vysokomolekul. Soedin.*, **3**, 1140 (1961).

78. S. G. Matsoyan, M. G. Avetyan, and M. G. Voskanyan, *Vysokomolekul. Soedin.*, **4**, 882 (1962).

79. S. G. Matsoyan, M. G. Voskanyan, and A. A. Cholakyan, *Vysokomolekul. Soedin.*, **5**, 1035 (1963).

80. J. C. H. Hwa and L. Miller, *J. Polymer Sci.*, **55**, 197 (1961).

81. W. E. Gibbs, *J. Polymer Sci.*, **A2**, 4815 (1964).

82. J. Roovers and G. Smets, *Makromol. Chem.*, **60**, 89 (1963).

83. G. Van Paesschen, R. Janssen, and R. Hart, *Makromol. Chem.*, **37**, 47 (1960).

84. W. E. Gibbs and R. J. McHenry, *J. Polymer Sci.*, **A2**, 5277 (1964).

85. J. K. Stille and D. W. Thomson, *J. Polymer Sci.*, **62**, 556 (1962).

86. G. B. Butler, *J. Polymer Sci.*, **48**, 279 (1960).

87. E. Y. Chang and C. C. Price, *J. Am. Chem. Soc.*, **83**, 4650 (1961).

88. J. M. Barton, G. B. Butler, and E. C. Chapin, *J. Polymer Sci.*, **A3**, 501 (1965).

89. L. E. Ball and H. J. Harwood, *Abstracts 139th Meeting American Chemical Society*, St. Louis, 1961.

90. B. Reichel, C. S. Marvel, and R. Z. Greenlee, *J. Polymer Sci.*, **A1**, 2935 (1963).

91. R. Dowbenko and W. H. Chang, *J. Polymer Sci.*, **B2**, 469 (1964).

92. J. P. Kennedy and J. A. Hinlicky, *Polymer*, **6**, 133 (1965).

93. G. B. Butler and M. L. Miles, *J. Polymer Sci.*, **A3**, 1609 (1965).

94. N. L. Zutty, *J. Polymer Sci.*, **A1**, 2231 (1963).

95. H. Brunner, A. L. L. Pallvel, and D. J. Wallbridge, *J. Polymer Sci.*, **28**, 629 (1958).

96. A. A. D'onofrio, *J. Appl. Polymer Sci.*, **8**, 521 (1964).

97. C. G. Overberger, S. Ishida, and H. Ringsdorf, *J. Polymer Sci.*, **62**, 51 (1962).

98. C. Aso and Y. Aito, *Makromol. Chem.*, **58**, 195 (1962).

99. W. W. Moyer and D. A. Drew, *J. Polymer Sci.*, **B1**, 29 (1963).

100. J. K. Stille and B. M. Culbertson, *J. Polymer Sci.*, **A2**, 405 (1964).

101. Y. Iwakura, K. Uno, and K. Ichkawa, *J. Polymer Sci.*, **A2**, 3387 (1964).

102. G. V. D. Tiers and F. A. Bovey, *J. Polymer Sci.*, **47**, 479 (1960).

103. W. L. Miller, W. S. Brey, Jr., and G. B. Butler, *J. Polymer Sci.*, **54**, 329 (1961).

104. G. B. Butler, *Pure Appl. Chem.*, **4**, 299 (1962).

105. J. C. H. Hwa, *J. Polymer Sci.*, **60**, S12 (1962).

106. J. C. H. Hwa and H. E. Ries, Jr., *J. Polymer Sci.*, **B2**, 389 (1964).

107. J. Mercier and G. Smets, *J. Polymer Sci.*, **A1**, 1491 (1963).

108. J. Mercier and G. Smets, *J. Polymer Sci.*, **57**, 763 (1962).

108a. G. Smets, N. Deval, and P. Hous, *J. Polymer Sci.*, **A2**, 4825 (1964).

109. P. D. Bartlett and R. Altschul, *J. Am. Chem. Soc.*, **7**, 812, 816 (1945).

110. P. J. Flory, *in Principles of Polymer Chemistry*, Cornell Univ. Press, Ithaca, New York, 1953, p. 158.

111. P. J. Flory, *in Principles of Polymer Chemistry*, Cornell Univ. Press, Ithaca, New York, 1953, p. 202.

112. P. J. Flory, *in Principles of Polymer Chemistry*, Cornell Univ. Press, Ithaca, New York, 1953, p. 123.

113. C. Walling and E. R. Briggs, *J. Am. Chem. Soc.*, **67**, 1774 (1945).

114. I. S. Sokolnikoff and E. S. Sokolnikoff, *Higher Mathematics for Engineers and Physicists*, 2nd ed., McGraw-Hill, New York, 1941, p. 107.

115. W. E. Gibbs, *J. Polymer Sci.*, **A2**, 4809 (1964).

116. R. H. Wiley and E. E. Sale, *J. Polymer Sci.*, **42**, 479, 491 (1960).

117. Y. Minoura and M. Mitoh, *J. Polymer Sci.*, **A3**, 2149 (1965).

118. W. E. Gibbs and J. T. Murray, unpublished results, 1962.

119. M. Okada, K. Hayashi, K. Hayashi, and S. Okamura, *Ann. Rept. Japan. Assoc. Radiation Res. Polymers*, **5**, 95 (1963–64); AEC-tr-6565, p. 119, CFSTI, NBS, U.S. Dept. of Commerce transl.

120. C. Aso, *J. Polymer Sci.*, **39**, 475 (1959).

121. K. I. Benyon and E. J. Haward, *J. Polymer Sci.*, **A3**, 1793 (1965).

122. R. W. Roth and R. F. Church, *J. Polymer Sci.*, **55**, 41 (1961).

123. K. I. Benyon, *J. Polymer Sci.*, **A1**, 3343 (1963).

124. K. I. Benyon, *J. Polymer Sci.*, **A1**, 3357 (1963).

125a. G. Takashi, *Kobunshi Kagaku*, **14**, 151 (1957); *CA*, **52**, 1670c (1948).

125b. T. Alfrey, Jr., J. Bohrer, and H. Mark, *Copolymerization, High Polymer Series VIII*, Wiley (Interscience), New York, 1952, p. 40.

126. T. Alfrey, Jr., J. Bohrer, and H. Mark, *Copolymerization, High Polymer Series XVIII*, Wiley (Interscience), New York, 1946, Appendix A.

127. W. E. Gibbs and J. T. Murray, to be submitted to *J. Polymer Sci.*

127a. G. Smets, N. Deval, and P. Hous, *J. Polymer Sci.*, **A2**, 4835 (1964).

128. E. W. Spanagel and W. H. Carothers, *J. Am. Chem. Soc.*, **57**, 929 (1935).

129. W. H. Carothers and J. W. Hill, *J. Am. Chem. Soc.*, **55**, 5043 (1933).

130. M. Stoll and A. Rouve, *Helv. Chim. Acta*, **18**, 1087 (1935).

131. M. Stoll, A. Rouve, and G. Stoll-Comte, *Helv. Chim. Acta*, **17**, 1289 (1934).

132. G. Salomon, *Trans. Faraday Soc.*, **34**, 1311 (1938).

133. K. Ziegler and W. Hechelhammer, *Ann.*, **528**, 114 (1937).

134. K. Ziegler and H. Holl, *Ann.*, **528**, 143 (1937).

135. K. Ziegler and M. Luttringhaus, *Ann.*, **528**, 162, 181 (1937).

136. A review of this general work was given by G. M. Bennett, *Trans. Faraday Soc.*, **37**, 794 (1941).

137. M. D. Barnett and G. B. Butler, *J. Org. Chem.*, **25**, 309 (1960).

138. I. A. Arbuzova and S. A. Plotkina, *Vysokomolekul. Soedin.*, **6**, 729 (1964).

139. C. F. Wilcox, S. Winstein, and W. G. McMillan, *J. Am. Chem. Soc.*, **82**, 5450 (1960).

140. H. H. Jaffe and M. Orchin, *Theory and Applications of Ultraviolet Spectroscopy*, Wiley, New York, 1962, p. 441.

141. S. Winstein and M. Shatavsky, *Chem. & Ind.*, **1956**, 56.

142. L. Schmerling, J. P. Luvisi, and R. W. Welch, *J. Am. Chem. Soc.*, **78**, 2819 (1956).

143. S. Winstein and M. Shatavsky, *J. Am. Chem. Soc.*, **78**, 592 (1956).

144. S. Winstein, *J. Am. Chem. Soc.*, **83**, 1516 (1961).

145. G. B. Butler and T. W. Brooks, *J. Org. Chem.*, **28**, 2699 (1963).

146. G. B. Butler and M. A. Raymond, paper presented before the *Div. of Organic Chemistry*, *ACS*, Denver, Colorado, Jan. 1964.

147. N. O. Brace, *J. Am. Chem. Soc.*, **86**, 523 (1964).

148. R. L. Van Deusen and W. E. Gibbs, unpublished results, 1964.

CHAPTER 3

Styrene

Maurice H. George†

Department of Chemistry, University of Queensland, Brisbane, Queensland, Australia

† Current affiliation: Department of Chemistry, Imperial College of Science and Technology, University of London, England.

3-1. GENERAL INTRODUCTION

Styrene has been studied academically more extensively than any other vinyl monomer, partly because it is of commercial importance and relatively cheap and partly because simple methods of purification and exclusion of oxygen are usually sufficient to ensure reproducible kinetic behavior when polymerization proceeds solely by a free-radical mechanism (1). Furthermore, the physical properties of monomer and polymer, including their ultraviolet (1–3), infrared (1,2(e),3–6), and Raman spectra [1,2(e),6(a),7,469,470], have been examined in detail, and analytical procedures (1,7) are available for purity estimation. Much of the physical data (1,7) and results of kinetic studies of polymerization have been critically collated (8–12).

Densities of monomer, d_m, and polymer, d_p, commonly used in dilatometric rate calculations have been tabulated (1,13,14) and enable percentage volume contractions for 100% conversions to be calculated

$$\begin{matrix} \% \text{ volume contraction} \\ \text{for } 100\% \text{ conversion} \end{matrix} = \left(\frac{1/d_m - 1/d_p}{1/d_m} \times 100 \right) \tag{3-1}$$

At constant temperature the density of the solid polymer is less than that of the polymer dissolved in monomer or other good solvent (13,14). There is no systematic change of polymer density with polymer concentration (15), and the apparent specific volume of polystyrene in solution does not vary with the degree of polymerization, if the latter is sufficiently high (16).

Methods of determining molecular weights and molecular-weight distributions of polystyrene are of general applicability (17). Viscometric determinations of molecular weight are facilitated by the recent tabulation of K and α constants of the Mark-Houwink equation (3-2), relating intrinsic viscosity $[\eta]$ to molecular weight M for a wide variety of solvents (18):

$$[\eta] = KM^\alpha \tag{3-2}$$

Low-resolution nuclear magnetic spectroscopy (relaxation spectroscopy) has been used to study solutions of polystyrene and solid polymer (3,19–23,471), and some high-resolution measurements of solutions have also been made (3,4,24,25). The NMR spectrum of monomeric styrene has been analyzed, and NMR methods have also been used for studying copolymers of styrene, especially those containing methyl methacrylate units. Electron spin resonance spectroscopy has been used chiefly for investigating radical formation and destruction on exposure of polystyrene to ionizing radiation or attack by excited rare-gas atoms (26–35), on milling of the polymer (472), or on heating it with initiator (473). Attempts have also been made at identifying the intermediate radicals in styrene polymerizations retarded by nitro and nitroso compounds (36), and the growth process of a styrene–p-divinylbenzene popcorn copolymer in styrene has been followed (474). The reactions between polystyryl radicals and other substrates has also received some attention with ESR, and the field has been reviewed recently (37).

From a thermodynamic viewpoint styrene and polystyrene were the first monomer-polymer pair on which sufficient specific heat data became available for calculating the thermodynamic functions $S_T - S_{0°K}$, $H_T - H_{0°K}$, and $G_T - G_{0°K}$. Warfield and Petree (38) calculated the entropy of polystyrene prepared with free radicals at 298.16°K ($S_{298.16} - S_{0°K}$) to be 30.70 cal deg^{-1} mole^{-1} and that of styrene to be 57.39 cal deg^{-1} mole^{-1}. Hence, the entropy of polymerization equals 26.69 cal deg^{-1} mole^{-1} on the usual assumptions. This is in reasonable agreement with the corresponding values (in calories per degree Kelvin per mole) of Dainton and Ivin (39) of 32.23 (polystyrene), 57.16 (styrene), and 24.93 (entropy of polymerization) at 298.16°K.

Heats of polymerization are equal to $-\Delta H_{xy}$, where x and y represent the initial and final states, respectively, and refer to the liquid l, condensed phase c, crystalline state c', and solution s. The heat of polymerization was first measured by Tong and Kenyon (40), who found that $-\Delta H_{lc}$ was 16.1 kcal mole^{-1} (of monomer) at 76.8°C, whereas more accurate values of 16.68 $\pm$ 0.14 at 25°C, 16.9 $\pm$ 0.3 (mean value) (42), and 16.4 $\pm$ 0.3 at 26.9°C (15) have been reported. If the relatively precise value of 16.68 $\pm$ 0.14 at 25°C (41) is taken with a value for the heat of solution of polystyrene in monomer (6.9% solution by weight of polymer in monomer), 0.86 at 25°C, then $-\Delta H_{ls} = 17.54 \pm 0.14$ kcal mole^{-1} at 25°C. This is in good agreement with the 17.4 $\pm$ 0.2 at 26.9°C, found by Dainton and co-workers (15). Heats of copolymerization of styrene with other monomers have also been measured (43–45), and heat-capacity measurements have enabled the entropy of completely crystalline isotactic polystyrene to be calculated (46) as 30.7 $\pm$ 0.2 cal deg^{-1} mole^{-1} at 25°C. The data of Dainton and co-workers (39,46) thus reveal the higher entropy of atactic polystyrene compared with the isotactic polymer to be 1.53 $\pm$ 0.2 cal deg^{-1} mole^{-1} at 25°C. The effects of molecular configuration (tacticity) and crystallinity on the specific heats and related thermodynamic quantities of polystyrene have been assessed, and the results have been interpreted (475,476). A review of the thermodynamics of addition polymerization and depolymerization has been published (39).

3-2. SCOPE OF CHAPTER, SYMBOLS, AND CONVENTIONS

The literature dealing with the chemistry of styrene and polystyrene is already enormous and continues to grow rapidly. This chapter will necessarily be limited to a consideration of those aspects of the polymerization of styrene by free-radical mechanisms which the author feels are of importance or interest. In particular, there is no detailed account of either the effects of ionizing radiation on monomer and polymer or of copolymerization.

Many initiators, In, when added to styrene in bulk or solution, produce free radicals and a corresponding increase in rate of polymerization over and above the thermal rate proceeding in their absence. Observed rates of polymerization, $R_{p(obs)}$, may be corrected to allow for the relatively small thermal rate of polymerization due to monomer alone, $R_{p(th)}$, to give the rate due to initiator alone, R_p, by means of Eq. (3-3):

$$R_p^2 = R_{p(obs)}^2 - R_{p(th)}^2 \qquad (3-3)$$

The results of many studies of free-radical polymerization will be discussed by reference to the following kinetic scheme.

A. Initiation

For initiators, In, decomposing thermally to give two primary radicals, R_c,

$$\text{In} \xrightarrow{k_d} 2R_c \qquad d[R_c]/dt = 2k_d[\text{In}] \qquad (3\text{-}4a)$$

where symbols inside brackets designate concentrations.

Some of the R_c radicals then add to monomer, M, to give a "polymeric" type of radical with a $-CH_2CHPh$ end:

$$R_c + M \xrightarrow{k_i} R_1 \qquad (3\text{-}4b)$$

The two steps (4a) and (4b) are collectively called the initiation step, and the over-all production of R_1 radicals, called the rate of initiation, I, is written

$$I = d[R_1]/dt = 2fk_d[\text{In}] \qquad (3\text{-}4c)$$

where f is called the initiator efficiency. This quantity f, then, is a measure of the wastage of radicals initially formed that do not successfully initiate polymerization but are destroyed by other reactions. For an initiator giving y primary radicals:

$$f = \frac{\text{rate of initiation of polymer chains}}{y \times \text{rate of decomposition of initiator}} = \frac{I}{yk_d[\text{In}]} \qquad (3\text{-}4d)$$

The rate of initiation of polymerization due to any other mechanism will also be represented generally as I.

B. Propagation

The propagation reaction may be written

$$R_n + M \xrightarrow{k_p} R_{n+1} \qquad (3\text{-}4e)$$

C. Mutual Termination of Polymer Radicals

The following method (8,10), particularly widespread in America, will be used to define the velocity constants k_{td} and k_{tc} for disproportionation and combination, respectively.

Disproportionation of polymer radicals may be written

$$R_r \cdot + R_s \cdot \xrightarrow{k_{td}} P_r + P_s \qquad (3\text{-}4f)$$

where the symbol P represents a polymer molecule. The velocity constant of this reaction will be defined:

$$-d[R\cdot]/dt = 2k_{td}[R\cdot]^2 \quad \text{and} \quad d[P]/dt = 2k_{td}[R\cdot]^2 \qquad (3\text{-}4g)$$

Combination of polymer radicals may be written

$$R_r \cdot + R_s \cdot \xrightarrow{k_{tc}} P_{r+s} \qquad (3\text{-}4h)$$

and the velocity constant of this reaction will be defined:

$$-d[R\cdot]/dt = 2k_{tc}[R\cdot]^2 \quad \text{and} \quad d[P]/dt = k_{tc}[R\cdot]^2 \qquad (3\text{-}4i)$$

where $[R\cdot]$ designates the total polymer radical concentration.

In a later section it will be indicated that in styrene polymerization the termination of polymer radicals occurs exclusively by combination ($k_{td} = 0$), so that in future the velocity constant for mutual termination of polystyryl radicals will be abbreviated to k_t.

It might be noted that another method (9,11,12), which might be called the British method, as follows, has been used to define these velocity constants.

For disproportionation:

$$-d[R\cdot]/dt = k_{td}[R\cdot]^2 \quad \text{and} \quad d[P]/dt = k_{td}[R\cdot]^2 \qquad (3\text{-}4j)$$

For combination:

$$-d[R\cdot]/dt = k_{tc}[R\cdot]^2 \quad \text{and} \quad d[P]/dt = \tfrac{1}{2}k_{tc}[R\cdot]^2 \qquad (3\text{-}4k)$$

Simple equations derived with the British convention or the American convention may be readily interchanged, since

$$2k_{tc} \text{ (American)} = k_{tc} \text{ (British)} \qquad (3\text{-}4l)$$

$$2k_{td} \text{ (American)} = k_{td} \text{ (British)} \qquad (3\text{-}4m)$$

D. Transfer

Transfer to monomer, to added solvent if present, and to other species will be dealt with in later sections.

By using the kinetic scheme outlined above one obtains for a rate of initiation I;

$$R_p = -d[M]/dt = k_p[M][R\cdot] = [k_p[M]/(2k_t)^{1/2}]I^{1/2} \qquad (3\text{-}4n)$$

$$= k_p[M](fk_d/k_t)^{1/2}[In]^{1/2} \qquad (3\text{-}4o)$$

for polymerization due to added initiator giving $2R_c\cdot$ radicals.

3-3. EARLY HISTORICAL BACKGROUND

Although the monomer had been isolated from natural sources earlier (1), Simon (47) in 1839 was the first to name the liquid "styrene" and demonstrated that in air it slowly changed into a gelatinous solid, mistakenly thought to be an oxidation product. Many properties of styrene were quickly established (48), and in 1876 van't Hoff (49) ended a period of controversy by demonstrating that the same product, styrene, could be isolated not only from natural products but also by heating cinnamates (47,50) and cinnamic acid (51–53) or by passing a mixture of benzene and ethylene through a red-hot tube (54,55).

Blyth and Hofmann (56) in 1845 prepared solid polystyrenes by heating styrene in air. They observed that the product had the same atomic composition as the monomer and that the exothermic reaction could also be induced by light. The polymers depolymerized, giving styrene on heating. Berthelot (57) first used the term "polymerization" to describe the conversion of liquid styrene to gelatinous or solid material. He noted that concentrated sulfuric acid accelerated the reaction rates and successfully polymerized styrene in toluene solution. Lemoine (58) followed the course of polymerization in air gravimetrically, separating monomer from polymer by fractional distillation at low pressures. He established that styrene had a low rate of thermal polymerization and that ultraviolet light, in particular, produced accelerated rates. Kronstein (59) systematically studied the precipitation of polystyrene from monomer–polymer mixtures by addition of a nonsolvent, alcohol.

In 1910 Stobbe and Posnjak (60) noted that polystyrene produced negligible boiling-point elevations when dissolved in carbon tetrachloride. They concluded that polystyrene was a "colloidal body" and proposed cyclic formulae for the polymer, involving four or more monomeric units. Viscosity and refractive-index methods of following polymerization reactions were also developed.

Staudinger (61) in 1920, however, proposed the correct long-chain covalent structure for polystyrene, which became firmly established (62) by the early 1930's. From this time onwards many theoretical and experimental workers investigated the structure, size, and shape of polymer molecules and the distribution of their molecular weights. By the early 1940's much was known about the nature of polymers in general and of polystyrene in particular. An interesting account of these developments may be found elsewhere (8).

The mechanism by which polystyrene is formed from monomer was a matter of controversy for many years. Ostromysslensky (63) in 1911–16 regarded the formation of hydrocarbon polymers as being a "step-wise" synthesis, and Whitby and Katz (64), who investigated the polymerization of indene and other monomers by stannic chloride and antimony pentachloride in 1928, would have considered that the stepwise polymerization of styrene was a series of hydrogen transfer reactions, each species being of equal reactivity,

$$CH_2{=}CHPh + CH_2 = CHPh \longrightarrow CH_3 \cdot CHPh \cdot CH{=}CHPh \qquad (3\text{-}5)$$
$$\text{monomer} \hspace{6.5cm} \text{dimer}$$

$$\text{dimer} \quad + CH_2 = CHPh \longrightarrow CH_3 \cdot CHPh \cdot CH_2 \cdot CHPh \cdot CH{=}CHPh$$
$$\hspace{8cm} \text{trimer}$$
$$(3\text{-}6)$$

and so forth. An opposing "chain reaction" mechanism was developed by Staudinger (61), who considered that after opening of the double bond of a monomer molecule other monomer molecules added on successively, forming long-chain molecules with free valencies at both ends. The intermediate species shown below were not, however, considered to be reactive:

$$-CH_2 \cdot CHPh \cdot CH_2 \cdot CHPh \cdot CH_2 \cdot CHPh \cdot CH_2 \cdot CHPh- \qquad (3\text{-}7)$$

Staudinger assumed that an equilibrium between the various large molecules was established, although later (65), in 1929, he and his associates proposed instead the existence of large cyclic molecules. Other workers (66,67) seemed unsure which of the two alternative mechanisms was correct.

Taylor and co-workers investigated the polymerization of vinyl acetate (68,69), styrene (68), and ethylene (70), and from this work and that of others (71) Chalmers (72) in 1934 concluded that a chain mechanism was involved, in which a slow (initiation) step was followed by rapid growth (propagation).

Following earlier work (73), Mark et al. (74–76) studied the thermal polymerization of styrene in air at different temperatures. They calculated energies of activation for initiation and propagation of about 30 and 8 kcal mole^{-1}, respectively. From 1936 to 1939 very precise measurements of the bulk thermal polymerization of styrene in air (77), and under nitrogen (78) were made by Schulz and Husemann, while other workers studied the bulk (79) and solution polymerization of styrene (79–83) in vacuo or under nitrogen.

These investigations established that in vacuo or under nitrogen:
1. Styrene underwent a characteristic thermal polymerization.

2. Added oxygen usually retarded the polymerization but at high temperatures could cause a rate acceleration due to the formation of peroxides (*84*).

3. The rate of the bulk polymerization was approximately first order with respect to monomer at low conversions.

4. In solution there was an apparent second-order dependence of rate of polymerization on monomer concentration.

5. The molecular weights of polystyrenes produced by solution polymerization were lower than for the bulk reaction (*80*).

6. Pure monomer was necessary for reproducible rates.

Figure 3-1 shows some early rate results for solution polymerization, obtained by Schulz and co-workers in the 1930's.

Meanwhile styrene had polymerized in the presence of added substances that were correctly thought to decompose thermally to form free radicals. Small amounts of these so-called initiators gave thermal rates of polymerization much greater than those observed in their absence. Rates of polymerization were shown to be half-order with respect to initiator concentration for benzoyl peroxide (*85*) and tetraphenyl succinodinitrile (*86*).

By the early 1940's the free-radical nature of the polymerization of styrene and the mechanism of initiation, propagation, and termination were slowly becoming understood. Kinetic chain-reaction schemes involving free radicals satisfactorily explained the observed experimental results (*75,76,87*). A

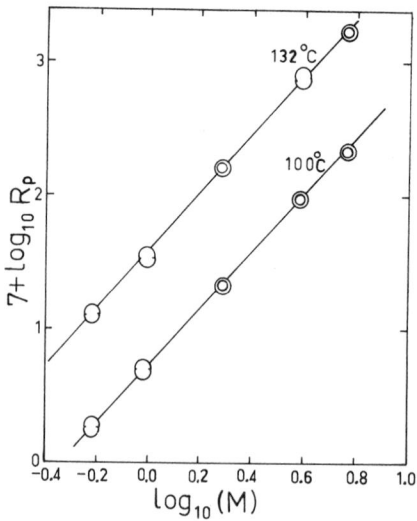

Fig. 3-1. Order of R_p in [M] for the thermal polymerization of styrene in toluene solution. No added initiator. R_p in moles per liter per second and [M] in moles per liter. At 132°C order = 2.18 and at 100°C order = 2.15. [Data from Schulz et al. (*83*).]

mechanism of chain transfer involving polymer radicals and solvent had also been suggested (87), and the possibility of branching reactions had been realized (87). Foord and others (88,89) had shown that a wide range of inhibitors and retarders could interact with the "active centers" in the thermal polymerization of styrene, and some of the differences between free-radical and ionic polymerizations were appreciated (90–92). Thus, the predominant features of free-radical polymerizations were understood, though much more detailed quantitative work was to follow.

Developments since the early 1940's will be discussed nonchronologically in later sections of this chapter.

3-4. THERMAL POLYMERIZATION IN BULK AND SOLUTION IN THE ABSENCE OF ADDED INITIATOR

A. Rates of Polymerization: Order of R_p and I in $[M]$

Purified styrene, like methyl methacrylate but unlike most other monomers, polymerizes slowly in vacuo or under nitrogen at a slow reproducible rate. Rubens and Boyer (93) have analyzed the results of several other workers and suggest that the initial rate of the thermal polymerization of bulk monomer between 60° and 120°C may be expressed as

$$\text{Initial rate (\% per hour)} = 3.55 \times 10^{11} \exp(-19{,}200/RT) \qquad (3\text{-}8)$$

A rate of polymerization of w weight per cent per hour at T (°K) corresponds to

$$w d_m/(104.1 \times 360) \text{ mole liter}^{-1} \text{ sec}^{-1},$$

where d_m is the density of the monomer at T (°K). Typical values (93) of the molecular weights of polymers prepared at different temperatures are shown in Table 3-1.

Now early work suggested that R_p in solution was approximately second order in monomer for a wide variety of solvents. This is reasonable, if the rate of thermal initiation I is also second order, for then

$$I = k_i[M]^2 \qquad (3\text{-}9)$$

and, assuming a stationary concentration of polymer radicals,

$$[R\cdot] = (k_i/2k_t)^{1/2}[M] \qquad (3\text{-}10)$$

whence

$$R_p = -d[M]/dt = k_p[M][R\cdot] = k_p(k_i/2k_t)^{1/2}[M]^2 = k_M[M]^2 \quad (3\text{-}11)$$

where k_M is a composite constant. Values of k_M and the over-all activation energy for the thermal polymerization reported by various workers differ

TABLE 3-1

Bulk Thermal Polymerization in Absence of Added Initiator

Polymerization temp., °C	Initial rate of polymerization, %/hr	Weight-average molecular weight $\overline{M}_W$
60	0.089	2,250,000
70	0.205	1,400,000
80	0.462	880,000
90	1.02	610,000
100	2.15	420,000
110	4.25	310,000
120	8.5	230,000
130	16.2	175,000
140	28.4	130,000
160		83,000

considerably. Thus, Bamford and Dewar (94) quote

$$k_M = 10^{6.8} \exp(-23{,}200/RT) \text{ mole}^{-1} \text{ liter sec}^{-1}$$

but this activation energy of 23.2 kcal mole^{-1} is much higher than the 19.2 kcal mole^{-1} in Eq. (3-8).

The apparent first-order dependence of rate on [M] in the bulk polymerization poses considerable problems. Walling et al. (95) calculated the activity of the monomer in the polymerizing system at 127°C to 95% conversion from monomer vapor-pressure measurements. Their results suggested that R_p was strictly proportional to the square of the monomer activity and only approximately proportional to [M]^1. In dilute solutions activities would be more nearly equal to concentrations, and a second-order dependence on [M] results.

Other explanations (8,9) imply that the lower order of reaction in bulk reaction is due to the "gel effect," which refers to the reduction of polymer radical termination rate with increasing conversion (96). The gel effect with styrene is real, though slight (97,98); it is discussed later.

Evidence found by Mayo (99), using bromobenzene as solvent, suggested that the over-all rate was 5/2 order in [M], which demands a third-order initiation process.

Thus, if

$$I = k_i[M]^3 \tag{3-12}$$

then

$$R_p = k_p(k_i/2k_t)^{1/2}[M]^{5/2} \tag{3-13}$$

Burnett and Loan (*100*) have criticized these results, because participation of solvent radicals in termination and reinitiating reactions was not considered, but the scheme of Burnett and Loan is also open to some doubt (*101*). Hiatt and Bartlett (*102*) polymerized styrene in ethyl thioglycollate solution and obtained results in support of third-order initiation. Termination by radicals derived by transfer with solvent do not appear to be important for this system or for *n*-butyl mercaptan–styrene (*103*) and carbon tetrachloride–styrene (*104*) systems. George and Onyon (*104*) show that in carbon tetrachloride solution *I* has an order in monomer of 1.64. This unexpected result is satisfactorily explained if *I* is increased by solvent, as suggested by other workers. Kinetic analysis demands that

$$I = k_i[M]^3 + k_s[M]^2[S] \tag{3-14}$$

where k_i and k_s relate to the initiation process.

Analysis of molecular-weight distribution curves of thermally produced polystyrenes has not been able to distinguish between initiation rates of second and third order in monomer concentration (*477*).

B. Mechanism of Initiation

The bulk of the evidence leads to a rejection of the original suggestion of Flory (*87*), that the initiation step involves simple bimolecular formation of a diradical, which then propagates:

$$2CH_2 = CHPh \longrightarrow \dot{C}HPh \cdot CH_2 \cdot CH_2 \cdot \dot{C}HPh \tag{3-15}$$

although ΔH for reaction (3-15) has been estimated as 20 to 30 kcal or even -10 kcal. Diradical formation from a single styrene molecule is unlikely, since it would involve about 58 kcal (*10*).

$$CH_2 = CHPh \longrightarrow \dot{C}H_2 \cdot \dot{C}HPh \tag{3-16}$$

Again, statistical calculations (*105,106*) indicate that small diradicals could not propagate to give high-molecular-weight polymer, because they would be very prone to undergo cyclization reactions. Johnson and Tobolsky (*107*) tentatively concluded, admittedly from scanty evidence, that the initiation process in the bulk reaction involved monoradicals. Russell and Tobolsky (*108*) found that the rate of consumption of diphenyl picrylhydrazyl (DPPH) in the bulk thermal reaction was much greater than the rate of initiation of polymer chains and concluded that diradicals, if formed, could have only a brief existence. Mayo (*99*), from studies of the amounts of low- and high-molecular-weight polymers formed in the styrene–bromobenzene system, thought that monoradicals were produced by the energetically feasible process

$$3CH_2{=}CHPh \longrightarrow CH_3{\cdot}\overset{\cdot}{C}HPh + CH_3{\cdot}CPh = CH{\cdot}\overset{\cdot}{C}HPh \quad (3\text{-}17)$$

Diradicals were assumed to form only low-molecular-weight compounds, mainly cyclic dimer.

Termolecular reactions in solution are rare (*109*), however, and a more reasonable suggestion for the formation of monoradicals is that initiation is a two-step process involving reversible inefficient bimolecular formation of a diradical (3-18) followed by a rapid transfer reaction (3-19):

$$2CH_2{=}CHPh \rightleftharpoons \overset{\cdot}{C}HPh{\cdot}CH_2{\cdot}CH_2{\cdot}\overset{\cdot}{C}HPh \quad (A) \qquad\qquad (3\text{-}18)$$

$$\overset{\cdot}{C}HPh{\cdot}CH_2{\cdot}CH_2{\cdot}\overset{\cdot}{C}HPh + CH_2{=}CHPh \longrightarrow CH_3{\cdot}\overset{\cdot}{C}HPh + \underset{\underset{CH_2{\cdot}CHPh}{|}}{CH{=}CHPh}$$

(A)

$$(3\text{-}19)$$

The diradical (A) would have to possess special reactivity in (3-19) for the scheme to be feasible, because the rate of transfer to monomer of polystyryl monoradicals is only about 10^{-5} the rate of propagation.

The diradical (A) could also be expected to accept a hydrogen atom or other atom from another molecule, such as ethyl thioglycollate (*102*), and donation of a chlorine atom from CCl_4 to the diradical would give a rate of initiation in accordance with Eq. (3-14).

Other workers (*110*), examining the polymerizations of 2,2-dideutero-styrene, have contested the existence of diradicals in this system and in the polymerization of styrene.

When styrene is initiated by monoradical-producing initiators, the rates of initiation of polymer chains are approximately equal to the rates of consumption of DPPH or benzoquinone, assuming a 1:1 radical/substrate stoichiometry. During the pure bulk thermal polymerization, however, rates of consumption of DPPH (*102*) and benzoquinone (*89*) are unexpectedly high. This led Hiatt and Bartlett (*102*) to suggest that DPPH and benzo-quinone could take the place of the third molecule of styrene in reaction (3-19) and accept or donate a hydrogen atom. Kern and Feuerstein (*111*) and Melville and Watson (*112*) have examined the low-molecular-weight products of the thermal polymerization of styrene in the presence of *p*-benzoquinone. Apart from hydroquinone and phenolic compounds, a product containing 2 moles of styrene to every mole of quinone was isolated, and a similar type of compound has been obtained with chloranil as inhibitor (*113*). Kern and Feuerstein (*111*) suggested a reaction of diradicals with quinone, but a one-step process such as (3-20) appears improbable:

$$(3\text{-}20)$$

The possibility that these compounds are Diels–Alder products has been reported (10,112,114). Indeed, a Diels–Alder product in equilibrium with two molecules of styrene could be formed in reaction (3-18) instead of a diradical (102). The precise mechanism of any Diels–Alder reaction still remains in doubt, however (109,115).

The thermal copolymerization of styrene and methyl methacrylate has been examined by Walling (116). By means of various known kinetic parameters, rates of initiation I were calculated from measured rates of copolymerization. A bimolecular initiation step for the individual monomers and for "cross initiation" being assumed, calculations showed preferential cross initiation, presumably due to polar effects in the transition state. Recalculations assuming third-order initiation would accentuate the effect (102). No cross initiation was observed in the styrene–diethyl fumarate system (117). Precise interpretation is difficult however, since the meaning of the value of ϕ in the usual copolymer rate equation is obscure, if the termination process is diffusion-controlled (118), and variations of chain flexibility with copolymer composition have been observed (119). The over-all activation energy for thermal polymerization increases in the series p-chlorostyrene, p-methystyrene, and styrene, corresponding to a decreasing order of conjugation between the π electrons of the vinyl and benzene ring, as revealed by analysis of Raman spectra [2(e)].

It may be noted that most cyclic peroxides (120–123), cyclic azo compounds (124), and cyclic disulfides (125), which would be expected to give diradicals on decomposition, are poor photoinitiators and thermal initiators for the polymerization of styrene and other monomers. A few efficient cyclic peroxides, such as dihydroascaridole (126) and cyclohexanone peroxide (121,126), appear to initiate by monoradicals rather than diradicals. Diradicals produced by the decay of N-nitroso-ε-caprolactam, however, successfully polymerize methyl methacrylate (127).

Bifunctional or polyfunctional initiators usually produce monoradical kinetics (128–131,483). A particularly detailed study has recently been made of the polymerization of styrene by a ferrous complex–organic dihydroperoxide (132). Excess ferrous complex produces "bifunctional" kinetics with termination by combination.

C. Molecular Weights

The effect of temperature T (°K) on degrees of polymerization $\overline{DP}$ of polymers formed by bulk thermal reaction may be predicted since, as long as the temperature is not high enough to cause significant depropagation, the following holds:

$$\overline{DP} = \frac{-d[M]/dt}{d[P]/dt} = \frac{k_p[M][R\cdot]}{k_t[R\cdot]^2 + k_{fm}[M][R\cdot]}$$

$$= \frac{[M]A_p \exp(-E_p/RT)}{(I/2)^{1/2}A_t^{1/2}\exp(-E_t/2RT) + [M]A_{fm}\exp(-E_{fm}/RT)} \quad (3\text{-}21)$$

since $[R\cdot] = (I/2k_t)^{1/2}$, and each velocity constant $k = A\exp(-E/RT)$, where A is a frequency factor and E the corresponding activation energy; k_{fm} is the velocity constant for transfer to monomer.

If transfer to monomer is the predominant termination reaction, a plot of log $\overline{DP}$ versus $1/T$ should give a straight line of slope $(E_{fm} - E_p)/2.303R$. The molecular weights of Table 3-1 are in reasonable agreement with this prediction, as has been shown by Rubens and Boyer (93), using typical values for E_{fm} and E_p.

Bamford and Dewar (94) and others (133) have also stressed the importance of termination by transfer to monomer in this system.

The process of chain transfer to solvents is dealt with in a later section.

Polystyrenes of unexpectedly high molecular weight are produced at very low conversions (134–136,462). The high-molecular-weight polymer is probably formed by a radical mechanism and has led to a re-examination of the concept of chain transfer (136). More recent experiments suggest that styrene dimer, perhaps the Diels–Alder product, is formed in the thermal polymerization. This has a large chain-transfer activity, and its production causes the observed molecular-weight decrease with increasing conversion (137).

3-5. PHOTOPOLYMERIZATION IN THE ABSENCE OF ADDED INITIATOR

Styrene polymerizes on exposure to ultraviolet light, having its main absorption band at 250 mμ (138). The mechanism of initiation unfortunately still remains in doubt. The initial absorption presumably corresponds to the promotion of an electron from the bonding to the antibonding π orbital without a change of spin (139). Since the Pauli principle does not demand spins of the electrons to remain paired in most excited states, spin inversion may occur and form a triplet excited state with a net spin angular momentum $S = 1$ (in a magnetic field separation into three energy states can occur). The electrons still couple strongly in the triplet state, but in the diradical state each electron has an orientation uncorrelated with that of the other. The distinction between the triplet and diradical state (140) will not be discussed further, however.

Haman and Eyring (141) considered that excitation to a triplet or diradical state occurred with styrene, while the formation of diradicals was assumed by Bamford and Dewar in their investigation of the direct photopolymerization (94). The objections to propagation by diradicals have been summarized in Section 3-4B. Johnson and Tobolsky (107) concluded from $R_p - \overline{DP}$ measurements that initiation occurred by monoradicals rather than diradicals. Initial diradical formation followed by a rapid transfer step to monomer or a splitting of the molecule following absorption, giving monoradicals, as shown below, may occur (87,107):

$$CH_2 = CHPh \longrightarrow CH_2 = \dot{C}H + \dot{P}h \qquad (3\text{-}22)$$

$$\longrightarrow H\cdot + \dot{C}H = \underset{\underset{Ph}{|}}{CH} \qquad (3\text{-}23)$$

Nonlinear plots of $\ln R_p$ versus $1/T$ for the low-temperature photopolymerization of styrene both in the presence and absence of added initiator have been noted (478). These results have been interpreted as due to the temperature dependence of E_i and E_t, the activation energies for initiation and termination, respectively.

Some "hot" radicals could be formed by photochemical initiation, and their effects on radical polymerization kinetics have been considered (502).

Methods of evaluation kinetic constants from studies of the photopolymerization of styrene have been developed by Burnett (142), and Bamford and Dewar (94). The results will be discussed in Section 3-12.

3-6. THERMAL AND PHOTOCHEMICAL POLYMERIZATION DUE TO ADDED INITIATOR

A wide variety of initiators successfully polymerize styrene, but only a few typical examples will be considered here. More extensive treatments of initiating systems are found elsewhere (8–12).

A. Initiating Species

1. DIACYL PEROXIDES

The properties and reaction of peroxides have been reviewed (143–145), while Cooper (146) has studied the effects of structure of seventy-four diacyl peroxides on rates of initiation of styrene polymerization at 70°C. Benzoyl peroxide, Bz_2O_2, is particularly useful for polymerizing styrene, and thermal decomposition at low concentrations proceeds by a first-order process in relatively inert solvents, initially by

$$Ph\cdot CO\cdot O\cdot O\cdot CO\cdot Ph \longrightarrow 2Ph\cdot CO\cdot O\cdot \qquad k_1 \qquad (3\text{-}24)$$

The over-all rate varies markedly with nature of solvent (146), but in the presence of styrene or other radical acceptor the order of the decomposition rate with respect to [In] is nearly unity (147,148). Activation energies for spontaneous decomposition are 29 to 34 kcal mole^{-1}, and frequency factors lie between 3×10^{13} and 6×10^{14}. At high concentrations induced decomposition of the benzoyl peroxide occurs, the effect of different solvents being more marked (149).

Investigations of the decompositions of ring-substituted benzoyl peroxides have been made (146,147,150), and some of the data have been reviewed elsewhere (10). Briefly, decomposition rates are increased by electron-donating groups such as $p-CH_3O-$, attached to the rings, owing to increased electrostatic repulsion between the two electron-attracting oxygen atoms of the $-O-O-$ bond, whereas electron-attracting substituents such as $Br-$ or $-NO_2$ decrease rates of decomposition. Thus, benzoyl peroxide itself is envisaged as

$$\underset{d+ \quad d-}{Ph \cdot \overset{\overset{\displaystyle O}{\|}}{C} \cdot O} \overset{\longrightarrow}{\underset{\longleftarrow}{}} \underset{d- \quad d+}{O \cdot \overset{\overset{\displaystyle O}{\|}}{C} \cdot Ph} \qquad (3\text{-}25)$$

Experimental data are generally correlated by Hammett plots of log (k/k_o) versus $\sigma_1 + \sigma_2$, where k_o is the velocity constant for decomposition of the unsubstituted benzoyl peroxide, k is the velocity constant for the substituted peroxide with *meta* or *para* substituents, and $\sigma_1 + \sigma_2$ represents the sum of the Hammett σ values for the substituents. The ρ value for the reaction has been estimated as -0.38 (147) or as between -0.5 and -1.0 (10). Variation in polar resonance in the transition states is not greatly important in affecting rates, though steric effects influence peroxide stability (144,145).

Recent work at 90°C, however, suggests that simple Hammett behavior does not occur and that both electrostatic repulsion at the $O-O$ bond and the stability of the radicals resulting from dissociation determine the rate of decomposition (482).

For benzoyl peroxide in styrene it has been known for some time (151,152) that both benzoyloxy and phenyl radicals initiate polymerization. Apart from reaction (3-24) one must consider

$$Ph \cdot CO \cdot O \cdot \longrightarrow Ph \cdot + CO_2 \qquad\qquad k_2 \quad (3\text{-}26)$$

$$Ph \cdot CO \cdot O \cdot + CH_2 = CHPh \longrightarrow Ph \cdot CO \cdot O \cdot CH_2 \cdot \dot{C}HPh \qquad k_3 \quad (3\text{-}27)$$

$$Ph \cdot + CH_2 = CHPh \longrightarrow Ph \cdot CH_2 \cdot \dot{C}HPh \qquad k_4 \quad (3\text{-}28)$$

In the absence of monomer or other scavenger virtually quantitative yields (153) of CO_2 are produced by the two-step processes (3-24) and (3-26), but photoreaction produces benzoyloxy and phenyl radicals simultaneously (154).

$$Ph \cdot CO \cdot O \cdot O \cdot CO \cdot Ph + h\nu \longrightarrow 2(1-y) Ph \cdot CO \cdot O \cdot + 2y Ph \cdot + 2y CO_2 \quad (3\text{-}29)$$

If the fraction of benzoyloxy radicals captured by styrene or other monomer is x, then, if all Ph· attack monomer,

$$x = \frac{k_3[\text{Ph·CO·O·}][\text{M}]}{k_3[\text{Ph·CO·O·}][\text{M}] + k_2[\text{Ph·CO·O·}]}$$

$$= \frac{\text{no. of benzoyloxy end groups in polymer}}{\text{total no. of benzoyloxy and phenyl groups in polymer}} \qquad (3\text{-}30)$$

Bevington (155) has evaluated x for styrene and other monomers by means of initiator labelled with ^{14}C only on the carboxyl carbon atoms and only in the benzene rings. The separate benzoyloxy and phenyl groups in polymer were then determined. In a third method the benzoyloxy end groups were hydrolyzed from polymers quantitatively (156,157). When a single ^{14}C-labelled initiator was used, comparison of the specific activities of polymer before and after hydrolysis enabled x to be determined (158). The quantity x increased with increase in [M] in accordance with

$$x^{-1} = 1 + k_2/k_3[\text{M}] \qquad (3\text{-}31)$$

and it also decreased with increasing temperature. Variation of x with [In] due to side reactions was small, and x could be corrected by extrapolation to zero concentration. Ayrey and Moore (159) have confirmed some of these results by a method of radioactivity, showing that at 60°C for styrene in benzene (50% vol/vol), the initiating radicals were 43% Ph· and 57% Ph·CO·O·. The work has been extended to include studies of ring-substituted benzoyl peroxides and substituted styrenes (160), and the field has been reviewed (12). Some of the data for styrene are shown in Table 3-2. The diluent used was benzene. Future work may involve the use of tritium-labelled benzoyl peroxide (500).

TABLE 3-2

Reactivity of Benzoyloxy-Type Radicals To Styrene

Radical	Temp., °C	k_2/k_3, mole liter^{-1}	Ref.
Benzoyloxy	60	0.4	155
	80	0.7	161
p-Methoxybenzoyloxy	60	0.02	162
	80	0.05	162
m-Methoxybenzoyloxy	60	0.3	163
	80	0.6	163
m-Bromobenzoyloxy	60	≥ 0.3	163
	80	≥ 0.5	163
3,5-Dibromo-4-methoxybenzoyloxy	60	≥ 0.06	163
	80	≥ 0.4	163

In all instances 100% efficiency was assumed in the tracer method, although this result has recently been questioned (482). Comparison of k_d values for various peroxides, determined by tracer and other methods, has been discussed (163). Electron-donating groups ($CH_3O—$) increase the stability with respect to further decomposition, whereas electron-accepting groups ($Br—$) decrease the stability of the corresponding radical. The energy of activation for dissociation of the benzoyloxy radical is estimated (161) as about 12 kcal mole^{-1}.

The bromine-substituted peroxides are extensively involved in induced decomposition, making the values of k_2/k_3 uncertain:

$$R\cdot + R'\cdot CO\cdot O\cdot O\cdot CO\cdot R' \longrightarrow R\cdot O\cdot CO\cdot R' + R'\cdot CO\cdot O\cdot \qquad (3\text{-}32)$$

where $R\cdot$ is a polymer radical. This is shown, for example, by the nonlinear plot of the reciprocal of the apparent chain length versus R_p for brominated peroxides. Bevington and Lewis (164) have indicated the importance of polar factors in such radical displacement reactions.

Haas (165–6) has studied the decomposition of Bz_2O_2 in polystyrene and noted the change of temperature dependence of rates at the second-order transition temperature.

Di-t-butyl peroxide is useful for initiating styrene polymerization at 80 to 130°C. Thermal and photoinitiation involve (167–169):

$$(CH_3)_3C\cdot O\cdot O\cdot C(CH_3)_3 \longrightarrow 2(CH_3)_3C\cdot O\cdot \qquad (3\text{-}33)$$

$$(CH_3)_3CO\cdot \longrightarrow CH_3\cdot + (CH_3)_2CO \qquad (3\text{-}34)$$

Tracer studies (167–168) show that t-butoxy radicals predominantly initiate polymerization except at low [M] and high temperature. At sufficiently low wavelengths some peroxide decomposes photochemically (170):

$$(CH_3)_3C\cdot O\cdot O\cdot C(CH_3)_3 + h\nu \longrightarrow 2(CH_3)_3C\cdot + O_2 \qquad (3\text{-}35)$$

Primary radicals from (3-33) can abstract hydrogen atoms from suitable solvent molecules and may form π complexes with aromatic solvents (171).

Tertiary amines increase the decomposition rates of diaroyl peroxides; the early work of Horner and Schwenk (172) has been reviewed (10). The dimethylaniline–benzoyl peroxide system has received most attention, and initiation involves formation of a reactive intermediate (173–175), which then forms benzoyloxy and phenyl radicals (176–177):

$$Ph\cdot N(CH_3)_2 + (Ph\cdot CO\cdot O)_2 \longrightarrow [Ph\cdot N(CH_3)_2\cdot O\cdot CO\cdot Ph]^+[Ph\cdot CO\cdot O]^-$$

$$\text{(I)} \qquad\qquad\qquad\qquad (3\text{-}36)$$

$$\text{(I)} \longrightarrow [Ph\cdot N(CH_3)_2]^+ + [Ph\cdot CO\cdot O]^- + Ph\cdot CO\cdot O\cdot \qquad (3\text{-}37)$$

$$Ph\cdot CO\cdot O\cdot \longrightarrow Ph\cdot + CO_2 \qquad (3\text{-}38)$$

Styrene and other monomers are polymerized by benzoyl peroxide–tertiary-amine systems, in accordance with the scheme (*178–182,489*), so that approximately:

$$R_p \propto ([Bz_2O_2][\text{tertiary amine}])^{1/2} \qquad (3\text{-}39)$$

Although most initiators decompose initially by homolytic scission, there is evidence that *t*-butyl hydroperoxide in styrene disappears by a polar reaction (*464*) and radical processes (*464,465*).

2. AZONITRILES

Azo initiators are favored for many studies because, unlike peroxides, they undergo no induced decomposition. That most widely used with styrene is 2,2′-azobisisobutyronitrile (AIBN). Its thermal decomposition in solution has been followed by N_2 evolution (*183–184*), by spectrophotometry (*185*), and by the use of radical scavengers such as iodine (*186*), oxygen (*186–187*), α,α'-diphenyl-β-picrylhydrazyl (DPPH), and ferric chloride (*189*), and found to be first order. Only small differences in rate were noted for various solvents (*9–11*), though low efficiencies are claimed in CCl_4 (*11*). The initial decomposition is

$$(CH_3)_2C(CN)\cdot N{=}N\cdot C(CH_3)_2(CN) \longrightarrow 2(CH_3)_2\dot{C}\cdot CN + N_2 \quad (3\text{-}40)$$

and the radicals produced are mesomeric with ketene imine radicals, $(CH_3)_2C{=}C{=}N\cdot$.

Tetramethylsuccinodinitrile (*186,190–192*) is the main product in solution, formed by recombination of the 2-cyano-2-propyl radicals, but smaller amounts of other materials are also formed (*193*), including dimethyl-N-(2-cyano-2-propyl) ketenimine (DKI) (*193–199*):

$$(CH_3)_2C(CN)\cdot N{=}C{=}C(CH_3)_2 \qquad \text{DKI} \qquad (3\text{-}41)$$

DKI is presumably formed when a ketene imine radical combines with a 2-cyano-2-propyl radical. It has been established that DKI can also act as an initiator of styrene polymerization (*199*). Fortunately, in studies of styrene involving AIBN no serious error is introduced into calculations that ignore the formation of DKI, provided that the conversion of AIBN does not exceed 15% (*189*). The presence of oxygen can cause $(CH_3)_2C(CN)\cdot O\cdot O\cdot$ radicals to be formed from AIBN in solution (*187*).

In aromatic solvents AIBN has a velocity constant for decomposition, k_d, best expressed (*185*) by

$$k_d = 1.58 \times 10^{15} \exp(-30{,}800/RT)\,\text{sec}^{-1} \qquad (3\text{-}42)$$

Many other aliphatic azo compounds have been studied (*10,11*), but not primarily as initiators in styrene polymerization. However, 2-cyano-2-

propylazoformamide has been used recently to polymerize styrene (*200,201*) at 100°C.

Initiation involves

$$(CH_3)_2C(CN)\cdot N=N\cdot CO\cdot NH_2 \longrightarrow (CH_3)\dot{C}(CN) + NH_2CO\cdot + N_2 \quad (3\text{-}43)$$

followed to a small extent by

$$NH_2\cdot CO\cdot \longrightarrow NH_2\cdot + CO \quad\quad\quad (3\text{-}44)$$

B. Efficiences of Initiation

If the rate of initiation I can be measured, then for an initiator initially giving two primary radicals $R_c\cdot$ it follows (see Section 3-2) that

$$I = 2k_d f[\text{In}] \quad\quad\quad (3\text{-}45)$$

Measurement of the rate of initiation due to a particular initiator in styrene may be determined by any of three methods. One is the inhibition method in which, for example, DPPH (*14*) or *p*-benzoquinone (*202*) (or retarders) are used, this method necessitating assumptions regarding the number of polymer radicals reacting with one inhibitor (or retarder) species. Another method is the molecular-weight method, which requires measurement of the rate of production of polymer molecules; in this method transfer reactions must be allowed for or must be negligible, and the mode of termination (combination for styrene) must be known. Finally, there are radioactive-tracer methods. One approach (*203*) involves a radioactive initiator and subsequent analysis of the number of initiator fragments in a given weight of polymer. This gives the kinetic chain length v and, subject to certain conditions,

$$v = R_p/I \quad\quad\quad (3\text{-}46)$$

Another technique depends on analysis for the products of low molecular weight produced from initiator by isotope dilution analysis (*204*). Reviews of the use of tracer methods in polymer chemistry have recently appeared (*160,205,206*).

The various approaches have been compared (*207*) for methyl methacrylate with AIBN, and values of I found by radioactive methods appear to give correct rates of initiation of high-molecular-weight polymer. A similar analysis has not been attempted for styrene, but some values of f for AIBN determined by radioactive methods are given in Table 3-3.

Recently ferric chloride was used as a radical scavenger for the decomposition of AIBN in dimethyl formamide in the presence or absence of styrene (*189*). A 1:1 stoichiometry between scavenger and radicals is assured, since the reaction probably is

$$R\cdot + FeCl_3 \longrightarrow R\cdot Cl + FeCl_2 \quad\quad\quad (3\text{-}47)$$

TABLE 3-3

Initiator Efficiences for AIBN–Styrene Determined by
Radioactive Methods

Temp., °C	f	Solvent	Ref.
50	0.52		208
50	0.50	Bromobenzene	208
50	0.55	Benzene, toluene, pyridine	208
50	0.51	Dioxane	208
50	0.70		209
60	0.61		204
60	0.48		210
60	0.64		211
60	0.70		212
60	0.80		209
80	0.65		490

Using ferric chloride at 60 to 78°C, the value of f is 0.73 (*189*). Determination of I for polymerization in dimethyl formamide by the ferric chloride technique has been considered in more detail by Bamford et al. (*213*). For styrene and three other monomers at 60°C the common value of f is 0.70. It was concluded that scavenging by monomer was not a competing step in determining the efficiency of initiation in normal circumstances.

With regard to peroxide initiators there is evidence of 100% efficiency in the initiation process (*155*), but this point is still controversial.

Experiments with 2-cyano-2-propylazoformamide (*200,201*) for the polymerization of styrene at 100°C have established that f is about 0.6.

Tobolsky and co-workers have recorded many rate and molecular-weight data on the polymerization of styrene at different temperatures, and analysis of the results gives values of I and f for various peroxides (*144,214–216*) and AIBN (*214–218*). Similar types of measurement have been made by other workers, especially with peroxides (*146,219,220*). A kinetic treatment of initiation with the use of mixed peroxides has also been given (*221*). In general, the dependence of R_p on $[In]^{1/2}$ for many initiators is well established, as shown in Fig. 3-2, whereas in the photopolymerization, R_p is proportional to both $[In]^{1/2}$ and (incident light intensity)$^{1/2}$ for low light intensities (*222*). Initiator exponents greater or less than 0.5, however, are sometimes observed, especially when R_p does not depend on the first power of $[M]$. Deviations of this type are discussed in later sections.

When cumene hydroperoxide is used as initiator in solution, the radicals appear to be formed by a bimolecular reaction between hydroperoxide and solvent or other species (*223*).

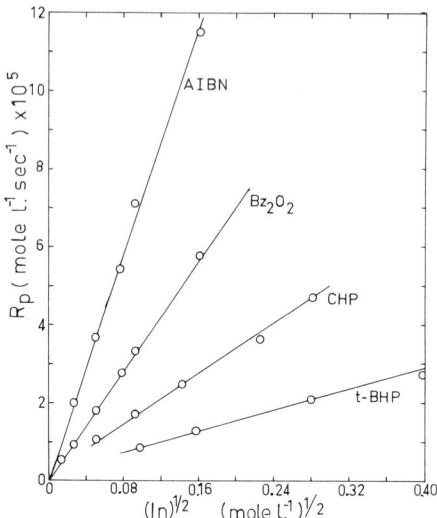

Fig. 3-2. Rates of polymerization of styrene, R_p (uncorrected for thermal rate) at 60°C versus $[In]^{1/2}$ for AIBN, Bz_2O_2, cumene hydroperoxide (CHP), and *tert*-butyl hydroperoxide (*t*-BHP). [Data from Baysal and Tobolsky (*214*).]

Values of f for AIBN have been measured in the polymerization of styrene at 60°C over a wide range of [M] with benzene as solvent (*204*). The efficiency f and rate of initiation I are almost independent of monomer concentration (*204,218*) except at low [M], as shown in Fig. 3-3. f may increase as [In] decreases, at constant [M] (*218*).

Values of R_p for styrene polymerization at temperature T (°K) with various initiators may be estimated by using the equations for I shown in Table 3-4

TABLE 3-4

Rates of Initiation I in Styrene Polymerization (*215*)

Initiator	Expression for $I/[In]$,[a] sec^{-1}
AIBN	$1.88 \times 10^{15} \exp(-30{,}700/RT)$
Benzoyl peroxide	$1.00 \times 10^{14} \exp(-29{,}400/RT)$
Lauroyl peroxide	$1.45 \times 10^{14} \exp(-28{,}900/RT)$
Bis-*p*-chlorobenzoyl peroxide	$1.74 \times 10^{13} \exp(-28{,}300/RT)$
Di-1-naphthoyl peroxide	$7.95 \times 10^{16} \exp(-31{,}500/RT)$
t-Butyl hydroperoxide	$1.15 \times 10^{11} \exp(-25{,}500/RT)$
t-Butyl perbenzoate	$8.15 \times 10^{15} \exp(-34{,}800/RT)$

[a] [In] = initiator concentration in mole liter^{-1}.

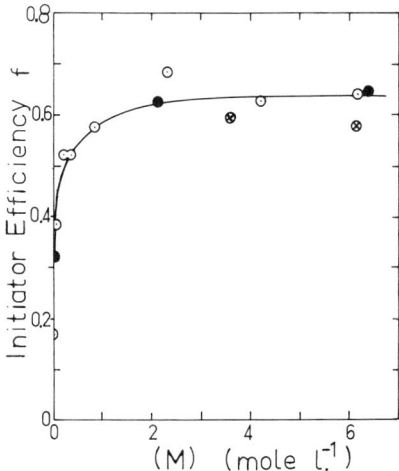

Fig. 3-3. Variation of initiator efficiency f of AIBN with styrene concentration [M] at 60°C. Benzene was used as diluent. Points ●, ⊙, and ⊗ represent results with [In] equal to 1.0, 0.5, and 0.2 g liter^{-1}, respectively (*204*).

together with equation (3-4n) and appropriate values of k_p and k_t computed from Table 3-12.

C. Dependence of R_p on [M]

From Eq. (3-4o) R_p should be proportional to [M] at constant [In], as long as f is independent of [M] and k_d, k_p, and k_t remain unaltered as [M] is varied.

Although a first-order dependence is reported in the case of some dilute-solution polymerizations with Bz_2O_2 (*225*), including polymerization in benzene (*226*), in other cases this is not so. Thus, R_p for styrene in toluene with Bz_2O_2 is alleged to follow a rate expression (*85,227*),

$$R_p = -d[\text{M}]/dt = \text{constant } [\text{M}][\text{In}]^{1/2}(K[\text{M}]/1 + K[\text{M}])^{1/2} \quad (3\text{-}48)$$

where K is a constant. This equation predicts a first-order dependence at high [M], increasing to 3/2 order in very dilute solutions. Again, Horikx and Hermans (*228*), using a flow reactor, have shown that for styrene in toluene at 80°C with Bz_2O_2 the order in monomer concentration apparently increases from 1.18 at [M] = 1.8 mole liter^{-1} to 1.36 at [M] = 0.4 mole liter^{-1}. Orders in monomer concentration greater than unity but not varying greatly with [M] have been claimed for a wide variety of solvents with AIBN by Henrici-Olivé and Olivé (*229*) over a concentration of 5 to 100% monomer and by George and Onyon for carbon tetrachloride (*230*), dimethyl formamide (*231*), and dimethyl acetamide (*231*).

To account for these observations various modifications to the simple reaction scheme have been proposed, none of which appears to be completely satisfactory (232). These alternatives will only be briefly mentioned here.

1. COMPLEX FORMATION

If a complex between initiator and monomer is formed and undergoes first-order decomposition (85,227,233),

$$In + M \rightleftharpoons complex \tag{3-49}$$

$$Complex \longrightarrow R_c \cdot \tag{3-50}$$

then Eq. (3-48) can be deduced, where K is the equilibrium constant for reaction (3-49). This theory is untenable, because widely different systems give closely similar values of K (232), just as orders in monomer for systems involving solvents of widely different dielectric constants do not vary greatly (229). Other physical measurements (226,234) show no evidence of complex formation with initiators such as benzoyl peroxide in styrene. However, there is good evidence that t-butyl hydroperoxide forms complexes with styrene (479), and a radical–monomer–solvent complex may be involved in the polymerization of methyl methacrylate with AIBN in halogenated solvents (480).

2. THE CAGE EFFECT: GEMINATE RECOMBINATION

The "cage effect" was originally suggested by Matheson (234) and has been developed and modified by Noyes (503). Kinetic considerations suggest that, if there is real competition between caged radicals and monomer, an equation of type (3-48) can be deduced. The original cage-effect theory has been criticized by Flory (8) and others (232), who argue that monomer is unlikely to influence combination except by altering rates of diffusion of radicals. The possibility that geminate recombination is influenced by the presence of solvents has been suggested (230,231).

3. TERMINATION BY PRIMARY RADICALS

A reaction order in [M] greater than unity is also a consequence of termination by primary radicals, $R_c \cdot$, which escape from their initial cages. This also results in orders in [In] of less than one half. Special limiting cases have been considered by Bamford and co-workers (235) and others (236,468). The rate constant for the reaction $R \cdot + R_c \cdot$ is about 60 times as great as that of $R_c \cdot + R_c \cdot$ in the polymerization of styrene in dimethyl formamide initiated by AIBN (235,237). Allen and Patrick (237) have examined the effects of diffusion control of primary-radical termination on R_p and $\overline{DP}$ in various polymerizations and also show that some of the kinetic assumptions of Bamford et al. (235) may be inexact. Other attempts have been made to assess the importance of primary-radical termination (238–241,463) and

Allen and Bevington (*167*) have shown by a tracer method that benzoyloxy radicals can combine with polystyryl radicals at 60°C under favorable conditions.

4. SOLVENT RETARDATION MECHANISM

This theory was developed by Burnett and Loan (*100*) and suggests that radicals of low reactivity are produced by transfer to solvent and can react with monomer to reinitiate chains or become involved in termination reactions. Data on styrene were not analyzed, however. This theory has been criticized (*11*), and various limiting possibilities of an alternative treatment have been considered by Jenkins (*101*). An initiator exponent of 0.5 to 1.0 is expected in all cases. The theory is adequate for systems showing marked retardation but not for systems such as the Bz_2O_2-initiated polymerization of styrene in toluene, in which retardation is slight.

3-7. PROPAGATION: VARIATION OF k_p AND k_{fs} WITH CHAIN LENGTH

The addition of a polystyryl radical $R{\cdot}CH_2{\cdot}\dot{C}H{\cdot}Ph$ to a molecule of styrene proceeds to give predominantly a head-to-tail, or 1,3, structure (3-51) in accordance with theoretical considerations (*8*) and limited experimental evidence (*242*):

$$R{\cdot}CH_2{\cdot}\dot{C}HPh + CH_2{=}CHPh \longrightarrow R{\cdot}CH_2{\cdot}CHPh{\cdot}CH_2{\cdot}\dot{C}HPh \qquad (3\text{-}51)$$

Occasional head-to-tail linkages will occur, however, when two polystyryl radicals terminate by combination.

When the stereochemistry of propagation is considered, the phenyl group previously at the radical end can attain an isotactic (I) or a syndiotactic (II) configuration relative to the phenyl group of the previous unit along the chain:

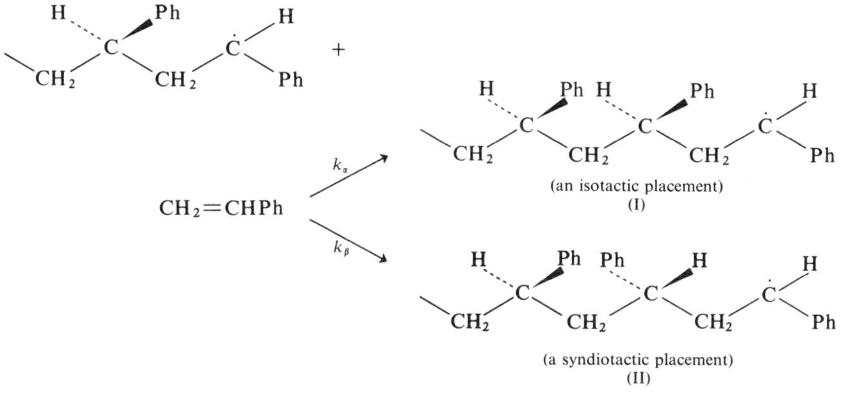

(an isotactic placement)
(I)

(a syndiotactic placement)
(II)

Repetition of such propagation steps could give completely isotactic polystyrene ($\alpha = 1$) or syndiotactic polystyrene ($\beta = 1$), whereas "atactic" polystyrenes having structures defined by the relative probabilities α and β of steps (I) and (II), respectively (*243*) can be formed. Development of these ideas in copolymer theory has been made (*244,245*). Completely random addition ($\alpha = \beta = \frac{1}{2}$), giving a "perfectly atactic" polystyrene, is unlikely because of the bulky phenyl group, and construction of models indicates that syndiotactic placements are favored. The conventional propagation velocity constant k_p is correctly expressed as

$$k_p = k_\alpha + k_\beta \qquad (3\text{-}52)$$

but the over-all kinetics of polymerization at any fixed temperature will not be affected. Consideration of steric effects indicates that the activation energy for the syndiotactic placement would be about 0.5 kcal less than that for the isotactic placement (*246,247*) since, unlike the case of other monomers (*248,249*), electrostatic effects for propagation involving styrene are negligible.

Low temperatures and polymerization in poor solvents (*250–252*) would be expected to give polystyrenes with increased syndiotactic structure by free-radical mechanisms. Unfortunately, there is a dearth of experimental data in this field, and at present heterogeneous catalyst systems (*249*) still afford the best method of controlling the stereospecificity of the propagation steps. However, Bamford and co-workers, using metal carbonyls in the presence of small amounts of organic halogen compounds, to generate free radicals (*253–262,499*), have shown that polymerization of methyl methacrylate gives polymers with increased isotacticity (*263*). No detailed results are available for polystyrenes.

Simple kinetic analyses of polymerizations usually assume that k_p is independent of the size of the polymer radical, although more general treatments have been given (*9,11*). Mayo (*264*) studied the polymerization of styrene initiated by Bz_2O_2 in the presence of high concentrations of carbon tetrachloride and showed by analysis of reaction products that the transfer constants C_s increased progressively from 6×10^{-4} for transfer involving $Cl_3C\cdot CH_2\cdot\dot{C}HPh$ to 115×10^{-4} for transfer involving $Cl_3C(CH_2CHPh)_3CH_2\dot{C}HPh$. The C_s values for larger radicals were essentially constant. Mayo suggested that the change was due to an increase in the value of the velocity constant for transfer, k_{fs},

$$R\cdot + CCl_4 \longrightarrow RCl + Cl_3C\cdot \qquad k_{fs} \qquad (3\text{-}53)$$

Robb and co-workers (*265,266*), however, studying the photochemically initiated polymerization of styrene with bromotrichloromethane, concluded that the reactivity of the Cl_3C-styryl radicals to both CCl_3Br and styrene monomer (both k_{fs} and k_p) and the values of C_s increase with increasing size, reaching an asymptotic limit for the Cl_3C-pentastyryl radical, but not for the Cl_3C-tristyryl radical, for which k_{fs} and k_p are reduced compared with the adjacent neighbors (266). Under these conditions termination reactivity seemed relatively unaffected by radical size. A more recent analysis (484) of the oligomerization kinetics of styrene in carbon tetrachloride initiated by AIBN led to the tentative suggestion that k_{fs} increased from almost zero to $\overline{DP} \approx 5$ and gradually increased thereafter with increasing $\overline{DP}$. For transfer with carbon tetrachloride involving larger polystyryl radicals, however, the observed increase of C_s with $\overline{DP}$ was attributed to preferential solvation by solvent at the reaction site (488). Other evidence of velocity-constant variation with length in the low-molecular-weight region has been observed with other monomers (267–269). Secondary isotope effects on the propagation step have been studied with styrenes containing deuterium or tritium atoms (497).

Although copolymerization will not be discussed here, a brief discussion of polar effects occurring in copolymerization, propagation, and chain transfer will be presented in Section 3-10B.

3-8. TERMINATION MECHANISMS

Most of the evidence to date suggests that the termination reaction between two polystyryl radicals is an exclusive combination process for temperatures up to 80°C:

$$\sim CH_2 \cdot \dot{C}HPh + \dot{C}HPh \cdot CH_2 \sim \longrightarrow \sim CH_2 \cdot CHPh \cdot CHPh \cdot CH_2 \sim \quad (3\text{-}54)$$

Most experimental evidence has involved the use of the radioactive initiator ^{14}C–AIBN (159,210,270–272,490) and the determination of the number of initiator fragments per polymer molecule. The presence of two initiator fragments per polymer molecule indicated that exclusive combination occurred. Cross termination in styrene–methyl methacrylate (210) and styrene–p-chlorostyrene (490) also involves combination, but the styrene–p-methoxystyrene system involves a significant amount of disproportionation (490). Emulsion polymerization of styrene initiated by ^{35}S–persulphate involves exclusive combination, though the results are more difficult to analyze (273–275).

Bamford and Jenkins (276) have developed another method of distinguishing between combination and disproportionation by preparing polymers with substituted azo nitriles such as γ,γ'-azobis(γ-cyanovaleric acid),

$$CH_3 \cdot C(CN)(CH_2CH_2COOH) \cdot N{=}N \cdot C(CN)(CH_2CH_2COOH) \cdot CH_3$$

δ,δ'-azobis(δ-cyano-n-pentanol) as initiator. Polystyrenes then contain two COOH or two OH end groups per molecule, and coupling of such polymer molecules by means of difunctional reagents produces a large increase in molecular weight. This increase in molecular weight was observed by the

viscosity technique. Comparable effects would not occur if disproportionation were the predominant termination process. Detailed analysis of the
coupling reaction has been made (277,278), and the method is suitable for
the preparation of block copolymers (278).

Palit and Saha (279) have used a dye test to detect the nature of end groups
in polystyrenes produced by solution polymerization and conclude that
combination of polystyryl radicals is predominant. Some of the evidence
obtained by analysis of molecular-weight distributions of polystyrenes
confirms these findings (280), but the results of Breitenbach and others (491)
indicate that the disproportionation reaction occurs to a significant extent
and increases in importance with increase of temperature.

Other reactions that remove polymer radicals, such as various transfer
reactions and primary-radical termination, are discussed elsewhere in this
chapter.

3-9. DIFFUSION CONTROL OF TERMINATION AND PROPAGATION

The termination reaction in the polymerization of methyl methacrylate
appears to be diffusion-controlled, from the beginning of the polymerization, over a wide temperature range (281–283), and k_t likewise depends on
diffusion for other monomers, including other methacrylates (284). The
termination process has been considered to involve diffusion together of
the radicals, followed by segmental rearrangement, so that the reactive radical
ends are correctly oriented and finally react (281). Hayden and Melville (258),
extending previous work (286), have shown that the propagation step for
methyl methacrylate photopolymerization also becomes diffusion-controlled
at conversions greater than 40%, while the termination process tends
progressively to become first order, and the intensity exponent after an initial
drop from about 0.5 eventually approaches unity. Burnett and Duncan (287)
have interpreted the polymerization of several methacrylates to high conversions and explained the "gel effect" in terms of occlusion of growing
radicals. Some of the kinetic effects at high conversion have also been
interpreted on the basis of increasing geminate chain recombination (288,289).

The termination reaction for styrene would likewise be expected to be
diffusion-controlled (237) from the start of the polymerization. Matheson
and co-workers (14) have examined the photosensitized polymerization of
styrene, and at 50°C values of k_p/k_t were obtained as a function of percentage
conversion. These values are shown in Table 3-5. If k_p and the rate of initiation can be assumed constant, then k_t falls progressively as the percentage
conversion increases. The initiator used in these experiments was 2-azobis-
propane.

The gel effect with styrene is real though small (97,98), and calculations
made by Vaughan (290), although open to some criticism (237), suggest that

TABLE 3-5

k_p/k_t as a Function of Percentage Conversion in Styrene Polymerization at 50°C *(14)*

Conversion, %	Rate, %/hr	Radical lifetime τ, sec[a]	Rel. value k_p/k_t
0.0	0.298	2.29	1.0
32.7	0.350	1.80	1.4
36.3	0.382	9.10	8.0
39.5	0.392	13.90	13.2
43.8	0.434	18.80	21.3

[a] The polystyrene radical lifetime τ is defined in Eqs. (3-106) and (3-107).

termination, propagation, and transfer to monomer may become diffusion-controlled during the bulk thermal polymerization of styrene at 125°C. The decrease in k_t for styrene at 30°C on increase of pressure may also be explained as due to the increased viscosity of the reaction medium *(291)*. A review of addition polymerization at high pressures is given elsewhere *(292)*.

The Bz_2O_2-initiated polymerization of styrene in the presence of aliphatic alcohols that may precipitate polymer and polymeric radicals has been studied *(459)*. Unusually high values of R_p were noted at low initial [M] in these mixtures. This effect and the accompanying increased $\overline{DP}$ values are explained by the decrease in k_t as polymer radicals precipitate and become occluded. Chapiro *(460)* used gamma radiation to polymerize the monomer in a variety of alcohols. Both monomer and the additive give initiating radicals, and detailed analysis of the results is thus complicated. However, the unusual dependence of R_p on [M] again suggests that k_t depends markedly on the nature of the environment.

Tobolsky, O'Driscoll, and co-workers *(293–295)* suggested that at a high initiator concentration and a temperature of 90°C or above complete conversion of styrene was not attained, owing to depletion of initiator. No complicating features due to the gel effect were encountered. This phenomenon is termed "dead-end polymerization"; and theoretical and experimental studies of it, involving styrene, have been made *(293–296,498)*. At temperatures of about 70°C dead-end kinetics did not apply, and it was suggested that the termination reaction becomes diffusion-controlled *(249)*.

3-10. CHAIN TRANSFER

A. To Monomer

Transfer to monomer in the polymerization of styrene probably proceeds by a hydrogen atom transfer from radical to monomer, as follows,

$$RCH_2 \cdot \dot{C}HPh + CH_2 = CHPh \longrightarrow R \cdot CH_2 = CHPh + CH_3 \cdot \dot{C}HPh \qquad k_{fm}$$

$$(3\text{-}55a)$$

although an alternative hydrogen atom transfer process has also been proposed:

$$R \cdot CH_2 \cdot \dot{C}HPh + CH_2 = CHPh \longrightarrow R \cdot CH_2 \cdot CH_2 Ph + CH_2 = \dot{C}Ph \quad (3\text{-}55b)$$

Values of k_{fm} and corresponding activation energies are shown in Table 3-12. The transfer constant to monomer will be represented by $C_m (= k_{fm}/k_p)$.

B. To Solvents

1. METHODS OF DETERMINING C_S

Constants of transfer to solvents, $C_S (= k_{fs}/k_p)$. are generally deduced from measurements of degrees of polymerization, $\overline{DP}$, of polymers prepared in solution at known $[S]/[M]$ ratios and equation (3-56) given below. Experimental precautions necessary if correct C_S values are to be obtained have been reviewed (11). In the absence of complicating features, for the polymerization of styrene with initiation rate I:

$$1/\overline{DP} = \{(Ik_t)^{1/2}/\sqrt{2}k_p[M]\} + C_M + C_S([S]/[M]) \quad (3\text{-}56)$$

For thermal polymerizations in the presence of a transfer agent, if the rate of initiation I is second order in $[M]$, the first two terms on the right-hand side of Eq. (3-56) are constant, and

$$1/\overline{DP} = (1/\overline{DP_0}) + C_S([S]/[M]) \quad (3\text{-}57)$$

This equation is called Mayo's equation (297), and C_S is again derived by plotting $1/\overline{DP}$ versus $[S]/[M]$.

The exact nature of the dependence of I upon $[M]$, however, has negligible influence on the value of C_S derived from a Mayo plot, if the value of C_S is large enough to make the first term on the right-hand side of (3-57) very small compared with the second term. When $\overline{DP}$ values are low, loss of low-molecular-weight material during polymer isolation may markedly affect the derived values of $\overline{DP}$ and, to a lesser extent, values of R_p (104). Typical results of Mayo plots for some aromatic solvents and n-heptane are shown in Fig. 3-4.

For polymerizations in the presence of added initiator

$$I = 2k_d f[In] \quad (3\text{-}58)$$

for AIBN and similar initiators giving $2R_c \cdot$ radicals. The constant C_S may be determined by plotting $1/\overline{DP}$ against $[S]/[M]$, maintaining $[In]^{1/2}/[M]$ constant.

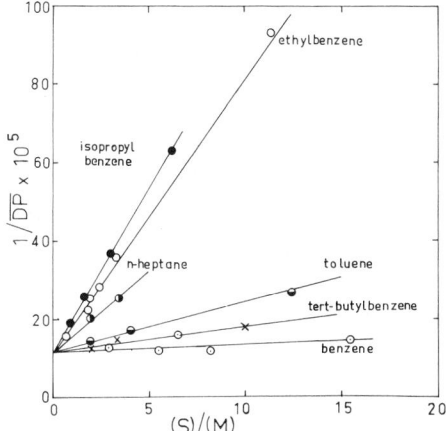

Fig. 3-4. $1/\overline{\rm DP}$ versus [S]/[M] for the thermal polymerization of styrene at 60°C. No added initiator. [Data from Gregg and Mayo (*304*).]

Another method of determining transfer constants of solvents with fairly high values of C_S depends on measuring rates of consumption of solvent and monomer and application of the equation

$$\frac{-d[\mathrm{M}]/dt}{-d[\mathrm{S}]/dt} = 1 + \frac{[\mathrm{M}]}{C_S[\mathrm{S}]} \tag{3-59}$$

Particular care has to be taken in calculations of $\overline{\rm DP}$ values from intrinsic viscosities [η] of polymer samples prepared by polymerization in solution. However, equations governing the molecular-weight distribution resulting from the simultaneous occurrence of chain transfer and combination of radicals, as in styrene polymerization, and a method of calculating $\overline{\rm DP}$ values from [η] of polymer samples having this distribution have been given (*11,298*). An alternative method of calculating $\overline{\rm DP}$ from [η] and over-all rates of polymerization R_p has been suggested and applied to the styrene system (*299*).

When transfer is accompanied by retardation, the molecular-weight method may give erroneous results, unless due account is taken of the various types of termination reaction occurring (*300*).

Tracer techniques involving isotopically labelled transfer agents have been used to a limited extent in the past (*301,302*), but recent interest has been shown by Bevington and co-workers, and typical procedures have been reviewed (*12,303*).

2. RESULTS: POLAR EFFECTS IN PROPAGATION AND TRANSFER REACTIONS

A considerable number of C_S values for a wide variety of solvents has now been accumulated for polystyryl radicals, particularly by Gregg and Mayo (304–306) and others (300–467). Many transfer reactions proceed by hydrogen atom abstraction:

$$R \cdot + R'H \longrightarrow RH + R' \cdot \qquad (3\text{-}60)$$

The results of Gregg and Mayo (304) with toluene, ethylbenzene, and iso-propylbenzene are usually interpreted as involving breaking of the relatively weak benzyl-hydrogen bond,

$$R \cdot + Ph \cdot CHR_1R_2 \longrightarrow RH + Ph \cdot \dot{C}R_1R_2 \qquad (3\text{-}61)$$

since transfer constants for these reagents are much higher than those for t-butylbenzene. Hydrogen atoms in alicyclic hydrocarbons give C_S values covering a wide range. Diphenylmethane, triphenylmethane, fluorene, and pentaphenylethane have increasing values of C_S owing to increasing resonance stabilization of the radical formed by the transfer reaction. A plot of the logarithm of the frequency factor, $\ln A_f$ versus the corresponding activation energy E_f for the hydrocarbons in Table 3-6 gives a straight-line (304), but this relationship does not hold for different related sets of transfer agents. The C_S values in Table 3-6 for hydrocarbons and halogenated compounds may require minor correction because of application of the Mark–Houwink equation without consideration of molecular-weight distributions.

Bevington and Troth (307) have established, using deuterated triphenylmethane with vinyl acetate, that the transfer reaction is one of hydrogen abstraction:

$$R \cdot + C(Ph)_3H \longrightarrow RH + \dot{C}(Ph)_3 \qquad (3\text{-}62)$$

Anomalous results were obtained from styrene and triphenylmethane with tritium-labelled benzene rings, possibly because of the presence of peroxide impurities (308). The true value of C_S at 80°C for styrene–triphenylmethane was 60×10^{-5}.

Care must be taken in interpretation of the results involving aromatic compounds. Thus, both vinyl acetate (309) and methyl methacrylate (310) on transferring to benzene incorporate benzene molecules in the chain, presumably by a process of copolymerization:

$$(3\text{-}63)$$

It is claimed that polystyrenes formed by polymerization in chlorobenzene solution contain no chlorine (311,312), and similar effects have been established for bromobenzene (99) and for polymethyl methacrylates formed in

TABLE 3-6

Transfer Constants of Hydrocarbons and Halogenated Compounds in
Styrene Polymerization

Transfer agent	$C_S \times 10^5$		$E_{fs} - E_p$, kcal mole^{-1}	Ref.
	60°C	100°C		
Hydrocarbons				
Toluene	1.25	6.5	10.1	*304*
Ethylbenzene	6.7	16.2	5.5	*304*
Isopropylbenzene	8.2	20	5.5	*304*
t-Butylbenzene	0.6	5.5	13.7	*304*
Benzene	0.18	1.84	14.8	*304*
Cyclohexane	0.24	1.6	13.4	*304*
Decalin	4			*304*
Diphenylmethane	23	42	3.7	*304*
Triphenylmethane	35	80	5.1	*304*
Fluorene	750	1,240	3.1	*304*
Pentaphenylethane	200,000			*304*
Halogenated Compounds				
n-Butyl chloride	0.4	3.7	14	*306*
n-Butyl bromide	0.6	3.5	11	*306*
n-Butyl iodide	18.5	55	7	*306*
Methylene chloride	1.5			*306*
Ethylene dichloride	3.2		15	*319*
Ethylene dibromide		66	10	*319*
Tetrachloroethane		180		*319*
Chloroform	5			*306*
Carbon tetrachloride	920	1,810	5	*305*
Carbon tetrachloride	1,350 (mean)			*104,230*
Carbon tetrabromide	136,000	235,000	3	*306*
Benzyl chloride	15.6			*306*
Benzal chloride	500			*306*
Benzotrichloride	575			*306*

the presence of labelled bromobenzene (*313*). Mayo (*99*) suggests two
possibilities for chain transfer without incorporation of solvent fragments
into polymer:

$$(3-64)$$

In the first step toward forming (A) or (B) the hydrogen atom or substituted benzyl radical is complexed with bromobenzene or forms a bond with a carbon atom in the ring. In the second step bromobenzene is regenerated, and the net effect may be that of transfer to monomer. Such processes may lead to discrepancies between analytic and molecular-weight methods of determining C_S values.

The site of radical attack may be established by the isotope effect, and with the use of deuterium it has been established that polystyryl radicals attack 2-propanol by removal of the secondary hydrogen atom but 2-methyl-2-propanol by removal of the hydroxyl hydrogen (314).

Table 3-6 also lists some data for halogenated compounds. Alkyl chlorides and bromides have values of C_S similar to that for cyclohexane, which may mean that a hydrogen and not a halogen atom is removed by the transfer reaction. The greater transfer constants for compounds containing more than one halogen atom may be due to the increased reactivity of the hydrogen atoms present (99). Since alkyl radicals abstract hydrogen from $CHCl_3$ to produce a trichloromethyl radical (315–317), the transfer reaction with a polymer radical $R\cdot$ is expected to be

$$R\cdot + CHCl_3 \longrightarrow RH + Cl_3C\cdot \qquad (3\text{-}65)$$

Carbon tetrachloride and tetrabromide are very reactive transfer agents, and polystyrene molecules formed in the presence of CCl_4 contain four chlorine atoms per molecule (305,318), the transfer reaction being

$$R\cdot + CCl_4 \longrightarrow R\cdot Cl + Cl_3C\cdot \qquad (3\text{-}66)$$

Now, Walling and others (320–323) have suggested that transition states in addition and transfer reactions involving free radicals may be stabilized by contributions from polar structures, and the possibility of correlating transfer constants for different systems by the Alfrey–Price Q–e scheme (324) has been attempted (325–328). For example, the value of C_S for styrene and carbon tetrachloride is at first sight unexpectedly higher than that for the same solvent with methyl methacrylate, methyl acrylate, and acrylonitrile. However, the "donor" polystyryl radicals ($e = -0.8$), unlike the "acceptor" polymethyl methacrylate radicals ($e = +0.4$), are able to make contributions to the transition state with the electron acceptor (electrophilic) CCl_4 and increase the velocity constant for the transfer step:

$$\sim CH_2\cdot \overset{}{\underset{Ph}{CH}} + Cl{-}CCl_3 \longleftrightarrow \sim CH_2\cdot \overset{+}{\underset{Ph}{CH}} \ldots \overset{}{Cl} \ldots \overset{-}{CCl_3} \qquad (3\text{-}67)$$

If Q_{tr} and e_{tr} define the general reactivity and polarity of the transfer agent, respectively, and Q and e are the corresponding values for the monomer (*e* is taken as the same for monomer and derived polymer radical), then (*326*)

$$C_S = k_{fs}/k_p = (Q_{tr}/Q)\exp[-e(e_{tr} - e)] \qquad (3\text{-}68)$$

Most amines have transfer constants similar to those of hydrocarbons for styrene polymerization (*306*). Tertiary amines are thought to be involved in abstraction of a hydrogen atom attached to an α carbon atom in the amine molecule (*329*):

$$R\cdot + \overset{\diagdown}{\underset{\diagup}{C}}H - N\overset{\diagup}{\diagdown} \longrightarrow RH + \overset{\diagdown}{\underset{\diagup}{\dot{C}}} - N\overset{\diagup}{\diagdown} \qquad (3\text{-}69)$$

Mayo plots were still obtained, even in the presence of retardation, and from studies with other monomers it was deduced that electron-acceptor polymer radicals from acrylonitrile and methyl methacrylate tend to stabilize the transition state with the electron-donating base. Electron-donating polystyryl radicals do not make great contributions to these polar structures.

Diphenylamine has been shown, by labelling of the benzene rings with tritium, to be involved in the transfer reaction (*330*):

$$R\cdot + (Ph)_2NH \longrightarrow RH + (Ph)_2N\cdot \qquad (3\text{-}70)$$

The possibility that the diphenyl nitrogen radicals disproportionate with polymer radicals has been considered.

Thiols have relatively high transfer constants and are thus used as "short-stops" in industrial reactions, such as the emulsion copolymerization of styrene and butadiene. The transfer reaction involves hydrogen abstraction from the HS group (*273,331*). The thiyl radical, like the peroxy radical, is electrophilic, and the transition state for reaction of a polystyryl radical with a thiol would involve contributions from (*301*)

$$\overset{H}{\underset{Ph}{\sim CH_2\cdot\overset{|}{C}\cdot}} + H - SR' \longleftrightarrow \overset{H}{\underset{Ph}{\sim CH_2\cdot\overset{|}{C}+}} \ldots \dot{H} \ldots \bar{S}R' \qquad (3\text{-}71)$$

Radical displacement on disulfides has been well studied, and the field has been recently reviewed (*332*). The transfer reaction involves predominantly

$$R\cdot + R'\cdot S\cdot S\cdot R'' \longrightarrow R\cdot S\cdot R' + R''\cdot S\cdot \qquad (3\text{-}72)$$

in spite of the fact that hydrogen atoms α to a sulfur atom have a reactivity similar to benzylic hydrogen atoms [*224(a)*].

The constant for transfer of polystyryl radicals to Bz_2S_2 at 60°C is 5 times less than that to Bz_2O_2, owing to the $-O-O-$ bond being weaker than the $-S-S-$ [*224(b)*]. The rate of attack decreases as the sulfur atom is more hindered [224(c)], in agreement with a backside Walden inversion mode of attack on sulfur. The analogy between the S_N2 reaction at carbon and the bimolecular displacement reaction by radicals, S_H2, is striking [224(a)].

Some values of transfer constants with thiols and disulfides are shown in Tables 3-7 and 3-8. A larger collection is recorded elsewhere (332). In support of mechanism (3-72) it has been shown that only two sulfur atoms become incorporated in polymer chains when involved in transfer with aliphatic (333) or aryl (334) disulfides. Furthermore, cyclic disulfides become copolymerized with styrene (333) and vinyl acetate (335).

Phosphines are very active transfer agents in styrene polymerization and have been studied by Pellon (327) and Perry (341). For a monosubstituted phosphine the reaction is

$$R\cdot + R'PH_2 \longrightarrow RH + R'\dot{P}H \tag{3-73}$$

Comparison of e_{tr} values in Table 3-8 shows that phosphines are less electrophilic than thiols and are more sensitive to the nature of the substituent (327). The lower polar effects with phosphines are probably associated with the lower electronegativity of the phosphorus atom (2.1) than of the sulfur atom (2.5) (342).

TABLE 3-7

Transfer Constants of Thiols and Disulfides in Styrene Polymerization
(cf. also Table 3-8)

Transfer agent	Temp., °C	C_S	Ref.
Thiolbenzoic acid	99	>6	338
Thiolacetic acid	99	>15	338
Thiophenol	99	0.08	338[a]
Benzyl mercaptan	99	25	338
n-Octyl thiol	50	19	337
Methyl disulfide	60	0.0094	339
Ethyl disulfide	60	0.005	338
Propyl disulfide	60	0:0023	339
n-Butyl disulfide	60	0.0023	339
t-Butyl disulfide	60	0.00014	339
Phenyl disulfide	50	0.06	340,334
Benzyl disulfide	50	0.03	334
Benzoyl disulfide	50	<0.005	340
2-Naphthyl disulfide	50	0.19	334

[a] Other values for thiophenol at 60°C are very high (336).

TABLE 3-8

Transfer Reactivity of Thiols and Phosphines at 60°C (327)

Transfer agent	C_S	Q_{tr}	e_{tr}
Phenyl phosphine	44	13	0.69
2-Cyanoethyl phosphine	5.0	1.3	0.92
Bis(2-cyanoethyl) phosphine	5.0	2.4	1.0
Octyl phosphine	3.6	1.6	0.22
Carboethyoxymethyl thiol	58	1.69	3.62
n-Butyl thiol	22	1.27	2.77
t-Butyl thiol	3.6	0.29	2.35

Similar types of calculation have been made for transfer to benzaldehyde and p-chlorobenzaldehyde (328).

By a study of deuterium isotope effects for phenols in the polymerization of styrene it has been established that transfer involves hydrogen abstraction (343):

$$R\cdot + PhOH \longrightarrow RH + PhO\cdot \qquad (3\text{-}74)$$

Phenols with C_S values less than 8×10^{-3} do not retard styrene polymerization markedly, but phenols with C_S greater than this value, and especially those with C_S of 10^{-2} to 10^{-1}, give marked retardation (344).

Bamford et al. (345) have devised a different treatment of the polar effects observed in propagation and transfer reactions. For a given polymer radical–substrate reaction with a velocity constant $k_s \, (= k_{fs}$ for transfer to solvent and $= k_p$ for homopolymerization propagations)

$$\log k_s = \log k_T + \alpha\sigma + \beta \qquad (3\text{-}75)$$

where k_T is the velocity constant for the transfer reaction between the polymer radical $PCH_2\dot{C}XY$ and toluene at 60°C, which defines the general (nonpolar) reactivity of the radical:

$$PCH_2\dot{C}XY + PhCH_3 \longrightarrow PCH_2CHXY + Ph\dot{C}H_2 \qquad (3\text{-}76)$$

The polymer radical is regarded as a substituted ethyl radical, and polar contributions to the transition state made by this radical are approximately measured by the sum of the Hammett p substituent constants for X and Y in certain simple cases, giving the value σ.

The tendency of the substrate, relative to toluene, to be involved in polar contributions to the transition state is measured by α ($\alpha = 0$ for toluene and hydrocarbons). Positive values of α are for tertiary amines and N,N-dimethyl formamide (both transfer reactions) and p-methoxystyrene (addition). In these cases there is electron donation from the substrate to the polymer radical $PCH_2\dot{C}XY$ in the transition state. Negative values of α are given by ferric chloride, mercaptans, carbon tetrachloride (all types of transfer reactions) and monomers such as acrylonitrile (addition), and this signifies that the substrate is an electron acceptor.

In Eq. (3-75) β is a measure of the general reactivity of the substrate in the absence of polar effects. Experimental evidence of the justification of Eq. (3-75) has been compiled (345,346), and values of α and β for various transfer agents and many vinyl monomers (347) have been published.

For the polymerization of a single monomer there is a relation between σ for the polymer radical and α for the conjugate monomer (346),

$$\alpha = -5.3\sigma \tag{3-77}$$

and values of σ for polymer radicals may be calculated from this relationship, but appreciable errors, as in the case of vinyl acetate, are sometimes observed. The monomer values of α may be obtained from experimentally determined reactivity ratios (348).

Values of α and β for a transfer agent can be deduced from the transfer constants for two polymer radicals, if k_T and σ for these radicals are already known. A few typical parameters applicable at 60°C are shown in Table 3-9.

There is considerable similarity between the scheme described above and the Q–e scheme (347,349). To obtain complete similarity it would be necessary, however, to choose $e = 0$ for styrene instead of the presently accepted $e = -0.8$. The precise value of e for styrene is still a controversial matter (350,351), though Price (352) has recently presented evidence in support of the assignment of $e = -0.8$ for styrene.

The effect of pressure on chain-transfer constants has been investigated (353,354,485). Thus, the value of C_S for triethylamine decreases with increasing pressure from 75×10^{-5} at 1 atm (355), to 14×10^{-5} at 4400 atm (354) with AIBN as initiator at 50°C. Deviations from a first-order dependence of rate on $[M]$ were observed at high pressures. Propagation and transfer constants, both designated k in Eq. (3-78), increase with increasing pressure (292), since the transition-state volume change ΔV^* is negative for both propagation and transfer reactions:

$$(d \log k)/dP = -\Delta V^*/RT \tag{3-78}$$

Walling and Pellon (353), however, found that the value of C_S for carbon tetrachloride was reduced by only about 15% on an increase in pressure to 4000 atm, so that for this reaction k_{f_S} and k_p must be increased to nearly the same extent. Thus, ΔV^* for transfer to CCl_4 must be greater than ΔV^* for transfer to $(C_2H_5)_3N$. The transition state for the radical–CCl_4 reaction

TABLE 3-9

Reactivity Parameters

Substrate	α	β	Polymer radical σ^a
Ferric chloride[b]	-5.65	7.4	
N-Butyl mercaptan	-4.8	6.05	
Carbon tetrabromide	-4.3	5.25	
Chloroform	-1.4	0.9	
Benzene	0	-0.82	
Toluene	(0)	(0.00)	
t-Butylbenzene	0	0.38	
Ethylbenzene	0	0.62	
Isopropylbenzene	0	0.75	
N,N-Dimethyl formamide	1.0	-0.2	
Triethylamine	2.4	1.8	
Styrene	0	4.85	-0.01
Methyl methacrylate	-1.5	4.90	0.28
Vinyl acetate	0	3.00	0.31
Acrylonitrile	-3	5.30	0.66

[a] Values of σ determined from experimental data and not calculated from Eq. (3-77).
[b] Solution in N,N-dimethyl formamide.

may therefore be more polar and more solvated than for the radical–$(C_2H_5)_3N$ transfer reaction.

C. To Polymer

The type of transfer to polymer usually postulated during the polymerization of styrene involves growing polymer radicals R· and dead polymer:

$$R\cdot + P\cdot CH_2\cdot \underset{\underset{Ph}{|}}{CH}\cdot P \xrightarrow{k_{pP}} RH + P\cdot CH_2\cdot \underset{\underset{Ph}{|}}{\dot{C}}\cdot P \qquad (3\text{-}79)(a)$$

The new radical may add monomer to form a branched molecule. Branching will rapidly become more important as the extent of conversion of monomer increases.

The branching density ρ, which is the average number of branches in polymer molecules per monomer unit in the chain, is given by (8,501)

$$\rho = -C_{poly}[1 + (1/\alpha)\ln(1-\alpha)] \qquad (3\text{-}79)(b)$$

where α is the fractional extent of conversion of monomer to polymer and C_{poly} is the constant of transfer to polymer, equal to k_{pP}/k_p.

The highly resonance-stabilized polystyryl radicals do not readily form branch polymers, in contrast to the more reactive polyvinyl acetate radicals, for example. Viscosity measurements of dilute polystyrene solutions reveal little branching (356,357), whereas combined light-scattering and viscosity measurements (358) show no differences between ordinary polystyrenes and polymers from α and β deuterostyrenes prepared similarly. Meyerhoff and Cantow (359) have shown that in solution there are differences between isotactic and normal atactic polystyrenes. In their thermal atactic polymer, prepared to 80% conversion, there was one branch for every 4×10^3 to 10×10^3 monomer units for molecular weights 10^5 to 10^6.

By means of ^{14}C-labelled styrene and unlabelled polystyrene the radioactive branches on inactive backbone polymer have been determined (360). The transfer constant C_{poly} was about 11×10^{-4} at 129°C, thus being slightly less than C_S for the model compound ethylbenzene. The activation energy for transfer to polymer was estimated as $7 \, kcal \, mole^{-1}$, but this value is probably too small.

Using polystyrene of very low molecular weight (oligomer) as a transfer agent and later separating oligomer from the high-molecular-weight polymer formed during the polymerization, Morton and Piirma (361) found no evidence of transfer to polymer even at 130°C. C_{poly} thus appeared to be much less than 10^{-4}. Other polymer-radical–polymer systems have been examined by the same method (361,362). Transfer to end groups of oligomers was not apparent. However, Schulz and co-workers (363,300) found C_{poly} equal to 2×10^{-4} at 50°C. The latter value, from equation (3-79b), would lead to only one branch in about 10^5 monomer units incorporated in polymer chains, for 10% conversion. Polymer samples used for determining C_{poly} must be carefully chosen, because polymer end groups (329) or groups pendant from the backbone (364), have reactivities similar to those of small molecules, and transfer to these groups may occur preferentially.

The possibility that initiator radicals $R_c\cdot$ may produce branching in polystyrene by a reaction similar to (3-79a) is usually discounted (365) because of the small value of $[R_c\cdot]$ compared with that of $[R\cdot]$. Henrici-Olivé and Olivé (272,366), however, have found that at conversions greater than 5% there are slightly more than two initiator fragments per polymer molecule and that the number increases with increasing conversion. This cannot be explained by the "self-branching" mechanism (3-79a), and transfer of $R_c\cdot$ with dead polymer is postulated. However, the ratio of k_{tr}, the velocity constant for the $R_c\cdot$–polymer reaction, to k_i, the velocity constant for addition of $R_c\cdot$ to M, has the unexpectedly high value of about 0.2 at 50°C. A more acceptable explanation involving copolymerization with ^{14}C–methacrylonitrile (a decomposition product of AIBN) has been made (206). For polystyrene radicals statistical calculations indicate that branching by a "back-biting" mechanism could produce branch points most likely 6 to 30 carbon atoms from the polymer end at low conversions (367). The activation energy for the branching reaction is greater than that of the growth reaction, indicating that low-temperature polymerization should favor the production of linear polystyrenes. Such effects have been noted in other systems (12).

Polystyrenes have been brominated photochemically with bromine atoms preferentially attached to the tertiary carbon atoms. This brominated polymer has been used as a photoinitiator for the polymerization of styrene–β-^{14}C, gelation being suppressed by the addition of carbon tetrachloride (368,369). After separation of the branched polymer the weight percentage of branches was determined by measurements of the radioactive content of the material, while the number of branches was calculated from bromine contents of linear (initial) and branched (final) polystyrene determined by neutron activation. Light-scattering studies of such polymers have also been made (370).

D. To Initiator

Transfer to initiator, or induced decomposition, has already been mentioned in Section 3-6-A-1. For aroyl peroxides the reaction probably involves attack of the polymer radical on one of the peroxide oxygen atoms, although other possibilities exist (481).

$$\text{R} \cdot + (\text{R}'\text{COO})_2 \longrightarrow \text{ROCOR}' + \text{R}'\text{COO} \cdot \qquad k_{f\text{In}} \qquad (3\text{-}80)$$

Polar contributions to the transition state are important in determining the rate of this reaction. Thus, for bis(4-methoxy-3,5-dibromobenzoyl) peroxide values of $\alpha = -7.57$ and $\beta = 4.96$ were obtained (12), indicating the importance of (R^+)–$(\text{peroxide})^-$ structures.

The molecular-weight method of studying transfer to initiator involves a study of the relationship between $1/\overline{\text{DP}}$ and $[\text{In}]^{1/2}$ or R_p, for polymerizations produced in the presence of varying $[\text{In}]$. Thus, in the absence of solvent, for an initiator giving two $R_c \cdot$ radicals,

$$1/\overline{\text{DP}} = \{k_t R_p/(k_p[\text{M}])^2\} + C_M + C_{\text{In}} k_t R_p^2/k_p^2 f k_d[\text{M}]^3 \qquad (3\text{-}81)$$

where C_{In} is the transfer constant to initiator.

At constant $[\text{M}]$ a plot of $1/\overline{\text{DP}}$ versus R_p or $[\text{In}]^{1/2}$ will be linear, only if C_{In} is zero or if the last term in (3-81) is negligibly small. Suitable analysis of the data gives values of C_{In}. Some results obtained by this method with styrene at 70°C are given in Table 3-10.

Electron-attracting substituents in the *para* position clearly increase the extent of transfer with initiator. These same substituents reduce the value of k_d for dissociation of the initiator. A typical plot of $1/\overline{\text{DP}}$ versus R_p, indicating considerable transfer to two hydroperoxides, slight transfer to

TABLE 3-10

Transfer Constants C_{In} for Substituted
Benzoyl Peroxides in Styrene Polymerization
at 70°C (*371*)

Substituent	C_{In} $(=k_{fIn}/k_p)$	Substituent	C_{In}
p-*t*-Butyl	0	*m*-Fluorine	0.246
p-Methyl	0.003	*m*-Chlorine	0.346
p-Methoxy	0.074	*m*-Bromine	0.465
Hydrogen	0.075	*m*-Iodine	0.262
p-Fluorine	0.219	*m*-Nitro	6.2
p-Chlorine	0.216		
p-Bromine	0.193	*o*-Methyl	0.175
p-Iodine	0.293	*o*-Fluorine	0.40
p-Cyanide	0.804	*o*-Chlorine	1.91
p-Nitro	7.4	*o*-Bromine	2.17

Bz_2O_2, and none to AIBN, is shown in Fig. 3-5. Discussion of other styrene–
peroxide systems is found elsewhere (*144,214–216,219,220*). It has been
suggested (*482*) that the induced decomposition rate constants k_{fIn} for
various bis-substituted benzoyl peroxides at 90°C in styrene give reasonable
Hammett plots.

The constants of transfer of polystyryl radicals to aliphatic peroxides, such
as *tert*-butyl [*224(d),224(e)*], *sec*-butyl [*224(f)*], butyl [*224(g)*], propyl [*224(h)*],
isopropyl [*224(f)*], and ethyl [*224(f)*] peroxides, have been determined by

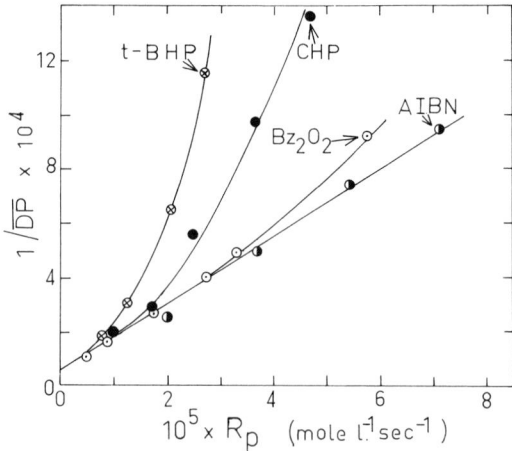

Fig. 3-5. $1/\overline{DP}$ versus R_p for the polymerization of styrene at 60°C with initiators as indicated.
[Data from Baysal and Tobolsky (*214*).]

Pryor and co-workers. There is some evidence that transfer involves α-hydrogen abstraction [224(b)].

As Fig. 3-5 indicates, hydroperoxides such as t-butyl and cumene hydroperoxides, engage readily in transfer reactions with polystyryl radicals (107,214,372,373). Transfer may involve hydrogen atom abstraction:

$$R\cdot + (CH_3)_3COOH \longrightarrow RH + (CH_3)_3COO\cdot \qquad (3\text{-}82)$$

However, recent evidence for the styrene–cumene hydroperoxide system indicates that the initiation mechanism may involve a bimolecular reaction with solvent, monomer, or other species (223).

Tetramethyl thiuram disulfide is an initiator of styrene polymerization (374–376), and there is evidence of the breakdown (377):

$$(CH_3)_2N\cdot\underset{\underset{S}{\|}}{C}\cdot S\cdot S\cdot\underset{\underset{S}{\|}}{C}\cdot N(CH_3)_2 \longrightarrow 2(CH_3)_2N\cdot\underset{\underset{S}{\|}}{C}\cdot S\cdot \longrightarrow 2(CH_3)_2N\cdot + 2CS_2 \qquad (3\text{-}83)$$

Transfer to initiator has also been postulated (378), and experiments with ^{14}C–tetraethyl thiuram disulfide suggest that $(C_2H_5)_2N\cdot CS\cdot S\cdot$ is both the radical produced by transfer to initiator and the radical initiating polymerization (486).

Certain disulfide initiators decompose,

$$R'\cdot S\cdot S\cdot R' \longrightarrow 2R'\cdot S\cdot \qquad (3\text{-}84)$$

and may also be involved in transfer reactions with polymer radicals [224(a)–(c),378,487]:

$$R\cdot + R'\cdot S\cdot S\cdot R' \longrightarrow RR' + R'\cdot S\cdot S\cdot \qquad (3\text{-}85))$$

3-11. INHIBITION AND RETARDATION

The polymerization of styrene may be prevented or reaction limited to very slow formation of low-molecular-weight polymers by the addition of small amounts of inhibitors. Induction or inhibition periods are observed, the length of which is proportional to the inhibitor concentration, after which R_p increases rapidly to reach approximately the rate expected in the absence of inhibitor. Retarders do not produce marked inhibition periods but cause decreased rates of polymerization usually throughout the reaction. The difference between retardation and inhibition is not clear-cut (379); the results of Foord (88) and others (380), who examined a wide range of additives, show that the difference is only one of degree. In fact, classification of additives on the basis of observed behavior depends on the sensitivity of the method used for detecting slow rates of polymerization. There are many different mechanisms that can cause pronounced retardation or inhibition; some of these possibilities are outlined below.

A. Molecular Compounds: Quinones

Quinones are regarded as inhibitors of the polymerization of styrene; p-benzoquinone has been particularly well studied. Breitenbach and Breitenbach ($89,381$) observed that in the bulk thermal polymerization low-molecular-weight compounds were formed from various quinones, and some hydroquinone was formed from p-benzoquinone (381). The nature of some of these low-molecular-weight products has received attention ($111,112$) and led to the suggestion that they were formed in some way from diradicals. This does not exclude the possibility that some copolymerization of the quinone with styrene occurs in the thermal polymerization. Mayo and Gregg (382) in polymerizations with added Bz_2O_2 found evidence of copolymerization with p-benzoquinone. Low-molecular-weight compounds were also isolated from the styrene-chloranil system ($113,383–385$), and a copolymer structure was suggested (383) for some of them,

$$-CH_2 \cdot CHPh \cdot O - \underset{\overset{Cl \quad Cl}{\underset{Cl \quad Cl}{}}}{\bigcirc} - O - \qquad (3\text{-}86)$$

although other workers (388) considered there was only one chloranil unit per polymer chain.

Cohen ($386,387$) observed characteristic induction periods in the styrene–Bz_2O_2–p-benzoquinone system. He concluded that two radicals from the initiator after a small period of growth were finally stopped by one quinone molecule. Induced decomposition of initiator also occurred, however, and a $1:1$ stoichiometry is also arguable. Two possible types of initial attack were proposed:

$$\sim CH_2\overset{\cdot}{C}HPh \; + \; \underset{\overset{\|}{O}}{\overset{O}{\bigcirc}} \; \longrightarrow \; \underset{\overset{|}{O\cdot}}{\overset{\overset{\sim CH_2CHPh}{\overset{|}{O}}}{\bigcirc}} \qquad (3\text{-}87)$$

$$\text{(I)}$$

$$\text{or} \; \longrightarrow \; \underset{\overset{|}{O\cdot}}{\overset{OH}{\bigcirc}} \; + \sim CH{=}CHPh \qquad (3\text{-}88)$$

$$\text{(II)}$$

Price and Read (*388,389*), however, suggested an initial polymer radical attack on the aromatic nucleus.

$$\text{(3-89)}$$

The precise radical/quinone stoichiometry clearly depends on the fate of the inhibitor radicals (I), (II) and (III) and on whether they are completely unreactive, dimerize, disproportionate among themselves or with other polymer radicals, or undergo further growth to give copolymers.

With the use of *p*-benzoquinone–^{14}C and AIBN–^{14}C in the polymerization of styrene at 60°C it has been confirmed (*390*) that low-molecular-weight polymer was formed during the induction period, and about 90% of the quinone was incorporated into polymer in this period. There was considerable polymer-radical–quinone interaction but only slight direct reaction of inhibitor with primary radicals. The existence of ether linkages in the polymer confirmed that radicals of type (I) were involved initially, and that limited growth of these rather unreactive radicals occurred by addition of monomer. On an average there were two molecules of quinone per polymer molecule during the induction period, and the preferred termination mechanism was

$$\sim CH_2CHPh-OC_6H_4O-\sim CH_2\dot{C}HPh + \dot{O}-C_6H_4-OCHPhCH_2\sim$$

$$\longrightarrow \sim CH_2CHPhOC_6H_4O\sim CH_2CHPhOC_6H_4OCHPhCH_2\sim \quad \text{(3-90)}$$

The effects of *p*-benzoquinone on the copolymerization of styrene and methyl methacrylate in the presence of AIBN can be explained by reference to the effects observed with the two monomers singly (*391*). Bickel and Waters (*392*) have observed that small radicals of the type $(CH_3)_2\dot{C}X$, where X = $-CN$ or $-COOCH_3$, also attack the oxygen atom of *p*-benzoquinone and chloranil initially (*392*), no evidence of nuclear substitution being observed.

Tüdös and co-workers have studied the inhibition of both thermal and initiated polymerization (*393,394*). They propose that only part of the inhibitor radicals formed by addition of polymer radicals to inhibitor molecules are able to attack monomer further. Whether retardation or complete inhibition occurs depends on the relative proportions of these two types of radical. The relative reactivities of quinones are related to their redox potentials, and chlorinated quinone derivatives may form charge-transfer complexes with styrene in 1 : 1 ratio.

Copolymerization of styrene with quinones increases as the reaction temperature increases, since the activation energy of reaction (3-87) is 4.3 kcal mole^{-1}, compared with 9.4 kcal mole^{-1} for the growth reaction (395). That the inhibitory efficiency of quinones is higher with styrene than with other monomers suggests that polar effects are important, the polystyryl radicals being electron donors and the quinones the acceptors.

B. Molecular Compounds: Nitro and Nitroso Derivatives

Aromatic compounds containing nitro (88,396–398) or nitroso (88) groups usually act as retarders or weak inhibitors (444) of styrene polymerization. Walling (10) has reviewed some of the evidence relating to the initial radical–molecule reaction, and Price (389,397,398) has suggested that the initial polymer radical attack is on the aromatic nucleus. The fate of the resultant radicals is uncertain. Transfer to monomer may occur (388), or copolymerization with monomer may be involved.

An alternative suggestion is that polymer radicals initially attack the oxygen atom of the nitro compound (399–403):

$$R\cdot + Ph\cdot NO_2 \longrightarrow Ph\cdot N \begin{matrix} O\cdot \\ \diagup \\ \diagdown \\ O-R \end{matrix} \qquad (3\text{-}91)$$

The results of Bevington and Ghanem (404), who used picric acid and m-dinitrobenzene, are in agreement with this postulate. The intermediate radicals may undergo some growth by monomer addition before being terminated by other polymer radicals, e.g., with m-dinitrobenzene:

$$(NO_2)\cdot C_6H_4\cdot N \begin{matrix} O\cdot \\ \diagup \\ \diagdown \\ OR \end{matrix} + \cdot CHPh\cdot CH_2 \diagdown\diagdown\diagdown$$

$$\longrightarrow (NO_2)\cdot C_6H_4\cdot N \begin{matrix} OH \\ \diagup \\ \diagdown \\ OR \end{matrix} + CHPh=CH\diagdown\diagdown\diagdown \qquad (3\text{-}92)$$

Other possible reactions have been discussed (405). The reactivity to polystyryl radicals of various substituted s-trinitrobenzenes obeys the Hammett rule as long as substituents are small, this reactivity being higher the greater the electron-accepting properties of the substituent (405).

The retarding action of nitroso compounds and aliphatic nitro compounds is even less understood (88,492). Tüdös et al. have used electron spin resonance in an attempt to identify the intermediate radicals in polymerizations in the presence of nitro and nitroso compounds besides quinones and condensed aromatic hydrocarbons (36).

C. Stable Radicals

α,α-Diphenyl-β-picrylhydrazyl (DPPH) is a free radical that owes its stability to the delocalization of the unpaired electron. It has a characteristic absorption spectrum in organic solvents, and the rate of fading of its purple color has been used for measuring rates of radical production (407,424). DPPH is usually assumed to behave as an ideal inhibitor, reacting with small polymer radicals R· with 1:1 stoichiometry:

$$R· + DPPH \longrightarrow \text{inactive products} \qquad (3\text{-}93)$$

It gives rise to marked induction periods in styrene polymerization even at concentrations of $< 10^{-4}$ molar, but its rates of consumption in the bulk thermal polymerization are much greater than expected (102) (cf. Section 3-4-B). Hammond and co-workers (408) and others (187) have indicated that the reaction between the radicals $(CH_3)_2\dot{C}(CN)$ and DPPH in inert solvents need not be 1:1 stoichiometric and is very sensitive to the presence of oxygen and that DPPH–solvent intermediates are possible (409,410). The inefficiency of DPPH as a scavenger for primary radicals from AIBN has been demonstrated (411–413). Nevertheless, when the rate of consumption of DPPH was used for evaluating the rate of initiation in the polymerization of styrene with added initiator, reasonable agreement was obtained with other methods, assuming that one polystyryl radical reacted with one DPPH radical (14). This result may be fortuitous, because in the case of methyl methacrylate rates of initiation with DPPH were higher than those measured by other methods (207).

The mechanism of the reaction of DPPH with radicals is obscure. The attack of isobutyronitrile radicals on DPPH does not take place directly on the nitrogen atom (188,413). There is some evidence that initial attack is at the *para* position of one of the phenyl groups for isobutyronitrile (188) and triphenylmethyl radicals (408). The over-all reaction may be

$$\text{(3-94)}$$

Such derivatives have been identified (414) and a mechanism proposed (415). ^{14}C radioactive-tracer methods have established that some of the DPPH is incorporated into polystyrene molecules (413). Polymethyl methacrylate degraded in the presence of DPPH leaves some polymer with DPPH residues attached (*416*). It may be noted that DPPH abstracts hydrogen atoms from mercaptans (*417*), other hydroaromatic compounds (*418*), isopropyl radicals produced photolytically (*419*), amines, and phenols (*420–423*).

The reaction products of polystyryl radicals with DPPH most probably act as retarders in the polymerization (*414*), and the nitro groups may be involved.

Triphenylmethyl radicals inhibit styrene polymerization at 100°C, but Mayo and Gregg (*425*) have shown that 1:1 stoichiometry is far from being observed. The radicals are presumed to act partly as inhibitors and to some extent as chain initiators.

Another stable free radical has received attention as an inhibitor of the AIBN-initiated styrene polymerization, but the stoichiometry of the initial radical–radical reaction is uncertain (*426*).

D. Other Materials

1. OXYGEN

The initial value of R_p for styrene at relatively low temperatures is greatly reduced by traces of oxygen because of the formation of peroxy radicals:

$$R\cdot + O_2 \longrightarrow RO_2\cdot \tag{3-95}$$

The oxygen may be regarded as a comonomer with styrene owing to the reaction

$$RO_2\cdot + M \longrightarrow RO_2M\cdot \tag{3-96}$$

These reactions can be repeated and lead to the formation of polyperoxides (*428,429*). The mode of termination has not been decided unequivocally, though a rapid cross termination of $R\cdot$ and $RO_2\cdot$ has been suggested (*429*). Absolute rate constants for the oxidation of styrene have been obtained by the rotating-sector technique (*493*). Other products formed by side reactions include benzaldehyde and formaldehyde (*430,431*) and styrene oxide (*11*). The polyperoxides may decompose at high temperatures to give $RO\cdot$ radicals (*427*) capable of initiating polymerization. Simultaneous copolymerization and polyperoxide decomposition may thus complicate kinetic measurements of such systems.

2. SULFUR

Sulfur, like oxygen, is able to inhibit the polymerization of styrene under suitable conditions. Bartlett and Trifan (*432*) showed that during the inhibition period the polymer contained eight sulfur atoms per styrene unit. The primary reaction involves opening of S_8 rings:

$$R\cdot + S_8 \longrightarrow R\cdot S_7\cdot S\cdot \tag{3-97}$$

TABLE 3-11

Velocity Constants for Reaction of Radicals with S_8 and O_2

Radical	Substrate	k, $\text{mole}^{-1}\,\text{liter}\,\text{sec}^{-1}$	Temp., °C	Ref.
Polystyryl	Styrene	332	81	*14*
Polystyryl	O_2	ca. $1 \times 10^{8\,a}$	50	*448*
Polystyryl	S_8	ca. $3 \times 10^{4\,b}$	81	*432,433*
Polymethyl Methacrylate	S_8	17^c	44.1	*434*

[a] Calculated from data (*448*) by use of the value of $k_p = 123\ \text{mole}^{-1}\,\text{liter}\,\text{sec}^{-1}$ at 50°C (*14*).

[b] Calculated from data (*432*) by use of the value of $k_p = 332\ \text{mole}^{-1}\,\text{liter}\,\text{sec}^{-1}$ at 81°C (*14*).

[c] Calculated from data (*434*) by use of the value of $k_p = 231\ \text{mole}^{-1}\,\text{liter}\,\text{sec}^{-1}$ at 44.1°C (*449*).

The reaction proceeds much faster than attack of R· on monomer or oxygen, as Table 3-11 indicates. The faster attack on O_2 compared with S_8 may be due partly to the diradical nature of O_2, the stability of the S_8 ring, and the greater energy needed for the —S—S— cleavage reaction. The polystyryl (electron donor) radical attacks sulfur faster than it attacks monomeric styrene, but this is not true of the polymethyl methacrylate radical (electron acceptor). The results indicate that S—S bonds are preferentially broken by nucleophilic rather than electrophilic attack.

3. CARBON

Carbon blacks inhibit the thermal polymerization of styrene (*435*), and inhibition periods are observed with AIBN as initiator (*436*). The inhibition is not due to the stable free radicals that can be detected in carbon blacks by electron spin resonance (*437,438*). The inhibition reaction may involve surface quinone groups (*438,439,461*) but may also involve hydrogen abstraction from surface phenolic groups (*436*). Inhibition by carbon black was also noted in emulsion polymerization (*436*).

4. FERRIC SALTS

Ferric salts retard or inhibit the polymerization of vinyl monomers in organic (*440,441*) or aqueous solution (*442*). A $1:1$ stoichiometry is assured,

$$\text{R·} + \text{FeCl}_3 \longrightarrow \text{R·Cl} + \text{FeCl}_2 \tag{3-98}$$

and with styrene inhibition occurs in dimethyl formamide solution (*189,213*), when the rate of (3-98) is much greater than the propagation rate. With monomers that are not such good electron donors as styrene, retardation occurs. Clearly, polar contributions to the transition state are important. If (FeCl$_3$) is high enough, mutual termination of polymer radicals is prevented. Entwistle (443) has shown, however, that different ferric salts have varying effects on the polymerization of monomers.

5. SOLVENT RETARDATION

Several examples of retardation involving chain transfer to solvents have been mentioned in Section 3-10.

E. Kinetics of Inhibited and Retarded Polymerization

In the presence of a strong retarder, such as FeCl$_3$, Bamford and co-workers (11,440) have expanded the simple kinetic scheme to include the reaction between retarder Z and polymer radicals R·, which give completely inert products,

$$\text{R· + Z} \longrightarrow \text{inert products} \qquad k_z \qquad (3\text{-}99)$$

besides the reaction

$$\text{R· + R·} \longrightarrow \text{polymer} \qquad k_t \qquad (3\text{-}100)$$

The stationary-state assumption appears to be a good approximation throughout the course of the reaction, in spite of the fact that at the end of the induction period R_p and hence [R·] change rapidly with time. It may be shown that if $[Z]_0$ is the inhibitor concentration initially, then

$$\tau = [Z]_0/I \qquad (3\text{-}101)$$

where τ is the time for the rate of polymerization to reach a fraction 0.648 of the final rate. The time τ is considered more important than the inhibition period found by linear extrapolation and, once obtained, enables I to be calculated. Further if the mutual reaction of polymer radicals during the inhibition period is negligibly small, then

$$I = k_z[\text{R·}][Z] = -d[Z]/dt \qquad (3\text{-}102)$$

and the rate of disappearance of Z (FeCl$_3$) enables I to be obtained.

For the styrene–AIBN–FeCl$_3$ system in dimethyl formamide at 60°C $k_z/k_p = 536$.

Bartlett and Kwart (400) have developed the stationary-state treatment to determine k_z/k_p for vinyl acetate and various inhibitors. Other schemes are necessary when radicals Z·, and not inert products, are formed in reaction (3-99), and a typical scheme has been presented by Flory (8). The values of k_z/k_p for styrene at 90°C with benzoquinone, p-xyloquinone, and duroquinone are 560, 43, and 0.67, respectively.

Other alternatives have been suggested (434,445,446) although usually applied to other monomers. The kinetic methods of Tüdös et al. (36,393–395, 444) have been applied mainly to styrene systems.

Relatively slight retardation by transfer to solvent has been discussed in previous sections, and data have been analyzed by means of the kinetic schemes of various workers (*100,101,447*).

3-12. EVALUATION OF ABSOLUTE KINETIC CONSTANTS

From Eq. [3-4(n)]

$$k_p^2/k_t = 2R_p^2/[M]^2 I \qquad (3\text{-}103)$$

Thus, once the rate of initiation I for a given system involving styrene is known—for example, from measurements of rate of decomposition of initiator with known f value, measurements with radioactive initiators, or experiments with inhibitors or retarders—the value of k_p^2/k_t can be found.

Alternatively, k_p^2/k_t may be determined from plots of $1/\overline{DP}$ versus R_p, since in the absence of transfer to initiator for the bulk reaction

$$1/\overline{DP} = C_M + k_t R_p/k_p^2[M]^2 \qquad (3\text{-}104)$$

The slope then gives $k_t/k_p^2[M]^2$, and the intercept gives C_M.

Determinations of k_p^2/k_t for styrene, made by various workers prominent in the field, are shown in Fig. 3-6, the agreement being marked. The line

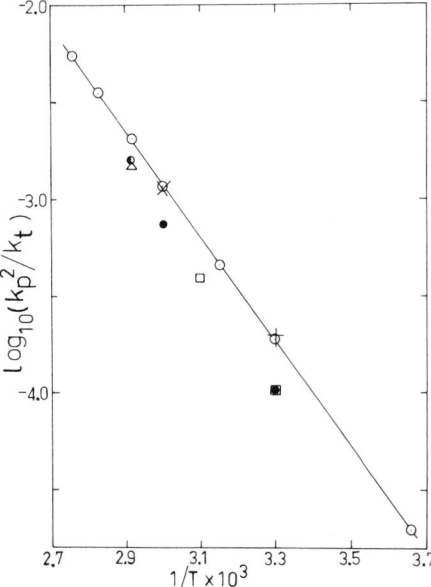

Fig. 3-6. $\log_{10}(k_p^2/k_t)$ versus $1/T$ for the polymerization of styrene. The line is drawn for the results collected by Tobolsky and Offenbach. ⊙ (*216*). Other results. ● (*14*); × (*226*) recalculated by Matheson et al. (*14*), □ (*85*) recalculated by Matheson et al. (*14*), + (*222*) recalculated by assuming combination, ◖ (*220*), △ (*144*).

is drawn through the results of Tobolsky and co-workers, which cover the widest temperature range. The equation of this line is (216)

$$k_p^2/k_t = (A_p^2/A_t) \exp\left[-(2E_p - E_t)/RT\right] = 1.76 \times 10^5 \exp\left(-12,460/RT\right)$$

(3-105)

Individual values of the kinetic constants shown in Table 3-12 are not in such good agreement. Bamford and Dewar (94) studied the thermal and photochemical polymerization of styrene by a viscometric technique, and further measurements of the photochemical after-effect (decay of radical concentration after illumination stopped) enabled k_p, k_{fm}, and k_t to be determined, and k_i could also be calculated for the thermal polymerization. They assumed initiation by diradicals and termination by disproportionation, and Onyon (450) has recalculated the data at 25°C, assuming monoradical initiation and radical combination. The recalculated values differ only slightly from the original results.

Melville and Valentine (222) studied the Bz_2O_2-initiated photopolymerization at 30°C by a rotating-sector method (494). Essentially this method measures the lifetime τ of the growing polymer radicals and, since

$$\tau = (2k_t I)^{-1/2}$$

(3-106)

then

$$\tau^{-1} = 2k_t R_p/k_p[M]$$

(3-107)

Thus a plot of τ^{-1} versus R_p yields a value of k_t/k_p. This value together with a value of k_t/k_p^2 enables the individual kinetic parameters to be evaluated. The values of Melville and Valentine have been recalculated by assuming termination by combination with the value $k_t/k_p^2[M]^2$ at 30°C, where $[M] = 8.71$ mole liter^{-1}, equal to 52.4 mole^{-1} liter sec, as established by a plot of $1/\overline{DP}$ versus R_p. The existence of the dark rate was ignored by these workers, but further correction (9) still gives k_t values much lower than those of Matheson et al. (14).

Burnett (142) studied the pre-effect for the direct photopolymerization, using a sensitive dilatometer at 15°C and 25°C, the original results being calculated by assuming disproportionation. The results at 25°C have been corrected for combination of radicals by assuming that the value of $k_t/k_p^2[M]^2$ found by Melville and Valentine (222) at 30°C is applicable. It was not possible to recalculate the values of A_i and k_i obtained from data in the thermal polymerization, so these values are quoted unaltered. The photochemical pre-effect in the presence of diacetyl has also been studied (466).

Matheson et al. (14) determined I from the rate of decomposition of AIBN and the use of DPPH, these results being in excellent agreement in spite

TABLE 3-12

Rate Constants for the Polymerization of Styrene (Velocity Constants in Terms of moles, liters, and seconds)

	Bamford and Dewar (94)	Onyon (450)	Burnett (142)[a]	Melville and Valentine (222)	Matheson et al. (14)	Imoto et al. (496)
k_i	(0°C) 4.51×10^{-18} (25°C) 1.35×10^{-15}	(25°C) 9.51×10^{-16}	(15°C) [1.48×10^{-16}] (25°C) [1.34×10^{-15}]			
E_i, kcal mole^{-1}	37.0 ± 2		36.4			
A_i	1.23×10^{10}		[4.15×10^{11}]			
k_p	(0°C) 6.91 (25°C) 18.7	(25°C) 25.1	(25°C) 19.0	(30°C) 25.5	(0°C) 13.2 (25°C) 44 (30°C) 55 (50°C) 123 (60°C) 176	(30°C) 106
E_p, kcal mole^{-1}	6.5 ± 1		6.3		7.76	
A_p	1.02×10^6		6.93×10^5		2.16×10^7	
k_{fm}	(0°C) 7.47×10^{-5} (25°C) 6.68×10^{-4}	(25°C) 8.81×10^{-4}	(25°C) 6.08×10^{-4}	(30°C) 3.32×10^{-3}	(60°C) 10.6×10^{-3}	
E_{fm}, kcal mole^{-1}	14.2 ± 1		14.4			
A_{fm}	1.50×10^7		1.97×10^7			
$k_t \times 10^{-7}$	(0°C) 0.092 (25°C) 0.140	(25°C) 0.18	(25°C) 0.14	(30°C) 0.26	(0°C) 1.66 (25°C) 2.38 (30°C) 2.53 (60°C) 3.6	(30°C) 5.4
E_t, kcal mole^{-1}	2.8 ± 1		1.9		2.37	
A_t	1.54×10^8		3.44×10^7		1.30×10^9	

[a] Values in brackets are the results quoted in the paper of Burnett. All other values corrected for combination of radicals.

of the difficulties of estimating the precise end of the inhibition periods. The rotating-sector technique enabled kinetic constants to be evaluated over a wide range of temperature. Similar types of measurement have recently been made at 30°C with a rotating sector and with DPPH and p-benzo-quinone as inhibitors (496).

Barb (451) has studied the kinetics of copolymerization of styrene and sulfur dioxide, and rotating-sector measurements enabled k_t and k_p to be evaluated at 20°C. Walling (452) has given a simpler treatment of the kinetics.

Burrell et al. (453) have studied the nonstationary state by observing the decrease in dielectric constant due to heat produced under essentially adiabatic conditions. Their value of k_p/k_t at 15°C for the AIBN-photo-initiated polymerization was 3.4×10^{-7} mole liter^{-1} sec, in good agreement with Matheson's value. Grassie and Melville (454) used a sensitive interferom-eter to measure refractive-index changes during the nonstationary state under adiabatic conditions. With benzoyl peroxide as photoinitiator k_p/k_t was 1.0×10^{-6} mole liter^{-1} sec at 15°C.

It is clear that for styrene, as for other monomers, there is still much uncertainty regarding the true values of k_p and k_t, which is usually associated with measurements of τ or experimental difficulties connected with investiga-tions of the nonstationary state. Walling (10) has selected a set of "best values" of k_p and k_t with associated activation energies and frequency factors, preference being given to the results of Tobolsky for k_p^2/k_t, and of Matheson for k_p/k_t. However, different workers give little indication of the magnitude of the likely errors involved, so that correct "weighting" of the results is difficult. The use of Matheson's values, determined over the widest temperature range, is therefore recommended for the purposes of calcula-tions.

Absolute values of the propagation velocity constant k_p have also been obtained for the emulsion polymerization of styrene by use of the Smith–Ewart theory (455), when

$$R_p = k_p[M](N/2) \tag{3-108}$$

where N is the number of latex particles per milliliter of aqueous phase in the emulsion. Rates of polymerization have been determined gravimetrically by Smith (456) and Morton et al. (457) and dilatometrically by Paoletti and Billmeyer (458).

Paoletti and Billmeyer (458) have analyzed their results, and with the exception of the values of k_p determined at the extremes of temperature, 30.5°C and 70.9°C, a good plot of $\log k_p$ versus $1/T$ was obtained with

$$k_p = 2.24 \times 10^{14} \exp(-17,570/RT) \tag{3-109}$$

The data of Smith (456) and Morton et al. (457) lead to (458)

$$k_p = 2.71 \times 10^{14} \exp(-17{,}570/RT) \qquad (3\text{-}110)$$

The reasons for the relatively high activation energy and frequency factor involved in the emulsion systems compared with the corresponding values for the homogeneous systems is not yet clear. The emulsion polymerization of styrene induced both by normal methods and by intermittent free-radical production has recently received attention (495).

REFERENCES

1. R. H. Boundy, R. F. Boyer, and S. M. Stoesser, eds., *Styrene: Its Polymers, Co-Polymers and Derivatives*, Reinhold, New York, 1952.

2. *Monomer and polymer spectra:*
   (a) M. J. Kamlet and H. E. Ungnade, eds., *Organic Electronic Spectral Data*, Vol. I (1960), Vol. II (1960), and Vol. III (1963), Wiley (Interscience), New York.
   Monomer spectrum:
   (b) S. S. Dubov and O. G. Strukov, *Zh. Vses. Khim. Obshchestva im. D. I. Mendeleeva*, **8**, 699 (1963).
   (c) G. V. Klimusheva, O. V. Bragin, E. A. Mikhailova, and I. L. Satonova, *Opt. i Spektroskopiya*, **15**, 72 (1963).
   (d) V. L. Broude and G. V. Klimusheva, *Fiz. Probl. Spektroskopii, Akad. Nauk SSSR, Materially*, 13-go (*Trinadtsatogo*) *Soveshch.*, Leningrad, **2**, 184 (1960).
   (e) P. S. Yu, V. N. Nikitin, and M. V. Volkenshtein, *Zh. Fiz. Khim.*, **36**, 681 (1962).
   (f) A. K. Chandra, *J. Am. Chem. Soc.*, **83**, 4177 (1961).
   (g) J. E. Bloor, *Can. J. Chem.*, **39**, 2256 (1961).
   (h) K. Kimura and S. Nagakura, *Theoret. Chim. Acta*, **3**, 164 (1965).
   Polymer spectrum:
   (i) M. T. Vala and S. A. Rice, *J. Chem. Phys.*, **39**, 2348 (1963).
   M. T. Vala, R. Silbey, S. A. Rice, and J. Jortner, *J. Chem. Phys.*, **41**, 2846 (1964).

3. G. M. Kline, ed., *Analytical Chemistry of Polymers*, Pt. II, Wiley (Interscience), New York, 1962, Chaps. VII and VIII.

4. B. Ke, ed., *Newer Methods of Polymer Characterization*, Wiley (Interscience), New York, 1964, Chap. II.

5. L. J. Bellamy, *The Infra-Red Spectra of Complex Molecules*, 2nd ed., Methuen, London, 1958.

6. *Monomer:*
   (a) E. Briner, C. Christol, H. Christol, S. Fliszar, and G. Rossetti, *Helv. Chim. Acta*, **46**, 2249 (1963).
   (b) W. Lüttke, *Ann. Chem.*, **668**, 184 (1963); W. G. Fately, R. K. Harris, F. A. Miller, and R. E. Witkowski, *Spectrochim. Acta*, **21**, 231 (1965).
   Polymer:
   (c) S. Krimm, *Fortschr. Hochpolymer.-Forsch.*, **2**, 51 (1960).
   (d) J. Braunbeck, *Angew. Chem.*, **72**, 31 (1960).
   (e) J. A. Bittles, A. K. Chaudhuri, and S. W. Benson, *J. Polymer Sci.*, **A2**, 1221 (1964).
   (f) A. Hadni, C. Bouster, E. Decamps, J. Munier, and P. Poinsot, *Colloq. Spectros. Intern. 9th*, Lyons, **3**, 11 (1961); D. Grandjean and A. Hadni, ibid. p. 44.
   (g) W. Kawai and S. Tstsumi, *Kogyo Kagaku Zasshi*, **62**, 1469 (1959).
   (h) H. Tadokoro, T. Kitazawa, S. Nazakura, and S. Murahashi, *Bull. Chem. Soc. Japan*, **34**, 1209 (1961).

(*i*) T. Onishi and S. Krimm, *J. Appl. Phys.*, **32**, 2320 (1961).

(*j*) *Tables of Wavenumbers for the Calibration of Infra-Red Spectrometers*, I.U.P.A.C., Butterworth, London, 1961.

(*k*) D. O. Hummel, *Kunstoffe*, **55**, 102 (1965).

7. G. M. Kline, ed., *Analytical Chemistry of Polymers*, Pt. I, Wiley (Interscience), New York, 1959.

8. P. J. Flory, *Principles of Polymer Chemistry*, Cornell Univ. Press, Ithaca, New York, 1953.

9. G. M. Burnett, *Mechanism of Polymer Reactions*, Wiley (Interscience), New York, 1954.

10. C. Walling, *Free Radicals in Solution*, Wiley, New York, 1957.

11. C. H. Bamford, W. G. Barb, A. D. Jenkins, and P. F. Onyon, *The Kinetics of Vinyl Polymerization by Radical Mechanisms*, Butterworth, London, 1958.

12. J. C. Bevington, *Radical Polymerization*, Academic, New York, 1961.

13. W. Patnode and W. J. Scheiber, *J. Am. Chem. Soc.*, **61**, 3449 (1939).

14. M. S. Matheson, E. E. Auer, E. B. Bevilacqua, and E. J. Hart, *J. Am. Chem. Soc.*, **73**, 1700 (1951).

15. F. S. Dainton, K. J. Ivin, and D. A. G. Walmsley, *Trans. Faraday Soc.*, **56**, 1784 (1960).

16. G. V. Schulz and M. Hoffmann, *Makromol. Chem.*, **23**, 220 (1957).

17. P. W. Allen, ed., *Techniques of Polymer Characterization*, Butterworth, London, 1959.

18. G. Meyerhoff, *Fortschr. Hochpolymer-Forsch.*, **3**, 59 (1961).

19. W. P. Slichter, *Fortschr. Hochpolymer-Forsch.*, **1**, 35 (1958).

20. J. A. Sauer and A. E. Woodward, *Rev. Mod. Phys.*, **32**, 88 (1960).

21. J. G. Powles, *Polymer*, **1**, 219 (1960).

22. B. I. Hunt, J. G. Powles, and A. E. Woodward, *Polymer*, **5**, 323 (1964).

23. F. Borsa and G. Lanzi, *J. Polymer Sci.*, **A2**, 2623 (1964).

24. F. A. Bovey and G. V. D. Tiers, *Fortschr. Hochpolymer-Forsch.*, **3**, 139 (1963); F. A. Bovey, F. P. Hood, E. W. Anderson, and L. C. Snyder, *J. Chem. Phys.*, **42**, 3900 (1965).

25. S. Brownstein, S. Bywater, and D. J. Worsfield, *J. Phys. Chem.*, **66**, 2067 (1962).

26. E. E. Schneider, *Discussions Faraday Soc.*, **19**, 158 (1955).

27. D. J. E. Ingram, M. C. R. Symons, and M. G. Townsend, *Trans. Faraday Soc.*, **54**, 409 (1958).

28. R. J. Abraham and D. H. Whiffen, *Trans. Faraday Soc.*, **54**, 1291 (1958).

29. D. J. E. Ingram, *Free Radicals as Studied by Electron Spin Resonance*, Butterworth, London, 1958.

30. A. T. Koritskii, Yu. N. Molin, V. N. Shamshev, N. Ya. Buben, and V. V. Voevodskii, *Vysokomolekul. Soedin.*, **1**, 1182 (1959).

31. Yu. D. Tsvetkov, Yu. H. Molin, and V. V. Voevodskii, *Vysokomolekul. Soedin.*, **1**, 1807 (1959).

32. D. H. Whiffen, *Makromol. Chem.*, **34**, 170 (1959).

33. R. E. Florin, L. A. Wall, and D. W. Brown, *Trans. Faraday Soc.*, **56**, 1304 (1960).

34. R. B. Ingalls and L. A. Wall, *J. Chem. Phys.*, **35**, 370 (1961); R. B. Ingalls and W. A. Young, *J. Chem. Phys.*, **43**, 1759 (1965).

35. L. A. Wall and R. B. Ingalls, *J. Polymer Sci.*, **62**, S5 (1962).

36. F. Tüdös, I. Kende, T. Bereznich, S. Solodovnikov, and V. Voevodskii, *Magy. Kem. Folyoirat*, **69**, 371 (1963); *Kinetika i Kataliz*, **6**, 203 (1965).

37. S. E. Bresler and E. N. Kazbekov, *Fortschr. Hochpolymer.-Forsch.*, **3**, 688 (1964).

38. R. W. Warfield and M. C. Petree, *J. Polymer Sci.*, **55**, 497 (1961); (*a*) I. V. Sochava and O. D. Trapeznikova, *Vestn. Leningr. Univ. Ser. Fiz. i Khim.*, **13**(3), 65 (1958); (*b*) K. Ueberreiter and E. Otto-Laupenmuhlen, *Z. Naturforsch.*, **8a**, 664 (1953); (*c*) K. S. Pitzer, L. Guttman, and E. F. Westrum, *J. Am. Chem. Soc.*, **68**, 2209 (1946).

39. F. S. Dainton and K. J. Ivin, *Quart. Rev.*, **12**, 61 (1958).

40. L. K. J. Tong and W. O. Kenyon, *J. Am. Chem. Soc.*, **69**, 1402 (1947).

41. D. E. Roberts, W. W. Walton, and R. S. Jessup, *J. Polymer Sci.*, **2**, 420 (1947).

42. R. M. Joshi, *J. Polymer Sci.*, **56**, 313 (1962).

43. H. Miyama and S. Fujimoto, *J. Polymer Sci.*, **54**, S32 (1961).

44. M. Suzuki, H. Miyama, and S. Fujimoto, *J. Polymer Sci.*, **31**, 212 (1958); *J. Chem. Soc. Japan*, **79**, 609 (1958).

45. R. J. Orr, *Polymer*, **2**, 74 (1961).

46. F. S. Dainton, D. M. Evans, F. E. Hoare, and T. P. Melia, *Polymer*, **3**, 286 (1962).

47. E. Simon, *Ann.*, **31**, 265 (1839).

48. E. Kopp, *Compt. Rend.*, **21**, 1376 (1845).

49. J. H. van't Hoff, *Ber.*, **9**, 5 (1876).

50. C. W. Hempel, *Ann.*, **59**, 316 (1846).

51. C. Gerhardt and A. Cahours, *Ann.*, **38**, 67 (1841).

52. M. Herzog, *Ann.*, **53**, 323 (1845).

53. D. Howard, *J. Chem. Soc.*, **13**, 135 (1861).

54. M. Berthelot, *Compt. Rend.*, **63**, 788 (1866).

55. M. Berthelot, *Ann.*, **142**, 257 (1867).

56. J. Blyth and A. W. Hofmann, *Ann.*, **53**, 289, 311 (1845).

57. M. Berthelot, *Bull. Soc. Chim. France*, **6**, 294 (1866).

58. G. Lemoine, *Compt. Rend.*, **125**, 530 (1897); **129**, 719 (1899).

59. A. Kronstein, *Ber.*, **35**, 4150 (1902).

60. H. Stobbe and G. Posnjak, *Ann.*, **371**, 259 (1910).

61. H. Staudinger, *Ber.*, **53**, 1073 (1920).

62. H. Staudinger, *Die hochmolekularen organischen Verbindungen*, Springer, Berlin, 1932.

63. J. Ostromysslensky, *J. Russ. Phys. Chem.*, **44**, 204 (1911); **47**, 1472, 1928 (1915); **48**, 1132 (1916).

64. G. S. Whitby and M. Katz, *J. Am. Chem. Soc.*, **50**, 1160 (1928).

65. H. Staudinger, M. Brunner, K. Frey, P. Garbsch, R. Signer, and S. Wehrli, *Ber.*, **62**, 241 (1929).

66. W. H. Carothers, *J. Am. Chem. Soc.*, **51**, 2548 (1929); **51**, 2560 (1929).

67. K. H. Meyer and H. Mark, *Der Aufbau der Hochpolymeren Organischen Naturstoffe*, Leipzig, 1930.

68. H. S. Taylor and A. A. Vernon, *J. Am. Chem. Soc.*, **53**, 2527 (1931).

69. H. W. Starkweather and G. B. Taylor, *J. Am. Chem. Soc.*, **52**, 4708 (1930).

70. H. S. Taylor and W. H. Jones, *J. Am. Chem. Soc.*, **52**, 1111 (1930).

71. G. S. Whitby and R. N. Crozier, *Can. J. Res.*, **6**, 203 (1922).

72. W. Chalmers, *J. Am. Chem. Soc.*, **56**, 912 (1934).

73. H. Staudinger and W. Frost, *Ber.*, **68**, 2351 (1935).

74. H. Mark and R. Raff, *Z. Physik. Chem. Leipzig*, **B31**, 275 (1936).

75. H. Dostal and H. Mark, *Z. Physik. Chem. Leipzig*, **B29**, 299 (1935).

76. H. Dostal and H. Mark, *Trans. Faraday Soc.*, **32**, 54 (1936).

77. G. V. Schulz and E. Husemann, *Z. Physik. Chem. Leipzig*, **B34**, 187 (1936).

78. G. V. Schulz and E. Husemann, *Z. Physik. Chem. Leipzig*, **B36**, 184 (1937).

79. J. W. Breitenbach and H. Rudorfer, *Monatsh.*, **70**, 37 (1937).

80. H. Suess, K. Pilch, and H. Rudorfer, *Z. Physik. Chem. Leipzig*, **A179**, 361 (1937).

81. H. Suess and A. Springer, *Z. Physik. Chem. Leipzig*, **A181**, 81 (1938).

82. H. Dostal and W. Jorde, *Z. Physik. Chem. Leipzig*, **A179**, 23 (1937).

83. G. V. Schulz, A. Dinglinger, and E. Husemann, *Z. Physik. Chem. Leipzig*, **B43**, 384 (1939).

84. F. A. Bovey and I. M. Kolthoff, *Chem. Rev.*, **42**, 491 (1948).

85. G. V. Schulz and E. Husemann, *Z. Physik. Chem. Leipzig*, **B39**, 246 (1938).

86. G. V. Schulz and G. Wittig, *Naturwiss.*, **27**, 387, 456 (1939).

87. P. J. Flory, *J. Am. Chem. Soc.*, **59**, 241 (1937).

88. S. G. Foord, *J. Chem. Soc.*, **1940**, 48.

89. J. W. Breitenbach and H. L. Breitenbach, *Z. Physik. Chem. Leipzig*, **A190**, 361 (1942).

90. G. Williams, *J. Chem. Soc.*, **1940**, 775.

91. C. C. Price, *Ann. N.Y. Acad. Sci.*, **44**, 35 (1943).

92. A. G. Evans and M. Polanyi, *Nature*, **152**, 738 (1943).

93. L. C. Rubens and R. F. Boyer, Ref. *1*, Chap. 7.

94. C. H. Bamford and M. J. S. Dewar, *Proc. Roy. Soc.* (*London*), **A192**, 308 (1948).

95. C. Walling, E. R. Briggs, and F. R. Mayo, *J. Am. Chem. Soc.*, **68**, 1145 (1946).

96. E. Trommsdorff, *Colloquium on High Polymers*, Freiburg, 1944.

97. R. N. Haward, W. Simpson, and J. Elly, *J. Appl. Chem.*, **1**, 347 (1951).

98. M. F. Vaughan, *Chem. & Ind.*, **1950**, 76.

99. F. R. Mayo, *J. Am. Chem. Soc.*, **75**, 6133 (1953).

100. G. M. Burnett and L. D. Loan, *Trans. Faraday Soc.*, **51**, 214, 219 (1955).

101. A. D. Jenkins, *Trans. Faraday Soc.*, **54**, 1885, 1895 (1958).

102. R. R. Hiatt and P. D. Bartlett, *J. Am. Chem. Soc.*, **81**, 1149 (1959).

103. R. Back, G. Trich, C. McDonald, and C. Sivertz, *Can. J. Chem.*, **32**, 1078 (1954); M. Onyszchuck and C. Sivertz, ibid., **33**, 1034 (1955).

104. M. H. George and P. F. Onyon, *Trans. Faraday Soc.*, **59**, 134 (1963).

105. R. N. Haward, *Trans. Faraday Soc.*, **46**, 204 (1950).

106. B. H. Zimm and J. K. Bragg, *J. Polymer Sci.*, **9**, 476 (1952).

107. D. H. Johnson and A. V. Tobolsky, *J. Am. Chem. Soc.*, **74**, 938 (1952).

108. K. E. Russell and A. V. Tobolsky, *J. Am. Chem. Soc.*, **75**, 5052 (1953).

109. S. W. Benson, *Foundations of Chemical Kinetics*, McGraw-Hill, New York, 1960.

110. G. S. Hammond and K. R. Kopecky, *J. Polymer Sci.*, **60**, S54 (1962).

111. W. Kern and K. Feuerstein, *J. Prakt. Chem.*, **158**, 186 (1941).

112. H. W. Melville and W. F. Watson, *Trans. Faraday Soc.*, **44**, 886 (1948).

113. J. W. Breitenbach and H. Schneider, *Ber.*, **B76**, 1088 (1943).

114. F. R. Mayo and C. Walling, *Chem. Rev.*, **46**, 191 (1950).

115. B. Capon and C. W. Rees, *Ann. Rept. Progr. Chem.*, **60**, 247 (1963).

116. C. Walling, *J. Am. Chem. Soc.*, **71**, 1930 (1949).

117. C. Walling and E. A. McElhill, *J. Am. Chem. Soc.*, **73**, 2819 (1951).

118. A. M. North, *Polymer*, **4**, 129 (1964).

119. R. B. Beevers, *Trans. Faraday Soc.*, **58**, 1465 (1962).

120. H. A. Shah, F. Leonard, and A. V. Tobolsky, *J. Polymer Sci.*, **7**, 537 (1951).

121. B. Baysal, *J. Polymer Sci.*, **33**, 381 (1958).

122. W. Hahn and A. Fischer, *Makromol. Chem.*, **21**, 106 (1956).

123. J. W. Breitenbach and A. Kastell, *Monatsh.*, **85**, 676 (1954).

124. C. G. Overberger and M. Lapkin, *J. Am. Chem. Soc.*, **77**, 4651 (1955).

125. K. E. Russell and A. V. Tobolsky, *J. Am. Chem. Soc.*, **76**, 395 (1954).

126. R. Zand and R. B. Mesrobian, *J. Am. Chem. Soc.*, **77**, 6523 (1955).

127. H. Craubner and A. Hrubesch, *Makromol. Chem.*, **72**, 38 (1964).

128. W. Hahn and A. Fischer, *Makromol. Chem.*, **16**, 36 (1955).

129. G. Smets, A. Poot, M. Mullier, and J. P. Bex, *J. Polymer Sci.*, **34**, 287 (1959).

130. C. P. J. Glaudemans, *Makromol. Chem.*, **47**, 1 (1961).

131. W. Hahn and A. Fischer, *Makromol. Chem.*, **21**, 77 (1956).

132. G. M. Burnett and A. M. North, *Makromol. Chem.*, **73**, 60, 67, 77 (1964).

133. J. W. Breitenbach and H. G. Burger, *Makromol. Chem.*, **54**, 60 (1962).

134. C. Loucheux and H. Benoit, *Compt. Rend.*, **251**, 382 (1960).

135. A. Lebovits and W. C. Teach, *J. Polymer Sci.*, **47**, 527 (1961).
136. G. Henrici-Olivé and S. Olivé, *Makromol. Chem.*, **53**, 122 (1962).
137. K. F. Müeller, *Makromol. Chem.*, **79**, 128 (1964).
138. O. H. Wheeler and C. B. Covarrubias, *Can. J. Chem.*, **40**, 1224 (1962).
139. S. F. Mason, *Quart. Rev.*, **15**, 287 (1961).
140. D. H. Whiffen, *Quart. Rev.*, **12**, 250 (1958).
141. R. A. Haman and H. Eyring, *J. Chem. Phys.*, **10**, 557 (1942).
142. G. M. Burnett, *Trans. Faraday Soc.*, **46**, 772 (1950).
143. E. G. E. Hawkins, *Quart. Rev.*, **4**, 251 (1950); *Organic Peroxides*, Van Nostrand, Princeton, N.J., 1961.
144. A. V. Tobolsky and R. B. Mesrobian, *Organic Peroxides*, Wiley (Interscience), New York, 1954.
145. J. O. Edwards, ed., *Peroxide Reaction Mechanisms*, Wiley (Interscience), New York, 1962; A. G. Davies, *Organic Peroxides*, Butterworth, London, 1961.
146. W. Cooper, *J. Chem. Soc.*, **1951**, 3106.
147. C. G. Swain, W. H. Stockmayer, and J. T. Clarke, *J. Am. Chem. Soc.*, **72**, 5426 (1950).
148. C. E. H. Bawn and S. F. Mellish, *Trans. Faraday Soc.*, **47**, 1216 (1951).
149. P. D. Bartlett and K. Nozaki, *J. Am. Chem. Soc.*, **68**, 1686 (1946); **69**, 2299 (1947).
150. A. T. Blomquist and A. J. Buselli, *J. Am. Chem. Soc.*, **73**, 3883 (1951).
151. M. M. Koton, T. M. Kiseleva, and M. I. Bessenov, *Zh. Fiz. Khim.*, **28**, 2137 (1954).
152. M. M. Koton, T. M. Kiseleva, and M. I. Bessenov, *Dokl. Akad. Nauk SSSR*, **96**, 85 (1954).
153. C. A. Barson and J. C. Bevington, *Tetrahedron*, **4**, 147 (1958).
154. J. C. Bevington and T. D. Lewis, *Trans. Faraday Soc.*, **54**, 1340 (1958).
155. J. C. Bevington, *Proc. Roy. Soc.* (*London*), **A239**, 420 (1957).
156. P. D. Bartlett and S. G. Cohen, *J. Am. Chem. Soc.*, **65**, 543 (1943).
157. J. C. Bevington and C. S. Brooks, *J. Polymer Sci.*, **22**, 257 (1956).
158. J. C. Bevington and C. S. Brooks, *Makromol. Chem.*, **28**, 173 (1958).
159. G. Ayrey and C. G. Moore, *J. Polymer Sci.*, **36**, 41 (1959).
160. J. C. Bevington, *Makromol. Chem.*, **34**, 152 (1959).
161. J. C. Bevington and J. Toole, *J. Polymer Sci.*, **28**, 413 (1958).
162. J. C. Bevington, J. Toole, and L. Trossarelli, *Trans. Faraday Soc.*, **54**, 863 (1958).
163. J. C. Bevington, J. Toole, and L. Trossarelli, *Makromol. Chem.*, **28**, 237 (1959).
164. J. C. Bevington and T. D. Lewis, *Polymer*, **1**, 1 (1960).
165. H. C. Haas, *J. Polymer Sci.*, **39**, 493 (1959).
166. H. C. Haas, *J. Polymer Sci.*, **54**, 287 (1961); **55**, 33 (1961).
167. J. K. Allen and J. C. Bevington, *Trans. Faraday Soc.*, **56**, 1762 (1960).
168. J. C. Bevington, J. Toole, and L. Trossarelli, *Makromol. Chem.*, **32**, 57 (1959).
169. L. M. Dorfman and Z. W. Salsburg, *J. Am. Chem. Soc.*, **73**, 255 (1951).
170. H. M. Frey, *Proc. Chem. Soc.*, **1959**, 385.
171. G. A. Russell, *J. Org. Chem.*, **24**, 300 (1959).
172. L. Horner and E. Schwenk, *Angew. Chem.*, **61**, 411 (1949).
173. K. F. O'Driscoll and E. N. Ricchezza, *J. Polymer Sci.*, **46**, 211 (1960).
174. K. Takemoto, A. Nishio, Y. Iikubo, and M. Imoto, *Makromol. Chem.*, **42**, 97 (1960).
175. L. Horner and H. Junkerman, *Ann.*, **591**, 53 (1955).
176. L. Horner and E. Schwenk, *Ann.*, **566**, 69 (1950).
177. J. C. Bevington and T. D. Lewis, *Radical Polymerization*, Academic, New York, 1961, p. 15.
178. K. F. O'Driscoll and S. McArdie, *J. Polymer Sci.*, **40**, 557 (1959).
179. K. F. O'Driscoll and J. F. Schmidt, *J. Polymer Sci.*, **45**, 189 (1960).
180. T. H. Meltzer and A. V. Tobolsky, *J. Am. Chem. Soc.*, **76**, 5178 (1954).
181. C. Walling and N. Indictor, *J. Am. Chem. Soc.*, **80**, 5814 (1958).

182. K. F. O'Driscoll and E. N. Ricchezza, *Makromol. Chem.*, **47**, 15 (1961).

183. F. M. Lewis and M. S. Matheson, *J. Am. Chem. Soc.*, **71**, 747 (1949).

184. C. G. Overberger, M. T. O'Shaughnessy, and H. Shalit, *J. Am. Chem. Soc.*, **71**, 2661 (1949).

185. J. P. van Hook and A. V. Tobolsky, *J. Am. Chem. Soc.*, **80**, 779 (1958).

186. G. S. Hammond, J. N. Sen, and C. E. Boozer, *J. Am. Chem. Soc.*, **77**, 3244 (1955).

187. D. Verdin, *Trans. Faraday Soc.*, **56**, 823 (1960); J. C. Bevington and H. G. Troth, *Makromol. Chem.*, **53**, 200 (1962).

188. C. E. H. Bawn and D. Verdin, *Trans. Faraday Soc.*, **56**, 815 (1960).

189. J. Betts, F. S. Dainton, and K. J. Ivin, *Trans. Faraday Soc.*, **58**, 1203 (1962).

190. A. F. Bickel and W. A. Waters, *Rec. Trav. Chim.*, **69**, 1490 (1950).

191. J. C. Bevington, *J. Chem. Soc.*, **1954**, 3707.

192. P. Smith and A. M. Rosenberg, *J. Am. Chem. Soc.*, **81**, 2037 (1959).

193. P. Smith, N. Muller, and W. C. Tosch, *J. Polymer Sci.*, **57**, 823 (1962).

194. P. Smith and S. Carbone, *J. Am. Chem. Soc.*, **81**, 6174 (1959).

195. M. Talât-Erben and S. Bywater, *J. Am. Chem. Soc.*, **77**, 3710, 3712 (1955).

196. M. Talât-Erben and A. N. Isfendiyaroğlu, *Can. J. Chem.*, **37**, 1156 (1959); **37**, 1165 (1959).

197. G. S. Hammond, C-H. S. Wu, O. D. Trapp, J. Warkentin, and R. T. Keys, *J. Am. Chem. Soc.*, **82**, 5394 (1960).

198. G. S. Hammond, O. D. Trapp, R. T. Keys, and D. L. Neff, *J. Am. Chem. Soc.*, **81**, 4878 (1959).

199. J. C. Bevington and H. G. Troth, *Trans. Faraday Soc.*, **58**, 186 (1962).

200. J. C. Bevington and A. Wahid, *Polymer*, **3**, 585 (1962).

201. J. C. Bevington and A. Wahid, *Polymer*, **4**, 129 (1963).

202. S. G. Cohen, *J. Am. Chem. Soc.*, **67**, 17 (1945); **69**, 1057 (1947).

203. J. C. Bevington, J. H. Bradbury, and G. M. Burnett, *J. Polymer Sci.*, **12**, 469 (1954).

204. J. C. Bevington, *Trans. Faraday Soc.*, **51**, 1392 (1955).

205. J. C. Bevington, *Fortschr. Hochpolymer.-Forsch.*, **2**, 1 (1960).

206. G. Ayrey, *Chem. Rev.*, **63**, 645 (1963).

207. W. I. Bengough, W. Henderson, and R. A. M. Thomson, *Trans. Faraday Soc.*, **60**, 1137 (1964).

208. G. Henrici-Olivé and S. Olivé, *Makromol. Chem.*, **58**, 188 (1962).

209. L. M. Arnett and J. H. Peterson, *J. Am. Chem. Soc.*, **74**, 2031 (1952).

210. J. C. Bevington, H. W. Melville, and R. P. Taylor, *J. Polymer Sci.*, **14**, 463 (1954).

211. J. C. Bevington, *Symp. Intern. Chim. Macromol. 3rd, Milan*, 1954.

212. J. H. Bradbury and H. W. Melville, *Proc. Roy. Soc. (London)*, **A222**, 456 (1954).

213. C. H. Bamford, A. D. Jenkins, and R. Johnston, *Trans. Faraday Soc.*, **58**, 1212 (1962).

214. B. Baysal and A. V. Tobolsky, *J. Polymer Sci.*, **8**, 529 (1952).

215. A. V. Tobolsky and B. Baysal, *J. Polymer Sci.*, **11**, 471 (1953).

216. A. V. Tobolsky and J. Offenbach, *J. Polymer Sci.*, **16**, 311 (1955).

217. J. P. van Hook and A. V. Tobolsky, *J. Polymer Sci.*, **33**, 429 (1958).

218. J. P. van Hook and A. V. Tobolsky, *J. Phys. Chem.*, **62**, 257 (1958).

219. L. Redington, *J. Polymer Sci.*, **3**, 503 (1948).

220. A. I. Lowell and J. R. Price, *J. Polymer Sci.*, **43**, 1 (1960).

221. A. I. Lowell and J. R. Price, *J. Polymer Sci.*, **50**, S37 (1961).

222. H. W. Melville and L. Valentine, *Trans. Faraday Soc.*, **46**, 210 (1950).

223. A. V. Tobolsky and L. R. Matlock, *J. Polymer Sci.*, **55**, 49 (1961).

224. (*a*) W. A. Pryor and H. Guard, *J. Am. Chem. Soc.*, **86**, 1150 (1964);
    (*b*) W. A. Pryor, *Tetrahedron Letters*, **1963**, 1201;

(c) W. A. Pryor and T. L. Pickering, *J. Am. Chem. Soc.*, **84**, 2705 (1962);

(d) W. A. Pryor, *J. Phys. Chem.*, **67**, 519 (1963);

(e) W. A. Pryor, A. Lee, and C. E. Witt, *J. Am. Chem. Soc.*, **86**, 4229 (1964);

(f) W. A. Pryor, D. M. Huston, T. R. Fiske, J. L. Pickering, and E. Ciuffarin, ibid., **86**, 4237 (1964);

(g) W. A. Pryor and G. L. Kaplan, ibid., **86**, 4234 (1964);

(h) W. A. Pryor and E. P. Pultinas, ibid., **85**, 133 (1963).

225. A. Conix and G. Smets, *J. Polymer Sci.*, **10**, 525 (1953).

226. F. R. Mayo, R. A. Gregg, and M. S. Matheson, *J. Am. Chem. Soc.*, **73**, 1691 (1951).

227. H. F. Mark and D. Josefowitz, *Polymer Bull.*, **1**, 140 (1945).

228. M. M. Horikx and J. J. Hermans, *J. Polymer Sci.*, **11**, 325 (1953).

229. G. Henrici-Olivé and S. Olivé, *Makromol. Chem.*, **42**, 251 (1961).

230. M. H. George and P. F. Onyon, *Trans. Faraday Soc.*, **59**, 1390 (1963).

231. M. H. George, *J. Polymer Sci.*, **A2**, 3169 (1964).

232. A. D. Jenkins, *J. Polymer Sci.*, **29**, 245 (1958).

233. S. Kamenskaya and S. S. Medvedev, *Acta Physicochim. URSS*, **13**, 565 (1940).

234. M. S. Matheson, *J. Chem. Phys.*, **13**, 584 (1945).

235. C. H. Bamford, A. D. Jenkins, and R. Johnston, *Trans. Faraday Soc.*, **55**, 1451 (1959).

236. A. Chapiro, M. Magat, J. Sebban, and P. Wahl, *Ric. Sci. Suppl.*, **25A**, 73 (1955).

237. P. E. M. Allen and C. R. Patrick, *Makromol. Chem.*, **47**, 154 (1961).

238. S. Okamura and T. Manabe, *Chem. High Polymers Tokyo*, **15**, 688 (1958).

239. S. Okamura and T. Manabe, *Polymer*, **2**, 83 (1961).

240. T. Manabe, T. Utsumi, and S. Okamura, *J. Polymer Sci.*, **58**, 121 (1962).

241. G. Henrici-Olivé and S. Olivé, *Makromol. Chem.*, **37**, 71 (1960).

242. H. Staudinger and A. Steinhofer, *Ann.*, **517**, 35 (1935).

243. B. D. Coleman, *J. Polymer Sci.*, **31**, 155 (1958).

244. R. L. Miller and L. E. Nielsen, *J. Polymer Sci.*, **46**, 303 (1960).

245. G. E. Ham, *J. Polymer Sci.*, **61**, 9 (1962).

246. J. W. L. Fordham, *J. Polymer Sci.*, **39**, 321 (1959).

247. J. W. L. Fordham, P. H. Burleigh, and C. L. Sturm, *J. Polymer Sci.*, **41**, 73 (1959).

248. J. W. L. Fordham, G. H. McCain, and L. E. Alexander, *J. Polymer Sci.*, **39**, 335 (1959).

249. C. E. H. Bawn and A. Ledwith, *Quart. Rev.*, **16**, 361 (1962).

250. M. Szwarc, *Chem. & Ind.* (*London*), **1958**, 1589.

251. G. E. Ham, *J. Polymer Sci.*, **40**, 569 (1959).

252. G. E. Ham, *J. Polymer Sci.*, **46**, 475 (1960).

253. C. H. Bamford and C. A. Finch, *Proc. Chem. Soc.*, **1962**, 110.

254. C. H. Bamford and C. A. Finch, *Proc. Roy. Soc.* (*London*), **A268**, 553 (1962).

255. C. H. Bamford and C. A. Finch, *Z. Naturforsch.*, **17b**, 500 (1962).

256. C. H. Bamford and C. A. Finch, *Trans. Faraday Soc.*, **59**, 118 (1963).

257. C. H. Bamford and C. A. Finch, *Trans. Faraday Soc.*, **59**, 540 (1963).

258. C. H. Bamford and C. A. Finch, *Trans. Faraday Soc.*, **59**, 548 (1963).

259. C. H. Bamford and C. A. Finch, *Z. Naturforsch.*, **17b**, 804 (1962).

260. C. H. Bamford, G. C. Eastmond, and W. R. Maltman, *Trans. Faraday Soc.*, **60**, 1432 (1964).

261. C. H. Bamford, G. C. Eastmond, and V. J. Robinson, *Trans. Faraday Soc.*, **60**, 751 (1964); C. H. Bamford and D. J. Lind, *Chem. & Ind.* (*London*), **1965**, 1627.

262. C. H. Bamford, G. C. Eastmond, and J. A. Rippon, *Trans. Faraday Soc.*, **59**, 2548 (1963).

263. C. H. Bamford, M. S. Blackie, and C. A. Finch, *Chem. & Ind.* (*London*), **1962**, 1763.

264. F. R. Mayo, *J. Am. Chem. Soc.*, **70**, 3689 (1948).

265. J. C. Robb and D. Vofsi, *Trans. Faraday Soc.*, **55**, 558 (1959).

266. W. J. Kirkham and J. C. Robb, *Trans. Faraday Soc.*, **57**, 1757 (1961).
267. H. W. Melville, J. C. Robb, and R. C. Tutton, *Discussions Faraday Soc.*, **14**, 150 (1953).
268. W. I. Bengough and R. A. M. Thomson, *Trans. Faraday. Soc.*, **56**, 407 (1960).
269. J. C. Robb and E. Senogles, *Trans. Faraday Soc.*, **58**, 708 (1962).
270. J. C. Bevington, H. W. Melville, and R. P. Taylor, *J. Polymer Sci.*, **12**, 449 (1954).
271. B. L. Funt and W. Pasika, *Can. J. Chem.*, **38**, 1865 (1960).
272. G. Henrici-Olivé and S. Olivé, *J. Polymer Sci.*, **48**, 329 (1960).
273. I. M. Kolthoff, P. R. O'Connor, and J. L. Hausen, *J. Polymer Sci.*, **15**, 459 (1955).
274. W. V. Smith and H. N. Campbell, *J. Chem. Phys.*, **15**, 338 (1947).
275. W. V. Smith, *J. Am. Chem. Soc.*, **71**, 4077 (1949).
276. C. H. Bamford and A. D. Jenkins, *Nature*, **176**, 78 (1955).
277. C. H. Bamford and A. D. Jenkins, *Trans. Faraday Soc.*, **56**, 907 (1960).
278. C. H. Bamford, A. D. Jenkins, and R. P. Wayne, *Trans. Faraday Soc.*, **56**, 932 (1960).
279. S. R. Palit and M. K. Saha, *J. Polymer Sci.*, **58**, 1233 (1962).
280. C. A. Baker and R. J. P. Williams, *J. Chem. Soc.*, **1956**, 2352.
281. S. W. Benson and A. M. North, *J. Am. Chem. Soc.*, **81**, 1339 (1959). For general reading cf. A. M. North, *The Collision Theory of Chemical Reactions in Liquids*, Methuen monograph, London, 1964.
282. A. M. North and G. A. Reed, *Trans. Faraday Soc.*, **57**, 859 (1961).
283. J. Hughes and A. M. North, *Trans. Faraday Soc.*, **60**, 960 (1964).
284. A. M. North and G. A. Reed, *J. Polymer Sci.*, **A1**, 1311 (1963).
285. P. Hayden and H. W. Melville, *J. Polymer Sci.*, **43**, 201 (1960).
286. W. I. Bengough and H. W. Melville, *Proc. Roy. Soc. (London)*, **A249**, 455 (1959).
287. G. M. Burnett and G. L. Duncan, *Makromol. Chem.*, **51**, 154, 171, 177 (1962).
288. P. E. M. Allen and C. R. Patrick, *Nature*, **191**, 1194 (1961).
289. P. E. M. Allen and C. R. Patrick, *Trans. Faraday Soc.*, **59**, 1819 (1963).
290. M. Vaughan, *Trans. Faraday Soc.*, **48**, 576 (1952).
291. A. E. Nicholson and R. G. W. Norrish, *Discussions Faraday Soc.*, **22**, 97, 104 (1956).
292. K. E. Weale, *Quart. Rev.*, **16**, 267 (1962).
293. A. V. Tobolsky, *J. Am. Chem. Soc.*, **80**, 5927 (1958).
294. A. V. Tobolsky, C. E. Rogers, and R. D. Brickman, *J. Am. Chem. Soc.*, **82**, 1277 (1960).
295. K. F. O'Driscoll and P. J. White, *J. Polymer Sci.*, **B1**, 597 (1963).
296. K. F. O'Driscoll, *J. Polymer Sci.*, **61**, S4 (1962).
297. F. R. Mayo, *J. Am. Chem. Soc.*, **65**, 2324 (1943).
298. C. H. Bamford, A. D. Jenkins, R. Johnston, and E. F. T. White, *Trans. Faraday Soc.*, **55**, 168 (1959).
299. G. Henrici-Olivé, S. Olivé, and G. V. Schulz, *J. Polymer Sci.*, **56**, 233 (1962).
300. G. Henrici-Olivé and S. Olivé, *Fortschr. Hochpolymer.-Forsch.*, **2**, 496 (1961).
301. C. Walling, *J. Am. Chem. Soc.*, **70**, 2561 (1948).
302. L. A. Wall and D. W. Brown, *J. Polymer Sci.*, **14**, 513 (1954).
303. J. C. Bevington, *Fortschr. Hochpolymer.-Forsch.*, **2**, 1 (1960).
304. R. A. Gregg and F. R. Mayo, *Discussions Faraday Soc.*, **2**, 328 (1947).
305. R. A. Gregg and F. R. Mayo, *J. Am. Chem. Soc.*, **70**, 2373 (1948).
306. R. A. Gregg and F. R. Mayo, *J. Am. Chem. Soc.*, **75**, 3530 (1953).
307. J. C. Bevington and H. G. Troth, *Trans. Faraday Soc.*, **59**, 127 (1963).
308. J. C. Bevington and H. G. Troth, *Trans. Faraday Soc.*, **58**, 2005 (1963).
309. W. H. Stockmayer and L. H. Peebles, *J. Am. Chem. Soc.*, **75**, 2278 (1953).
310. D. B. Anderson and G. M. Burnett, unpublished data; G. M. Burnett, *Progr. Reaction Kinetics*, **3**, 449 (1965).
311. J. W. Breitenbach, *Naturwiss.*, **29**, 708 (1941).

312. J. W. Breitenbach, *Makromol. Chem.*, **8**, 147 (1952).
313. D. B. Anderson, G. M. Burnett, and A. C. Gowan, *J. Polymer Sci.*, **A1**, 1465 (1963).
314. M. Morton, J. A. Cala, and I. Piirma, *J. Am. Chem. Soc.*, **78**, 5394 (1956).
315. M. S. Kharasch, E. V. Jensen, and W. H. Urry, *J. Am. Chem. Soc.*, **69**, 1100 (1947).
316. D. F. de Tar and D. V. Wells, *J. Am. Chem. Soc.*, **82**, 5839 (1960).
317. J. Harmon, T. A. Ford, W. E. Hanford, and R. M. Joyce, *J. Am. Chem. Soc.*, **72**, 2213 (1950).
318. J. W. Breitenbach and A. Maschin, *Z. Physik. Chem. Leipzig*, **A187**, 175 (1940).
319. C. H. Bamford and M. J. S. Dewar, *Discussions Faraday Soc.*, **2**, 314 (1947).
320. C. Walling, E. R. Briggs, K. B. Wolfstirn, and F. R. Mayo, *J. Am. Chem. Soc.*, **70**, 1537 (1948).
321. C. Walling, E. R. Briggs, and K. B. Wolfstirn, *J. Am. Chem. Soc.*, **70**, 1543 (1948).
322. C. Walling, D. Seymour, and K. B. Wolfstirn, *J. Am. Chem. Soc.*, **70**, 2259 (1948).
323. C. Walling, *J. Am. Chem. Soc.*, **70**, 2561 (1948).
324. T. Alfrey, Jr., J. J. Bohrer, and H. Mark, *Copolymerization*, Wiley (Interscience), New York, 1957; G. E. Ham, ed., *Copolymerization*, Wiley (Interscience), New York, 1964.
325. K. Katagiri, K. Uno, and S. O. Okamura, *J. Polymer Sci.*, **17**, 142 (1955); K. Katagiri and S. Okamura, *J. Polymer Sci.*, **17**, 309 (1955).
326. N. Fuhrman and R. B. Mesrobian, *J. Am. Chem. Soc.*, **76**, 3281 (1954).
327. J. Pellon, *J. Polymer Sci.*, **43**, 537 (1960).
328. G. Platau, F. R. Eirich, R. B. Mesrobian, and A. E. Woodward, *J. Polymer Sci.*, **39**, 357 (1959).
329. C. H. Bamford and E. F. T. White, *Trans. Faraday Soc.*, **52**, 716 (1956).
330. J. C. Bevington and H. G. Troth, *Trans. Faraday Soc.*, **59**, 1348 (1963).
331. W. E. Mochel and J. H. Peterson, *J. Am. Chem. Soc.*, **71**, 1426 (1949).
332. W. Pryor, *Mechanisms of Sulphur Reactions*, McGraw-Hill, New York, 1962.
333. A. V. Tobolsky and B. Baysal, *J. Am. Chem. Soc.*, **75**, 1757 (1953).
334. R. M. Pierson, A. J. Costanza, and A. H. Weinstein, *J. Polymer Sci.*, **17**, 221 (1955).
335. W. H. Stockmayer, R. O. Howard, and J. T. Clarke, *J. Am. Chem. Soc.*, **75**, 1756 (1953).
336. R. A. Gregg, D. M. Alderman, and F. R. Mayo, *J. Am. Chem. Soc.*, **70**, 3740 (1948).
337. E. J. Meehan, I. M. Kolthoff, and P. R. Sinha, *J. Polymer Sci.*, **16**, 471 (1955).
338. V. A. Dinaburg and A. A. Vansheidt, *J. Gen. Chem. USSR (English Transl.)*, **24**, 839 (1954).
339. W. A. Pryor, *Mechanisms of Sulphur Reactions*, McGraw-Hill, New York, 1962, p. 53.
340. A. J. Costanza, R. J. Coleman, R. M. Pierson, C. S. Marvel, and C. King, *J. Polymer Sci.*, **17**, 319 (1955).
341. E. Perry, *J. Polymer Sci.*, **54**, S46 (1961).
342. L. Pauling, *The Nature of the Chemical Bond*, Cornell Univ. Press, Ithaca, N.Y., 1945.
343. R. A. Bird, G. A. Harpell, and K. E. Russell, *Can. J. Chem.*, **40**, 701 (1962).
344. M. P. Godsay, G. A. Harpell, and K. E. Russell, *J. Polymer Sci.*, **57**, 641 (1962).
345. C. H. Bamford, A. D. Jenkins, and R. Johnston, *Trans. Faraday Soc.*, **55**, 418 (1959).
346. C. H. Bamford and A. D. Jenkins, *J. Polymer Sci.*, **53**, 149 (1961).
347. C. H. Bamford and A. D. Jenkins, *Trans. Faraday Soc.*, **59**, 530 (1963).
348. L. J. Young, *J. Polymer Sci.*, **54**, 411 (1961).
349. M. C. Shen, *J. Polymer Sci.*, **B1**, 11 (1963).
350. N. Kawabata, T. Tsuruta, and J. Furukawa, *Makromol. Chem.*, **51**, 70 (1962).
351. R. D. Burkhart and N. L. Zutty, *J. Polymer Sci.*, **A1**, 1137 (1963).
352. C. C. Price, *J. Polymer Sci.*, **B1**, 433 (1963).
353. C. Walling and J. Pellon, *J. Am. Chem. Soc.*, **79**, 4776 (1957).
354. A. C. Toohey and K. E. Weale, *Trans. Faraday Soc.*, **58**, 2446 (1962).
355. A. C. Toohey and K. E. Weale, *Trans. Faraday Soc.*, **58**, 2439 (1962).
356. C. D. Thurmond and B. H. Zimm, *J. Polymer Sci.*, **8**, 477 (1952).

357. O. J. Walker and C. A. Winkler, *Can. J. Chem.*, **B28**, 298 (1950).
358. L. A. Wall and D. W. Brown, *J. Polymer Sci.*, **14**, 513 (1954).
359. G. Meyerhoff and M. Cantow, *J. Polymer Sci.*, **34**, 503 (1959), and discussion.
360. J. C. Bevington, G. M. Guzman, and H. W. Melville, *Proc. Roy. Soc. (London)*, **A221**, 453 (1954).
361. M. Morton and I. Piirma, *J. Am. Chem. Soc.*, **80**, 5596 (1958).
362. M. Morton and I. Piirma, *J. Polymer Sci.*, **A1**, 3043 (1963).
363. G. Henrici-Olivé, S. Olivé, and G. V. Schulz, *Z. Physik. Chem. (Frankfurt)*, **20**, 176 (1959).
364. M. S. Gluckman, M. J. Kampf, J. L. O'Brien, T. G. Fox, and R. K. Graham, *J. Polymer Sci.*, **37**, 411 (1959).
365. M. Morton, J. A. Cala, and I. Piirma, *J. Am. Chem. Soc.*, **78**, 5398 (1956).
366. G. Henrici-Olivé and S. Olivé, *Mazhdunar. Simpozium Makromol. Khim.*, *Dokl. Moscow Sektsiya*, **3**, 243 (1960).
367. G. W. King, Ref. *1*, p. 231.
368. M. H. Jones, H. W. Melville, and W. P. Robertson, *Nature*, **174**, 78 (1954).
369. M. H. Jones, H. W. Melville, and W. P. Robertson, *Simp. Intern. Chim. Macromol.*, Milan, 1954, p. 271.
370. I. G. Sobelova, N. V. Makletsova, and S. S. Medvedev, *Kolloidn. Zh.*, **19**, 619 (1957).
371. W. Cooper, *J. Chem. Soc.*, **1952**, 2408.
372. C. Walling and Y. W. Chang, *J. Am. Chem. Soc.*, **76**, 4878 (1954).
373. R. N. Haward and W. Simpson, *Trans. Faraday Soc.*, **47**, 212 (1951).
374. T. Otsu, K. Nayatani, I. Muto, and M. Imai, *Makromol. Chem.*, **27**, 149 (1958).
375. T. E. Ferington and A. V. Tobolsky, *J. Am. Chem. Soc.*, **77**, 4510 (1955).
376. T. Otsu and K. Nayatani, *Makromol. Chem.*, **27**, 149 (1958).
377. T. Otsu, *J. Polymer Sci.*, **26**, 236 (1957).
378. T. Ferington and A. V. Tobolsky, *J. Am. Chem. Soc.*, **80**, 3215 (1958).
379. G. V. Schulz, *Ber.*, **80**, 232 (1947).
380. R. L. Frank and C. E. Adams, *J. Am. Chem. Soc.*, **68**, 908 (1946).
381. J. W. Breitenbach and H. L. Breitenbach, *Z. Physik. Chem. Leipzig*, **A190**, 361 (1941).
382. F. R. Mayo and R. A. Gregg, *J. Am. Chem. Soc.*, **70**, 1285 (1948).
383. J. W. Breitenbach and A. J. Renner, *Can. J. Res.*, **B28**, 507 (1950).
384. J. W. Breitenbach and H. Tschamler, *Monatsh.*, **82**, 179 (1951).
385. J. W. Breitenbach and H. Karlinger, *Monatsh.*, **82**, 95 (1951).
386. S. G. Cohen, *J. Polymer Sci.*, **2**, 511 (1947).
387. S. G. Cohen, *J. Am. Chem. Soc.*, **67**, 17 (1945); **69**, 1057 (1947).
388. C. C. Price, *J. Am. Chem. Soc.*, **65**, 2380 (1943); C. C. Price and D. H. Read, *J. Polymer Sci.*, **1**, 44 (1946).
389. C. C. Price, *Mechanisms of Reactions at Carbon–Carbon Double Bonds*, Wiley (Interscience), New York, 1946.
390. J. C. Bevington, N. A. Ghanem, and H. W. Melville, *J. Chem. Soc.*, **1955**, 2822.
391. J. C. Bevington and N. A. Ghanem, *Makromol. Chem.*, **43**, 61 (1961).
392. A. F. Bickel and W. A. Waters, *J. Chem. Soc.*, **1950**, 1764.
393. F. Tüdös and N. I. Smirnow, *Acta Chim. Hung.*, **15**, 389, 401, 409 (1958); F. Tüdös and V. Furst, ibid., 417.
394. F. Tüdös and L. Simandi, *Vysokomolekul. Soedin.*, **4**, 1271, 1425, 1431 (1962); F. Tüdös, T. Bereznich, and B. Turcsanyi, ibid., 1584.
395. F. Tüdös, *J. Polymer Sci.*, **30**, 343 (1958).
396. G. V. Schulz, *Ber.*, **80**, 232 (1947).
397. C. C. Price, reference 389, p. 85.

398. C. C. Price and D. A. Durham, *J. Am. Chem. Soc.*, **65**, 757 (1943).
399. P. D. Bartlett, G. S. Hammond, and H. Kwart, *Discussions Faraday Soc.*, **2**, 342 (1947).
400. P. D. Bartlett and H. Kwart, *J. Am. Chem. Soc.*, **72**, 1051 (1950).
401. G. S. Hammond and P. D. Bartlett, *J. Polymer Sci.*, **6**, 617 (1951).
402. N. Inamoto and O. Simamura, *J. Org. Chem.*, **23**, 408 (1958).
403. W. P. Norris, *J. Am. Chem. Soc.*, **81**, 4239 (1959).
404. J. C. Bevington and N. A. Ghanem, *J. Chem. Soc.*, **1959**, 2071.
405. F. Tüdös, I. Kende, and M. Azori, *J. Polymer Sci.*, **53**, 17 (1961).
406. F. Tüdös, I. Kende, T. Bereznich, S. Solodovnikov, and V. Voevodskii, *Magy. Kem. Folyoirat*, **69**, 371 (1963).
407. C. E. H. Bawn and S. F. Mellish, *Trans. Faraday Soc.*, **47**, 1216 (1951).
408. G. S. Hammond, J. N. Sen, and C. E. Boozer, *J. Am. Chem. Soc.*, **77**, 3244 (1955).
409. J. A. Lyons and W. F. Watson, *J. Polymer Sci.*, **18**, 141 (1955).
410. P. J. Proll and L. H. Sutcliffe, *Trans. Faraday Soc.*, **59**, 2090 (1963).
411. C. Walling, *J. Polymer Sci.*, **14**, 214 (1954).
412. J. C. Bevington, *Nature*, **175**, 477 (1955).
413. J. C. Bevington, *J. Chem. Soc.*, **1956**, 1127.
414. S. Goldschmidt and K. Renn, *Ber.*, **B55**, 628 (1922).
415. R. H. Poirier, E. J. Kahler, and F. Bennington, *J. Org. Chem.*, **17**, 1437 (1952).
416. A. Henglein, *Makromol. Chem.*, **15**, 188 (1955).
417. K. E. Russell, *J. Phys. Chem.*, **58**, 437 (1954).
418. E. A. Braude, A. G. Brook, and R. P. Linstead, *J. Chem. Soc.*, **1954**, 3574.
419. Z. Laita and Z. Macháček, *J. Polymer Sci.*, **38**, 459 (1959).
420. J. C. McGowan, T. Powell, and R. Raw, *J. Chem. Soc.*, **1959**, 3103.
421. J. S. Hogg, D. H. Lohmann, and K. E. Russell, *Can. J. Chem.*, **39**, 1588 (1961).
422. J. S. Hogg, D. H. Lohmann, and K. E. Russell, *Can. J. Chem.*, **39**, 1394 (1961).
423. J. C. McGowan and T. Powell, *J. Chem. Soc.*, **1961**, 2160.
424. W. I. Bengough, *Chem. & Ind. (London)*, **1955**, 599.
425. F. R. Mayo and R. A. Gregg, *J. Am. Chem. Soc.*, **70**, 1284 (1948).
426. J. C. Bevington, *J. Chem. Soc.*, **1956**, 3506.
427. F. R. Mayo and A. A. Miller, *J. Am. Chem. Soc.*, **78**, 1023 (1956).
428. C. E. Barnes, R. M. Elofson, and G. D. Jones, *J. Am. Chem. Soc.*, **72**, 210 (1950).
429. A. A. Miller and F. R. Mayo, *J. Am. Chem. Soc.*, **78**, 1017 (1956).
430. S. Medvedev and P. Tseitlin, *Acta Physicochim. URSS*, **20**, 3 (1945); *J. Phys. Chem. USSR*, **18**, 13 (1944).
431. H. Trenne, *Chemiker-Zeitung*, **74**, 692 (1950).
432. P. D. Bartlett and D. S. Trifan, *J. Polymer Sci.*, **20**, 457 (1956).
433. D. M. Gardner and G. K. Fraenkel, *J. Am. Chem. Soc.*, **78**, 3279 (1956).
434. J. L. Kice, *J. Am. Chem. Soc.*, **76**, 6274 (1954).
435. G. Kraus, J. T. Gruver, and K. W. Rollmann, *J. Polymer Sci.*, **36**, 564 (1959).
436. A. I. Medalia, E. Hagopian, and J. P. Hall, *J. Polymer Sci.*, **57**, 693 (1962).
437. G. Kraus and R. L. Collins, *Rubber World*, **139**, 219 (1958).
438. R. L. Collins, M. D. Bell, and G. Kraus, *J. Appl. Phys.*, **30**, 56 (1959).
439. G. Kraus, J. T. Gruver, and K. W. Rollmann, *Proc. Fourth Carbon Conf.*, Pergamon, London, 1960, p. 291.
440. C. H. Bamford, A. D. Jenkins, and R. Johnston, *Proc. Roy. Soc. (London)*, **A239**, 214 (1957).
441. C. H. Bamford, A. D. Jenkins, and R. Johnston, *Nature*, **177**, 992 (1956).
442. E. Collinson, F. S. Dainton, and G. S. McNaughton, *J. Chim. Phys.*, **52**, 556 (1955).
443. E. R. Entwistle, *Trans. Faraday Soc.*, **56**, 284 (1960).

444. F. Tüdös, I. Kende, and M. Azori, *J. Polymer Sci.*, **A1**, 1353, 1369 (1963).

445. J. L. Kice, *J. Polymer Sci.*, **19**, 123 (1956).

446. G. M. Burnett and P. R. E. J. Cowley, *Trans. Faraday Soc.*, **49**, 1490 (1953).

447. P. W. Allen, F. M. Merrett, and J. Scanlan, *Trans. Faraday Soc.*, **51**, 95 (1955).

448. F. R. Mayo, *J. Am. Chem. Soc.*, **80**, 2465 (1958).

449. M. S. Matheson, E. B. Bevilacqua, E. E. Auer, and E. J. Hart, *J. Am. Chem. Soc.*, **71**, 497 (1949).

450. P. F. Onyon, *Trans. Faraday Soc.*, **51**, 400 (1955).

451. W. G. Barb, *Proc. Roy. Soc. (London)*, **A212**, 66, 177 (1952).

452. C. Walling, *J. Polymer Sci.*, **16**, 315 (1955).

453. C. M. Burrell, T. G. Majury, and H. W. Melville, *Proc. Roy. Soc. (London)*, **A205**, 309 (1951); T. G. Majury and H. W. Melville, **A205**, 323 (1951).

454. N. Grassie and H. W. Melville, *Proc. Roy. Soc. (London)*, **A207**, 285 (1951).

455. W. V. Smith and R. H. Ewart, *J. Chem. Phys.*, **16**, 592 (1948).

456. W. V. Smith, *J. Am. Chem. Soc.*, **70**, 3695 (1948).

457. M. Morton, P. Salatiello, and H. Landfield, *J. Polymer Sci.*, **8**, 279 (1952).

458. K. P. Paoletti and F. W. Billmeyer, *J. Polymer Sci.*, **A2**, 2049 (1964).

459. J. Abere, G. Goldfinger, H. Naidus, and H. Mark, *J. Phys. Chem.*, **49**, 211 (1945).

460. A. Chapiro, *J. Chim. Phys.*, **47**, 747, 764 (1950).

461. J. B. Donnet, L. Geldreich, G. Henrick, and G. Riess, *Colloq. Nationaux Centre Natl. Rech. Sci. (Paris)*, **24**, 143 (1963).

462. C. Loucheux, *Ann. Chim.*, **9**, 143 (1964).

463. N. S. Tsvetkov, E. S. Beletskaya, and L. N. Bondarchuk, *Vysokomolekul. Soedin. Karbotsepnye Vysokomolekul.*, **1963**, 131.

464. C. Walling and L. Heaton, *J. Am. Chem. Soc.*, **87**, 38 (1965).

465. E. T. Denisov and L. N. Denisova, *Dokl. Akad. Nauk SSSR*, **157**, 907 (1964).

466. G. P. Gladyshev, *Trans. Inst. Khim. Nauk Akad. Nauk Kaz. SSR*, **11**, 25 (1964).

467. J. N. Sen, U. Nandi, and S. R. Palit, *J. Indian Chem. Soc.*, **40**, 729 (1963).

468. M. R. Gopalan and M. Santappa, *Makromol. Chem.*, **50**, 83 (1961).

469. J. R. Nielsen, *J. Polymer Sci.*, **C7**, 19 (1964).

470. N. V. Zubova, M. M. Sushchinskii, and V. A. Zubov, *Zh. Eksperim. i Teor. Fiz. Pis'ma v Redaktsiyu*, **2**, 63 (1965).

471. A. Odajima, J. A. Sauer, and A. E. Woodward, *J. Polymer Sci.*, **57**, 107 (1962); A. I. Maklakov and G. G. Pimenov, *Vysokomolekul. Soedin.*, **7**, 536 (1965); A. I. Maklakov, G. G. Pimenov, and V. I. Shepelev, *Vysokomolekul. Soedin.*, **7**, 1894 (1965).

472. A. M. Dubinskeya, P. Yu. Butyagin, and A. A. Berlin, *Dokl. Akad. Nauk SSSR*, **159**, 595 (1964).

473. R. Rado, F. Srocs, and M. Lazar, *Collection Czech. Chem. Commun.*, **30**, 894 (1965).

474. J. W. Breitenbach, D. Campbell, and A. Schindler, *J. Polymer Sci.*, **B3**, 1017 (1965).

475. I. Abu-Isa and M. Dole, *J. Phys. Chem.*, **69**, 2668 (1965); M. Dole, *Fortschr. Hochpolymer.-Forsch.*, **2**, 221 (1960).

476. F. E. Karasz, H. E. Blair, and J. M. O'Rielly, *J. Phys. Chem.*, **69**, 2657 (1965).

477. F. C. Goodrich and M. Cantow, *J. Polymer Sci.*, **C8**, 269 (1965).

478. G. P. Gladyshev and N. F. Khasanova, *Dokl. Akad. Nauk SSSR*, **163**, 1193, 1423 (1965).

479. C. Walling and L. Heaton, *J. Am. Chem. Soc.*, **87**, 48 (1965).

480. G. M. Burnett, W. S. Dailey, and J. M. Pearson, *Trans. Faraday Soc.*, **61**, 1216 (1965).

481. C. Walling and E. S. Savas, *J. Am. Chem. Soc.*, **82**, 1738 (1960).

482. K. F. O'Driscoll and P. J. White, *J. Polymer Sci.*, **A3**, 283 (1965).

483. V. D. Enalev, V. V. Zaitseva, Y. S. Sadovskii, T. N. Sadovskaya, and Z. F. Nazarova, *Vysokomolekul. Soedin.*, **7**, 275 (1965).

484. E. Tsuchida and S. Mimashi, *J. Polymer Sci.*, **A3**, 1401 (1965).
485. V. M. Zhulin, M. G. Gonikberg, and V. N. Zagorbinina, *Dokl. Akad. Nauk SSSR*, **163**, 106 (1965).
486. A. F. Barton and J. C. Bevington, *Trans. Faraday Soc.*, **62**, 433 (1966).
487. K. Tsuda, S. Kobayashi, and T. Otsu, *Bull. Chem. Soc. (Japan)*, **38**, 1517 (1965).
488. J. W. Breitenbach, O. F. Olaj, K. Kuchner, and H. Horaček, *Makromol. Chem.*, **87**, 295 (1965).
489. K. F. O'Driscoll, P. F. Lyons, and R. A. Patsiga, *J. Polymer Sci.*, **A3**, 1567 (1965).
490. G. Ayrey, F. G. Levitt, and R. J. Mazza, *Polymer*, **6**, 157 (1965).
491. J. W. Breitenbach and H. G. Burger, *Monatsh.*, **93**, 733 (1962); O. F. Olaj, J. W. Breitenbach, and B. Wolf, *Monatsh.*, **95**, 1646 (1964); J. W. Breitenbach, H. Gabler, and O. F. Olaj, *Makromol. Chem.*, **81**, 32 (1965).
492. K. Szyc-Lewanska and M. Sycewski, *Nitro Compounds, Proc. Intern. Symp.*, Warsaw, 1963, p. 257.
493. J. A. Howard and K. U. Ingold, *Can. J. Chem.*, **40**, 1851 (1965); **43**, 2729 (1965).
494. G. M. Burnett and H. W. Melville, in *Technique of Organic Chemistry*, Vol. VIII, Pt. II. (S. L. Friess, E. S. Lewis, and A. Weissberger, eds.), Wiley (Interscience), New York, 1963, Chap. 20.
495. S. Jovanović, J. Romatowski, and G. V. Schulz, *Makromol. Chem.*, **85**, 187 (1965); G. V. Schulz and J. Romatowski, **85**, 195, 227 (1965).
496. M. Imoto, M. Kinoshita, and M. Nishigaki, *Makromol. Chem.*, **86**, 217 (1965).
497. W. A. Pryor, R. W. Henderson, R. A. Patsiga, and N. Carroll, *J. Am. Chem. Soc.*, **88**, 1199 (1966).
498. A. V. Tobolsky, R. H. Gobran, R. Böhme, and R. Schaffhauser, *J. Phys. Chem.*, **67**, 2336 (1963); Z. Tadmor and J. A. Biesenberger, *J. Polymer Sci.*, **B3**, 753 (1965).
499. C. H. Bamford, G. C. Eastmond, and W. R. Maltman, *Trans. Faraday Soc.*, **61**, 267 (1965); C. H. Bamford, R. Denyer, and G. C. Eastmond, **61**, 1459 (1965); **62**, 688 (1966).
500. J. C. Bevington and G. Sinatti, *J. Polymer Sci.*, **B4**, 7 (1966).
501. P. J. Flory, *J. Am. Chem. Soc.*, **69**, 2893 (1947).
502. F. Tüdös, *Acta Chim. Acad. Sci. Hung.*, **43**, 397 (1965).
503. R. M. Noyes, *J. Am. Chem. Soc.*, **77**, 2042 (1955); *J. Phys. Chem.*, **65**, 763 (1961); *Progr. Reaction Kinetics*, **1**, 129 (1961).

CHAPTER 4

The Mechanism
of Vinyl Acetate Polymerization

Martin K. Lindemann†

Cumberland Chemical Corp., A Subsidiary of Air Reduction Co., Inc.
Bound Brook, New Jersey

† Present address: Mobil Chemical Co., Metuchen, N.J.

4-1. INTRODUCTION

Vinyl acetate has become an important monomer during the last fifteen years. Although the polymerization characteristics of vinyl acetate have been studied extensively over the years, a need exists to summarize and evaluate the present knowledge. The following chapter was designed to help fill that need. It was, of course, impossible to cover and include all of the numerous references pertaining to the polymerization of vinyl acetate that were published during the last thirty years. An attempt has been made to cover the often inaccessible, and therefore ignored, Japanese vinyl acetate literature.

4-2. KINETICS OF BULK AND SOLUTION POLYMERIZATION

In a free-radical polymerization there are four main reactions to consider, although a number of lesser reactions may also be important. The four main reactions are initiation, propagation, transfer, and termination. The following scheme represents the reaction steps:

Initiation:

$$I \xrightarrow{k_d} 2R \cdot \quad R + M \xrightarrow{f} M_i \cdot \qquad R_i = 2k_d f[I] \qquad (4\text{-}1)$$

Propagation:

$$M_n \cdot + M \xrightarrow{k_p} M_{n+1} \cdot \qquad R_p = k_p[M \cdot][M] \qquad (4\text{-}2)$$

Transfer to solvent:

$$M_n \cdot + S \xrightarrow{k_{trs}} M_n + S \cdot \qquad k_{trs}[M \cdot][S] \qquad (4\text{-}3)$$

Transfer to initiator:

$$M_n \cdot + I \xrightarrow{k_{tri}} M_n + I \cdot \qquad k_{tri}[M \cdot][I]$$

Transfer to monomer:

$$M_n \cdot + M \xrightarrow{k_{trm}} M_n + N \cdot \qquad k_{trm}[M \cdot][M] \qquad (4\text{-}4)$$

Reinitiation:

$$N \cdot + M \xrightarrow{k_{pm}} M_1 \cdot \qquad k_{pm}[N \cdot][M] \qquad (4\text{-}5)$$

Reinitiation:

$$S \cdot + M \xrightarrow{k_{ps}} M_1 \cdot \qquad k_{ps}[S \cdot][M] \qquad (4\text{-}6)$$

Termination (terminated and stabilized radical):

$$M_n \cdot + M_m \cdot \xrightarrow{k_t} \qquad k_t[M \cdot]^2 \qquad (4\text{-}7)$$

$$M_n \cdot + S \cdot \xrightarrow{k_{ts}} \qquad k_{ts}[S \cdot][M \cdot] \qquad (4\text{-}8)$$

$$S \cdot + S \cdot \xrightarrow{k_{tss}} \qquad k_{tss}[S \cdot]^2 \qquad (4\text{-}9)$$

A. Initiation and Initiators

During the initiation step the initiator decomposes and produces free radicals, which in turn react with monomer and start a polymer chain or abstract a labile hydrogen or halogen from any organic compound present. As a side reaction two free radicals produced by the initiator may terminate each other without starting a polymer chain.

A number of compounds can serve as initiators of vinyl acetate polymerization: for example, peroxides, hydroperoxides, and azo compounds. These decompose in solution either by heat or photochemically, following a certain rate. Not all free radicals thus produced start a polymerization reaction; in fact, even in the most favorable case not more than 50 to 60% of the radicals generated start a polymerization reaction. The initiator efficiency can be expressed as follows:

$$f = R_i/2k_d[\text{I}]$$

Table 4-1 lists the initiators that have been used in vinyl acetate polymerization. Only relatively few initiators are being used commercially in solution polymerization of vinyl acetate: benzoyl peroxide (BPO), lauroyl peroxide (LPO), t-butyl hydroperoxide $(t\text{-BHPO})$ (551), diisopropyl peroxydicarbonate (DPP) $(417,447)$, and azobisisobutyronitrile (AIBN) $(130,256)$.

AIBN has the advantage that its decomposition is essentially a first-order reaction not influenced by the solvent $(447,319,21)$. The latter statement is not exactly true $(318,9,110)$, since rate of decomposition differences, especially in various aromatic solvents, have been detected (456). A summary of the chemistry of azo initiators as it pertains to polymerization reactions has recently been published (595). The efficiency of AIBN is only 50% or less in vinyl acetate polymerization $(342,22,65)$. AIBN has the advantage over most peroxides of having a low transfer constant, which results in polymers of higher molecular weight than those made with organic peroxides (485). The chain-transfer constant of benzoyl peroxide was determined by Matsumoto (339) to be $C_i = 0.09$. Figure 4-1 compares AIBN and BPO in a vinyl acetate polymerization. It can be seen that, when $1/\overline{\text{DP}}$ is plotted against $R_p/[\text{M}]^{-2}$, AIBN gives a straight line denoting no transfer to initiator, whereas BPO shows a large deviation from linearity. Sakurada et al. (485) studied the decomposition of AIBN in vinyl acetate at various temperatures and calculated rates of decomposition. He found for AIBN:

$$k_d = 7.9 \times 10^{16} \exp\left(-34,000/RT\right) \quad \sec^{-1}$$

Barsom et al. (41) studied the reactivity of vinyl acetate and other monomers to the benzoyloxy radical. They found that the e values for monomers of Price (462) can be correlated with the relative reactivities of the monomers

TABLE 4-1

Vinyl Acetate Polymerization with Various Initiators

Initiator	Mode of polymerization	Ref.
Azobisisobutyronitrile	Solution	43,22
Azobisisobutyronitrile	Solution	485,342
Dibenzoyl peroxide	Solution	41
Dianisoyl peroxide	Solution	16
Di-o-bromobenzoyl peroxide	Solution	98
Di-m-bromobenzoyl peroxide	Solution	98
Di-p-bromobenzoyl peroxide	Solution	98
Lauroyl peroxide	Solution	98
Palmitoyl peroxide	Solution	98
Benzoyl peroxide	Solution	98
Perester of polymethyl acrylate	Solution	477
Phenyl(phenyl sulfonyl)	Solution	446
Acetoxymethyl hyponitrile	Solution	317
Di-m-nitrobenzoyl peroxide	Solution	113
m-Nitrobenzoylbenzoyl peroxide	Solution	113
Di(2,3,4,5-tetrachlorobenzoyl) peroxide	Solution	113
N-Nitrosoacetanilide	Solution	121
Dioleoyl peroxide	Solution	569
Distearoyl peroxide	Solution	569
t-Butyl hydroperoxide	Solution	551
o-Chlorobenzoyl peroxide	Solution	404
Isopropyl peroxidicarbonate	Solution	580
Bis(trifluoromethyl) peroxide	Solution	118
α,α'-azobis(α,γ-dimethyl valeronitrile	Solution	308
α,α'-azobisdimethyl isobutyrate	Solution	357
4,4'azobis(4-cyanopentanonic acid)	Solution	357
Tetraalkylthiuram disulfides	Solution	443
t-Butyl hydroperoxide	Emulsion	594
Azodisulfonic acid	Emulsion	468
o-Methoxy benzoylperoxide	Suspension	341

to the benzoyloxy radical, suggesting that polar factors are important in the reaction of an initiator radical and the monomer.

Although redox polymerization of vinyl acetate is industrially performed primarily in an emulsion system, work has also been reported on redox polymerization in solution. One of the reasons for considering redox polymerizations is the fact that the activation energy of polymerization is greatly reduced with redox systems. This affords an opportunity to study the low-temperature polymerization and the resulting polymerization products.

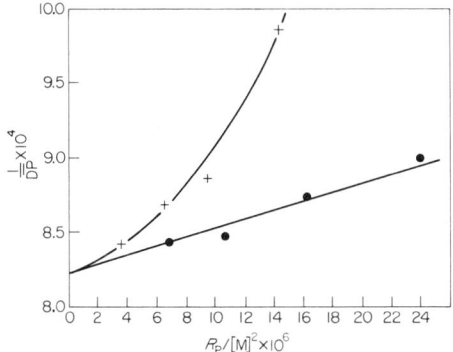

Fig. 4-1. Rate of polymerization and reciprocal degree of polymerization for two initiators (*343*). ●, azobisisobutyronitrile; +, benzoyl peroxide.

In the case of vinyl acetate this has been important for obtaining information on head-to-tail versus head-to-head polymerization and also for the preparation of stereoregular polyvinyl acetates and polyvinyl alcohols. Table 4-2 shows some typical redox systems for vinyl acetate. For example, a solution polymerization of vinyl acetate in methanol (VAcMeOH=70:30) was completed to 97% conversion in 24 hours at 0°C with the use of the *t*-butyl perbenzoate-1–ascorbic acid redox system (4:1 moles) at a level of 0.4% (*410*). Typical activation energies are shown in Table 4-3. It can be seen how much lower the activation energies are for redox polymerizations; only light and irradiation polymerizations are favored even more.

B. Propagation

The propagation step can be separated into two competing reactions: the head-to-tail addition and the head-to-head addition. The frequency of head-to-head addition for vinyl acetate polymerization was first measured by Flory and Leutner (*141*). They hydrolyzed polyvinyl acetates prepared at various temperatures and then determined the 1,2-glycol structure quantitatively by degradative oxidation. The activation energy difference between these two reactions was found to be about 1.3 kcal/mole: the lower the temperature the fewer 1,2-glycol structures were found.

Hayashi and Okamura (*221*) determined that the difference in activation energy between these two reactions was rather 3.4 kcal/mole; they had obtained the polyvinyl acetate in an emulsion system. It is interesting to speculate that in emulsion the vinyl acetate monomer is hydrated and therefore may react differently. Matsumoto and Imai (*340*) found the value of the activation-energy difference between the two reactions to be very close

TABLE 4-2

Redox-Initiated Vinyl Acetate Polymerization

Initiator system	Mode of polymerization	Ref.
Hydrogen (activated) with peroxide	Bulk	*114*
Hydrogen and palladiumsol with peroxide	Emulsion	*225*
Sodium perchlorate (sodium sulfite)	Emulsion	*583*
Peroxides and organic-metal salts	Solution	*227*
Peroxide and titanium sulfate	Solution	*268*
Hydrazine, cupric ions, oxygen	Solution	*359*
Metal salt–sulfuric acid– benzoyl peroxide	Solution	*547*
p-Chlorosulfuric acid–aminebenzoyl peroxide	Solution	*549*
p-Chlorosulfuric acid–dimethyl aniline–benzoyl peroxide	Solution	*550*
Azobisisobutyronitrile-p-chlorobenzene sulfuric acid	Solution	*256*
Diisopropyl dicarbonate peroxide–N,N-dimethylaniline	Solution	*416,417*
Tetrakis (hydroxymethyl) phosphine oxide–Ce^{4+}, Mn^{4+}	Solution	*265*
Chlorate–sulfite	Suspension	*234*
Benzoin–ferric salts–benzoyl peroxide	Solution	*283,548,215*
t-Butyl perbenzoate–ascorbic acid	Solution	*410,418–420*
Hydrogen peroxide–ascorbic acid	Solution	*216–218*
Hydrogen peroxide–Rongalite	Solution	*219*
Potassium persulfate–sodium dithionite	Solution, Emulsion	*194,297*

TABLE 4-3

Activation Energy of Polymerization of Vinyl Acetate for Various Initiators

Initiator	Activation energy, kcal/mole	Ref.
Azobisisobutyronitrile	26	*485*
Isopropyl peroxydicarbonate	18.5	*410*
Tributyl borate	15–16	*247*
Isopropyl peroxydicarbonate– N,N-dimethyl aniline	11.4	*410*
t-Butyl perbenzoate–1-ascorbic acid	10	*410*
Irradiation	3.7	*433*
Light	3.2	*387*

to that of Flory and Leutner, but they also used polyvinyl acetate prepared in solution.

The over-all rate constant of propagation has been measured by many investigators. Table 4-4 gives a survey of all the velocity constants in vinyl acetate polymerization. Schulz and Stein (*495*) found that the values of the propagation and termination rate constants were much higher than was previously thought.

Matheson's et al. (*337*) measurements are given in Table 4-5. There is some confusion in the literature about these rate constants. Matheson, for example, assumed termination by combination. It has, however, been fairly well established that termination in vinyl acetate polymerization occurs by disproportionation. All of Matheson's values should, therefore, be doubled.

The rate constants of propagation and termination are very much dependent on the degree of conversion of monomer to polymer. Melville (*356*) and Miyama (*372*) showed that the rate constant for polymerization at 65% conversion had decreased to less than 5% of its original value at 5% conversion at 25°C (see Table 4-6). By raising the temperature the original value of k_p was maintained longer owing to increased mobility (see Fig. 4-2). The termination rate constant was affected even more by increasing conversion (*223*). This is shown in Fig. 4-3, where the lifetime of radicals is plotted against conversion at various temperatures. It is important to remember that diffusion-controlled processes such as propagation and termination quickly have an influence on apparent reactivity when the velocity constants are large, as is the case of vinyl acetate.

Although the mechanism and kinetics of vinyl acetate polymerization have been studied frequently, the values of the velocity constants do not often show good reproducibility. One of the chief reasons has been the difficulty in obtaining pure monomer. Ultraviolet absorption spectra of vinyl acetate used by various investigators have shown considerable differences (*337*). During the catalyzed or photoinitiated polymerization a gel effect similar to that occurring in methyl methacrylate polymerization was observed (see

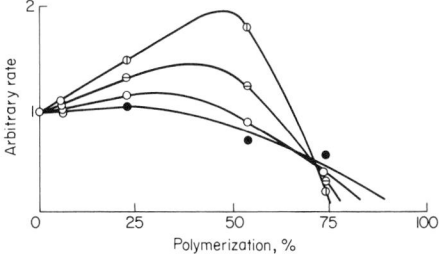

Fig. 4-2. Variation of rate of polymerization of vinyl acetate as a function of temperature and percentage conversion. Temperatures (°C): ①, 0, ⊖, 25; ○, 50; ●, 75 (*355*).

TABLE 44

Summary of Velocity Constants for Vinyl Acetate Polymerization

	k_p	$\bar{E}_p$, kcal/mole	k_{trm}	$\bar{E}_{trm}$, kcal/mole	k_t, $\times 10^{-6}$	$\bar{E}_t$, kcal/mole	$(k_t/k_p^2) \times 10^{-3}$, mole liter^{-1} sec^{-1} (70°C)
Swain and Bartlett (522)	1100 (25°C)				80 (25°C)		
Burnett and Melville (88,89)	780 (25°C)				390 (25°C)		
Burnett et al. (91)	1012 (25°C)	4.4 (25°C)			58.8 (25°C)	0	2.28
Matheson et al. (337)	2640 (50°C)	7.3			116.8 (50°C)		
Dixon-Lewis (123)	4600 (25°C)	3.2 (25°C)	0.36 (25°C)	6.1	220 (25°C)	5.2	3.38
Kwart et al. (310)	1000 (25°C)		0.23 (25°C)		59 (25°C)	0	2.76
Motoyama and Okamura (389)							3.6
Bevington (64)		7.3 (60°C)		10 (60°C)			
Matsumoto and Maeda (342)	7730 (60°C)						3.0
Sakurada et al. (485)							2.3
Schulz and Stein (495)	19000 (60°C)				760 (60°C)		2.1

TABLE 4-5

Temperature Dependence of the Rate Constants for Propagation and
Termination of Vinyl Acetate (*337*)

Temp., °C	0	15.9	25	50	60
k_p, mole^{-1} liter sec^{-1}	320	690	1012	2640	3700
$2k_t \times 10^{-7}$	2.7	4.5	5.88	11.68	14.8

TABLE 4-6

Rate Constants of Propagation and Termination as a Function of
Conversion for Vinyl Acetate Polymerization at 25°C (*356*)

Conversion, %	4	23	46	57	65
k_p, mole^{-1} liter sec^{-1}	860	990	1070	238	30
k_t, $\times 10^{-5}$	240	126	90	6.7	1.15

Table 4-6). The kinetic order with respect to initiator concentration is 0.5
in the case of pure monomer (*115*), and also in benzene (*85*) and toluene (*84*)
solution. The square-root dependence also holds true for the intensity in
photopolymerizations (*31*).

The dependence of rate on monomer concentration is more complex.
Burnett and Melville (*89*) observed a first-order dependence on monomer
concentration (1.5 to 4.5 molar) in ethyl acetate, but Conix and Smets (*112*)
found an order of 1.5 in the same solvent in the range 5 to 10 molar. Loan

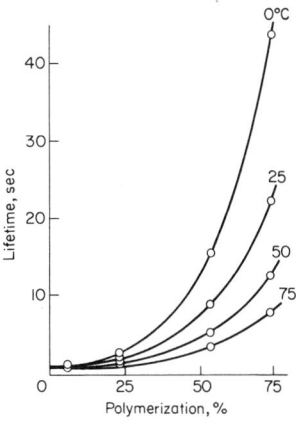

Fig. 4-3. Variation of radical lifetime with temperature and percentage conversion (*355*).

TABLE 4-7

Heat of Polymerization of Vinyl Acetate

Heat of polymerization, kcal/mole	Temp. determined at, °C	Ref.
21.4	25	*54*
20.1 ± 1.0	25	*53*
21.0 ± 0.5	75	*270*
8.0 ± 0.4	80	*186*
21.3 ± 0.2	77	*542*

and Burnett (*325*) showed that the rate dropped rapidly with decreasing monomer concentration in benzene.

The heat of polymerization of vinyl acetate has been determined several times (see Table 4-7). The value of 8 kcal/mole reported very early (*186*) was too low. Otherwise there is good agreement between various determinations at different temperatures.

C. Chain Transfer

1. KINETICS OF CHAIN TRANSFER

It was recognized early by Flory (*138*) that a reaction was taking place during the course of polymerization that limited the molecular weight of the resulting polymer without affecting substantially the rate of polymerization. He concluded that the activity of the growing radical was transferred either to a monomer or to a solvent molecule. This concept was first experimentally verified by Breitenbach and Maschin (*76*), who found four chlorine atoms per molecule in polystyrene that had been polymerized in the presence of carbon tetrachloride.

Cuthbertson and co-workers (*115*) also found that the concept of chain transfer explained the fact that the degree of polymerization of vinyl acetate, when polymerized in the presence of toluene, decreased, and they showed that toluene must have actually been incorporated into the polymer molecule by a transfer reaction.

Mayo (*350*), using published data on styrene polymerization, showed that a simple expression could be used for determining the so-called transfer constant C, which was defined as the ratio of the rate constants for the transfer and propagation reactions. In its simplest form the equation was written by Mayo as

$$1/\overline{DP} = C_s \frac{[S]}{[M]} + 1/\overline{DP}_0$$

where $\overline{DP}$ is the average degree of polymerization of the polymer obtained in the presence of solvent, $\overline{DP_0}$ is the average degree of polymerization obtained when pure monomer was polymerized, $|S|$ is the moles of solvent, $[M]$ is the moles of monomer, and C_s is the transfer constant, defined as k_{tr}/k_p.

This equation is valid only when several assumptions, which are generally valid for styrene, are made; the rate of polymerization is not affected by the transfer reaction (or, in other words, the radicals resulting from transfer have the same order of activity as the styrene radicals), the initiator does not enter into any transfer reaction (this is true only in certain cases in which ultraviolet light is used as initiator), and the average degree of polymerization measured is equal to twice the kinetic chain length.

There are a number of reviews dealing with this subject in detail (33,140, 226).

In the case of vinyl acetate the chain-transfer phenomenon has been studied extensively, because the high reactivity of the vinyl acetate radical causes large reductions in molecular weight in the presence of transfer agents, which are easily measured, and because the radicals produced by chain transfer usually have a lower activity and, therefore, the chain-transfer process retards the rate of polymerization much more than when styrene or methyl methacrylate is used for these studies. The transfer is then called "degradative." The kinetic analysis is, of course, quite different in this case.

The kinetics of retarded polymerizations have been discussed in several papers (19,90,267,286,287,526). Table 4-8 lists the kinetic possibilities (592).

By applying the steady-state conditions the following equations are derived

TABLE 4-8

Effect of Magnitude of Rate Constants on Rate and Degree of
Polymerization

Condition of polymerization	Definition	Effect on R_p	Effect on $\overline{DP}$
$k_p \ggg k_{tr}, k_{ps} \simeq k_p$	Regular chain transfer	No change	Decrease
$k_p \ggg k_{tr}, k_{ps} < k_p$	Retardation	Decrease	Decrease
$k_p \lll k_{tr}, k_{ps} \simeq k_p$	Modifier action, telomer formation	No change	Large decrease
$k_p \lll k_{tr}, k_{ps} < k_p$	Degradative chain transfer	Large decrease	Large decrease

for the case of regular chain transfer:

$$d[M\cdot]/d_t = R_i - k_{trm}[M][M\cdot] - k_{trs}[S][M\cdot] + k_{pm}[M][N\cdot] + k_{ps}[M][S\cdot]$$
$$- k_t[M\cdot]^2 = 0 \tag{4-10}$$

$$d[S\cdot]/d_t = k_{trs}[S][M\cdot] - k_{ps}[M][S\cdot] = 0 \tag{4-11}$$

$$d[N\cdot]/d_t = k_{trm}[M][M\cdot] - k_{pm}[M][N\cdot] = 0 \tag{4-12}$$

where $[M\cdot] = \sum_n[M_n\cdot]$ is the total polymer radical concentration. Addition of Eqs. (4-10), (4-11), and (4-12) gives

$$R_i = k_t[M\cdot]^2 \tag{4-13}$$

The rate of propagation is

$$-d[M]/d_t = k_p[M][M\cdot]$$

Substituting for $[M\cdot]$,

$$-d[M]/d_t = k_p[M]R_i^{1/2}k_t^{-1/2} \tag{4-14}$$

It can be seen that simple chain transfer has no effect on the rate of polymerization. In this case the additional assumption has been made that the radicals derived from the solvent $S\cdot$ do not take part in the termination reaction. This is true when k_{ps} is of an order of magnitude similar to k_p; then Eq. (4-2) becomes

$$k_{trs}[S][M\cdot] = k_{ps}[M][S\cdot] \tag{4-15}$$

$$\frac{[S\cdot]}{[M\cdot]} = (k_{trs}/k_p)/([S]/[M\cdot]) \tag{4-16... }$$

This quantity is usually very small; therefore, the assumption made above is valid. However, if k_{ps} is much smaller than k_p (see Table 4-8), then Eqs. (4-1), (4-2), and (4-3) change as follows:

$$d[M\cdot]/d_t = R_i - k_{trm}[M][M\cdot] - k_{trs}[S][M\cdot] + k_{pm}[M][N\cdot]$$
$$+ k_{ps}[M][S\cdot] - (k_t + k_{t'})[M\cdot]^2 - k_{ts}[M\cdot][S\cdot] = 0 \tag{4-16}$$

$$d[S\cdot]/d_t = k_{trs}[S][M\cdot] - k_{ps}[M][S\cdot] - k_{ts}[M\cdot][S\cdot] - k_{tss}[S\cdot]^2 = 0 \tag{4-17}$$

$$d[N\cdot]/d_t = k_{trm}[M][M\cdot] - k_{pm}[M][N\cdot] = 0 \tag{4-18}$$

Adding Eqs. (4-16), (4-17), and (4-18), we obtain

$$R_i = k_t[M\cdot]^2 + 2k_{ts}[M\cdot][S\cdot] + k_{tss}[S\cdot]^2 \tag{4-19}$$

The fraction of $[S\cdot]$ that disappears by reaction (4-8) is equal to

$$\Omega = \frac{k_{ts}[M\cdot]}{k_p[M] + k_{ts}[M\cdot] + k_{tss}[S\cdot]} \tag{4-20}$$

The fraction of [S·] disappearing by reaction (4-9) is

$$\beta = \frac{k_{tss}[S\cdot]}{k_p[M] + k_{ts}[M\cdot] + k_{tss}[S\cdot]} \tag{4-21}$$

It is clear from the steady-state assumption that the number of S· radicals consumed must be equal to the number produced, which is $k_{trs}[M\cdot][S]$. Therefore, the number of radicals disappearing by reaction (4-8) is $k_{trs}[M\cdot][S]\Omega$, and by reaction (4-9) it is $k_{trs}[M\cdot][S]\beta$. Each S· consumed in reaction (4-8) stops two kinetic chains, whereas each S· consumed in reaction (4-9) stops one chain. Therefore, Eq. (4-19) can be rewritten:

$$R_i = 2k_{trs}[M\cdot][S]\Omega + k_{trs}[M\cdot][S]\beta + (k_t + t')[M\cdot]^2 \tag{4-22}$$

Substituting Ω and β we get

$$R_i = (k_t + k_{t'})[M\cdot]^2 + k_{trs}[M\cdot][S]\frac{2k_{ts}[M\cdot][S\cdot] + k_{tss}[S\cdot]^2}{k_{ps}[S\cdot][M] + k_{ts}[M\cdot][S\cdot] + k_{tss}[S\cdot]^2} \tag{4-23}$$

The rate of polymerization is

$$R_p = k_p[M\cdot][M] \tag{4-24}$$

and in the case of unretarded polymerization it is

$$R_0 = k_p[M\cdot]_0[M]_0 \tag{4-25}$$

where the subscript 0 denotes the rate in the absence of a terminator. Then

$$R_i = k_t[M\cdot]_0^2 = k_t R_0^2/k_p^2[M]_0^2 \tag{4-26}$$

On combining Eqs. (4-23), (4-24), and (4-26) we obtain

$$\frac{k_t}{k_p^2}\left(\frac{R_0^2}{[M]_0^2} - \frac{R_p^2}{[M]^2}\right) = \frac{k_{trs}[S]R_p}{k_p[M]}\left(\frac{2k_{ts}[S]/k_p[M] + k_{tss}[S\cdot]}{k_{ps}[M] + k_{ts}[S]/k_p[M] + k_{tss}[S\cdot]}\right) \tag{4-27}$$

Dissolving Eqs. (4-19), (4-24), and (4-26) per [S·], we have

$$[S\cdot] = \frac{k_{ts}}{k_p k_{tss}}\left\{\left[\frac{R_p^2}{[M]^2} + \frac{k_t k_{tss}}{k_{ts}^2}\left(\frac{R_0^2}{[M]_0^2} - \frac{R_p^2}{[M]}\right)\right]^{1/2} - \frac{R_p}{[M]}\right\} \tag{4-28}$$

Now the mutual termination constant $\phi = k_{ts}/(k_t k_{tss})^{1/2}$ and the retardation coefficient $\lambda = R_p[M]_0/R_0[M]$ are introduced:

$$[S\cdot] = \frac{k_{ts}}{k_p k_{tss}}\left(\frac{R_p}{[M]}\right)\left[\left(1 + \frac{(1 - \lambda^2)}{\phi^2\lambda^2}\right)^{1/2} - 1\right] \tag{4-29}$$

Substituting this equation into (4-27) and rearranging gives

$$\frac{\lambda^2[S]}{1 - \lambda^2[M]}\left[\left(1 + \frac{1 - \lambda^2}{\phi^2\lambda^2}\right)^{1/2} + 1\right]$$

$$= \frac{k_{ps}k_t}{k_{trs}k_{ts}} + \frac{k_tR_p}{k_pk_{trs}[M]^2}\left(1 + \frac{1 - \lambda^2}{\phi^2\lambda^2}\right)^{1/2} \qquad (4\text{-}30)$$

The last equation is valid only if [S] remains constant long enough for the rate of polymerization to be measured, and, of course, the rate must be large enough to be measured accurately. This is rather difficult in the case of vinyl acetate, because this monomer is easily inhibited and thus gives very low rates.

Normally ϕ, the cross-termination constant, is very large, because k_{tss} is very small in most experiments (286). Then we can rewrite Eq. (4-30), taking $\phi \to \infty$

$$\frac{\lambda^2[S]}{1 - \lambda[M]} = \frac{k_{ps}k_t}{k_{trs}k_{ts}} + \frac{k_t}{k_pk_{trs}}\frac{R_p}{[M]^2} \qquad (4\text{-}31)$$

A plot of $R_p/[M]^2$ versus $\lambda^2[S]/(1 - \lambda^2[M])$ should give a straight line with the slope k_t/k_pk_{trs} and the intercept $k_{ps}k_t/k_{trs}k_{ts}$.

Equation (4-31) was tested by Takayama (526), who used a crotonaldehyde-retarded vinyl acetate polymerization. The crotonaldehyde content was varied from 0.05 to 0.5% and AIBN was the initiator. Figure 4-4 shows the linear plot with: $k_t/k_pk_{trs} = 15.08$ and $k_{ps}k_t/k_{trs}k_{ts} = 0.089 \times 10^{-4}$.

Since $k_t/k_p^2 = 2.64$ (342) and $k_p = 3700$ (337), then $k_{trs}/k_p = C_s = 0.18$ and $k_{ps}/k_{ts} = 1.6 \times 10^{-10}$, which shows that the cross-termination constant is very large. The termination reaction (4-8) is favored over the reinitiation reaction (4-5).

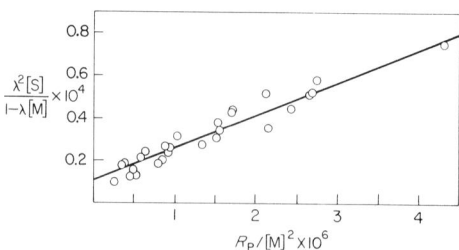

Fig. 4-4. Application of Kice's equation to the polymerization of vinyl acetate in the presence of crotonaldehyde (526).

To evaluate the effect of the magnitude of the cross-termination constant ϕ Jenkins (267) made the following derivations, using Eqs. (4-26) and (4-30):

$$k_{tr} = \frac{[(R_i k_t)^{1/2}\lambda(1 + (1 - \lambda^2)/\phi^2\lambda^2)^{1/2} + k_{ps}k_t[M]/k_{ts}](1 - \lambda^2)}{\lambda^2[S]\{[1 + (1 - \lambda^2)]/\phi^2\lambda^2)^{1/2} + 1} \tag{4-32}$$

The reactivities of the transfer and polymer radicals may be related by the following equations:

$$k_{ps} = \beta k_p, \qquad k_{ts} = \phi\alpha k_t, \qquad k_{tss} = \alpha^2 k_t \tag{4-33}$$

where α and β are constants. Substituting these equations gives

$$k_{tr} = \frac{[(R_i k_t)^{1/2}\lambda(1 + (1 - \lambda^2)/\phi^2\lambda^2)^{1/2} + (\beta/\phi\alpha)k_p[M]](1 - \lambda^2)}{\lambda^2[S][(1 + [1 - \lambda^2]/\phi^2\lambda^2)^{1/2} + 1]} \tag{4-34}$$

There are three special cases, $\phi = 1$, $\phi = \infty$, and $\phi \to 0$.

1. When $\phi = 1$, where the geometric mean assumption of cross termination is valid, then $k_{ts} = (k_t k_{tss})^{1/2}$ and

$$k_{trs} = [(R_i k_t)^{1/2} - (\alpha/\beta)k_p[M]](1 - \lambda)/\lambda[S] \tag{4-35}$$

and when $\beta = 0$,

$$k_{trs} = (R_i k_t)^{1/2}(\lambda^{-1} - 1)/[S] \tag{4-36}$$

This is the case in which most retardation is present, because when $\beta = 0$, then the rate of reinitiation k_{ps} must be very small. Conversely, when $\beta = \alpha$, no effect on the rate will be noticed, because the relative extents of participation in the termination and reinitiation reactions by the transfer radicals is equal to that of the polymer radicals in the termination and propagation reactions. When $\alpha = \beta = 1$, the absolute reactivities of the two types of radical are identical.

Equation (4-36) may be rewritten and solved for R_p by using $R_0 = k_p(R_i/k_t)^{1/2}[M]_0$:

$$R_p = k_p(R_i/k_t)^{1/2}[M]\frac{(R_i k_t)^{1/2}}{k_{trs}[S] + (R_i k_t)^{1/2}} \tag{4-37}$$

This equation predicts that the dependence of the rate of polymerization on initiator concentration will be a power between 0.5 and 1.0.

The value of the exponent depends on the relative values of $k_{tr}[S]$ and $(R_i k_t)^{1/2}$. In the case of vinyl acetate polymerization in the presence of crotonaldehyde (526)† it was found that $R_p \approx [I]^{0.70}$ and, in the case of the addition of benzaldehyde (527) to a vinyl acetate polymerization, $R_p \approx [I]^{0.65}$.

† This work was also summarized by Matsumoto et al. (349).

2. When $\phi = \infty$, where cross termination predominates, Eq. (4-34) becomes

$$k_{\text{trs}} = [(R_i k_t)^{1/2}\lambda + (\beta/\alpha\phi)k_p[\text{M}]](\lambda^{-2} - 1)/2[\text{S}] \qquad (4\text{-}38)$$

and when $\beta = 0$ for the case of most retardation,

$$k_{\text{trs}} = (R_i k_t)^{1/2}(\lambda^{-1} - \lambda)/2[\text{S}] \qquad (4\text{-}39)$$

3. When $\phi \to 0$, where cross termination is negligible,

$$k_{\text{trs}} = [(R_i k_t)^{1/2} + (\beta/\alpha)k_p[\text{M}]]/(1 - \lambda^2)^{1/2}(\lambda^{-1} - \lambda)[\text{S}] \qquad (4\text{-}40)$$

and when $\beta = 0$,

$$k_{\text{trs}} = (R_i k_t)^{1/2}(\lambda^{-1} - \lambda)/[\text{S}] \qquad (4\text{-}41)$$

When three quantities are introduced, namely the kinetic chain length

$$\gamma = k_p[\text{M}](R_i k_t)^{-1/2} \qquad (4\text{-}42)$$

the radical regeneration ratio *(108)* $\bar{D} = k_{\text{ps}}/\phi\alpha k_p$, and the chain transfer constant $C_s = k_{\text{trs}}/k_p$, the three cases [Eqs. (4-35) to (4-41)] previously defined become

$$\phi = 1: \qquad C_s[\text{S}]/[\text{M}] = (\lambda^{-1} - 1)(\gamma^{-1} + \bar{D}) \qquad (4\text{-}43)$$

$$\phi \to \infty: \qquad 2C_s[\text{S}]/[\text{M}] = (\lambda\gamma^{-1} + \bar{D})(\lambda^{-2} - 1) \qquad (4\text{-}44)$$

$$\phi \to 0: \qquad C_s[\text{S}]/[\text{M}] = [\gamma^{-1} + \bar{D}/(1 - \lambda^2)^{1/2}](\lambda^{-1} - \lambda) \qquad (4\text{-}45)$$

The degree of polymerization is given by:

$$\overline{\text{DP}} = \frac{\text{rate of propagation}}{\text{rate of termination}}$$

$$\overline{\text{DP}} = \frac{R_i + k_p[\text{M·}][\text{M}] + k_{\text{ps}}[\text{S·}][\text{M}]}{\frac{1}{2}k_t[\text{M·}]^2 + k_{\text{trm}}[\text{M·}][\text{M}] + k_{\text{trs}}[\text{M·}][\text{S}] + k_{\text{ts}}[\text{M·}][\text{S·}]} \qquad (4\text{-}46)$$

When R_i and $k_{\text{ps}}[\text{S·}][\text{M}]$ are very much smaller than $k_p[\text{M·}][\text{M}]$, they can be neglected. Rearranging, we obtain:

$$\frac{1}{\overline{\text{DP}}} = \frac{k_{\text{trm}}}{k_p} + \frac{k_{\text{trs}}[\text{S}]}{k_p[\text{M}]} + \frac{k_t R_p}{k_p^2[\text{M}]^2} + \frac{k_{\text{ts}}[\text{S·}]}{k_p[\text{M}]} \qquad (4\text{-}47)$$

In steady-state condition $R_i = k_t[\text{M·}]^2 + k_{\text{ts}}[\text{M·}][\text{S·}]$, $\gamma = R_p/R_i$ [see Eq. (4-42)], $k_{\text{trm}}/k_p = C_m$ (the so-called transfer constant to monomer), and $k_{\text{trs}}/k_p = C_s$ (the transfer constant to solvent).

We obtain from Eq. (4-47)

$$\frac{1}{\overline{\text{DP}}} = \frac{1}{2\gamma} + C_m + C_s\frac{[\text{S}]}{[\text{M}]} \qquad (4\text{-}48)$$

and
$$R_i = k_t[\text{M·}]_0^2 = k_t R_0^2/k_p[\text{M}]_0^2 = k_t R/k_p^2[\text{M}]^2 \lambda^2 = AR\lambda^{-2} \qquad (4\text{-}49)$$
where
$$A = k_t/k_p^2[\text{M}]^2, \qquad (4\text{-}50)$$
and
$$\frac{1}{\overline{DP}} = AR\lambda^{-2} + C_m + C_s\frac{[\text{S}]}{[\text{M}]} \qquad (4\text{-}51)$$

When the retardation caused by solvent is small, $\lambda = 1$, and we can neglect $k_{ts}[\text{M·}][\text{S·}]$ to obtain
$$\frac{1}{\overline{DP}} = AR + C_m + C_s\frac{[\text{S}]}{[\text{M}]} \qquad (4\text{-}52)$$

Plotting $1/\overline{DP} - AR\lambda^{-2}$ against $[\text{S}]/[\text{M}]$ should give a straight line with C_m as intercept and C_s as slope (see Fig. 4-5). This is shown (526) again for crotonaldehyde-retarded vinyl acetate polymerization, where $C_m = 1.9 \times 10^{-4}$ and $C_s = 0.18$.

In this case the initiator was AIBN, which essentially does not enter into the transfer reaction. However, other initiators may, and an additional term has to be added to Eq. (4-52). We obtain, then,
$$\frac{1}{\overline{DP}} = AR + C_m + C_s\frac{[\text{S}]}{[\text{M}]} + C_i\frac{[\text{I}]}{[\text{M}]} \qquad (4\text{-}53)$$

The importance of this term can be experimentally determined very easily by plotting the reciprocal of $\overline{DP}$ against $[\text{I}]^{1/2}$ or against R_p. The curve will be linear only when k_{tri} or, therefore, C_i is zero or when the initiator concentration is so low that the term is negligible. Figure 4-6 shows the catalyzed polymerization of methyl methacrylate with various initiators. It can be seen that transfer to catalyst for AIBN and benzoyl peroxide is negligible but that it is substantial for cumene hydroperoxide and t-BHPO.

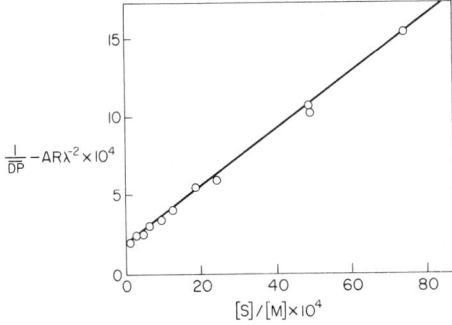

Fig. 4-5. Polymerization of vinyl acetate in the presence of crotonaldehyde (526).

A very extensive study of chain transfer in vinyl acetate polymerization has been made by Clarke et al. (*108*). Using the above-described kinetic scheme, they distinguish between "mildly" degradative and "strongly" degradative chain transfer. They discuss only two limiting cases, $\phi = 1$ and $\phi \gg 1$, as follows.

When $\phi = 1$, then

$$C_s\frac{[S]}{[M]} = (\lambda^{-1} - 1)(\bar{D} + \gamma^{-1}) \tag{4-54}$$

and the degree of polymerization is given by

$$\frac{1}{\overline{DP}} = (1 - \tfrac{1}{2}\lambda)\gamma^{-1} + C_m + C_s\frac{[S]}{[M]} \tag{4-55}$$

Since γ^{-1} is much smaller than C_m, Eq. (4-55) does not differ much from the unretarded case, namely:

$$\frac{1}{\overline{DP}} = \frac{1}{2\gamma} + C_m + C_s\frac{[S]}{[M]} \tag{4-56}$$

As we have seen, ϕ is frequently larger than 1, the second limiting case. When $\phi \gg 1$, then

$$2C_s\frac{[S]}{[M]} = (\lambda^{-2} - 1)(\bar{D} + \lambda\gamma^{-1}) \tag{4-57}$$

and the degree of polymerization is given by

$$\frac{1}{\overline{DP}} = (2\gamma\lambda)^{-1} + C_m + C_s\frac{[S]}{[M]} \tag{4-58}$$

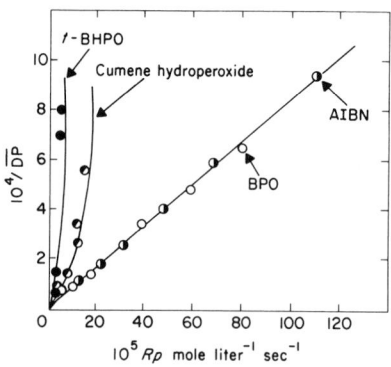

Fig. 4-6. $1/\overline{DP}$ versus R_p for the polymerization of methyl methacrylate at 60°C.

The first term of Eq. (4-58) can be very important; in fact, in the case of very strong retardation, when $\lambda \ll 1$ and $\bar{D} \ll \lambda\gamma^{-1}$, the equation changes to

$$\frac{1}{\overline{DP}} = C_m + 2C_s\frac{[S]}{[M]} \qquad (4\text{-}59)$$

When $1/\overline{DP}$ versus $[S]/[M]$ is plotted, a straight line always results. The slope C_s' of this line, however, which Clarke calls the apparent transfer constant, is only the upper limit of the true transfer constant when the system is retarded. A lower limit of C_s can be calculated from Eq. (4-58). The absolute maximum of C_s' (in the absence of copolymerization) is, moreover, $2C_s$.

When the rate found by Clarke et al. (108) was so little retarded that the difference between lower limit of C_s and C_s' calculated from the plot of $1/\overline{DP}$ versus $[S]/[M]$ was no greater than 10%, the transfer agent was called "mildly" degradative. When the difference was more than 10%, it was called "strongly" degradative.

2. TRANSFER TO MONOMER (227)

Table 4-9 lists the constants of transfer to monomer for vinyl acetate. Clarke et al. (108) showed that an Arrhenius plot could be constructed by conforming to the equation $\log_{10} C_m = -1.59 - 670\, T^{-1}$, which gives the activation energy difference of

$$\bar{E}_{trm} - \bar{E}_p \simeq 3.1 \,\text{kcal mole}^{-1}$$

and

$$\Delta S^*_{trm} - \Delta S^*_p \simeq -7.3 \,\text{cal deg}^{-1}\,\text{mole}^{-1}$$

as the difference in entropy of activation.

There are indications that most of the monomer transfer took place at the hydrogen atoms of the acetyl group (316). This was shown by comparing the partial transfer constant of the acetate group with C for vinyl acetate, the latter being $C_m = 1.7 \times 10^{-4}$ and C_s (acetate) $= 1.3 \times 10^{-4}$. It was determined by Imoto et al. (257) that transfer took place forty times as much on the acetyl hydrogens as on the backbone tertiary hydrogen in the case of polyvinyl acetate.

The constant of transfer to monomer has been determined many times; Table 4-9 gives only a partial list of values. In general there is good agreement, with the exception of the value $C_m = 20 \times 10^{-4}$ of Matheson et al. (337). This value is clearly too high. Sakurada and Yoshizaki (491) determined the transfer constant from titrations of the carboxyl end group of the hydrolyzed polymer. They found $C_m = 5.7 \times 10^{-4}$ at 45°C, which is in very good agreement with other published values, considering the method used.

TABLE 4-9

Constants of Transfer to Monomer for Vinyl Acetate

Temp., °C	C_m	Ref.
−15	0.36	123
0	0.9[a]	123
2	1.05	502
20	0.94	494
25	1.45[a]	123
25	1.3[a]	310
40	1.32	28
40	1.32	494
45	5.7	491
45	2.0	69
50	20	337
50	1.38	28
60	2.8[a]	449
60	2.4	454
60	2.5	108
60	1.9	342,346,349
60	2.8	98
70	2.9[a]	579
75	3.0	109

[a] Recalculated by Clarke et al. (108).

Since the Arrhenius plot was a straight line, the activation energy for the polymerization of the allylic double bond must be very close to the activation energy of transfer to monomer.

Moreover, when the transfer constants for dimethyl oxalate ($C_s = 0.0001$), acetic anhydride ($C_s = 0.0008$), and methyl acetate ($C_s = 0.00025$), are compared with each other and with C_m, it becomes clear that most of the transfer to monomer is caused by abstraction of hydrogen from the acetate group; this leads to a long-chain vinyl ester, which can later be incorporated as a branch into the polymer molecule. Imoto et al. (259) found that transfer to monomer resulted in 0.02 to 0.04 mole-% double bonds in the resulting polyvinyl acetate. This is also in agreement with the monomer transfer constant.

The following transfer reaction cannot be ruled out:

$$\text{\textasciitilde CH}_2\text{--CH}\cdot + \text{CH}_2\text{=CH} \longrightarrow \text{\textasciitilde CH}_2\text{=CH} + \text{CH}_3\text{--CH}\cdot \qquad (4\text{-}60)$$
$$\qquad \underset{\text{OAc}}{|} \qquad \underset{\text{OAc}}{|} \qquad\qquad \underset{\text{OAc}}{|} \qquad \underset{\text{OAc}}{|}$$

The allyl double bond, however, will not be very reactive.

3. TRANSFER TO POLYMER

The constant of transfer to polymer has been determined by many workers. Table 4-10 lists some of the results obtained. Imoto et al. (*257*) polymerized vinyl trimethyl acetate in the presence of polyvinyl acetate. After separating and saponifying the graft copolymer and determining the composition of the polymers they determined that chain transfer was taking place on site (C) forty times more frequently than on site (B).

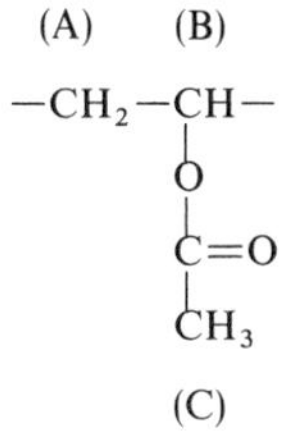

$$
\begin{array}{cc}
\text{(A)} & \text{(B)} \\
-CH_2-CH- \\
\;O \\
\;C=O \\
\;CH_3 \\
\text{(C)}
\end{array}
$$

TABLE 4-10

Constants of Transfer to Polyvinyl Acetate for Vinyl Acetate

Temp., °C	$C_p \times 10^4$	Remarks	Ref.
40	30.9	Radioactive determination	66
40	3.2		458
40	11.2		28
40	32	Telomer of VAc used	378
45	1.35	By COO⁻ analysis	491
50	10.2	α polymer	28
50	3.0	Radioactive determination	66
60	3.3		108
60	2.6		349
60	2.96		494
60	4.8		458
60	3.1	α polymer	255
60	1.4		258
60	7.0	α polymer	109
60	6.8	α polymer	28
60	2.5	Increasing conversion	495
60	1.8		515
60	3.5	Calculated from hydrolysis data (*347*)	517
70	3.0	Increase of $\overline{DP}$ with conversion	579
75	9.0		109
80	2.8		568
88	15.0		62
90	15.0		63

When it happened on site (C), the branch that was formed would hydrolyze easily, resulting in a decreased molecular weight of the resulting polyvinyl alcohol. Wheeler and co-workers (578,579) performed a thorough kinetic analysis and thus explained the lower molecular weight of polyvinyl alcohol than of the parent polyvinyl acetate; this had been noticed for a long time but had not been accounted for satisfactorily. Since the concentration of polymer increases gradually in a polymerization, the extent of branching also increases gradually. Wheeler (577) calculated the extent of branching and related it to the conversion of monomer to polymer.

If the acetyl group is the main site of transfer then the transfer constants for monomer and polymer should be close, which is being found (see Table 4-10). Some of the transfer constants in this table are rather high: for example, the one found by Morton and Piirma (378). One of the reasons for this high value might be the use of benzene-derived and toluene-derived vinyl acetate telomers of very low molecular weight in place of ordinary vinyl acetate polymer. Since toluene must be a significant part of the telomer by weight, the transfer constant to this telomer may also partly reflect the higher transfer of vinyl acetate to toluene. The other transfer constant out of line is the one determined at 40°C by Bevington and co-workers (66). The transfer constant determined at 55°C seems to be similar to other workers', although Bevington feels that it is more uncertain because of the experimental conditions. The radioactive method of Bevington is based on the ability to separate quantitatively a weakly radioactive high polymer from a strongly radioactive polymer of low molecular weight. Only small amounts of this latter polymer not separated can cause a large error.

Transfer to polymer can also occur on the tertiary hydrogen atom of the polyvinyl acetate backbone (108),

$$\sim CH_2-CH\sim \; + \; M\cdot \longrightarrow -CH_2-\dot{C}\sim \; + \; MH \tag{4-61}$$
$$\quad\quad\; \underset{OAc}{|} \qquad\qquad\qquad\qquad \underset{OAc}{|}$$

$$\sim CH_2-\dot{C}\sim \; + \; CH_2{=}CH \longrightarrow \sim CH{=}C\sim \; + \; CH_3-CH\cdot \tag{4-62}$$
$$\quad\; \underset{OAc}{|} \qquad\quad \underset{OAc}{|} \qquad\qquad \underset{OAc}{|} \qquad\qquad \underset{OAc}{|}$$

or (254) as follows:

$$M\cdot \; + \; CH_2{=}CH \longrightarrow CH_2{=}\dot{C} \; + \; MH \tag{4-63}$$
$$\qquad\qquad \underset{OAc}{|} \qquad\qquad\; \underset{OAc}{|}$$

$$CH_2{=}\dot{C} \; + \; M \longrightarrow CH{=}CH\sim \tag{4-64}$$
$$\quad\; \underset{OAc}{|} \qquad\qquad\qquad\; \underset{OAc}{|}$$

$$CH{=}CH\sim \; + \; M\cdot \longrightarrow M-CH_2-\dot{C}\sim \tag{4-65}$$
$$\quad\; \underset{OAc}{|} \qquad\qquad\qquad\qquad\quad \underset{OAc}{|}$$

$$M-CH_2-\dot{C}\sim \; + \; CH_2{=}CH \longrightarrow M-CH{=}C\sim \; + \; CH_3-CH\cdot \tag{4-62}$$
$$\qquad\quad \underset{OAc}{|} \qquad\quad \underset{OAc}{|} \qquad\qquad\; \underset{OAc}{|} \qquad\qquad \underset{OAc}{|}$$

TABLE 4-11

Inhibiting Action of Fractionated and Unfractionated Polymers (*495*)

Sample no.	$\overline{DP}$	R_p/R_{po}	Double bonds[a]		
			Total	End group	Allyl
Fractionated polymers					
4/2/3	123	0.88	0.076	0.015	0.061
4/3	94	0.88	0.093	0.020	0.073
5/5	127	0.80	0.118	0.013	0.105
5/6	82	0.68	0.181	0.020	0.161
5/7	61	0.65	0.232	0.026	0.206
Unfractionated polymers					
PI	91	0.99	0.056	0.019	0.037
PII	146	0.99	0.022	0.015	0.007

[a] Moles double bond per mole vinyl acetate.

Both these mechanisms lead to some internal allylic double bonds. These do not readily copolymerize with vinyl acetate, and they retard the rate of polymerization (*254*). Schulz and Stein (*495*) have determined the influence of the double bonds on the rate of polymerization. Table 4-11 and Fig. 4-7 show that the rate decreases as the number of allyl groups increases. By using the Kice (*286*) equations they determined that the transfer constant of the allyl group is $C_{allyl} = 0.4$, which is close to the value for allyl acetate (see Table 4-19).

Stein and Schulz (*517*) calculated C_p from the paper by Matsumoto and Ohyanagi (*347*) and obtained

$$C_p = 3.5 \times 10^{-4}$$

Intramolecular transfer is possible, as it is in the case of ethylene. Experimental evidence of short-chain branching, however, has not been obtained.

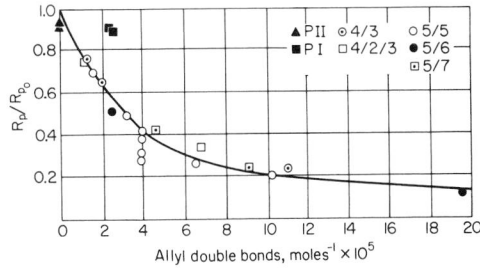

Fig. 4-7. Inhibitor action of allyl-containing polymers, no solvents, at 60°C (*495*).

The activation-energy difference of transfer and propagation for polymer is approximately the same as for monomer, 3 kcal/mole.

Sakurada (491) measured the constant of transfer to polymer by a quantitative analysis of carboxyl groups of the hydrolyzed polymer. He found $C_p = 1.35 \times 10^{-4}$ at 45°C, which shows very good agreement with the other methods employed.

In comparison, Table 4-12 lists some constants of transfer to model substances for vinyl acetate. It can be seen that they are all approximately similar to the constant of transfer to polyvinyl acetate.

Some transfer constants have been determined for other polymers, such as polyvinyl alcohol (438), polyvinyl chloride (255), polystyrene (378), and polymethyl methacrylate (378) (see Table 4-13). The constant of transfer to polyvinyl chloride is greatest, as expected. This transfer reaction undoubtedly leads to considerable branching during vinyl acetate–vinyl chloride copolymerizations (255) as well as to the formation of graft copolymers when vinyl acetate is polymerized in the presence of polyvinyl chloride (224,289). The transfer to polystyrene is of the same order as the transfer to toluene; that to polymethyl methacrylate, of the same order as that to methyl isobutyrate. For comparison, constants of transfer to polyvinyl acetate for styrene and methyl methacrylate are listed too. They are, as expected, lower by one order.

4. BRANCHING

Because the constant of transfer to polymer of vinyl acetate is larger than that of most other monomers, branching of polyvinyl acetate is of great practical importance. The properties, not only of the polyvinyl acetate, but even more of the derived polyvinyl alcohols, are profoundly affected by branching.

TABLE 4-12

Transfer Constants of Model Compounds for Vinyl Acetate Polymerization (495)

Compound	Model $\overline{DP}$	Temp., °C	$C_s \times 10^4$	Ref.
$CH_3-CH-CH_3$ $\quad\ \ OCOCH_3$	1	50 60	1.5 ± 0.5 3.1	322 349
CH_3-CH_2 $\quad\ \ OCOCH_3$	1	60 60	2.6 1.9	349 449
$CH_3-CH-CH_2-CH-CH_3$ $\quad\ \ OCOCH_3\quad OCOCH_3$	2	50	2.0 ± 0.5	322
$CH_3-CH-CH_2-CH-CH_2-CH-CH_3$ $\quad\ \ OCOCH_3\quad OCOCH_3\quad OCOCH_3$	3	50	2.0 ± 0.5	322

TABLE 4-13

Transfer Constants of Other Polymers for Vinyl Acetate, Styrene, and
Methyl Methacrylate

Polymer	C_p	Temp., °C	Ref.
For vinyl acetate			
Polyvinyl alcohol	3.5×10^{-3}	60	*438*
Polyvinyl chloride	0.21	60	*255,289*
Polystyrene	1.5×10^{-3}	60	*378*
Polystyrene	1.9×10^{-3}	75	*378*
Polymethyl methacrylate	2.1×10^{-3}	60	*378*
Polymethyl methacrylate	2.6×10^{-3}	75	*378*
Polyvinyl acetate	1.5×10^{-4}	60	*438*
For styrene			
Polyvinyl acetate	6.6×10^{-4}	100	*378*
Polyvinyl acetate	9.2×10^{-4}	130	*378*
For methyl methacrylate			
Polyvinyl acetate	2.0×10^{-4}	60	*378*
Polyvinyl acetate	2.8×10^{-4}	80	*378*

A number of studies have been made to elucidate the branching mechanism. Wheeler and co-workers (*579*) have examined some polyvinyl acetates
obtained by photopolymerization to different conversions at 70°C. They
interpreted the mechanism in terms of the following seven reactions:

$$R\cdot + M \longrightarrow R\cdot \tag{4-66}$$

$$R\cdot + M \longrightarrow RH + CH_2{=}CH{-}O{-}\underset{\underset{O}{\|}}{C}{-}CH_2\cdot \tag{4-67}$$

$$R\cdot + M \longrightarrow RH + CH_2{=}\dot{C}{-}\underset{\underset{O}{\|}}{O}C{-}CH_3 \tag{4-68}$$

$$R\cdot + P \longrightarrow RH + CH_2{-}\underset{\underset{OAc}{|}}{\dot{C}}{\sim} \tag{4-69}$$

$$R\cdot + P \longrightarrow RH + CH_2{-}\underset{\underset{\underset{O}{\|}}{O\underset{}{C}{-}CH_2\cdot}}{CH}{\sim} \tag{4-70}$$

$$R\cdot + CH_2{=}CHO{-}\overset{\overset{O}{\|}}{C}{-}CH_2 \longrightarrow R{-}CH_2{-}\underset{\underset{\underset{O}{\|}}{O{-}C{-}CH_2\sim}}{\dot{C}H} \tag{4-71}$$

$$R\cdot + CH_2{=}C\!\!\sim \longrightarrow R{-}CH_2{-}\overset{\cdot}{C}\!\!\sim \qquad\qquad (4\text{-}72)$$
$$\underset{\underset{O}{\overset{\|}{\underset{}{}}}}{O{-}C{-}CH_3} \qquad\quad OAc$$

They obtained some rate constants. They could not obtain a good indication of the relative importance of transfer to the α and β hydrogens and to the acetyl group. They only suggested a number for the ratio of the constants of transfer to α and β hydrogens to those of acetyl hydrogen, equal to 0.33 to 0.50. Howard (241) studied extensively the transfer to solvents, monomer, and polymer. He concluded that, since the transfer to polymer was three times the value of transfer to monomer, most transfer took place at the α or β hydrogen, leading to nonhydrolyzable branches. About one third of the branches were hydrolyzable. The ratio of transfer to the α and β hydrogens and to the acetyl hydrogen was in close agreement with Wheeler, and the kinetic predictions were consistent with the solution properties obtained (518). Ethylene was polymerized in the presence of polyvinyl acetate by Roland and Richards (473), who found in this case that ethylene grafted more at the α or β hydrogen position, but that some grafting also occurred on the acetyl group. On the other hand, Imoto et al. (257) found that the methyl group of the acetate was the principal transfer point—in fact, forty times more so than the α or β hydrogen of the backbone of the polymer.

Unfortunately, this question has not been completely resolved; however, the evidence thus far points to the validity of Imoto's finding.

Melville and Sewell (358) have introduced another factor. They found some evidence that an intramolecular transfer reaction took place. They plotted the number of branches against the number-average molecular weight as shown in Fig. 4-8. The branches produced by this mechanism should be hydrolyzable. Berry (62) and Berry and Craig (63) performed a

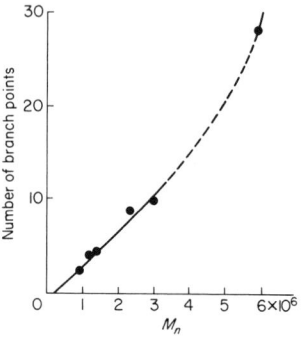

Fig. 4-8. Variation of number of branch points with number-average molecular weight of polyvinyl acetate fractions (358).

kinetic analysis of the reactions important in the polymerization of a monomer in the presence of its polymer and a chain-transfer solvent. They found that the average number of branches per molecule n_B grafted onto the backbone is given approximately by

$$n_B = C_p \overline{DP}_B X \qquad (4\text{-}73)$$

where C_p is the polymer chain-transfer constant, $\overline{DP}_B$ is the average degree of polymerization of the backbone material, and X is the degree of conversion of monomer to polymer. Then the fraction F of the new polymer formed that is grafted to the backbone is given approximately by

$$F = \frac{C_p[B/M]}{C_s([S]/[M]) + C_m} \qquad (4\text{-}74)$$

where $[B/M]$ is the ratio of the weight of polymer to the weight of monomer, $[S]/[M]$ is the ratio of the moles of solvent to the moles of monomer, C_s is the solvent chain-transfer constant, and C_m is the monomer chain-transfer constant. For a typical set of conditions the number of branches could be calculated.

It was shown that only about 6 to 8 branches resulted from a single graft copolymerization. To introduce more branches more than one graft polymerization was performed. Equation (4-73) then becomes:

$$n_B = C_p \overline{DP}_B \sum X \qquad (4\text{-}75)$$

where $\sum X$ is now the sum of the degrees of conversion, X, obtained for each of the graft polymerizations on a particular linear backbone polymer. The average number of branches per molecule may be computed from the expression

$$n_B = (M_g - M_l)/M_b \qquad (4\text{-}76)$$

where M_g, M_l and M_b are the average molecular weights of the graft, linear backbone, and linear branch polymer, respectively. Figure 4-9 shows the values of n_B calculated from Eq. (4-76) for the conditions used. It follows that the data best fit when C_p is 15×10^{-4} at 90°C.

Other studies of the branching reaction of vinyl acetate during its polymerization were made by Bevington et al. (66), who used an isotope method and whose constant for transfer to polymer at 40°C, as mentioned before, seems to be too high, although the one determined at 55°C seems to be correct.

Matsumoto and Ohyanagi (347) confirmed Long's (327) finding that at low conversion of monomer to polymer essentially no degradation on hydrolysis takes place, indicating no branches have formed. They polymerized vinyl acetate with catalyst and ultraviolet light at 0 and −30°C.

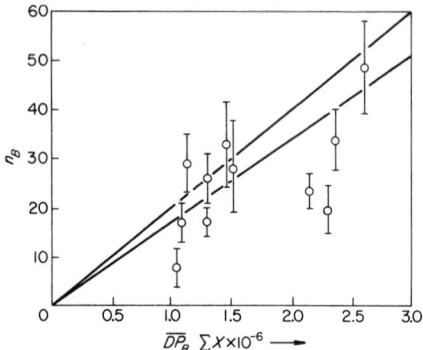

Fig. 4-9. Number of branches per molecule and degree of conversion [Eq. (4-75)] (*63*).

This is in contradiction to the findings of Melville and Sewell (*358*), who found even at low conversion a degradation on hydrolysis, which they tried to explain by an intramolecular transfer mechanism.

Schulz and Stein (*495*) determined the constant of transfer to polyvinyl acetate for vinyl acetate by the method of the α polymer. They also analyzed the kinetics. They found that small amounts of oxygen increased the value of C_p in an uncontrollable fashion. Their value is very close to the value found by Wheeler and co-workers (*579*), which is quite remarkable, because Wheeler worked with undiluted vinyl acetate that was polymerized to high conversions.

The latter method was used again by Stein (*515*), who determined C_p from the change in molecular weight at increasing conversions during a vinyl acetate polymerization. He determined the molecular weights very carefully by viscosity, light-scattering, and osmotic-pressure measurements. The value of $C_p = 1.8 \times 10^{-4}$ at 60°C checks well with previous results. He also confirmed Wheeler's result that the double bond at the end of the polymer molecule introduced by transfer to monomer is almost as reactive as the monomer itself; this means that the large polymer molecule does not shield this double bond effectively. The number of branches per polymer molecule as a function of conversion at 60°C is shown in Fig. 4-10.

The transfer reaction to polymer occurs mainly on the hydrogen atoms of the acetyl group, because the radical so formed is stabilized by the neighboring carbonyl group. Schulz and Roberts-Nowakowska (*494*) determined the activation energy of transfer to polyvinyl acetate for vinyl acetate as 3.3 ± 0.3 kcal/mole. After reviewing literature data they came to the conclusion that the polymer transfer constant was equal to the monomer transfer constant. The degree of branching can be calculated if C_m, C_p, $k_{p'}/k_p$, and

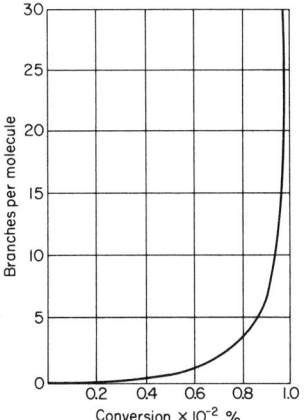

Fig. 4-10. Number of branches and percentage conversion for vinyl acetate polymerization at 60°C (*515*).

the temperature dependence of the values are known:

$$\log C_p = -1.54 - 723/T \tag{4-77}$$

$$\ln C_m = 5.8 - 3.4/RT \tag{4-78}$$

$$k_{p'}/k_p = 0.8 \text{ (temperature-independent)}$$

where $k_{p'}$ is the rate constant of propagation for the terminal double bond in the polymer molecule introduced by transfer to monomer.

5. TRANSFER TO LOW-MOLECULAR-WEIGHT COMPOUNDS

a. Hydrocarbons. Chain transfer for vinyl acetate to hydrocarbons has been extensively studied. Transfer constants have been determined for a number of aliphatic and aromatic hydrocarbons; these are listed in Table 4-14. The determination of the transfer constant for aliphatic hydrocarbons is difficult. It was observed that beyond a solvent-to-monomer ratio of 0.3 the degree of polymerization and the molecular weight increase again. This is probably due to a decreased rate of termination, which becomes important when a nonsolvent such as an aliphatic hydrocarbon is added in a vinyl acetate (*316*) polymerization.

The transfer constants for aromatic hydrocarbons follow the well-known sequence depending upon the reactivity of the hydrogen atoms in the transfer agent. Thus, it was found that the transfer constants increased in the following order: normal < secondary < tertiary: for example, C_s toluene < C_s ethyl benzene < C_s isopropyl benzene. According to the lability of the hydrogen atom in general or the sum of the effects of the lability of individual hydrogen

TABLE 4-14

Transfer Constants to Hydrocarbons for Vinyl acetate

Compound	$C_s \times 10^4$	Temp., °C	Retardation[a]	Ref.
n-Heptane	17.0	50		316
Isooctane	8.0	50		316
Benzene	0.7	40		378
	1.2	60	S	108
	2.96	60		449
	2.4	60		98
	5.27	70		566
	3.6	75		276
Toluene	34	60	S	108
	20.75	60		98
	20.89	60		449
	21.6	60		541
	36	50		92[b]
	29.2	70		541
	21.8	70		566
	66	75		276
Xylene	278	70		566
	166	75		276
Ethyl benzene	100	60	S	108
Ethyl benzene	55.15	60		449
Isopropyl benzene (cumene)	100	60	S	108
	89.9	60		449
	139	70		566
	356	75		276
Triphenyl methane	850	60		67
Triphenyl methane				
(partly deuterated)	540	60		67
Triphenyl methane (tritiated)	150	60		67
Cyclohexane	100	60	M	108
	6.59	60		449
Methyl cyclohexane	24	60	M	108
	11.75	60		449
Cyclohexane	620	60	S	108
	770	75		276
Decalin	48	60	M	108
Dipentene	1,900	60	S	108
9-Phenyl fluorene	16,240	70		566
Fluorene	4,700	60	S	108
	3,610	70		566
Dihydromyrcene	700	60		19
Diphenyl	6.4	60		198
Naphthalene	1,715	70		566
Phenanthrene	3,380	70		566

atoms we obtain the following sequence: C_s benzene $<$ C_s toluene $<$ xylene $<$ fluorine $<$ 9-phenyl fluorene. Table 4-14 allows more of these sequences to be easily constructed. There are some discrepancies in the literature; for example the constant for cyclohexane is given as both $C_s = 100 \times 10^{-4}$ (108) and $C_s = 6.6 \times 10^{-4}$ (449). Clarke and co-workers (108) determined the transfer constant in the presence of benzene and, although they showed that the latter generally did not affect the former, they showed an exception in the case of cyclohexane. This was explained by possible copolymerization. However, since they found the transfer constant of methyl cyclohexane to be $C_s = 24 \times 10^{-4}$, which is more in line with the other value for cyclohexane, the benzene possibly also interfered with the cyclohexane polymerization of Clarke and, therefore, a high value was obtained.

A controversy has arisen whether benzene has been incorporated into polyvinyl acetate or other polymers only by chain transfer or also by copolymerization.

Peebles et al. (454) and Stockmayer and Peebles (520) studied the free-radical polymerization of vinyl acetate in ^{14}C-labelled benzene and found that twenty times more benzene was incorporated into the polymer than could be expected by the chain-transfer constant. This corresponded to a copolymerization ratio of $r_1 = 350$ for vinyl acetate and $r_2 \approx 0$ for benzene. Henrici-Olivé and Olivé (228) found that benzene copolymerized with styrene, and Burnett and co-workers proved copolymerization of benzene and methyl methacrylate (20).

More recently Henrici-Olivé and Olivé (229) repeated their experiments with styrene and found only one benzene molecule per chain. Breitenbach and co-workers (74) repeated Stockmayer's experiments and found that by using a specific ^{14}C-tagged benzene, which was prepared by a trimerization of ^{14}C-labelled acetylene, they also obtained polyvinyl acetates with high radioactivity, only explainable by copolymerization of benzene. However, when they used a ^{14}C-labelled benzene prepared by dehydrogenation of ^{14}C-labelled cyclohexane, they found only one benzene molecule per polymer chain. Mortimer and Arnold (385) studied the question of possible benzene copolymerization in an ethylene polymerization system. They also came to the conclusion that a simple transfer reaction was involved and not

---

[a] S = strong, M = mild.

[b] All transfer constants quoted in this paper (92) were unusually low originally and have been recalculated here by means of the relationship between intrinsic viscosity and molecular weight for vinyl acetate, $[\eta] = 1.02 \times 10^{-2} \overline{M}_w^{0.72}$, which was taken from M. Matsumoto and Y. Ohyanagi, J. Polymer Sci., **46**, 441 (1960). It had been suggested previously (349) that the use of benzoyl peroxide as initiator had caused the abnormally low transfer constants. This is apparently not the case; rather, an incorrect relationship between intrinsic viscosity and molecular weight was the cause of the discrepancy.

copolymerization of benzene. Haas and Husek (*198*) tried to copolymerize diphenyl and vinyl acetate, but they came to the conclusion that only transfer was involved. However, they did not agree that a simple transfer step was involved, such as

$$R\cdot + C_6H_6 \longrightarrow RH + C_6H_5\cdot$$

but, rather, the following step:

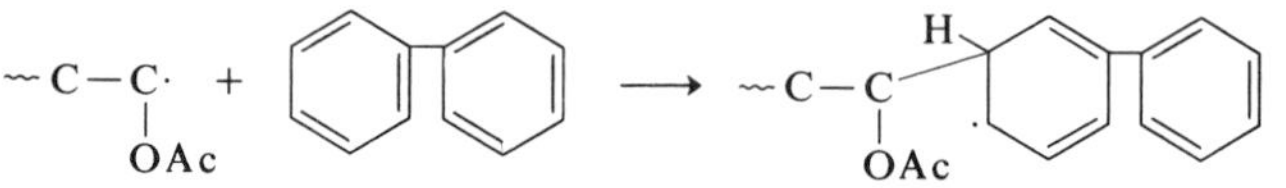

where the radical produced either ejects hydrogen or abstracts it from vinyl acetate. This would account for the kinetics and retardation of vinyl acetate in benzene polymerization, which cannot be explained by the usual chain-transfer mechanism.

It would be interesting in this connection to study further the kinetics of polymerization of vinyl benzoate, in which was also postulated by Ham and Ringwald (*203*) a copolymerization mechanism involving the benzene ring of vinyl benzoate, to account for cross-linking at high conversion of monomer to polymer, especially in a vinyl acetate–vinyl benzoate copolymerization.

b. Halogen Compounds. The reactivity in the transfer step is much higher for halogen compounds than it is for hydrocarbons. Table 4-15 lists a summary of transfer constants of halogen compounds in vinyl acetate polymerization. Again, we can put compounds in sequences regarding their transfer reactivity, C_s of RCl $< C_s$ of RBr $< C_s$ of RJ, or regarding their chain-transfer reactivity, $CCl_4 > CHCl_3 > Cl_2CHCHCl_2 > CH_3CCl_3 > ClCH_2CH_2Cl > ClC_6H_5$.

An explanation of the relatively low transfer constant of chlorobenzene may be the fact that the bond energy between a chlorine and a carbon is higher in an aromatic compound than it is in an aliphatic compound (*565*).

In the case of bromotrichloromethane (*57*) it has been found that the chain-transfer constant varied depending on the solvent-to-monomer ratio. This implies that the rate of polymerization as a function of solvent concentration changes in a way different from that of the rate of transfer.

c. Alcohols. Table 4-16 lists the transfer constants of alcohols. The same rules as those of primary H $<$ secondary H $<$ tertiary H transfer constants are valid here. It is noteworthy that, for example, *t*-butanol has a very small transfer constant. This shows that the α hydrogen atoms are very important transfer sites and that the hydroxyl hydrogen is of small activity. Table 4-17 shows transfer constants of phenol and some substituted phenols (*69*). The constants in columns 1 and 2 were determined by molecular-weight data and kinetic data, respectively. Phenols and, even more so, alkylated phenols

TABLE 4-15

Transfer Constants of Halogen Compounds for Vinyl Acetate

Compound	$C_s \times 10^4$	Temp., °C	Retardation[a]	Ref.
Methylene chloride	4	60	M	108
1,2-Dichloroethane	5	60	M	108
	7	60	M	119,449
	10	70		565
1,1-Dichloroethane	65	60	M	108
1,1-Dibromoethane	1100	60	M	108
Chloroform	150	60	M	108
	125	60	M	269
	540	70		565
Carbon tetrachloride	960	60	M	108
	2023	70		565
	1050	75	M	108
	4700	20	M	466
Carbon tetrabromide	39×10^4	60		149
	28.7×10^4	70		565
Bromotrichloromethane	40×10^4			57
	6363	70		565
1,1,1,-Trichloroethane	71	60		269,449
1,1,2-Trichloroethane	36	60		449
1,1,2,2,-Tetrachloroethane	107	60		449
	160	60	M	108
	67.7	70		565
Pentachloroethane	1384	70		565
Hexachloroethane	1210	70		565
1,2-Dibromoethane	134	70		565
1,1,2,2,-Tetrabromoethane	6000	60	M	108
Tetrachloroethylene	465	70		565
Trichloroethylene	3810	70		565
Tetrabromoethylene	2800	70		565
Tribromoethylene	3.472×10^4	70		565
Allyl chloride	3100	60	M	108
n-Butyl chloride	10	60	M	108
t-Butyl chloride	26	60	M	108
n-Butyl bromide	50	60	M	108
n-Butyl bromide	1100	70		565
t-Butyl bromide	150	60	M	108
n-Butyl iodide	800	60	M	108
Methyl iodide	1230	70		565
Chlorobenzene	80	60	S	108
	8	60		449
	2.61	70		565
	13	75		276
Bromobenzene	134.2	70		565

TABLE 4-15 (continued)

Compound	$C_s \times 10^4$	Temp., °C	Retardation[a]	Ref.
Bromobenzene	25	75		276
o-Chlorotoluene	92.86	70		565
p-Chlorotoluene	195	70		565
o-Dichlorobenzene	42	75		276
p-Dichlorobenzene	11.8	70		565
α-Trichlorotoluene	350	60		62
Benzyl chloride	118	75		276
	584	70		565
	450	60	S	108
Butyl bromide	1100	70		565
Chlorobenzene	2.61	70		565
Dichlorodiethyl ether	245	70		565
Monochloroacetic acid	2550	70		565
Monobromoacetic acid	4450	70		565
Trichloroacetic acid	1445	70		565
Chloral hydrate	4312	70		565
Chloral	4927	70		565
Benzoyl chloride	300	70		565
1,3,3,3,-Tetrachloropropyl acetate	423.2	70		565
Methallyl chloride	400	60	S	108

[a] M = mild, S = strong.

are strong retarders of vinyl acetate polymerization (69). The deuterated phenols have a lower transfer constant and retard the polymerization less, indicating that the acidic hydrogen is the main transfer point.

d. Carbonyl Compounds. The transfer to acetaldehyde was studied in telomerization experiments (371). It was found that most of the end groups were of the ketonic form, a few remaining aldehydes. It was estimated that the chain-transfer constant of the aldehyde group is $C_s = 2 \times 10^{-2}$, whereas that of the methyl group is $C_s = 0.72 \times 10^{-4}$. The partial constant of the methyl groups was estimated by Lazar and co-workers (316) to be $C_s = 0.2 \times 10^{-4}$, which shows good agreement.

The transfer to aldehydes and its effect on the rate of polymerization is very important in vinyl acetate polymerization, because small amounts of aldehydes are always present in vinyl esters (see Table 4-18).

e. Other Transfer Constants. All other transfer constants are summarized in Tables 4-19 and 4-20. Again, the same rules apply and have been sufficiently covered.

TABLE 4-16

Transfer Constants of Alcohols for Vinyl Acetate

Compound	$C_s \times 10^4$	Temp., °C	Retardation[a]	Ref.
Methanol	3.4	10		280
	6	60	M	108
	1.9	60		342
	3.2	60		382
	4.3	60		484
	5.5	70		484
Ethanol	18	50		305
	25	60	M	108
	26.3	70		566
Isopropyl alcohol	44.6	70		566
n-Butanol	20.39	60		449
	29.1	70		566
Isobutanol	21.75	60		449
	32.4	70		566
sec-Butanol	31.74	60		449
	6.21	70		566
	95	75		276
tert-Butanol	1.3	60	M	108
	0.46	60		449
	1.2	70		566
n-Amyl alcohol	56	75		276
3-Methyl-butyn-3-ol	400	60	S	108
Polyethylene glycol:				
n = 8.7	250	60		426
n = 22.3	460	60		426
n = 34.6	610	60		426
n = 136	2400	60		426
Ethylene glycol	83	70		566
Diethylene glycol	85.3	70		566
Benzyl alcohol	556	70		566
Cyclohexanol	127	70		566
Furfuryl alcohol	2520	70		566

[a] M = mild, S = strong.

Finally, this great mass of data makes it possible to assign partial transfer constants to groups of atoms. Table 4-21 lists these partial transfer constants (316). Buselli and co-workers (92) have done something similar for the fatty acid esters and have assigned partial transfer constants. They have also compared the transfer constants of the fatty acid ethyl esters with the degree of polymerization of the corresponding vinyl esters.

TABLE 4-17

Transfer Constants of Phenols and Deuterated Phenols for Vinyl Acetate at 45°C (69)

	Phenols		Deuterated phenols	
	C_{s1}	C_{s2}	C_{s1}	C_{s2}
Phenol	0.019	0.024	0.002	0.005
3-Chlorophenol	0.027	0.014	0.007	0.007
3-Methylphenol	0.046	0.029	0.012	0.005
3-Acetylphenol	0.160	0.121	0.137	0.121
3-Cyanophenol	0.069	0.095	0.067	0.094
4-Chlorophenol	0.046	0.034	0.010	0.006
4-Methylphenol	0.071	0.071	0.015	0.011
2,3,4,6-Tetramethylphenol	0.94	1.32	0.075	0.085

D. Termination

The exact termination mechanism of vinyl acetate polymerization is still subject to some uncertainty. There are three termination reactions that must be considered here: termination by chain transfer, a mechanism particular important in the case of vinyl acetate polymerization, termination by combination, and termination by disproportionation. The last two reactions probably proceed competitively, each with a definite activation energy. Unfortunately, very little work is reported in the literature concerning the exact mechanism of vinyl acetate polymerization termination or, for example, the influence of temperature on it.

TABLE 4-18

Transfer Constants of Carbonyl Compounds for Vinyl Acetate

Compound	$C_s \times 10^4$	Temp., °C	Retardation[a]	Ref.
Acetone	1.5	60	M	108
	11.7	60		449
	11	60		249
	25.6	70		566
	42	75		276
Methyl ethyl ketone	73.8	60		449
	55	60		249
	63.6	70		566
Methyl isopropyl ketone	118.16	60		449
	102	60		249
Methyl isobutyl ketone	34.52	60		449
	28	60		249

TABLE 4-18 (continued)

Compound	$C_s \times 10^4$	Temp., °C	Retardation[a]	Ref.
Diethyl ketone	100	60		249
Acetylacetone	10	60	M	108
	80.4	70		566
Cyclohexanone	180	60	M	108
	670	75		276
Acetophenone	100	60	S	108
	62	70		566
Benzaldehyde	540	60	S	108
	230	60	S	527
	421	70		566

Substituted benzaldehyde (R in [R — C₆H₄ — CHO])

	$C_s \times 10^4$	Temp., °C	Retardation[a]	Ref.
p-Cl	340	60		108
p-OCH₃	370	60		108
o-Cl	390	60		108
o-OCH₃	420	60		108
p-CH₃	440	60		108
H	540	60	S	108
p-CH(CH₃)₂	540	60		108
3,4-diOCH₃	550	60		108
m-CH₃	570	60		108
p-CN	610	60		108
m-Cl	860	60		108
m-CN	1070	60		108
m-OCH₃	2500	60		108
Acetaldehyde	530	45	M	108
	660	60		108
	200	60		349
	700	75		108
Propionaldehyde	1000	60	M	108
	457	70		566
n-Butyraldehyde	1000	60	M	108
	650	60		525
	388	70		566
Crotonaldehyde	1800	60	S	526
Paraldehyde	136	70		566
Dimedone	5580	70		566
Chloral	5000	60	M	108
Benzoin	800	60	S	108
Biacetyl	670	60	S	108
Furfural	15000	60	S	108

[a] M = mild, S = strong.

TABLE 4-19

Transfer Constants of Organic Compounds for Vinyl Acetate

Compound	$C_s \times 10^4$	Temp., °C	Retardation[a]	Ref.
Esters				
Methyl formate	3	60	M	108
Ethyl formate	8.1	50		92
Methyl acetate	2.5	60	M	108
	1.6	60		345
Ethyl acetate	1.52	20		494
	2.11	40		494
	2.9	50		316
	2.96	60		494
	1.07	60		287
	1.25	60		98
	4.0	50		92
	2.6	60		346
	3.3	60	M	108
	7.8	70		566
n-Propyl acetate	3.4	60		346
	6.2	50		316
Isopropyl acetate	1.5	50		322
	3.5	50		316
	3.1	60		346
	8	60	M	108
	9	67.5		108
	10	75		108
n-Butyl acetate	13.2	50		316
Isobutyl acetate	9.1	50		316
sec-Butyl acetate	8	60	M	108
	4.4	50		316
tert-Butyl acetate	6.2	60		346
	1.5	50		316
Amyl acetate	7.2	70		566
	8.7	75		276
Methyl n-butyrate	19	60	M	108
	18	60		346
Methyl isobutyrate	86	60	M	108
	58	60		346
Methyl glycolate	300	60	M	108
Methyl lactate	640	60	M	108
Ethyl lactate	700	60	M	108
Dimethyl oxalate	1	60	M	108
	2.0	60		346
Diethyl oxalate	4	60	M	108
Dimethyl malonate	17	60	M	108
Ethyldichloro acetate	210	60	M	108

TABLE 4-19 (continued)

Compound	$C_s \times 10^4$	Temp., °C	Retardation[a]	Ref.
Esters				
Ethyltrichloro acetate	4,400	60	M	108
Diethyldithio glycolate	14,100	60	M	108
Allyl acetate	900	60	S	108
Methyl oleate	1,000	60	S	108
Ethyl benzoate	26	60	S	108
Benzyl acetate	80	60	S	108
Methyl cyanoacetate	5,000	60	S	108
Methyl trimethylacetate	5	60		257
Ethyl stearate	48.9	50		92
Ethyl laurate	40	50		92
Ethyl pelargonate	29	50		92
Ethyl octanoate	25	50		92
Ethyl butyrate	17	50		92
Ethyl propionate	15.5	50		92
Ethyl 2-ethylhexanoate	24	50		92
Ethyl isobutyrate	55	50		92
Ethyl trifluoroacetate	10	50		92
Amines				
Anilin	210	60		242
N-Methylanilin	360	60		242
N,N-Dimethylanilin	260	60		242
p-Toluidin	750	60		242
N-Methyl-p-toluidin	830	60		242
N,N-Dimethyl-p-toluidin	380	60		242
Triethylamine	3,700	60		37
	360	60		242
Diphenylamine	230	60		68
Other nitrogen compounds				
Acetonitrile	10	60	M	108
Isobutyronitrile	100	60	M	108
Dimethyl formamide	50	60	M	108
N-n-Butyl acetamide	40	60	M	108
Nitromethane	2,300	60	S	108
Methyl cyanoacetate	5,000	60	S	108
Benzyl cyanide	2,100	60	S	108
Ethers				
n-Butyl ether	76	60	M	108
Benzyl methyl ether	280	60	M	108
Anisol	10	60	S	108

TABLE 4-19 (continued)

Compound	$C_s \times 10^4$	Temp., °C	Retardation[a]	Ref.
Polyethylene glycol dodecylether:				
$n = 6$	140	60		426
$n = 16$	310	60		426
$n = 33$	530	60		426
$n = 45$	710	60		426
Dioxane	20	60	M	108
	49.1	70		566
Dodecyl ethyl ether	57.2	60		6
Diethyl ether	45.3	60		6
Dodecyl vinyl ether	73.5	60		6
Sulfur compounds				
Di-n-butyl sulfide	260	60	M	108
Diethyl dithioglycolate	14,100	60	M	108
1-Oxa-4.5,-dithiacycloheptane	2,500	60	S	519
Di-n-butyl disulfide	10,000	60	S	108
Diacetyl disulfide	2,900	60	S	108
n-Butyl mercaptan	$(48 \pm 14) \times 10^4$	60	S	571
Acetoxyethyl thioacetate	132	60	S	205
Benzyl mercaptan	8,850	70		566
Acids				
Acetic acid	10	60	M	108
	13	60	M	109
	1.13	60		269
Acetic anhydride	8	60	M	108
Benzoic acid	50	60	S	108
Benzoic anhydride	130	60	S	108
Phenylacetic acid	400	60	S	108
Phenol	600	60	S	108
Isobutyric acid	5.02	60		108
Bromoacetic acid	489	60	S	560
Salicylic acid	296	70		566

[a] M = mild, S = strong.

One recent study by Funt and Pasika (*152*) indicated that at 60°C disproportionation was the predominant termination reaction for vinyl acetate. They determined this with ^{14}C-tagged AIBN and found generally at this temperature only one initiator fragment per chain. The same experiment performed with styrene showed that termination by combination predominated.

TABLE 4-20

Transfer Constants of Initiators for
Vinyl Acetate at 60°C

Initiator	C_i	Ref.
Benzoyl peroxide	0.15	98
Benzoyl peroxide	0.09	343
o-Bromobenzoyl peroxide	0.25	98
m-Bromobenzoyl peroxide	0.24	98
p-Bromobenzoyl peroxide	0.17	98
Lauroyl peroxide	0.10	98
Palmitoyl peroxide	0.10	98
Oxygen–vinyl acetate adduct	0.26	516
Benzoin	0.1	434

Funt and Pasika found that at 30°C more than one initiator fragment was present in one polyvinyl acetate molecule. However, they did not draw any conclusions from this study, since the data were tentative.

The rate constant of termination for vinyl acetate has been determined by a number of investigators (see Table 4-4). Bengough and Melville (56) have shown that the energy of activation for termination increased with increasing conversion and that k_t decreased at the same time. This suggests that some of the termination rate constants that were obtained may not be right, since k_t is diffusion-dependent.

TABLE 4-21

Partial Transfer Constants of Constit-
uent Groups of Transfer Agents for
Vinyl Acetate at 50°C (316)

Group	$C \times 10^4$
$-CH_3$	0.2
$-CH_2-$	3.3
$=CH$	4.5
$-O-CH_2-$	1.4
$-O-CH\diagdown$	1.8
$CH_3-C\diagup\diagdown_{O^-}^{O}$	1.3

In vinyl acetate polymerization the termination step occurred more often than not by transfer to monomer, solvent, polymer, or impurities. Kice (286) has treated chain transfer to terminator rigorously; some of his derivations were presented herein [Eqs. (4-10) to (4-14)]. Bartlett and Kwart (48,49) also treated inhibition and retardation in vinyl acetate polymerization. Flory (139) reduced the kinetics of inhibition and retardation to a simple scheme as follows:

$$k_{trz} \qquad M\cdot + Z \xrightarrow{k_{trz}} Z \qquad\qquad \text{Transfer to} $$
$$\text{terminator } Z \qquad (4\text{-}79)$$

$$k_r = k_{pz} \qquad Z\cdot + M \xrightarrow{k_{pz}} M \qquad\qquad \text{Reinitiation} \qquad (4\text{-}80)$$

$$k_{tzz} = k_{zt} \qquad 2Z\cdot \xrightarrow{k_{tzz}} \text{nonradical products} \qquad \text{Termination} \qquad (4\text{-}81)$$

$$M\cdot + Z\cdot \xrightarrow{k_{tz}} \text{nonradical products} \quad \text{Termination} \qquad (4\text{-}82)$$

Assuming that the concentration sequence is

$$[M\cdot] \ll [Z\cdot] \ll [Z]$$

then we obtain

$$-d[Z]/d_t = k_{trz}[M\cdot][Z] - y k_{tzz}[Z\cdot]^2 \qquad (4\text{-}83)$$

which represents the rate of consumption of inhibitor, where y may be set equal to zero if the annihilation process of Equation (4-81) occurs by combination; if it occurs by disproportionation with a release of one molecule of inhibitor, y will be unity.

It is possible to deduce the rate constants ratio k_{trz}/k_p from the relative rates of reaction of inhibitor and monomer in this region. Equation (4-83) yields the following, when divided by the rate of consumption of monomer,

$$\frac{d[Z]}{d[M]} = \frac{k_{trz}}{k_p}\left(\frac{[Z]}{[M]}\right) \qquad (4\text{-}84)$$

and, after integration,

$$\log \frac{[Z]}{[Z_0]} = \frac{k_{trz}}{k_p} \log \frac{[M]}{[M]_0} \qquad (4\text{-}85)$$

For a good inhibitor k_{trz}/k_p is very large, and the monomer concentration will not change appreciably before the inhibitor concentration has decreased by many orders of magnitude. This means that, if $k_{trz}/k_p \gg 1$, the inhibitor will be completely exhausted before polymerization starts. Table 4-22 gives some of these inhibition-rate ratios, the data for which were partially taken from a

TABLE 4-22

Inihibition-Rate Ratios (*47,48*)

Inhibitor or retarder	k_{trz}/k_p	Temp., °C	Ref.
Nitrobenzene	20	45	*139*
Duroquinone	90	45	*139*
o-Dinitrobenzene	95	45	*139*
m-Dinitrobenzene	105	45	*139*
p-Dinitrobenzene	265	45	*139*
Divinyl acetylene	130	60	*530*
Crotonaldehyde	0.28	60	*530*

paper by Bartlett and co-workers (*47,48*). The value of k_{trz}/k_p has been obtained, assuming $y = 0$, from the slope of $\log[Z]$ plotted against $\log[M]$ with the aid of the equation $[Z] = [Z_0] -$ constant $\times$ time (*48*).

4-3. BULK AND SOLUTION POLYMERIZATION

A. Introduction

Bulk polymerization of vinyl acetate is not important industrially. The difficulty of removing the heat of polymerization and, therefore, of controlling the polymerization reaction and the occurrence of branching at high polymer-to-monomer ratios, which leads to insolubilization, have made bulk polymerization unattractive. Some processes were developed earlier for the control of a bulk polymerization, such as a continuous-tower process (*127*) or the use of chain-transfer agents for the production of low-molecular-weight polyvinyl acetate, which has a relatively low melting point, the melted polymer being then removed from reactors even at high conversions (*235*).

The mechanism and kinetics of bulk and solution polymerizations are so similar that only the case of solution polymerization will be treated here. Commercially, solution polymerizations are preferred when polyvinyl acetate is sold as a solution polymer, such as for adhesive applications in ethyl acetate or toluene or when the polyvinyl acetate is only an intermediate product, as it is in polyvinyl alcohol preparation.

The solution polymerization mechanism is mainly determined by the type of initiation used (free-radical and cationic initiation, heat and ultraviolet radiation) and by the type of solvent employed. The solvent will influence the final molecular weight and the nature of the polymer end groups. The extent of that influence depends on the solvent transfer constant. The solvent could also determine the degree of stereoregularity of the resulting polymer, as in the case of polyvinyl chloride (83,474). No such solvent effect, however, has been noted with vinyl acetate. Finally, a solvent that dissolves the monomeric vinyl acetate but not the polymer, such as an aliphatic hydrocarbon, will bring about a heterogeneous polymerization by precipitating the polymer as soon as it is formed.

B. Determination of Rate of Polymerization

Rates of polymerization are most conveniently determined in a dilatometer. A large number of experiments in which solvents, initiators, and their concentrations are varied can be conveniently and rapidly performed. A very thorough study of vinyl acetate polymerization with a dilatometer has been made by Matsumoto and Maeda (342).

They first investigated the method of purification for vinyl acetate and found that only a careful fractionation followed by partial polymerization and degassing resulted in reproducible rates of polymerization.

It is interesting to note in this connection that the volume contraction of vinyl acetate on polymerization has been determined or calculated from the densities of monomer and polymer. Values found in the literature are listed in Table 4-23. It can be seen that the contraction value for emulsion polymerization is smaller than that for bulk or solution polymerization. Dunn and Taylor (128) propose the explanation that vinyl acetate is solvated in water and effectively has a larger density. Patsiga (452) and also Vanzo (567) used in their emulsion polymerization work a calculated value which may be wrong. A correction factor should be applied to their conversions.

TABLE 4-23

Relationship of Volume Contraction and Conversion in
Vinyl Acetate Polymerization

Solvent	Temp., °C	Contraction, %	Ref.
Toluene	82	25.6	514
	101	26.8	514
	111	27.2	514
None	45	23.6	48
Benzene	70	26.8	89
	56	21.6	191
	25	20.9[a]	400
Water	60	15.7	128,398
	60	23.6[a]	452
None	—	20.12[b]	544

[a] Contraction calculated from monomer and polymer densities.

[b] Calculated from molar refractions.

TABLE 4-24

Polymerization of Twice-Purified Vinyl Acetate with Azobisisobutyronitrile and Benzoyl Peroxide at 60°C (342)

Initiator concn.		Uncorrd.[a] rate R_p		Corrd. rate,	Convsn, %	$[\eta]$	$\overline{DP}$	$(R_p/M^2) \times 10^5$	$R_p/I \times 10^2$
%	mole liter⁻¹ × 10⁴	%/min	mole liter⁻¹ sec⁻¹ × 10⁴	mole liter⁻¹ sec⁻¹ × 10⁴					
Initiator AIBN									
0.100	54.3	0.649	11.18	9.22	10.24	0.1653	4582	1.065	1.25
0.0493	26.74	0.440	7.58	6.62	7.55	0.1679	4693	0.723	1.28
0.0233	12.65	0.288	4.96	4.60	6.02	0.1723	4885	0.472	1.29
0.0115	6.24	0.189	3.25	3.10	6.37	0.1757	5047	0.309	1.24
0.00472	2.56	0.1125	1.94	1.92	6.03	0.1765	5088	0.185	1.20
Initiator BPO									
0.300	110.3	0.637	11.00	9.10	11.36	0.1408	3563	1.049	0.86
0.0954	35.05	0.359	6.16	5.55	8.08	0.1662	4624	0.587	0.94
0.0509	18.07	0.266	4.58	4.30	7.40	0.1652	4591	0.437	1.01
0.0216	7.93	0.152	2.62	2.55	7.55	0.1687	4743	0.250	0.90
0.0102	3.75	0.096	1.65	1.63	7.02	0.1726	4898	0.157	0.85

[a] Diameter of dilatometer bulb, 14 mm.

Matsumoto and Maeda (*342*) determined the rate of polymerization of vinyl acetate (see Table 4-24) catalyzed by AIBN and BPO. They found the following rate expressions at 60°C:

$$R_p = 1.25 \times 10^{-2}[\text{AIBN}]^{1/2}$$

$$R_p = 0.95 \times 10^{-2}[\text{BPO}]^{1/2}$$

$$\frac{k_t}{k_p^2} = 2.6$$

This compares well with the results of Allen et al. (*19*), who found for a concentration of 0.2 g/liter of AIBN a rate of polymerization of 0.262%/min and for 0.4 g/liter of BPO a rate of 0.227%/min.

C. Impurities in Vinyl Acetate Polymerization

Commercially available vinyl acetate monomer has a number of impurities, which influence the rate of polymerization. A list of all known impurities has been compiled by Nishino (*403*); a partial list with the indications of their effects on polymerization is given in Table 4-25.

The effect of crotonaldehyde on vinyl acetate polymerization has been investigated by Usami (*554*). He found that 0.005% of crotonaldehyde retarded the polymerization of vinyl acetate by about 15%; 0.02%, by about 40%. Gregor and Macho (*191*) also investigated the influence of impurities on the polymerization of vinyl acetate. Acetic acid and acetic anhydride

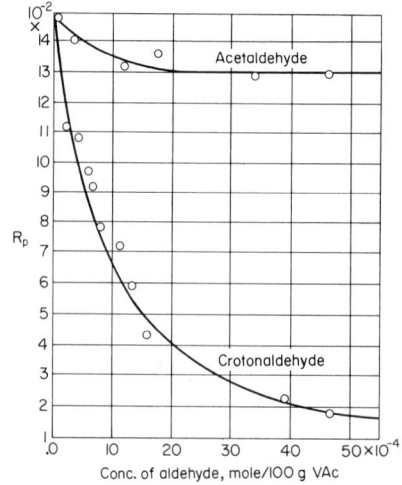

Fig. 4-11. Polymerization of vinyl acetate in the presence of aldehydes (*191*).

TABLE 4-25

Impurities in Monomeric Vinyl Acetate and Their Effects on Polymerization

Impurity	Effect	Remarks[a]	Ref.
Oxygen	Inhibition	Copolymerizes	40,590
Reaction product of oxygen and vinyl acetate	Chain transfer	$C_s = 0.26$	516
Water	No effect up to 5%		95
Acetic acid	Chain transfer	$C_s = 10 \times 10^{-4}; C_s = 1.13 \times 10^{-4}$	526,269
Acetaldehyde	Chain transfer	$C_s = 0.066$ at 60°C	108
Acetone	Chain transfer	$C_s = 11.70 \times 10^{-4}$ at 60°C	108,276
Crotonaldehyde	Retardation	$yk_{r_1}/k_p = 0.28, yk_{r_2}/k_p = 0.14$	526
Crotonaldehyde	Chain transfer	$C_s = 0.18$ at 60°; $k_r/k_t = 1.6 \times 10^{-10}$	531
Methanol	Chain transfer	$C_s = 6 \times 10^{-4}, 1.9 \times 10^{-4}$	108,342
Methyl acetate	Chain transfer	$C_s = 2.5 \times 10^{-4}$	108
Divinyl acetylene	Retardation	$k_r = 107 \times 10^3$ at 60°C	174,393,546
Divinyl acetylene	Retardation	$k_{r_1}/k_p = 130, yk_{r_2}/k_p = 1.1$, at 60°C	531
Monovinyl acetylene	Retardation	$k_r = 10.2 \times 10^3$ at 60°C	393,532,546
Benzene	Chain transfer	$C_s = 2.96 \times 10^{-4}$ at 60°C	108,276
Toluene	Chain transfer	$C_s = 34 \times 10^{-4}$ at 60°C	108
Ethylidene diacetate	No effect up to 5% concn.		95
Methyl vinylketone	Copolymerization	$r_1 = 0.05, r_2 = 7.0$, at 70°C	199
Methyl propenylketone			386
Crotonic acid	Retardation	$k_r = 15.6$ at 60°C	100
Crotonic acid	Copolymerization	$r_1 = 0.33, r_2 = 0$	275
Methacrylonitrile	Copolymerization	$r_1 = 0.01, r_2 = 12$ at 70°C	144
Butadienyl acetylene	Retardation		174
Vinylisopropenyl acetate	Copolymerization (also retardation)		554
Vinyl crotonate	Copolymerization (also retardation)	Cross-linking	554
Copper acetate	Retardation	No polymerization at 1.5×10^{-5} moles per 100 g of vinyl acetate	191

[a] Here k_r is the rate constant of the reaction of retarder with the propagating radical. According to Bartlett and Kwart (48,49), $yk_r/k_p = -(1/[Z])(k_t/k_p^2)[-d \ln [M]/d_t - R_i/-d \ln [M]/d_t]$, k_{r_1} and k_{r_2} are the retarding rate constants in retarding steps 1 and 2, and y is the number of radicals stopped by 1 mole of retarder.

were found to be without effect, acetaldehyde had little effect, but croton-aldehyde stopped the polymerization completely at 1.3×10^{-2} moles per 100 g of vinyl acetate. He found copper salts to inhibit polymerization completely at a concentration of 1.5×10^{-5} moles per 100 g of vinyl acetate. Figures 4-11 and 4-12 show the influence of aldehydes and copper salts.

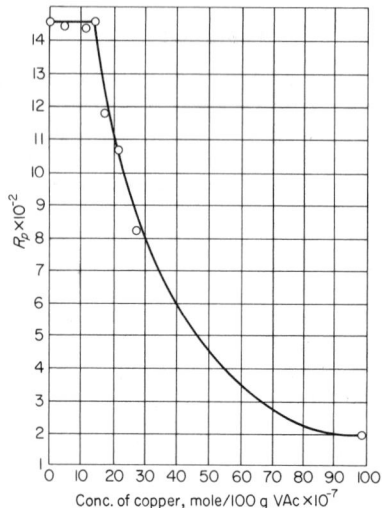

Fig. 4-12. Polymerization of vinyl acetate in the presence of copper traces (*191*).

Most impurities can be detected and identified by gas chromatographic means; for example, very small amounts of crotonaldehyde have been easily identified by this method (*70*).

Georgieff et al. (*175,176*) studied the influence on the polymerization of vinyl acetate of a number of other organic compounds, some of them occurring as impurities in vinyl acetate monomer. Figure 4-13 shows some of their results. The test was run adiabatically, and the time to boil for vinyl acetate after start of polymerization was plotted against the concentration of the impurity. It can be seen that the substituted acetylenes are the most powerful retarders and that some dienes are almost as bad.

D. Polymerizations of Vinyl Acetate in Solution

1. BENZENE

The questions arising from the solution polymerization kinetics of vinyl acetate in benzene, i.e. copolymerization versus chain transfer, have already been treated (page 237).

Benzene, even in small amounts, reduces the rate of polymerization appreciably (*112*); the order of reaction is rather complex, changing constantly as the monomer concentration increases (*344*). On the other hand, for a solution polymerization of vinyl acetate in ethyl acetate a 1.5 order was found with benzoyl peroxide (*112*) (see Table 4-26).

Loan and Burnett (*325*) explained this retardation effect as being due to the inefficiency of radicals found during a transfer reaction in reinitiating

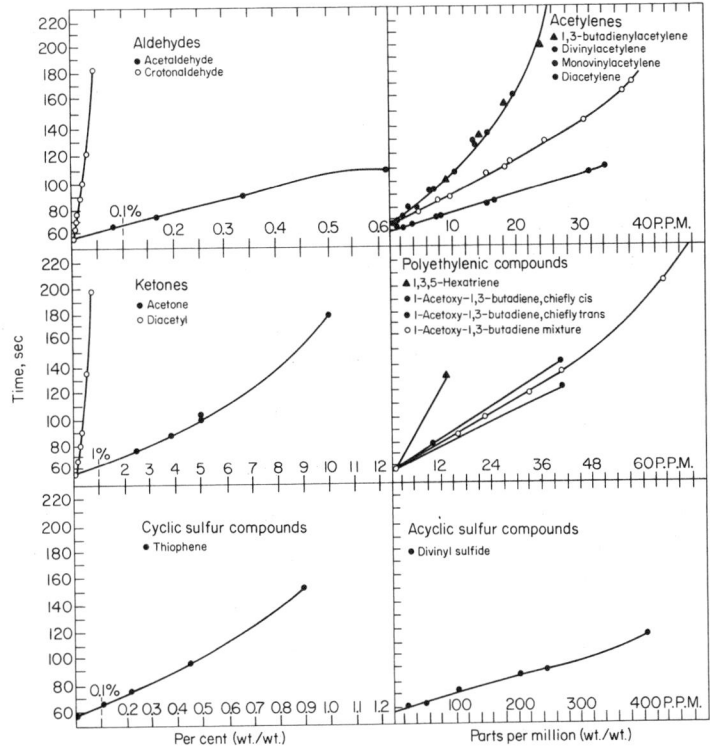

Fig. 4-13. Time lapse (in seconds) before the spontaneous boiling of vinyl acetate and concentrations of compounds added (*176*).

TABLE 4-26

Rate of Polymerization of Vinyl Acetate at 50°C (*112*)

In benzene		In ethyl acetate	
VAc, moles liter^{-1}	Rate $\times 10^{4}$,^{a} (moles liter^{-1}) sec^{-1}	VAc moles liter^{-1}	Rate $\times 10^{4}$,^{a} (moles liter^{-1}) sec^{-1}
10.36	6.6	10.36	6.6
9.98	4.5	9.94	5.8
9.93	4.4	9.50	5.4
9.45	2.9	8.65	4.4
9.31	2.2	7.87	3.8
8.92	1.7	5.93	3.0
		5.19	2.44

^{a} Initiator, benzoyl peroxide, 0.042 mole liter^{-1}.

polymerization chains. However, Barson et al. (*41*) discount this explanation, because they found phenyl radicals, probably produced by chain transfer, to initiate reactive chains efficiently. There must be some other mechanism, and this points again to the copolymerization scheme or to the explanation given by Haas and Husek (*198*) (see page 238).

2. METHANOL

Vinyl acetate polymerization in methanol solution is industrially important, because in some processes for the preparation of polyvinyl alcohol the polyvinyl acetate obtained by methanol solution polymerization is used as intermediate (*231*). The polymerization of vinyl acetate in methanol has been studied repeatedly. Transfer constants and other kinetic constants are shown in Tables 4-27 and 4-28. The difference between activation energy of transfer and that of polymerization was also calculated. It is found to be (*382*)

$$\bar{E} = \bar{E}_p - \tfrac{1}{2}\bar{E}_{tr} = 4.3 \text{ kcal/mole}$$

Vinyl acetate and methanol have been polymerized in various ratios, and the molecular weights of the resulting polyvinyl acetate and polyvinyl alcohol measured. Table 4-28 shows that the overriding influence on the molecular weight of the polyvinyl acetate is the methanol concentration. It has also been suggested that a small amount of acetaldehyde is formed in the system by transesterification of vinyl acetate with methanol, resulting in methyl acetate and acetaldehyde (*120*). Yano and Matsumoto (*591*) found that the rate of polymerization of vinyl acetate was not influenced by various ratios of methanol and methyl acetate but that the degree of polymerization increased as the methyl acetate concentration increased.

Alexandru and Opris (*10*) studied the polymerization of vinyl acetate in methanol, using various initiators for a mole ratio of vinyl acetate to methanol

TABLE 4-27

Chain Transfer Constants and Kinetic Constants for Vinyl Acetate Polymerization in Methanol (*382*)

	Temp. °C				
	40	50	60	60[a]	70
$C_m \times 10^4$ (monomer)	1.6	1.98	2.32	1.9	2.90
$C_s \times 10^4$ (methanol)	2.08	2.55	3.2	2.26	3.80
k_t/k_p^2	5.50	3.18	1.65		0.716

[a] Matsumoto and Maeda (*342*).

TABLE 4-28

Vinyl Acetate Polymerization in Methanol (295)

VAc/MeOH, %	BPO on VAc, %	Polymeriz. time, hr	Convsn., %	$\overline{DP}_{Ac}{}^{a}$	$\overline{DP}_{A}{}^{b}$
85/15	0.0504	16	96.2	1903	1177
67/33	0.0664	45	96.3	762	712
67/33	0.23	17	96.6	668	622
50/50	0.23	16	97.5	355	470

[a] Degree of polymerization of polyvinyl acetate.
[b] Degree of polymerization of derived polyvinyl alcohol.

of 0.55. They determined the rate constant of polymerization, k_p, for AIBN (6.25×10^{-6}), BPO (5.3×10^{-6}), and LPO (4.88×10^{-6}). They also found that the inhibiting action of oxygen is minimal with AIBN but is considerable with BPO and LPO.

Sakurada et al. (483) studied the same system extensively. They determined the effect of monomer concentration and the water content on conversion and degree of polymerization, the effect of temperature on conversion, and the effect of conversion on branching. A kinetic analysis (485) was also performed by the same authors. The activation energy and rate constant for the decomposition of AIBN was measured.

3. OTHER SOLVENTS

Vinyl acetate polymerization has been studied in other solvents, such as ethanol (305,306), methyl acetate (250,345), ethyl acetate (195), other esters (346,349), ketones (249), and water (439).

More recently t-butanol has been used as a solvent for vinyl acetate polymerization (44). The transfer constant is very low and allows the preparation of polymers of relatively high molecular weight (367).

E. Telomerization

A special case of solution polymerization is the preparation of so-called telomers. These are defined as low-molecular-weight polymers having end groups that contribute significantly to the properties of the polymer (209). A telomer is produced when the monomer-to-solvent ratio is small and when the solvent has a high transfer constant.

The following reaction scheme denotes the telomerization reaction:

$$I \quad \rightarrow R\cdot \qquad \text{radical formation}$$

$$R\cdot + YZ \quad \rightarrow RY + Z\cdot \qquad \text{transfer reaction to solvent}$$

$$Z\cdot + A \quad \rightarrow ZA\cdot \qquad \text{initiation}$$

$$ZA\cdot + A \quad \rightarrow ZAA\cdot \qquad \text{propagation}$$

$$ZA_n\cdot + YZ \rightarrow ZAY + Z\cdot \qquad \text{new transfer reaction}$$

Here the solvent YZ is called the telogen, the monomer A is called the taxogen, and the product ZA_nY is called the telomer. Termination takes place almost exclusively by transfer. When the propagation reaction is negligible, only 1:1 addition products are formed.

A number of good reviews have been published on telomerization in general (146,535). Specifically, vinyl acetate telomers have been prepared with various solvents (588).

The earliest example of a telomerization reaction was published by Harmon in a patent (209). Carbon tetrachloride formed mixtures of compounds with vinyl acetate having the following structure:

$$Cl_3C \underset{\underset{\displaystyle OAc}{|}}{+CH_2 - CH} \Big]_n Cl$$

where $n = 1$ to 8. When hydrolyzed, these products were said to be useful in surface-coating applications. Later Patrick received a patent (451) describing the isolated compounds, such as 1,3,3,3,-tetrachloropropyl acetate. Other carbon tetrachloride telomers have been described in the literature (512,523,597). Table 4-29 indicates some conditions used and the products obtained (511,512).

It was shown that the products A and B with $n = 2$ were actually diastereoisomers and had different melting points. Other chloride-containing

TABLE 4-29

Telomerization of Vinyl Acetate in Carbon Tetrachloride (512)

		$CCl_3 - (CH_2 - CHOAc)_nCl$ obtained, %				
			$n = 2$			
Polymeriz. temp., °C	CCl_4/VAc, moles	$n = 1$	A^a	B^b	$n = 3$	Losses, %
0	3	4.1	26.6	14.7	49.4	4.8
71–80	2	14.4	22.5	14.2	43.9	5.0

^{a} Telodimer A, m.p. 67.5°C.

^{b} Telodimer B, m.p. 51.5°C.

telomers were made from perchloroethylene, with the structure ($129,596$),

$$CCl_2{=}CCl{+}CH_2{-}\underset{\underset{OAc}{|}}{CH})_n Cl \qquad (19.36\% \text{ Cl, m.p.} \approx 100°C)$$

and from chloroform and chlorobenzene (500). Sakurada et al. (482), Noma and Nishiura (407), and Konishi and Ishizuka ($299,301$) prepared telomers with a degree of polymerization of less than 100 from phenol and aliphatic alcohols such as dodecyl and octadecyl alcohols. After hydrolysis of the telomers they produced surface-active agents. Alkyl halides were used by Noma and Nishiura (406) and Konishi and Ishizuka ($298,300$) as telogens for producing surface-active agents after saponification of the vinyl acetate telomers. Surface-active agents were also produced by cotelomerization of vinyl acetate and acrylamide in the presence of mercaptan (589).

Telomers were also prepared with aldehydes as telogens ($408,481$). One aldehyde group per molecule and a $\overline{DP} = 10$ was found. During saponification acetal groups were formed inter- and intramolecularly. Most of the end groups were ketonic in character, because most of the transfer took place on the aldehyde hydrogen ($370,371$). However, with increasing temperature the number of aldehyde end groups increased.

4-4. EMULSION POLYMERIZATION

A. Introduction

The emulsion polymerization process is most important for the commercial production of polyvinyl acetate, the suspension, solution, and bulk polymerization following in that order of importance. Unfortunately, the emulsion polymerization process for vinyl acetate is also the least understood. This is due in part to the complexity of the system. A typical emulsion polymerization recipe, as revealed in patents and trade literature, consists of:

Vinyl acetate	80 to 100 parts
Water	80 to 100 parts
Emulsifier	2 to 6 parts
Initiator	0.5 to 1.5 parts

The emulsifiers used are such polymers as polyvinyl alcohol, hydroxyethyl cellulose, maleic anhydride–vinyl alkyl ether copolymers, gum arabic, anionics such as sodium lauryl sulfate, alkyl aryl sulfonates, and nonionics such as polyethylene oxide alkylphenols, ethylene oxide–propylene oxide block copolymers, and polyethyleneoxide–fatty acid esters and fatty acid ethers.

The commonly used initiators include ammonium persulfate, potassium persulfate, hydrogen peroxide, water-soluble azo compounds such as

2,2'-azobis(2-methyl-4-carboxybutyronitrile) (469), and partially water-soluble organic peroxides such as succinic acid peroxide and *t*-butyl hydroperoxide.

The difference between the kinetics of styrene and vinyl acetate emulsion polymerization seems to be due mainly to the different water solubility of the monomers, but it should be due also to the different reactivities of the styrene and vinyl acetate radicals (see Table 4-30). For example, the chain-transfer activity of vinyl acetate is very much higher than that of styrene and, of course, influences the rate of emulsion polymerization, in which partially oil-soluble ingredients are used. This is especially true in the presence of emulsifiers that are more likely to be attacked by very active radicals, such as alkyl phenol–ethylene oxide adducts, in which the branched alkyl side chain of the phenol is a very likely attack point for a reactive radical. This not only reduces the rate of polymerization but also removes the emulsifier from the system by incorporating it into polymer particles, thereby changing the emulsifier concentration continuously.

Much of the data in the literature has to be viewed individually, but to arrive at a unifying theory is still impossible, because not enough comparative data are available. One of the reasons for this is the number and complexity of the variables. Temperatures, monomer-to-water ratio, kind and amount of emulsifiers, and initiators vary in most of the work reported. The influence of pH, both on the initiator efficiency and on the hydrolysis

TABLE 4-30

Water Solubility of Different Monomers

Monomer	Temp., °C	Water solubility		Weight ratio of monomer to polymer in latex particle	Ref.
		Wt-%	Molecules/cm^3		
Vinyl xylene	45	0.6×10^{-2}	2.7×10^{17}	0.9–1.7	180
Vinyl toluene	45	1.2×10^{-2}	6.1×10^{17}	0.6–0.9	180
Styrene	45	3.6×10^{-2}	2.1×10^{18}	1.1–1.7	42
Butadiene	25	8.2×10^{-2}	9.1×10^{18}	0.8	379
Chloroprene	25	1.1×10^{-1}	7.5×10^{18}	1.7	376
Isoprene				0.85	380
Vinyl chloride[a]	50	1.06	1.0×10^{20}	0.84	179
Methyl methacrylate	45	1.50	9.0×10^{19}	2.5[b]	179
Vinyl acetate	28	2.5	1.75×10^{20}	6.4	543
Methyl acrylate	45	5.6	3.9×10^{20}	6–7.5	245
Acrylonitrile[a]	50	8.5	9.6×10^{20}		179

[a] Polymer insoluble in monomer.

[b] Equilibrium solubility.

of vinyl acetate, which produces acetaldehyde, which in turn retards the rate of polymerization, and the influence of minor constituents such as impurities and oxygen, is often neglected. The following is a short review of the literature of vinyl acetate emulsion polymerization. It will serve to accentuate the differences between vinyl acetate and styrene emulsion polymerization. The emulsion polymerization of vinyl acetate in industrial practice as published in patents and trade literature is still in many respects an art, and much meaningful research will be necessary to elucidate the mechanism in each case.

More recently small amounts of water-soluble monomers, such as unsaturated carboxylic acids, unsaturated amides, and substituted amides, have been copolymerized with styrene, acrylic esters, and vinyl acetate, and have yielded products with specific properties. This again complicates the mechanism of emulsion polymerization and makes research work very cumbersome and difficult. Much of the work is being done in industrial laboratories and will probably not be published for some time.

B. Theory of Emulsion Polymerization

1. SMITH–EWART THEORY

The generally accepted qualitative theory of emulsion polymerization is based on work done by Harkins (*207,208*), which was later put into quantitative terms by Smith and Ewart (*508*) and Haward (*220*).† Essentially, an emulsion polymerization consists of a system of water, a monomer that is water-insoluble, an emulsifier, and a water-soluble initiator, which produces radicals when decomposing. Figure 4-14 shows schematically that the emulsifier forms micelles (about $10^{18}/cm^3$), solubilizing the monomer, which

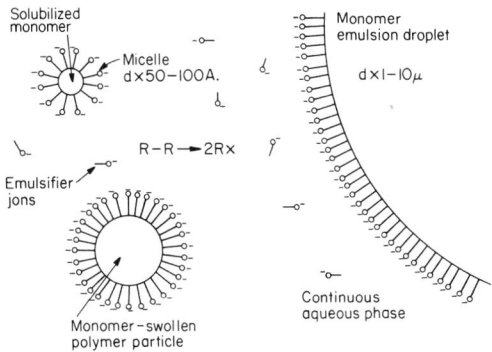

Fig. 4-14. Schematic representation of a conventional emulsion polymerization.

† The same conclusions were reached independently by Yurzhenko and Kolechova (*593*) in Russia and by Fikentscher et al. in Germany (*136*).

is transported by diffusion through the water phase from the monomer droplet into the emulsifier micelle. The initiator decomposes in the water phase, and the free radicals so formed diffuse into the micelles and start the polymerization. Since there are many more micelles than monomer droplets (about $10^{10}/cm^3$) the polymerization takes place essentially only in the micelle and not in the monomer droplets. The monomer in the micelle will be used up rapidly, but new monomer diffuses into the micelle, which is now swollen with polymer, until the monomer droplet disappears and the micelles have changed to polymer particles. No new micelles can be formed after a certain time, because the total surface area of the particles in the system increases, and thus the emulsifier concentration in the aqueous phase is reduced to below the critical micelle concentration for the surfactant. This occurs at about 15 to 20% conversion in the case of styrene emulsion polymerization.

Smith and Ewart in this country and Haward in England proposed a kinetic scheme to account for the known facts of the emulsion polymerization of styrene. They proposed three different cases for the polymerization occurring in the polymer–monomer particle, as follows.

Case 1. The rate of entry of radicals into the particle is low, but the rate of exit is high. This case is highly improbable, because a polymeric radical will not diffuse out of a particle faster than a small one will enter.

Case 2. The rate of exit or termination of radicals is much slower than the rate of entry. In this case the rate of polymerization can be described by the expression used for bulk polymerization:

$$R_p = k_p[M](kdIf/k_t)^{1/2} \qquad (4\text{-}86)$$

Case 3. The rate of termination is much faster than the rate of entry or of exit. This means that at any given time the particle would have one growing radical or none. The rate of polymerization is then described by the propagation step in any polymerization:

$$dM/dt = R_p = k_p[M][R] \qquad (4\text{-}87)$$

Since we will have one radical per particle half the time, Eq. (4-87) becomes

$$R_p = k_p[M](N/2) \qquad (4\text{-}88)$$

The absolute rate of propagation constant for several monomers has been measured (*34,35,51,88*).

One of the important points of this rate equation is the fact that an increase in initiator concentration does not lead to an increase in the rate of polymerization, although it will affect the molecular weight of the polymer.

Equation (4-88) can be used to calculate the molecular weight, assuming that no transfer reactions take place. The rate of decomposition of the initiator is given by

$$\rho = k_d[I]$$

where $[I]$ is the concentration of initiator and k_d is the rate constant of decomposition; N/ρ gives the time of growth of a chain, and the molecular weight is equal to $k_p(N/\rho)$. Any increase in $[I]$ results in an increase in ρ and thereby reduces the molecular weight.

A relationship between the number of particles formed and the initial concentration of emulsifier and initiator was also found by Ewart and Smith:

$$N = k([E]A_E)^{3/5}(\rho/\mu)^{2/5}$$

where $[E]$ is the concentration of emulsifier in grams per cubic centimeter, A_E is the area occupied by 1 g of emulsifier, ρ is the rate of radical generation, and μ is the rate of particle growth. In this equation one of the complicating factors, shown by Vanderhoff et al. (564), is the dependence of the rate of growth on the size of the particles.

In evaluating k Smith and Ewart made two assumptions: one was that no radicals would enter a particle as long as micelles still existed and therefore $k = 0.53$, and the other was that both micelles and particles compete for radicals and therefore $k = 0.37$. Experimentally, the value $k = 0.4$ is found. Gerrens et al. (42,177) verified the Smith–Ewart kinetics for styrene when he excluded oxygen rigorously. He found three distinct regions in the curve of conversion versus rate: in the first region $R_p = k_p[M](N/2)$, which verified Smith and Ewart's work, and in the second region this same equation applied, with the difference that a new rate constant had to be used:

$$R_p = k_1[M]/f$$

where $k_1 = k_p(N/2)f$. The point of transition between region 1 and region 2 was the conversion at which the monomer droplets disappeared; the rate was now first-order, since the monomer-to-polymer ratio decreased. In the third region the rate began to increase, because the particles were rather large; the time between the successive entry of radicals was given by t, and t represented the time between entry of the second radical and termination. Furthermore, the increasing viscosity produced the Trommsdorff effect, that is, a decrease in the rate of termination because of decreased mobility.

The Smith–Ewart theory has certain limitations:

1. It can be used only where the curve of rate versus conversion is linear.
2. Extremes of temperature, initiator concentration, and monomer-to-water ratio will change the particle number and size.

3. If the monomer is more water-soluble than styrene, the theory probably does not apply.

4. Interfacial tension will control diffusion.

5. Solubility of polymer in monomer is important. If it is not soluble continuously, new particles must form.

6. Allyl-type monomers terminate excessively by transfer. Under these conditions addition of more catalyst should increase R_p; this has been found (46).

Vanderhoff and co-workers have shown that particle growth can be given by the following formula (564):

$$\Delta V/\Delta t = kD^n$$

where D is the particle diameter. The exponent n will decrease as the particle size decreases. The small particles grow faster than the big ones when $n < 3$; when $n > 3$, the big ones grow faster. This means that a mono-dispersed latex can be produced by a delayed monomer addition.

2. NEWER THEORIES

Sheinker and Medvedev (499) have proposed a different mechanism of isoprene polymerization. For methyl methacrylate a similar mechanism, much like the one proposed by the Russian workers, was offered recently by Brodnyan et al. (79).

These last workers studied the emulsion polymerization of methyl methacrylate and n-butyl methacrylate and found that the water solubility of the monomer was relatively unimportant in determinations of the rate dependence and particle-number dependence. Monomers such as methyl methacrylate, vinyl acetate, n-butyl methacrylate, vinyl chloride, and styrene, which differ widely in water solubility, showed the same dependence of rate and particle number on emulsifier, initiator, and monomer concentrations over most of the range of variables studied. Brodnyan and co-workers found that the rate of polymerization obeyed the equation

$$R_p \approx [E]^{0.5}[I]^{0.5}$$

and the number of particles obeyed the equation

$$N_w \approx [E]^{3.0}[I]^{0.0}[M]^{0.0}$$

They compared the Smith–Ewart (508) and the Medvedev (354) theories, using methyl methacrylate and n-butyl acrylate. The dependence of the rate of polymerization on initiator concentration was found to conform to either theory, owing to some scattering of experimental points. Medvedev's theory predicts

$$R_p \approx [I]^{0.5}$$

and Smith–Ewart's predicts

$$R_p \approx [I]^{0.4}$$

The dependence of rate on emulsifier concentration for methyl methacrylate did not agree with either theory. It was found to be

$$R_p \approx [E]^{0.4}$$

Medvedev's theory predicts

$$R_p \approx [E]^{0.5}$$

and Smith–Ewart's theory predicts

$$R_p \approx [E]^{0.6}$$

For n-butyl methacrylate no differentiation between the theories could be made.

It is obvious that the kinetic data are not complete enough to differentiate between both theories. The number of particles was measured as a function of both emulsifier and initiator concentration. It did not significantly change over a thirty-fold range of initiator concentration, but it did change with emulsifier concentration. For methyl methacrylate it was found that

$$N \approx [E]^{3.0}$$

but for n-butyl methacrylate there appeared to be a change in the relationship depending on the range of the number of particles. For $N > 2 \times 10^{14}$ the cube expression seemed to hold, but for $N < 2 \times 10^{14}$ it seemed that $N \approx [E]^{0.5}$ was true.

In comparing the rate of polymerization per particle with the rate of polymerization per specific surface it was found that the rate per surface was nearly constant whereas the rate per particle increased considerably. This indicates that the Medvedev mechanism is the more realistic of the two. However, it is quite possible that, depending on the ratio of surface to volume, both mechanisms are operative.

Brodnyan et al. (79) showed that methyl methacrylate, which is more water-soluble than n-butyl methacrylate, behaved very similarly to it, and they pointed out that styrene, vinyl acetate, vinylidene chloride, and vinyl chloride behaved similarly. Van der Hoff (562) has shown that for all styrene emulsion polymerization data in the literature the following holds true:

$$R_p/N_w = \text{constant}, \qquad \text{when } N_w < 3 \times 10^{14}$$

$$R_p/N_w \approx N_w - 0.83, \qquad \text{when } N_w > 3 \times 10^{14}$$

and, since

$$R_p \approx [E]^{0.5}[I]^{0.5}$$

then

$$N_w \approx [E]^{0.5} \qquad \text{for } N_w < 3 \times 10^{14}$$

$$N_w \approx [E]^{3.0} \qquad \text{for } N_w > 3 \times 10^{14}$$

It was also found by Van der Hoff (563) that the number of particles was independent of the initiator concentration over a wide range. Ewart and Carr's data (135) on particle-number dependence on emulsifier concentration was replotted and found to conform to $N_w \approx [E]^{3.0}$ and to be independent of monomer concentration. Medvedev et al. (60) also found that in the case of styrene the rate of polymerization was linearly related to the specific surface of the emulsion.

French (148) found, by using Pluronics as emulsifiers, that in the case of vinyl acetate $N_w \approx [E]^{3.0}$, in conformity with the results with methyl methacrylate. Mesrobian et al. (421) found that $R_p \approx [E]^{0.6}$ and $R_p \approx [I]^{0.7}$ with polyvinyl alcohol and potassium persulfate. Combining these results, then: $R_p \approx N_w^{0.2}$, which was found by Stannett et al. (453), using sodium lauryl sulfate as emulsifier. Moll and Le Fevre (374) finally found that in the emulsion polymerization of vinylidene chloride and vinyl chloride the following relationships held true: $R_p \approx [E]$ and $N_w \approx [E]^{3.0}$.

C. Effect of Variables on Emulsion Polymerization of Vinyl Acetate (377, 379, 380, 381)

Since $N = ([E]A_E)^{3/5}(\rho/\mu)^{2/5}$, an increase in initiator during the first phase of polymerization will result in a larger particle number, which in turn will result in a rate increase, since $R_p = k_p[M](N/2)$. However, if the initiator is increased after the micelles have disappeared, no rate increase, but rather a decrease in molecular weight, should result. The rate will be affected if there is any mechanism by which more than two radicals can grow at the same time. In the case of styrene, isoprene, and butadiene, no increase in rate resulted when initiator was added during the linear portion of the rate–conversion curve.

According to Smith–Ewart, N should depend on the 3/5 power of an emulsifier factor; the values found are closer to 1/2. French (148) found that in vinyl acetate polymerization the rate was proportional to the third power of the emulsifier and that the monomer droplets disappeared at 8% conversion. Gerrens (178) suggests another explanation, namely that

$$N = ([E]A_E)^3/36\pi V_m^2$$

If the micelles did not take part in the initiation, the dependence on the third power of the emulsifier would be reasonable. Vinyl acetate is soluble up to 5% in water and, therefore, initiation takes place only in the water phase. It is reported (94) that, for example, if only a nonionic was used, no difference in particle size was observed when the concentration of emulsifier was increased, but that, when small amounts of sodium lauryl sulfate were added, differences in both rate and particle size were observed.

The critical micelle concentration depends on the particular emulsifier used and also on the amounts of other materials present, such as electrolytes.

The water-to-monomer ratio should not affect the kinetics of emulsion polymerization. This is true only if relatively high ratios are being used. For example, in styrene emulsion polymerization a water-to-monomer ratio of less than 2.3 should start to affect the kinetics (94).

The temperature will affect the rate of polymerization, because the propagation constant k_p and the initiator decomposition constant k_d are affected by temperature.

In emulsion as well as in bulk or solution polymerization the well-known chain-transfer relation is valid. Transfer may occur with monomer, polymer, emulsifier, and initiator. There apparently is no transfer involving water molecules (116,148,184). However, the equation for chain transfer,

$$\frac{1}{\overline{DP}} = \frac{1}{\overline{DP}_0} - C_{tr}\frac{[S]}{[M]}$$

may have to be modified to take into account different diffusion rates of monomer and transfer agent. The exact ratio of monomer and transfer agent at the site of polymerization will govern the influence of the various transfer reactions on the rate and degree of polymerization.

The effects of inhibitors and retarders are determined also by the locus of polymerization. If a water-soluble inhibitor is present, it will not affect the rate if the locus of polymerization is in the particle. Kolthoff and Bovey (292) have shown that by using dinitrobenzoic acid the pH of the system that governed the solubility of the retarder in water also affected the rate of polymerization.

The dependence of the rate of polymerization on the initiator varies from $[I]^{0.4}$ in styrene emulsion polymerization to $[I]^{0.5}$ in solution polymerization to $[I]^{>0.5}$ in a precipitation polymerization (103).

The influence of kind and concentration of emulsifier on the emulsion polymerization of methyl methacrylate and other monomers and their dependence on the water solubility of the monomers was investigated by Okamura et al. (430,431,437). They found that the rate of polymerization R_p of styrene and methyl methacrylate increased with increasing emulsifier concentration, but that in the case of methylacrylate, acrylonitrile, and vinyl acetate it went through a maximum and decreased at high emulsifier concentrations.

Agitation does not affect the rate of emulsion polymerization of vinyl acetate per se (128). In some of the early literature reference was made to the

TABLE 4-31

Effect of Air, Oxygen, and Stirring on Emulsion Polymerization of Vinyl
Acetate (*107*)[a]

		Conversion, %, after:				
Stirring	Medium	30 min	1 hr	2 hr	4 hr	$\overline{DP}_{Ac}$
No	Air	40.90	61.60	77.80	86.60	3,900
Yes	Air	72.60	73.60	74.80	76.00	4,150
No	N_2	58.80	71.60	82.50	84.30	
Yes	N_2	85.00	87.40	94.40	91.50	4,300
No	O_2					

[a] VAc, 0.9 mole/liter, KPS 5.55 × 10^{-3} mole/liter, 0.05 % Triton X-100,
40°C.

fact that agitation decreased the rate of polymerization. It was found later
that oxygen, which was still present in traces, was responsible for this effect.

Table 4-31 shows that a vinyl acetate emulsion polymerization is affected
by stirring in air, chiefly at low conversions, reflecting a longer induction
period. When the emulsion is not stirred even in the presence of oxygen,
the final conversion is higher than when it is stirred and compares well with
the polymerization conducted under nitrogen. In acrylonitrile polymerization
it was found that stirring did affect the rate of polymerization (*117,539*).
In a solution polymerization of vinyl acetate in water with potassium persulfate as initiator it was found that stirring did not affect the rate (*128,375*).
In some cases, however, it has been found that the diffusion of monomers or
modifiers may be influenced by the agitation, which would indirectly affect
the rate (*293,492*).

Okamura and Motoyama, on the other hand, found that the rate of agitation did influence the rate of polymerization and also the molecular weight
of the resulting polyvinyl acetate; when in an otherwise identical emulsion
polymerization the rate of agitation was varied, it was found that the degree
of polymerization of the resulting polyvinyl acetate increased substantially
when the rate of agitation was increased (*429*). This occurred whether the
polymerization was run under carbon dioxide or under air. The corresponding degree of polymerization of polyvinyl alcohol was always much lower,
indicating the occurrence of branching in the original polyvinyl acetate.
It was also found that in the case of an emulsion with very fine particle
size the difference between the degree of polymerization of polyvinyl acetate
and that of the resulting polyvinyl alcohol was quite small but that the
difference between the $\overline{DP}$'s, however, increased with increasing particle

size. Okamura and Motoyama (*429*) explained this by pointing out that the heat transfer is much faster from small particles than from large ones. Here again, however, the rate of agitation may indirectly affect the rate of polymerization and the molecular weight of the polymer in the direction opposite to that proposed in some of the earlier literature.

D. Effect of Water Solubility of Vinyl Acetate on Emulsion Polymerization

The solubility of vinyl acetate in water has been reported by Okamura et al. (*439*) to be 2.1 % at 50°C and 3.5 % at 70°C.

Okamura et al. (*439*) also studied the solution polymerization of vinyl acetate in water. They found that at very low conversions the rate of polymerization depended on the square root of the initiator concentration but was directly proportional to the monomer concentration: $R_p \approx [\mathrm{I}]^{0.5}[\mathrm{M}]^{1.0}$. Hummel et al. (*244,245*) investigated the influence of ionizing radiation on the emulsion polymerization of styrene, methyl methacrylate, ethyl acrylate, and methyl acrylate. They found that styrene (Fig. 4-15) obeyed Smith–Ewart kinetics quite well, with $R_p \approx [\mathrm{I}]^{0.5}$.

In the case of methyl methacrylate they did not vary the radiation doses. Figure 4-15 shows that R_p rose very rapidly within a few per cent of conversion, probably because of water-phase polymerization; then the rate remained almost constant until 30 % conversion, which is the point at which the monomer concentration remained constant. After 30 % conversion the monomer droplets had disappeared, and the viscosity in the particle produced a Trommsdorff effect. After 50 % conversion, when the maximum in R_p was reached, the diffusion started to be hindered, there was no more water-phase polymerization and, therefore, R_p decreased rapidly.

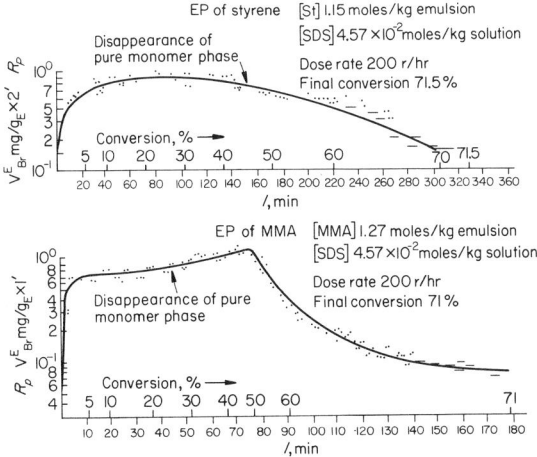

Fig. 4-15. Over-all reaction rate versus time (*245*).

In the case of ethyl acrylate, which is even more water-soluble than methyl methacrylate, a very high R_p also was found in the beginning. Then, however, the R_p decreased without staying at a plateau. Not enough data, especially about the distribution of monomer between water and polymer phases, is available to draw valid conclusions.

Methyl acrylate is very soluble in water (5 % at 30°C), so from the solubility point of view, at least, it is closely related to vinyl acetate. Here Hummel (244) found some seemingly contradictory facts. The influence of the initiator concentration was measured by varying the radiation intensity. He found $R_{p,\,max} \approx [I]^{0.55}$. This, according to Gerrens (178), is always true when the gel effect predominates. However, Hummel also found that the number of particles, N, and the degree of polymerization, $\overline{DP}$, depended on the radiation dose or [I]. The value of N increased with the initiator concentration, and the $\overline{DP}$ decreased. This was in contradiction to Gerrens, who found that N and $\overline{DP}$ were not affected by the initiator concentration.

Very often the point at which the monomer droplets disappear can be determined by a change in the rate of polymerization and also by a change in the monomer-to-polymer ratio in the polymer particle. For example, a latex without any monomer is saturated with monomer, and the distribution of monomer in the polymer and monomer phase is measured. The ratio of monomer to polymer in the particle is then expressed in per cent conversion of monomer to polymer and compared with the rate curve. Table 4-30 shows the water solubility and the weight ratio of monomer and polymer in the latex particle.

Patsiga (452) undertook a systematic study of the emulsion polymerization of vinyl acetate in the manner of Smith. He found a linear rate of polymerization over 80% of the conversion range. According to the Smith–Ewart theory, the rate should decrease after about 32% conversion.

The kinetic data were summarized by Patsiga as follows:

$$-dM/dt = kN^{0.15}[I]^{1.0}$$

He found no dependence on the emulsifier concentration. This means that the polymerization took place almost exclusively in the aqueous phase, in which vinyl acetate was dissolved. The polymer molecule so formed then precipitated and formed particles, which absorbed emulsifier from the micelles or from the solution. When salt was added and the monomer was salted out, the rate of polymerization increased, because then the polymerization took place in the particle.

Motoyama and Okamura (388,436) studied this matter by using vinyl hexanoate having a water solubility similar to that of styrene but a chain-transfer activity similar to that of vinyl acetate (92). They found that vinyl hexanoate behaved more like styrene in dependence of polymerization rate on the emulsifier concentration. When they increased the solubility of styrene in water by adding methanol, the emulsifier dependency was reduced to the 0.20 power, approaching that of vinyl acetate.

Vanzo (567) studied the kinetics of emulsion polymerization of vinyl acetate, vinyl hexanoate, and styrene, using 10 ml of monomer in 140 ml of water, emulsifier, and initiator. He also found first-power dependency of the rate on initiator concentration for vinyl acetate. For vinyl hexanoate he found that the rate depended on initiator to the 0.45 power and that the particle number depended on initiator to the 0.47 power, which indicated close agreement with the theoretical 0.40 power:

For vinyl acetate:

$$R_p \approx [\text{I}]^{1.0}$$

For vinyl hexanoate:

$$R_p \approx [\text{I}]^{0.45}$$

$$N \approx [\text{I}]^{0.47}$$

$$R_p \approx [\text{E}]^{0.46}$$

The dependence of the rate on emulsifier concentration was more like that found by Kolthoff et al. (73) for styrene.

The dependence of R_p on the number of particles was found to be equal to that of styrene: $R_p \approx N^{0.96}$. This was in direct contrast to the finding of Patsiga et al. (453) for vinyl acetate, for which R_p was proportional to the 0.2 power of the number of particles ($R_p \approx N^{0.2}$). At a constant number of particles the rate was found to be independent of initiator concentration, in agreement with the Smith–Ewart theory and in contrast to the first-power dependence found by Patsiga. The rate of polymerization per particle fluctuated widely but decreased as the concentration of particles increased. This has been confirmed in the range of particle concentrations considered by Smith (507) and Brodnyan (79) (see Fig. 4-16). The similarity in behavior in the region above 10^{14} particles is noteworthy. The rate per particle was influenced by the surface area, as confirmed by Brodnyan (79).

The decrease in the rate of polymerization was influenced by the particle size as follows. The amount of monomer within the particle increased with particle size. The surface area was a factor in the diffusion rate per particle, smaller particles normally accompanied the increase in particle concentration, and each of these factors tended to decrease the rate per particle as the number of particles increased by the use of initiator or emulsifier in a standard polymerization, assuming that diffusion control existed.

The value of k_p for vinyl hexanoate has been calculated by Vanzo (567). It is much lower than that for vinyl acetate, probably because of the influence of diffusion:

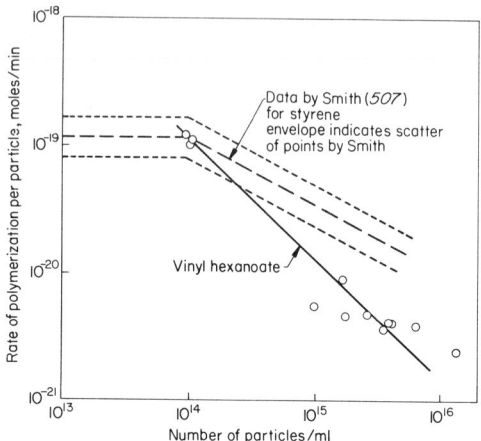

Fig. 4-16. Effect of particle concentration on the rate per particle (*567*).

Vinyl acetate:

$$k_p = 3700 \text{ liter/mole/sec}$$

Vinyl hexanoate:

$$k_p = 510 \text{ liter/mole/sec}$$

The shape of the polymerization curve may be deduced from the kinetic expression. The concentration of monomer on which the rate of polymerization depends remains constant as long as a free monomer phase is present. After the polymer fraction is large enough to absorb the monomer, the rate decreases, because the monomer now is not replenished in the particle.

Table 4-32 shows that the point of departure from linearity of R_p agrees with the calculated value for the disappearance of the monomer phase for styrene and vinyl hexanoate but not for vinyl acetate. Figure 4-17 shows the rate curves.

From these observations it is concluded that vinyl hexanoate behaves like styrene in emulsion polymerization. Motoyama (*388*) reported that the rates for vinyl acetate and vinyl hexanoate were the same and that they were five times higher than those for styrene. Vanzo found low values for vinyl hexanoate, because the particle size concentration remained in a range where diffusion controls the rate of polymerization.

Motoyama (*388*) also found that in a bulk polymerization chain-transfer constants of the two vinyl esters were similar and much greater than those of styrene. Therefore, one must conclude that solubility in water was a key factor in the different kinetics of vinyl acetate on the one hand and of vinyl hexanoate and styrene on the other.

TABLE 4-32

Calculated versus Observed Departure of Rate Curve
from Linearity (567)[a]

Solubility of monomer in polymer particles, moles/liter		Calculated point of disappearance (conversion), %	Observed point of departure from linearity (conversion), %
Styrene	5.42	40	38
Vinyl hexanoate	4.28	36	38–43
Vinyl acetate	7.60	32	77

[a] Departures from linearity were measured on standard (nonseeded) polymerizations.

Okamura and Motoyama (432) had come to the same conclusions earlier. They found that during an emulsion polymerization of styrene, vinyl caproate, methyl acrylate, and vinyl acetate, styrene and vinyl caproate behaved quite similarly. For example, the degree of polymerization increased with increasing emulsifier concentration for these two monomers, whereas it decreased for vinyl acetate. In bulk polymerization the $\overline{\text{DP}}$ as a function of the concentration of the same emulsifier stayed the same for styrene and

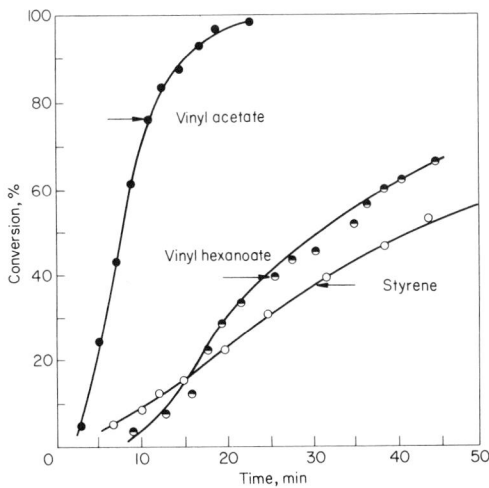

Fig. 4-17. Polymerization curves of vinyl acetate, styrene, and vinyl hexanoate (567).

TABLE 4-33

Results of Bulk and Emulsion Polymerization of Styrene, Vinyl Caproate, Methyl Acrylate, and Vinyl Acetate (432)

Monomer	Concn. of initiator, moles/liter	Concn. of emulsifier, g per 100 ml.	Rates of polymerization, mole/liter/sec $\times 10^{-4}$	Induction period, min	$\overline{DP}$
Bulk polymerization					
St	0.0182	0	1.2	27	230
	0.0182	0.85	1.2	25	240
	0.0182	10.04	1.1	74	240
VCp	0.0182	0	2.5	13	600
	0.0182	1.80	1.9	15	590
	0.0182	10.00	1.2	28	490
MA	0.0018	0	4.2	12	4000
	0.0018	1.62	3.6	16	3580
	0.0018	9.44	3.1	28	2170
VAc	0.0091	0	2.5	13	600
	0.0091	1.80	1.9	15	590
	0.0091	10.00	1.2	28	490
Emulsion polymerization					
St	0.15	0.2	1.3		780
	0.15	0.7	3.9		1280
	0.15	1.5	6.4		3520
VCp	0.1	1.0	1.6		600
	0.1	2.0	6.2		680
	0.1	3.0	7.8		810
	0.1	4.0	9.0		1030
MA	0.02	0	4.4		2440
	0.02	0.1	6.7		2470
	0.02	0.5	8.5		2500
VAc	0.05	0	14.4		3120
	0.05	0.2	8.6		1690
	0.05	1.0	5.7		1020

decreased for vinyl acetate and vinyl caproate, showing a similar reactivity of the radicals in chain-transfer reactions (see Table 4-33).

In emulsion polymerization the effects of the Smith–Ewart kinetics on the molecular weight, namely the increase in molecular weight with increasing emulsifier concentration, was not as pronounced with vinyl caproate as it was with styrene. However, the $\overline{DP}$ of vinyl acetate decreased considerably with increasing emulsifier concentration (a nonionic polyethylene oxide dodecyl ether was used). This may mean that in the case of vinyl caproate only transfer with monomer took place, whereas in the case of vinyl acetate

TABLE 4-34

Solubilization of Monomers in Sodium Dodecyl Sulfate
Solution at 30°C (*436*)

Monomer	Solubility in water, %	Solubility in 2% SDS solution
Vinyl acetate	2.3	4.0
Styrene	0.03	0.12

in addition to transfer with monomer there was also transfer with emulsifier. This implies a water-phase polymerization during most of the polymerization.

In a later paper Okamura and Motoyama (*436*) studied the emulsion polymerization of styrene, vinyl acetate, and vinyl caproate with both non-ionic and anionic emulsifiers. They compared first the solubility of the mono-mers in water and 2% sodium dodecyl sulfate solution (see Table 4-34). Then they determined the chain-transfer constant of polyethylene oxide dodecyl ether for vinyl acetate and styrene and also the retardation constant (which they defined as $R = R_0[E]^{-r}$, where R and R_0 represent the polymeri-zation rates in the presence and absence of surfactant E. Unfortunately, they did not determine these values for an anionic emulsifier (Table 4-35).

As predicted by the Smith–Ewart theory, the rate of polymerization of styrene was very small below the critical micelle concentration and increased abruptly above it. This was not so of vinyl acetate, which polymerized with an appreciable rate even without a surface-active agent (see Fig. 4-18).

The influence on rate of the emulsifier concentration can be seen in Fig. 4-19: for styrene $R_p \approx [E]^{0.6}$, for vinyl acetate with anionic soap $R_p \approx [E]^{0.0}$, and for nonionic soap, $R_p \approx [E]^{-0.3}$. The last result was due to the retarda-tion with increasing nonionic emulsifier concentration, since the polymeri-zation took place in the water phase. In the case of vinyl caproate, as Fig. 4-20

TABLE 4-35

Transfer and Retardation Constants of Vinyl Acetate and
Styrene toward Polyethylene Oxide Dodecyl Ether (*436*)

	k_{tr}/k_p	r
Vinyl acetate	0.075	930
Styrene	0.002	10
Vinyl caproate	0.078	870

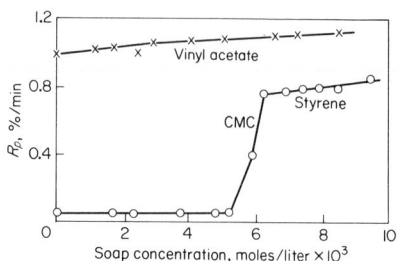

Fig. 4-18. Emulsion polymerizations in surfactant solution at concentrations near the critical micelle concentration: $\bigcirc$, styrene, ammonium persulfate, 0.1 g; $\times$, vinyl acetate, APS 0.02 g, H_2O 200 cm^3, monomer, 40 cm^3 (*436*).

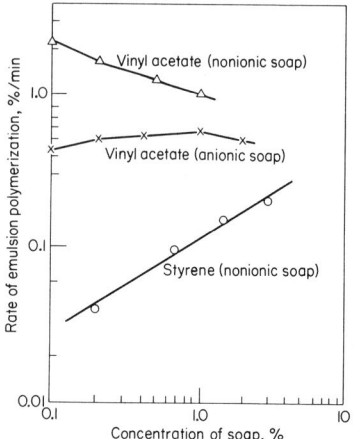

Fig. 4-19. Relation between rate of polymerization at 60°C and surfactant concentration (*436*).

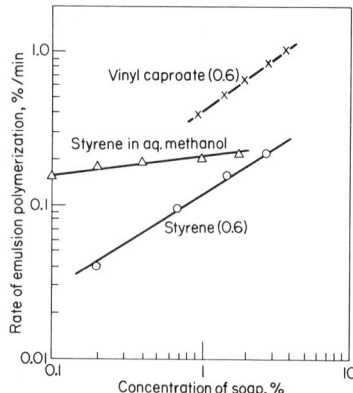

Fig. 4-20. Relation between rate of polymerization at 60°C and surfactant concentration. Numbers in figures indicate the exponent of the Smith–Ewart equation (*436*).

TABLE 4-36

Emulsion Polymerization of Vinyl Acetate (*348*)[a]

Run no.	Polymeriz. time, min	Temp., °C	Convsn., %	Degree of polymerization $\overline{DP}$ resulting[b]		
				$\overline{DP}_{PVAc}$	$\overline{DP}_{PVA}$	$\overline{DP}_{PVAc}/\overline{DP}_{PVA}$
1	20	66	5.5	3,400	2,300	1.49
2	40	67	17.7	3,260	2,780	1.17
3	50	67	27.6	3,770	2,830	1.30
4	60	67.5	44.2	3,800	2,650	1.43
5	70	72	80.8	13,520	2,200	6.15
6	80	81	89.4	16,150	1,810	8.92
7	90	78	90.5	16,607	1,790	9.27

[a] *Recipe:* vinyl acetate, 10 kg (contained 0.14% acetaldehyde); water, 50 kg; ammonium persulfate, 30 g.

[b] PVAc = polyvinyl acetate, PVA = polyvinyl alcohol.

shows, the rate was $R_p \approx [E]^{0.6}$, just as it was in the case of styrene. Adding methanol to the water decreased the rate dependence on emulsifier for styrene to $R_p \approx [E]^{0.2}$, because styrene became more soluble in the water–methanol medium.

Matsumoto et al. (*348*) studied the emulsion polymerization of vinyl acetate. They used an anionic emulsifier and found that the degree of polymerization of the polyvinyl acetate was low up to 40% conversion and then rose rapidly, probably because of branching reactions. Water-phase polymerization probably dominated during the first phase, giving a low-molecular-weight "solution polymer," and polymerization in the particle predominated during the second phase, giving rise to the branching reactions. Table 4-36 shows some of their results. The investigators found that the rate

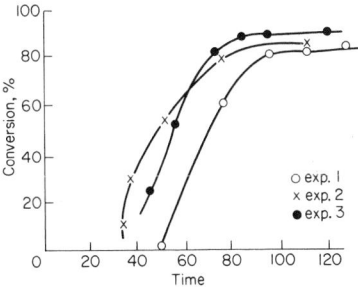

Fig. 4-21. Emulsion polymerization of vinyl acetate. VAc/H$_2$O = 1:37, 63°C; (NH$_4$)$_2$S$_2$O$_8$; ◯, 0.6%; ×, 0.75%; ●, 1.5% (*348*).

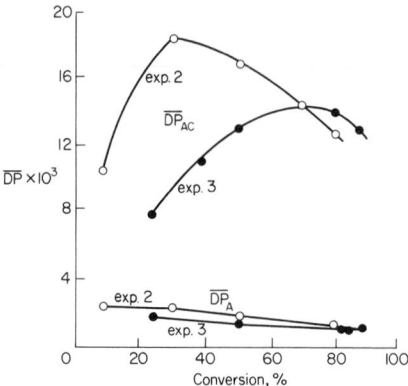

Fig. 4-22. Degree of polymerization and percentage conversion for two initiator levels. $\bigcirc$, 0.75%; $\bullet$, 1.5% (*348*).

of polymerization was linear up to about 80% conversion and not very dependent on the catalyst concentration in the range used, 0.6 to 1.5% of ammonium persulfate. This was a polymerization without emulsifier in dilute aqueous solution. In this case polyvinyl acetate of relatively low molecular weight was produced in the beginning, a maximum at about 40% conversion, and then a gradual fall again until 100% conversion (see Figs. 4-21 to 4-24).

Cherdron and co-workers (*106*) studied the emulsion polymerization of acrolein, another very water soluble monomer. They found the following relationships to be valid:

$$R_p \approx [\text{E}]^{0.2}$$

$$R_p \approx [\text{I}]^{0.4}$$

$$R_p \approx [\text{M}]^{1.0}$$

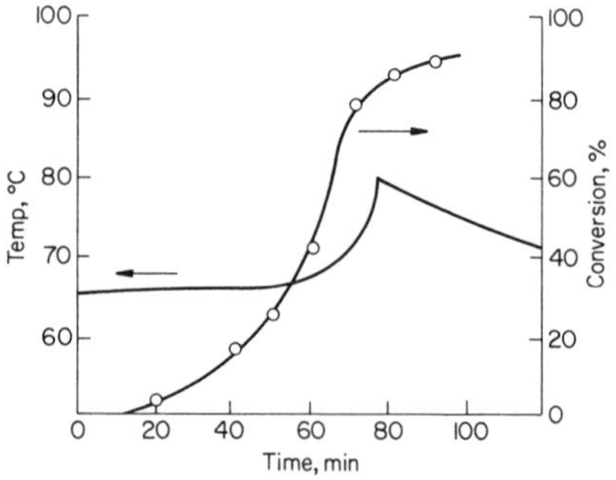

Fig. 4-23. Time, temperature, conversion relationship for vinyl acetate emulsion polymerization (*348*).

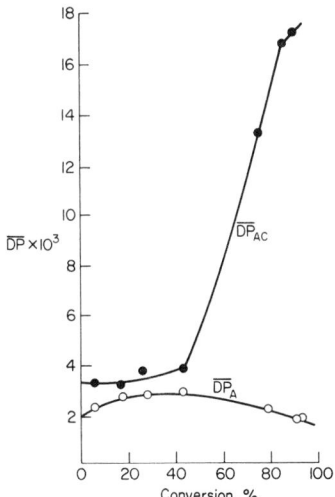

Fig. 4-24. Change in degree of polymerization with percentage conversion (*348*).

They used as the emulsifier a polyacrolein–sulfur dioxide addition product. The water solubility of acrolein (20 vol-%) explains the deviation from the Smith–Ewart kinetics.

Polymeric emulsifiers do not form micelles in the ordinary sense. However, polyvinyl alcohol, for example, does form aggregates of some kind, which have been found by light-scattering (*513*). These could act somewhat like micelles. A comparison of vinyl acetate, acrylonitrile, and acrolein is given in Fig. 4-25 (*105*). The most water-soluble monomer, acrolein (20.8%), shows $R_p \approx [E]^{0.2}$; acrylonitrile (9%) shows $R_p \approx [E]^{0.3}$ and vinyl acetate (2.5%) shows nearly $R_p \approx [E]^{0.6}$. This reveals again the importance of water solubility in the kinetic picture of emulsion polymerization.

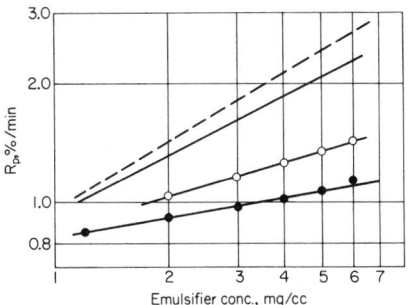

Fig. 4-25. Polymerization of water-soluble monomers. $\bigcirc$, acrylonitrile; $\bullet$, acrolein; - - -, vinyl acetate; ———, slope = 3/5 (Smith–Ewart) (*105*).

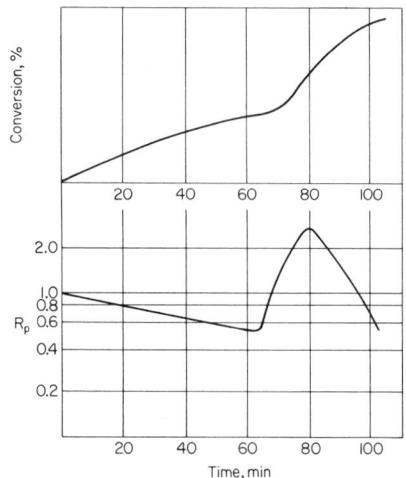

Fig. 4-26. Polymerization of methyl acrylate in water without addition of emulsifiers (*493*).

The polymerization of methyl acrylate in water was investigated by Schuller (*493*), who found a relatively slow first-order reaction in relation to monomer, which is characteristic of a solution polymerization (see Fig. 4-26). The reaction medium was completely transparent during this stage. Coincidental with a strong acceleration of the rate of polymerization the solution became very hazy, indicating the beginning of a true emulsion polymerization.

The emulsion polymerization of vinyl stearate was studied as an example of a monomer much less water-soluble than styrene (*450*). The water solubility of vinyl stearate is estimated to be somewhere between 10^{-11} to 10^{-8} moles/liter. A nonionic polyethylene oxide–alkyl phenol adduct was used as emulsifier. The rate of polymerization first increased and then decreased with increasing emulsifier concentrations. The increase can be explained by Smith–Ewart kinetics, because more particles are formed. The later decrease in rate is probably due to chain transfer with emulsifier. The number of particles was independent of initiator concentration, whereas R_p was directly proportional to the initiator concentration:

$$R_p \approx [\text{I}]^{1.0}$$

$$R_p \approx N^{0.0}$$

Obviously, diffusion of monomer to the growing particle was a very important step, being dependent on the size of the monomer droplets and on the size of the latex particles. Therefore, the rate of polymerization was proportional to the particle surface area. At the beginning the surface area of the latex particle was zero and the monomer droplets were large. Somewhere during the intermediate stages the surface area became large, while the monomer droplet size decreased; therefore, both the transfer to monomer and the rate of polymerization passed through maxima.

E. Other Studies of Emulsion Polymerization of Vinyl Acetate

The emulsion polymerization with and without emulsifier was studied by Napper et al. (397,398). They found that in the polymerization without emulsifier the third case of Smith–Ewart was applicable. The experimental conditions were a 0.33 molal solution of vinyl acetate in water, potassium persulfate heat activated at 40°C, and oxygen not removed before polymerization. The rate constant k_p was calculated for this system at 5% conversion and found to be 1860 liter mole^{-1} sec^{-1}, which compares well with the $k_p = 1320$ liter mole^{-1} sec^{-1} calculated by Bagdasaryan as reported by Napper and Parts (398). It is assumed that the rate increased constantly because of the increasing radical concentration in the growing latex particles. The number of particles per milliliter was found to be in the range of 1.2×10^{12} (at low conversion) to 1.7×10^{12} (at high conversion). The average radius changed from 0.78×10^{-5} cm to 1.33×10^{-5} cm. The rate of polymerization increased steadily up to 40% conversion and then decreased again. The time–conversion plot had a linear portion extending from 5 to 60% conversion. The rate of polymerization as a function of initiator concentration was found to be: $R_p \approx [\mathrm{I}]^{0.15}$ (this value was calculated from Napper's data with the use of rates between 20 and 40% conversion at various catalyst concentrations.

Napper and Parts found that in their system the polymerization of vinyl acetate consisted of three distinct stages. During the first stage vinyl acetate polymerized in solution, the polymer so formed precipitated, aggregated, and formed latex particles. These absorbed monomer and then became the locus of polymerization. The number of particles was constant during the second stage of polymerization, but the rate of polymerization increased with time, owing to the increase in the size of the particles and the increase in radical concentration.

At the same time a Trommsdorff effect may have been operative during this stage because of the increasing viscosity of the monomer–polymer mixture in the particle, and even a decrease in monomer concentration could be more than compensated for by the gel effect.

During the third stage the rate declined again owing to the decreasing monomer concentration in the particles.

The number of particles was found to be constant above 16% conversion, and the instantaneous rate of polymerization increased up to about 40% conversion and then decreased (see Fig. 4-27).

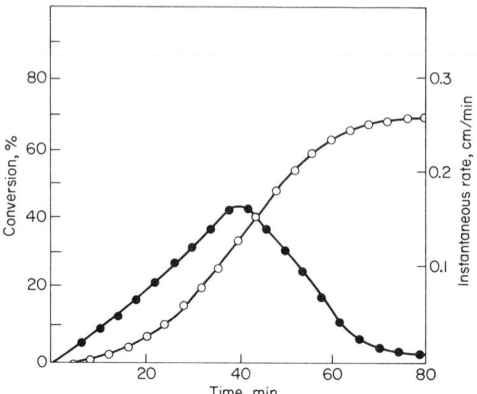

Fig. 4-27. ○, A typical sigmoidal conversion–time curve. ●, instantaneous rate of polymerization as a function of time. Vinyl acetate, 0.33 m; potassium peroxydisulfate, 7.5 mM; pH of solution, 3.80; temperature, 40.0°C (*398*).

The final conclusion of this study was that the kinetics of the vinyl acetate polymerization suggested that the polymerization occurred primarily in the polymer particle, which formed a stable suspension. The percentage conversion was found to be linear with the square of the time over a considerable range. The autoacceleration observed could be ascribed to an increase in the average number of free radicals per particle during the polymerization.

On adding cationic, anionic, and nonionic emulsifiers in amounts below the critical micelle concentration Napper and Alexander (*397*) found that the nonionic emulsifier did not affect the rate of polymerization; however, anionic emulsifier increased, and cationic emulsifier decreased, the rate of polymerization (see Fig. 4-28).

It was found that the particle size produced by anionic emulsifier was much smaller than those obtained without emulsifier, by nonionic it was the same, and by cationic emulsifier it was much larger. This proves that the anionic and nonionic emulsifiers interfered with the aggregation of the polymer particles, the effect being dependent upon the type of emulsifier and, of course, upon the nature of the initiator. The surface charges on the latex particles will become progressively more negative, since SO_4^{2-} end groups will result from the use of potassium peroxydisulfate.

It would have been interesting to observe the effect of hydrogen peroxide in this connection, because no charged end groups result when this initiator is used.

By virtue of the positive charge of the cationic emulsifier and the negative charge of the particle strong adsorption of the cationic emulsifier and a subsequent lowering of the zeta potential would promote coalescence

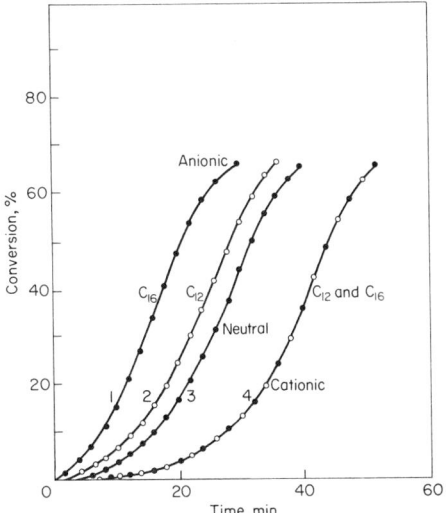

Fig. 4-28. Effects of soaps on the conversion–time curve. 1, sodium cetyl sulfate; 2, sodium dodecyl sulfate; 3, Triton X-100; 4, decyl trimethylammonium bromide or dodecyltrimethylammonium bromide. Vinyl acetate 0.33 m, potassium peroxydisulfate 0.015 M, pH of the solution 3.80 (*398*).

and lead to a larger particle size. In the presence of anionic emulsifier the polymer particle will adsorb the organic anion of the emulsifier, leading to an increase in zeta potential and a prevention of coalescence (a lowering of the critical charge value) and, therefore, producing a smaller particle size. The rate of increase may be explained by a decrease of mutual radical termination due to the smaller particle size.

End group analysis has been performed by tracer (*294*) and chemical methods (*50*) and has established the presence of sulfate end groups when potassium peroxydisulfate was used as initiator. Very sensitive end group determinations by a dye partition and interaction technique (*183*) have shown both sulfate and hydroxyl end groups. When the pH of the emulsion polymerization medium became acidic, the hydroxyl end groups predominated. Sulfate ion radicals and the surrounding water molecules can react as follows,

$$\dot{S}O_4^- + H_2O \longrightarrow HSO_4^- + \dot{O}H$$

or, in an acidic medium,

$$\dot{S}O_4^- + H_3O^+ \longrightarrow H_2SO_4 + \dot{O}H$$

This points to an additional complication in the evaluation of published emulsion polymerization studies, since this effect has been neglected in most cases. During an emulsion polymerization with potassium peroxydisulfate and a reducing agent the medium becomes more acidic, unless properly buffered. Further, the presence of heavy metal salts, such as Fe^{2+} or Ag^+, which may activate the polymerization, may produce polymers with both sulfate and OH end groups (*182*).

Greth and Wilson (*193*) related the so-called HLB number of an emulsifier, which indicates a specific hydrophobic-hydrophylic balance in the emulsifier with the rate of polymerization and with the emulsion stability and particle size of the resulting polymer emulsion. No conclusions can be drawn, however, from their data on the kinetics of vinyl acetate emulsion polymerization, because not only were protective colloids, such as polyvinyl alcohol and hydroxyethyl cellulose, used in conjunction with nonionic and anionic emulsifiers, making these systems extremely complicated, but also the pH of these emulsions was generally very low, giving rise to monomer hydrolysis and subsequent acetaldehyde formation, which may be considerable at the typical condition of the polymerizations (pH $= 2$ at 70°C for $2\frac{1}{2}$ hours), and because the monomer was added gradually during the polymerization, which introduced the most serious complication for kinetic studies.

Dunn and Taylor (*128*) investigated the emulsion polymerization of vinyl acetate in experiments similar to those of Napper and Parts. They found that

$$R_{p,\text{max}} \approx [\text{I}]^{0.64}$$

$$R_{p,\text{max}} \approx [\text{M}]^{0.3} \quad \text{(only up to 1.0, then constant)}$$

$$N \approx [\text{I}]^{0.22} \quad \text{at a concentration of 1\% } M$$

$$N \approx [\text{M}]^{1.0} \quad \text{at a concentration of 0.02\%}$$

The lack of degassing did not affect the rate of polymerization but only the induction period. The polymer phase soon became the more important locus of polymerization, as can be seen in Fig. 4-29. From 20 to 45% conversion R_p is fairly constant (see Fig. 4-30). The number of particles decreased

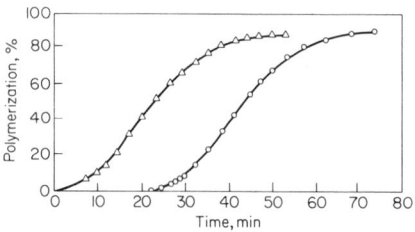

Fig. 4-29. Effect of oxygen. $\triangle$, rigorously degassed, maximal rate 3.24%/min; $\bigcirc$, oxygen content limited by use of boiled-out water, maximal rate 3.18%/min. Vinyl acetate concentration 1.0% v/v, persulfate concentration 0.01% w/v (*128*).

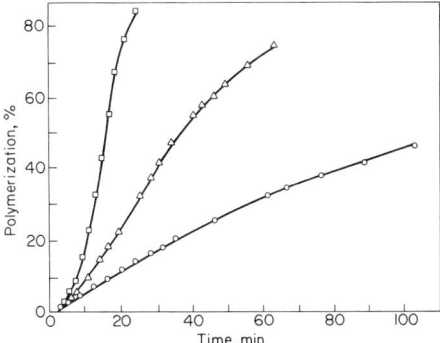

Fig. 4-30. Emulsion polymerization of vinyl acetate. □, Polymerization of 2% v/v vinyl acetate with 0.02% w/v persulfate; △, ionic strength increased by addition of 4% w/v potassium sulfate; ○, ferric–hydrogen peroxide initiation. (H_2O_2) 0.047 M, (Fe^{3+}) 3.5 × 10^{-5} M, giving a rate of initiation similar to that of 0.02% persulfate (*128*).

with conversion; only during the accelerating portion of the time conversion curve did the number of particles go up. The addition of sodium lauryl sulfate increased the rate of polymerization and increased the number of particles. Above the critical micelle concentration the particle number remained constant. The addition of polyvinyl alcohol reduced the maximal rate. Dunn and Taylor proved that much of the polymerization must have taken place in the polymer–monomer phase rather than in the aqueous phase. They calculated the rate of solution polymerization of a 0.23-M vinyl acetate solution by using $k_p/k_t^{1/2} = 0.6$ at 60°C, and the rate of initiation by using 3.6 × 10^{-7} mole liter^{-1} min^{-1} as 6.1 × 10^{-4} mole liter^{-1} min^{-1}, but the maximal rate in practice was 1.1 × 10^{-2} mole liter^{-1} min^{-1}, or twenty times larger. Table 4-37 shows the number of radicals per particle as a function of conversion and also the concentration of monomer in the polymer phase, [M_p], which is very low. The difference between this and a styrene type of emulsion polymerization is that here the monomer concentration decreases continuously throughout the reaction. However, since the weight of the polymer phase increases continuously, the monomer dissolved in the polymer phase passes through a maximum. Figure 4-31 shows a correlation of R_p and monomer in the polymer phase. The explanation of the coexistence of such a large number of particles must be based on the assumption that radicals can coexist if the medium is sufficiently viscous to prevent cross termination.

Transfer reactions between polyvinyl alcohol and vinyl acetate reduced the rate of polymerization with increasing amounts of polyvinyl alcohol. The transfer reactions retarded the rate of polymerization because of the introduction of an alternative termination reaction (*87*).

TABLE 4-37

Variation of the Number of Radicals (n) per Particle with Conversion (128)[a]

2.0 % monomer, 0.02 % persulfate					
Polymerization, %	5	16	37	62	100
[M_p], molar	4.4	3.4	2.1	0.6	
Rate × 10³, mole liter⁻¹ min⁻¹	3.36	6.26	10.45	9.6	
n	1.8	4.2	14.2	61.5	
1.0 % monomer, 0.01 % persulfate					
Polymerization, %	6	17	32	49	66
[M_p], molar	0.8	0.56	0.33	0.21	0.08
n	0.17	0.53	1.38	2.57	3.65

[a] [M_p] is the monomer concentration in the particle.

French (148) studied the emulsion polymerization of vinyl acetate, using ethylene oxide–propylene oxide block copolymers as emulsifiers. A standard commercial recipe was used with a high water-to-monomer ratio in comparison to previous studies, in which this ratio was always quite low.

French found that the number of particles remained constant from 20 to 100% conversion; the monomer droplets disappeared at about 13.5% conversion; the number of particles was found to be related to the emulsifier concentration,

$$N \approx [E]^{3.0}$$

and the total surface was proportional to the emulsifier concentration. French postulated that the vinyl acetate monomer diffused very rapidly into the polymer particle, so that after 15% conversion no monomer droplet existed. At this point the total surface in 1 cm³ was equal to $A_E \times [E]$, which is the total interface covered by the emulsifier in 1 cm³. The average radius

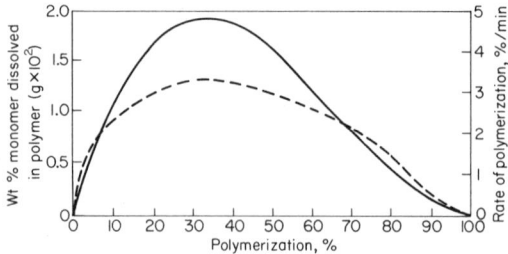

Fig. 4-31. Correlation of the rate of polymerization - - - with the total amount of monomer dissolved in the polymer phase —— (128).

d_0 is, then, given by

$$(A_E[\text{E}]) = \pi N d_0$$

$$N = A_E[\text{E}]/\pi d_0$$

If V_m is the volume of the monomer in 1 cm^3 at the start, and if the assumption is made that the particle has the density of monomer at 8 to 15% conversion, then

$$V_m = N \pi d_0^3/6$$

$$d_0 = (6V_m/N\pi)^{1/3}$$

$$N = (A_E[\text{E}])^3/\pi 36 V_m^2$$

which results in the third-order-dependence number of particles on emulsifier. Gerrens (*178*), who derived this calculation, had a different explanation of the proportionality of surface-to-emulsifier concentration. He said that the Pluronic emulsifiers do not solubilize any monomer. The latex particles were formed when the polymer, which was initiated in the water phase, precipitated, and coagulation was prevented by the emulsifier. Then only as many latex particles could be formed as could be protected by the emulsifier; therefore, the emulsifier and total surface area were proportional.

Elgood and co-workers (*134*) have studied some phases of an emulsion polymerization of vinyl acetate, in which the monomer, emulsifier, and initiator were continuously added over the course of the polymerization. This is industrially a very important process in which many vinyl acetate emulsion polymers are prepared at least by adding the monomer continuously and in some cases by adding also emulsifier and initiator continuously (*582*). They found that the particle surface area was an important parameter in controlling the rate of polymerization in systems with nonionic or with anionic emulsifiers. They also confirmed that the relationship between rate of polymerization and particle size changed at about 3×10^{14} particles per milliliter. This was similar to Van der Hoff's observation in the case of styrene (*562*). The particle surface, however, was found to be directly proportional to the rate of polymerization.

An extensive study of vinyl acetate polymerization with nonionic emulsifier was made by Chung and Han (*107*). They used Triton X-100, a polyoxyethylene alkylphenol adduct, and polyvinyl alcohol as emulsifiers. They too, found that the rate of polymerization goes through a maximum as a function of emulsifier concentration both for polyvinyl alcohol and the Triton X-100. The rate of polymerization as a function of initiator concentration was found to be:

$$R_p \approx [\text{I}]$$

Patsiga et al. (453) found that the rate of polymerization was independent of emulsifier concentration. They used an anionic emulsifier, $R_p \approx [E]^{0.0}$; presumably, this meant that the rate was also independent of the number of particles. They also found

$$R_p \approx [I]^{1.0}$$

The rate of polymerization was found to be constant up to 80% conversion after the initiation. The monomer phase disappeared at about 35% conversion. Patsiga used a recipe that started out with a seed and ended with about 25% solids.

The rate of polymerization was found to be $R_p \sim N^{0.2}$ for vinyl acetate; in comparison, for styrene it was found to be $R_p \approx N$. At the same time the rate for styrene was found to be zero when there were no particles, but for vinyl acetate it was 0.88 moles/min per 180 cm^3 of H$_2$O.

The final conclusion of the paper by Pastiga et al. was that most of the polymerization up to 80% conversion took place in the water phase, where the monomer was supplied from the monomer droplets at first and then from the monomer–polymer droplets. This theory is in direct conflict with those of Napper et al. (397,398) and French (148).

F. Emulsion Polymerization of Vinyl Acetate in the Presence of Polyvinyl Alcohol

O'Donnell et al. (421) studied the emulsion polymerization of vinyl acetate with a partially hydrolyzed polyvinyl alcohol as emulsifier. They found

$$R_p \approx [I]^{0.7}$$

$$R_p \approx [E]^{0.6}$$

The conversion–time curves were essentially linear up to 40 to 80% conversion. They used a polymerization recipe that is closer to those used in commercial practice than are the recipes in most of the other studies: 20 parts of vinyl acetate per 100 parts of total charge and polyvinyl alcohol concentrations of 0.75 to 2.04% per 100 cm^3 of water.

From surface-tension measurements they deduced an "apparent critical micelle concentration" at 0.25% of polyvinyl alcohol in solution, although light-scattering measurements of 0.12 to 0.75% polyvinyl alcohol solutions in water failed to give an indication of aggregates. The latter point is important; however, the experimental evidence given by O'Donnell et al. is not conclusive, because they not only chose a low-molecular-weight polyvinyl alcohol ($\overline{DP} = 350$) for the experiment, although a high-molecular-weight polyvinyl alcohol was given in the recipe, but also failed to do the light-scattering work at the temperature of the emulsion polymerization, i.e. 70°C.

There is evidence that partially saponified polyvinyl alcohol forms aggregates as a function of temperature (409). The lower the degree of hydrolysis and the higher the temperature, the greater the number of aggregates formed (cloud-point formation). Since partially saponified polyvinyl alcohol is really a mixture of fractions of polyvinyl alcohols of various degrees of hydrolysis, the average degree of hydrolysis being about 88%, the formation of aggregates is a progressing phenomenon with the increase of temperature. Unfortunately, no study of the emulsion polymerization of vinyl acetate with polyvinyl alcohol as emulsifier has been made at various polymerization temperatures.

Regarding the rate of polymerization as a function of emulsifier, another point is very important, which is chain transfer to polyvinyl alcohol, which decreases the rate of polymerization and therefore may compensate and obscure rate increases due to increasing emulsifier concentrations.

Measurements of surface tensions of partially saponified polyvinyl alcohols at room temperature do not show a sharp break at 0.25% but show a rather slowly decreasing function (574). Again, a study of surface tension as a function of temperature has not yet been reported for polyvinyl alcohol.

Commercially large amounts of polyvinyl acetate are prepared in the presence of polyvinyl alcohol to give stable dispersions. The mechanism and kinetics of the polymerization of these systems is not very well known. Relatively few studies have been published, and almost none are concerned with kinetic studies.

It has been established that graft copolymers easily form when vinyl acetate is polymerized in the presence of polyvinyl alcohol (214,405,441). This phenomenon complicates any kinetic examination of the emulsion polymerization process. This is so because the grafting process removes emulsifier from the system, thereby changing the concentration, and it may change the solubility characteristic of the polyvinyl alcohol that is left in solution by changing the ratio of hydroxyl and acetyl groups. Furthermore, the distribution of acetyl groups will be changed, which will affect the emulsion properties.

The first study of the emulsion polymerization of vinyl acetate with polyvinyl alcohol as emulsifying agent was made by Motoyama and co-workers (391). They found that the rate of polymerization was affected by the degree of hydrolysis of the polyvinyl alcohol used. The lower the degree of hydrolysis, the better the emulsifying action and the faster the rate of polymerization.

Okamura and Yamashita (442) studied the emulsion polymerization of vinyl acetate in the presence of polyvinyl alcohol, especially the formation of graft copolymer, and some emulsion properties such as particle size and stability. They found that the following variables increased the amount of graft copolymer of polyvinyl alcohol and vinyl acetate: increasing initiator concentration, increasing molecular weight of the polyvinyl alcohol and increasing acetyl content in the polyvinyl alcohol. However, only when ammonium or potassium persulfate was used as initiator was this result obtained. When hydrogen peroxide or AIBN was used, very little graft copolymer was recovered. It was found that 97% of the ammonium persulfate formed radicals with polyvinyl alcohol, but only 14% of the AIBN did so. It is known that carbon radicals are generally more inefficient hydrogen abstractors than are oxy or thiyl radicals (190,595). It is very possible that in the presence of polyvinyl alcohol the radical from the initiator attacks the polyvinyl alcohol, producing a macroradical, which in turn initiates vinyl acetate polymerization (438). The fact that the amount of graft copolymer increases with increasing acetyl content of the polyvinyl alcohol led to the determination of the chain-transfer constant for both polyvinyl acetate and polyvinyl alcohol in solution polymerization (438).

Vinyl acetate transfer constant to PVAc: 1.5×10^{-4}

Vinyl acetate transfer constant to PVA: 35×10^{-4}

The transfer constant to PVA is twenty times that of the polyvinyl acetate. This is surprising in view of the fact that as the acetyl groups—that is, the polyvinyl acetate content—of the polyvinyl alcohol increased, the graft efficiency also increased, even though the transfer constants indicate the opposite. It was found that the graft efficiency, when checked in a true solution polymerization, decreased with decreasing degree of saponification, as expected from the transfer constants.

The explanation of this phenomenon must be sought partly in the mechanism of emulsion polymerization. Moreover, partially hydrolyzed polyvinyl alcohol will orient itself in such a way that the acetyl part will tend to be in the particle and the hydrophilic OH− part toward the water phase. Therefore the acetyl group will come more in contact with the polymerizing species. Some other parameters were also measured by Okamura and coworkers (438). For example, the emulsion particle size decreased as the amount of acetate groups on the polyvinyl alcohol increased, and the emulsion viscosity increased as the amount of acetate groups in the polyvinyl alcohol increased. This was due partially to the finer particle size, which resulted in a higher emulsion viscosity, but it was also due to a loose agglomeration of particles (flocculation), which immobilized water and thereby removed it from the continuous phase, effectively increasing the solid phase.

4-5. SUSPENSION POLYMERIZATION

The suspension polymerization of vinyl acetate is an important industrial process. Surprisingly, only very few studies of the mechanism of suspension polymerization in general (238,239) and of vinyl acetate in particular (296,

488,533,534) have been reported. Numerous patents, however, deal with the vinyl acetate suspension polymerization, mainly describing various protective colloids and catalysts (*5,59,78*). The patent and other literature on suspension polymerization has been well summarized recently by Logemann (*326*).

It had been recognized long ago, although never really proven, that kinetically the suspension polymerization is a "water cooled bulk polymerization" (*237,543*). Since mainly oil-soluble initiators are used, the high water solubility of vinyl acetate is not as important in this case as in emulsion polymerization of vinyl acetate, in which the water solubility of the monomer influences the kinetics of polymerization profoundly.

The particles that are formed during suspension polymerization are usually spherically shaped with diameters of 0.1 to 3 mm. Small amounts of protective water-soluble colloids normally are used, to prevent the particles from coalescing. Some of the water-soluble colloids that have been used are polyvinyl alcohol (*476*), gelatin (*61*), the ammonium salt of a styrene–maleic anhydride or vinyl alkyl ether–maleic anhydride copolymer (*192,201*), and polyethylene oxide graft copolymers (*273,274*). Solid suspending agents such as calcium or barium carbonate or barium sulfate can also be used (*427,573*).

The effect of agitation and agitator geometry on the particle size distribution has been studied by Ishii (*266*). An extensive study of the suspension polymerization of methyl methacrylate, styrene, and vinyl acetate was made by Hopff and co-workers (*238,239*). They developed the following empirical equation:

$$\log L_0 = a_{n\overline{D}n} + b_n \log n + b_{\overline{D}} \log \overline{D} + b_\eta \log N_w$$

where L_0 is the original particle size, $\overline{D}$ is the vessel diameter, N_w is the viscosity of protective colloid solution, n is the revolutions per minute of the agitator, and a and b are constants.

Figure 4-32 shows the dependence of the particle size on agitation, and Fig. 4-33 shows the dependence of particle size on the viscosity of the

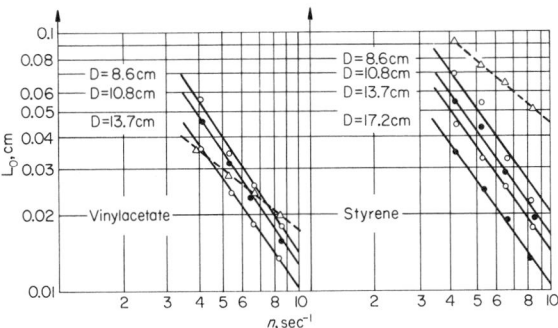

Fig. 4-32. Dependence of original bead size on agitation (n = revolutions per minute). Polyvinyl alcohol; ● and ○, 20 g/liter; △, 0.5 g/liter (*239*).

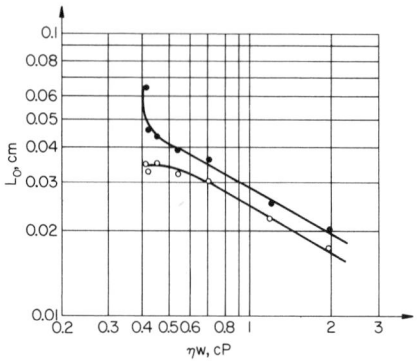

Fig. 4-33. Dependence of original bead size L_0 on viscosity η_w of the protective colloid solution ($n = 6.66 \, \text{sec}^{-1}$). ○, Vinyl acetate, $D = 10.8$; ●, styrene (*239*).

protective colloid solution both for vinyl acetate and for styrene. It can be seen that the smallest viscosity allowable, of the protective colloid solution for styrene and probably also of vinyl acetate, is about 0.4 centipoise.

Table 4-38 shows the constants of the equation for three different monomers. Figure 4-34 shows the yield of suspension polymer as a function of protective colloid concentration, the remainder of the polymer being in emulsion form. It can be seen that vinyl acetate does not tend to form emulsion polymer in this system.

Recently a study of suspension polymerization of vinyl acetate was made by Sakurada et al. (*488*), who confirmed that the kinetics are similar for bulk and suspension polymerizations.

TABLE 4-38

Characteristic Constants for the Suspension Polymerization of Different Monomers (*239*)

Monomers	Polymeriz. temp., °C	Protective colloid concn., g/liter	Constants		
			b_n	$b_{\overline{D}}$	b_η
Methyl methacrylate	50	20	-1.59	-0.80	-0.60
		0.5	-0.92		
Vinyl acetate	70	20	-1.51	-0.80	-0.60
		0.5	-0.83		
Styrene	70	20	-1.47	-0.94	-0.58
		0.5	-0.83		

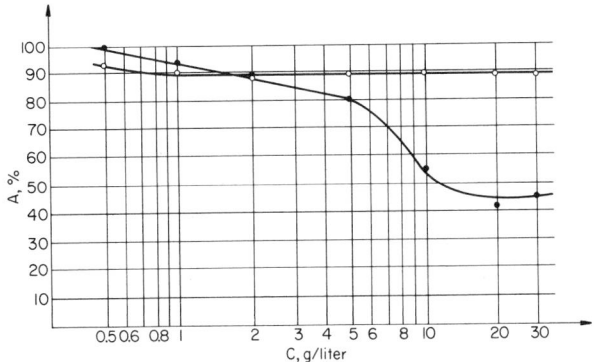

Fig. 4-34. Dependence of the yield A of suspension polymer on the protective colloid concentration. ○, Vinyl acetate; ●, sytrene (*239*).

4-6. POLYMERIZATION BY LIGHT

Melville determined rate constants of vinyl acetate polymerization by a rotating-sector method with light as initiator (*189,355*).

The most efficient light source is ultraviolet light, and each monomer responds best to a specific wavelength, corresponding to maximal absorption. For vinyl acetate this is at 2537 A; for sodium light, at 5890 A. The number of radicals formed by 1 quantum of light is called the primary quantum efficiency. This value is 0.3 for vinyl acetate (*387*).

To increase the efficiency of initiation sensitizers are often added (*89*). The sensitizer usually absorbs light over a wider wavelength range and thereby increases the efficiency. Guzman and Delgado (*196*) studied sensitized vinyl acetate photopolymerization. They found that $R_p \approx I^{1/2}[\text{sensitizer}]^{1/2}$ up to 30% conversion, where I is the light intensity. The sensitizer was AIBN. Azo compounds have been found to act as very good sensitizers: AIBN (*86*), α,α'-azobiscyclohexane carbonitrile (*55*), and azobispropane (*86*). Other sensitizers are carbonyl compounds such as benzoin and benzil (*434*), peroxides such as di-*t*-butyl peroxide (*310*) and benzoyl peroxide (*89,501*), uranyl salts (*435*), ω-bromo acetophenone (*448*), acriflavine–ascorbic acid (*528*) and, finally, ferrous salt–oxalic acid–persulfate (*422*).

Some sensitizers are also chain-transfer agents. The kinetic equations for light-induced polymerization are the same as for free-radical initiator polymerization:

$$1/\overline{DP} = \tfrac{1}{2}\gamma + C_m + C_i([I]/[M])$$

Burnett et al. (*86*), for example, found

$$1/\overline{DP} = 10^{-2}\exp(-850/T) + 0.935 \times 10^{-7}\exp(+2{,}200/T)$$

where they obtained the maximal molecular weight at 14°C.

The rate of polymerization is proportional to the 0.5 power of the light intensity without sensitizer and to the 0.6 power with sensitizer (*310*).

The activation energy for the polymerization reaction, in general, is

$$\bar{E}_a = \frac{\bar{E}_d}{2} - \left(\bar{E}_p - \frac{\bar{E}_{tr}}{2} \right)$$

where $\bar{E}_d$, $\bar{E}_p$, and $\bar{E}_{tr}$ are the activation energies of initiation, propagation, and transfer, respectively. Since the rate of initiation was found to be temperature-independent, in the case of light initiation the energy of activation reduces to

$$\bar{E} \text{ photo} = \bar{E}_p - \bar{E}_{tr}/2$$

Since the energy of activation for benzoyl peroxide and AIBN is 26 kcal/mole in a heat-activated system, $\bar{E}$ photo is less by 13 kcal/mole than $\bar{E}_a$ for normal heat-activated polymerizations.

Table 4-39 shows some energies of activation. It can be seen that uranyl salts, just as in radiation polymerization, have by far the most efficient sensitizing effect.

4-7. POLYMERIZATION BY RADIATION

The radiation polymerization of monomers has been reviewed by Charlesby (*104*) and Chapiro (*102*). Chapiro studied in detail the behavior of various monomers (*101*). Table 4-40 shows the polymerization activity of some monomers when initiated by radiation at 20°C. It can be seen that vinyl acetate is by far the most reactive.

Radiation polymerization can become important when conventional polymerization systems cannot be used as, for example, in the recently developed process of making "wood alloys," that is the impregnation of

TABLE 4-39

Energy of Activation for Light-Initiated Vinyl Acetate
Polymerization with Sensitizer

Sensitizer	Activation energy, kcal/mole	Ref.
No sensitizer	4.4	89
Uranyl salt	0–1.5	435
ω-bromo acetophenone	6.47	448
Acriflavine–ascorbic acid	6.2	528

TABLE 4-40

Polymerization of Vinyl Monomers by Gamma Radiation
$(101)^a$

Monomer	Rate of polymeriz., %/hr	Rate of polymeriz. per megarad, %
Butadiene	0.01	0.2
Styrene	0.2	3
Methyl methacrylate	4	67
Acrylamide	6	100
Acrylonitrile	9.5	160
Vinyl chloride	15	250
Methyl acrylate	18	300
Vinyl acetate	27	450

^{a} 10^3 rad/min at 20°C

wood with monomer and then polymerization of the monomer (282). Other cases in which radiation polymerization is of advantage are the preparation of polymers when no initiator residues can be tolerated, when low-temperature polymerization is used, when solvent initiation only can be used, and when solid-phase polymerization is desired (39). Graft and block copolymers can also be synthesized by means of ionizing radiation (82,97).

Bulk radiation polymerization has been investigated by Bagdasaryan (30). He found that up to a radiation intensity of 0.4×10^4 r/hr the rate of polymerization was equal to the square root of the intensity, $R_p \approx I^{1/2}$ but that the power decreased to less than half when higher intensities were used, because the incidence of recombination of radicals increased. Okamura and co-workers (434) found that the rate and the degree of polymerization were related in the same manner in radiation as in polymerization by free-radical initiator. At 20°C they found that the relation

$$\frac{1}{\overline{DP}} = C_m - \left(\frac{k_t}{k_p^2}\right)\frac{R_p}{[M]^2}$$

was valid (425). The G value, which is equal to the number of radicals produced by 100 eV of energy, was determined from $k_p/k_t^{1/2}$:

$$G = 1.4 \quad \text{for vinyl acetate}$$

$$G = 5.5 \quad \text{for methyl methacrylate}$$

$$G = 0.04 \text{ for styrene}$$

For vinyl acetate $k_p/k_t^{1/2} = 0.21$.

The higher the G value, the easier it is to form radicals. Other investigators found the G value for vinyl acetate to be 5.0 to 7.5 (30,206). The apparent activation energy for gamma-radiation polymerization of vinyl acetate was found to be 3.7 kcal/mole (39,433). At low temperatures the "gel effect" became pronounced, owing to the high viscosity of the system.

Additives in small amounts (0.1 mole/liter) reduced the rate of polymerization slightly. The following order of increasing retardation for organic additives was observed: acid anhydrides < alcohols < esters < hydrocarbons < ethers < ketones < halogen compounds < nitrogen compounds (204).

In solution polymerization by radiation the solvent generally accelerated the rate of polymerization (428,332).

The following kinetic scheme can be written (428):

$$M \longrightarrow M\cdot \qquad \varphi_m I[M]$$

$$S \longrightarrow S\cdot \qquad \varphi_s I[S]$$

$$M\cdot + M \longrightarrow MM\cdot$$

$$S\cdot + M \longrightarrow SM\cdot$$

$$MM\cdot + nM \longrightarrow MM_n\cdot$$

$$SM\cdot + nM \longrightarrow SM_n\cdot \qquad k_p[M]([M\cdot] + [S\cdot])$$

$$MM_n\cdot + SM_n\cdot \longrightarrow \text{polymer}$$

$$SM_n\cdot + SM_m\cdot \longrightarrow \text{polymer} \qquad k_t([M\cdot] + [S\cdot])^2$$

$$MM_n\cdot + MM_m\cdot \longrightarrow \text{polymer}$$

where S is the solvent, I is the radiation intensity, and φ_m and φ_s are the rate constants for radical formation from monomer and solvent, respectively, which are proportional to the G value. It is assumed that $M\cdot$ and $S\cdot$ are of equal activity. Then for steady-state conditions

$$R_p = -\frac{d[M]}{d_t} = \frac{k_p}{k_t^{1/2}}[M]^{3/2}(\varphi_m I)^{1/2}\left(1 + \frac{\varphi_s}{\varphi_m}\frac{[S]}{[M]}\right)^{1/2}$$

and, if R_0 and M_0 are rate and monomer concentration, respectively, then for bulk polymerization

$$\frac{R_p}{R_0} = \left(\frac{[M]}{[M_0]}\right)^{3/2}\left(1 + \frac{\varphi_s}{\varphi_m}\frac{[S]}{[M]}\right)^{1/2}$$

Plotting $(R_p/R_0)^2/([M]/[M_0])^3 - 1$ against $[S]/[M]$ will give φ_s/φ_m. For example, in acetic acid, water, and uranyl salt as sensitizer (332)

$$\frac{\varphi_{AcOH}}{\varphi_{VAc}} = 3.4, \qquad \frac{\varphi_{H_2O}}{\varphi_{VAc}} = 9.5, \qquad \text{and} \quad \frac{\varphi_{VAc}}{\varphi_{VAc}} = 10,700$$

The G value of the solvent, G_s, can also be calculated with the use of G_{VAc} for bulk polymerization, which is equal to 10.6:

$$G_s = \frac{\varphi_s}{\varphi_m}\left(\frac{MW_M}{MW_S}\right)G_{VAc}$$

where MW_M and MW_S are the molecular weights of monomer and solvent, respectively. For the vinyl acetate–solvent system the following G values were found: vinyl acetate–AcOH, $G_{AcOH} = 52$; vinyl acetate–AcOH–H$_2$O, $G_{H_2O} = 480$; and vinyl acetate–AcOH–H$_2$O–uranyl acetate, $G = 23,000$.

The rate and degree of polymerization are equally changed by changes in solvent composition. Uranyl acetate accelerates the R_p greatly.

The effect of temperature on the rate and degree of polymerization in the low-temperature radiation polymerization of vinyl acetate has been investigated at 0, -20, and $-78°$C (424). It was found that between 0 and $-78°$C the activation energy of polymerization was 3 kcal/mole, giving the highest molecular weight at 0°C. At lower temperatures the activation energy decreased to 2 kcal/mole and, in solution, 4 and 1 kcal/mole, respectively. In solution the maximal molecular weight was reached at $-20°$C. As the temperature decreased, less branching and less tail-to-tail polymerization (1,2 glycol units in the hydrolyzed polyvinyl acetate) were observed as expected.

The emulsion polymerization by radiation of vinyl acetate has been studied extensively (18,244,328–330). The rate of polymerization is ten to one hundred times faster than for bulk or solution polymerization, depending on the kind of emulsifier. Table 4-41 shows some emulsifiers and their influence on the rate of polymerization. It is seen that the presence of cationic emulsifiers resulted in the lowest rate. It was found that the activation energy of polymerization was 5.7 kcal/mole in the presence of cationic emulsifiers.

Graft copolymers were prepared by radiation in emulsion with vinyl acetate monomer (17). A number of patents were issued covering emulsion polymerization of vinyl acetate by gamma radiation. High molecular weights were obtained, which allowed the preparation of high-viscosity polyvinyl alcohol (307,315,509).

In another case Okamura (423) applied radiation to vinyl acetate in the presence of oxygen and formed a peroxy compound of vinyl acetate. He used this as polymerization initiator together with dimethyl anilin and ferrous sulfate.

TABLE 4-41

Emulsion Polymerization[a] of Vinyl Acetate by Gamma Radiation
(328)

Emulsifier	R_p, mole^{-1} sec^{-1} × 10^4	R_p/R_0
None	2.50	1.0
Sodium lauryl sulfate	76.39	30.5
Polyoxyethylene laurylether	85.38	34.1
Stearyl trimethyl ammonium chloride	45.83	18.3
Cetyl pyridinium chloride	3.77	1.5

[a] Emulsifier concentration, 0.1%; 2 × 10^4 rad/hr; 20°C, 10% conversion.

4-8. POLYMERIZATION BY ORGANOMETALLIC COMPOUNDS

It can be seen in Table 4-42 that only metal-organic compounds from the second and third group of the periodic table, with the exception of lead compounds, are efficient catalysts of vinyl acetate polymerization. The mechanism usually is not cationic, although in some cases it is not entirely of a free-radical type, either (576). The mechanism of polymerization has been studied by Inoue and co-workers (264). They classified organometallic compounds as catalysts for vinyl polymerization as shown in Table 4-43. The metal alkyls of the first and second group of the periodic system induce anionic polymerization. Alkyl compounds of the other metals cannot induce the vinyl polymerization by themselves, unless the C—M bond strengths are weak enough to break under the influence of light or heat:

$$RM \rightarrow R \cdot + M \cdot$$

TABLE 4-42

Polymerization of Vinyl Acetate by Organometallic Compounds

Initiator	Efficiency of polymerization[a]	Remarks	Ref.
Li	2	Li–naphthalenide	24
Li	1	Li–metal	281
LiBu	3		147
LiBu	2	Partially oxidized LiBu + cocatalysts ZnR$_2$ + H$_2$O	164
Na–iAm	2	TiCl$_4$/Na–iAm = 0.1 to 0.3 mole	383,384
NaAm	3		252,253

TABLE 4-42 (continued)

Initiator	Efficiency of polymerization[a]	Remarks	Ref.
AgEt	2	PbEt$_4$–AgNO$_3$, AgEt (in methanol)	111
BeEt$_2$		+ Cumene hydroperoxide	521
CaZnEt$_4$	3		154,262
CdEt$_2$	2	Rate and degree of polymerization increase by O$_2$	150,153,159
CdMe$_2$	1		150
CdEt$_2$	1	+ VOCl$_2$, VCl$_4$, AgNO$_3$, CdCl$_3$, and solvent	163,263
ZnEt$_2$	2	+ air, VOCl$_3$, VCl$_4$, ethanol, and water	156,166 263,479
HgBu$_2$	1	+ ZnCl$_2$, ZnBr$_2$, BiCl$_3$, VOCl$_3$, VCl$_4$	261,263
HgR$_2$	1	R = C$_6$H$_{11}$, R = phenyl–CH$_2$	302
HgR$_2$	2	R = phenyl	302
Hg(OAc)$_2$	2		260
BEt$_3$, −Bu$_3$	1		162,25
BEt$_3$, −Bu$_3$	1	Cocatalysts O$_2$, H$_2$O$_2$, MgO$_2$, V$_2$O$_5$, CuO, cumene hydroperoxide	158,161,247,412 26,165,415
BEt$_3$, NH$_3$	1		413,414
BBu$_3$	3	+ BF$_3$OEt$_2$, ZrCl$_4$	167
AlEt$_3$	2	Self-starting O$_2$-accelerated polymerization	151
AlEt$_3$	2	VCl$_3$, VOCl$_3$, V$_2$O$_5$	156,230,561
AlEt$_3$	1	+ BF$_3$OEt$_2$; AlEt$_3$/BF$_3$OEt$_2$ = 1 to 2 moles	279
AlR$_3$	1	+ Benzoyl peroxide	364,365
AlR$_3$	1	Large amounts of O$_2$ inhibit polymerization	576
AlEt$_3$	1	+ Dicyclohexyl percarbonate	363
AlEt$_3$	1	+ O$_2$, BZ$_2$O$_2$, cumene hydroperoxide	362
AlEt$_3$	1		58
Al–iBu$_3$	1	+ CoCl$_2$, NiCl$_2$, Co(NH$_3$)$_6$, Cl$_2$	171
Al–iBu$_3$	1		4,368,575
AlR$_3$	1	Benzoyl peroxide	133
AlEt$_3$	1	+ CS$_2$; also with ZnEt$_2$, CdEt$_2$	331
SnR$_4$	3	R = C$_6$H$_{11}$; some polymerization, R = Ph	166
PbEt$_4$	2		111,168
PbEt$_4$	2	+ Ultraviolet light	336
PbR$_4$			302
PEt$_3$	3	+ TiCl$_4$	166
SbEt$_3$, −Me$_3$	2	+ TiCl$_4$ decreased $\overline{DP}$; V$_2$O$_5$, WO$_3$ increased $\overline{DP}$	166
BiR$_3$	3		302
SeBu$_2$	3		478
TeBu$_2$	2	+ HgCl$_2$	478
TiBu$_4$	1		314

[a] 1 = efficient polymerization, 2 = little polymerization, 3 = no polymerization.

TABLE 4-43

Classification of Organometallic Compounds as Initiators of Vinyl Polymerization (*264*)

	I_A	II_A	III_A	IV_A	V_A	VI_A	VII_A	VIII			I_B	II_B	III_B	IV_B	V_B	VI_B	VII_B	O
1	H																	He
2	Li	Be									B	C	N	O	F			Ne
3	Na	Mg									Al	Si	P	S	Cl			A
4	K	Ca	Sc	Ti	V	Cr	Mn	Fe	Co	Ni	Cu	Zn	Ga	Ge	As	Se	Br	Kr
5	Rb	Sr	Y	Zr	Nb	Mo	Tc	Ru	Rh	Pd	Ag	Cd	In	Sn	Sb	Te	I	Xe
6	Cs	Ba	—	Hf	Ta	W	Re	Os	Ir	Pt	Au	Hg	Tl	Pb	Bi	Po	At	Rn

			Reaction type[a]			
Group	A	B	C	D	E
I	+	+	+		
II	−	+	+	+	
III	−	−	+	+	+

[a] Reaction type:

    A = Anionic polymerization.

    B = Oxygen-catalyzed radical polymerization [reaction (2)].

    C = Coordinated anionic polymerization by RM–MX system (4).

    D = Radical polymerization by RM–MX system (6).

    E = Polymerization by radical decomposition (1).

    + = Catalyst for the reaction.

    − = No catalyst for the reaction.

Some oxygen compounds were found to be effective catalysts for alkyl derivatives of Zn, Cd, B, Al, Sb, Bi, etc., by the following mechanism:

$$RM \xrightarrow{O_2} R-O-O-M \longrightarrow RO\cdot + MO\cdot$$

Even lithium alkyl, usually only inducing anionic polymerization, can induce free-radical polymerization under certain conditions (*396*).

The activation energies for a few catalysts have been tabulated in Table 4-44.

The effect of monomer and catalyst concentration on the rate of polymerization is tabulated in Table 4-45.

TABLE 4-44

Activation Energies for the Polymerization of
Vinyl Acetate with Some Organometallic
Catalysts

Catalyst	Energy of activation, kcal/mole	Ref.
BBu_3–O_2	15 to 16	247
BBu_3	5.8	280
AlR_3	13.0	576
$AlEt_3$	10.6	363

Ziegler catalysts of the structure RMe–MeX will induce coordinate anionic polymerization of olefins and diolefins:

$$RM + M'X \longrightarrow RM \cdot M'X \xrightarrow{C=C} \overset{\displaystyle C \cdots C}{\underset{(complex)}{RM \cdot M'X}}$$

In vinyl polymerization, however, the polymerization often also proceeds through a radical mechanism (263) by decomposition of the complex to radicals, which can then initiate polymerization.

Lithium metal and lithium alkyls as polymerization initiators have been investigated for polar and nonpolar monomers. A recent review covers possible polymerization mechanisms and kinetics (93).

Vinyl acetate gives only oligomers with butyllithium, just as do methyl acrylate and allyl acetate (147). Furukawa also did not obtain polymers either from vinyl acetate or from n-butyl vinylether (155). Vinyl acetate has

TABLE 4-45

Dependence of Rate of Polymerization of Vinyl
Acetate by Organometallic Catalysts on
Monomer and Catalyst Concentrations

Catalyst	Concentration effect		Ref.
	Monomer	Catalyst	
BBu_3	$[M]^2$	$[C]$	280
BBu–O_2	$[M]^2$	$[C]$	247
Al–iBu_3	$[M]^2$	$[C]$	576

been polymerized by lithium metal (probably by a free-radical mechanism), as copolymerization experiments confirmed (281). Partially preoxidized lithium alkyls were found to act as radical initiators in the polymerization of vinyl acetate (164), although the monolithium or dilithium salt of a tri-α-naphthylboron did not cause vinyl acetate polymerization (395). Anhydrous lithium perchlorate was found to initiate polymerization of vinyl formate, probably by a cationic mechanism, but not of vinyl acetate and higher vinyl alkylesters (236).

Using an aluminum triisobutyl–VOCl$_3$ system, Baker (32) found that vinyl acetate and vinyl chloride copolymerized in the ratio that would be expected in a free-radical polymerization. Moreover, the monomer reactivity ratios of acrylonitrile and vinyl acetate with BR$_3$ as initiator were very close to those measured by free-radical polymerization (27).

Copolymerization studies of styrene and methyl methacrylate with alkyl boron (143) and aluminum alkyl (160) gave proof of free-radical mechanism.

Furukawa and Fueno (157) polymerized vinyl acetate with zinc and t-butyl chloride. They found that after several hours the reaction mixture darkened. They could not eliminate the dark color by repeated precipitations of the polymer with methanol and hexane. They proposed the following mechanism:

$$BuCl + Zn \longrightarrow \overset{-}{Bu} \cdots \overset{+}{ZnCl}$$

$$\overset{-}{Bu} \cdots \overset{+}{ZnCl} + \underset{\underset{OAc}{|}}{CH_2=CH} \longrightarrow R-CH_2-\underset{\underset{OAc}{|}}{\overset{-}{CH}} \cdots \overset{+}{ZnCl}$$

$$\underset{\underset{OAc}{|}}{CH_2=CH}$$

$$R-CH_2-\underset{\underset{OAc}{|}}{CH}-CH_2-\underset{\underset{OAc}{|}}{\overset{-}{CH}} \cdots \overset{+}{ZnCl}$$

A truly cationic copolymerization of styrene and vinyl acetate resulted in $r_1 = 8.25$ (styrene) and $r_2 = 0.015$ (vinyl acetate) at 20°C in nitro benzene with SnB$_4$ catalyst (313). In an anionic copolymerization it was found (145) that $r_1 = 1.1$ (styrene) and $r_2 = 0.2$ (vinyl acetate) at -30°C in liquid ammonia by sodium.

Metal chelates together with activators have been reported to initiate vinyl acetate homopolymerization and copolymerization (572). For example, manganese(III)acetylacetonate together with carbon tetrachloride was used for copolymerizing styrene and vinyl acetate. The copolymerization suggests that the mechanism may not be truly free-radical. On the other hand, a truly cationic mechanism is also improbable, since the polymerization occurs in water.

4-9. COPOLYMERIZATION OF VINYL ACETATE

A. Introduction

For a modification of its polymer properties vinyl acetate has been extensively copolymerized with other monomers. Summaries of the subject of this copolymerization have been published by Alfrey et al. (12) and more recently by Ham (202).

B. Copolymerization

The following partial polymerization reactions take place between two monomers:

$$M_1\cdot + M_1 \xrightarrow{k_{11}} M_1\cdot \tag{4-89}$$

$$M_1\cdot + M_2 \xrightarrow{k_{12}} M_2\cdot \tag{4-90}$$

$$M_2\cdot + M_1 \xrightarrow{k_{21}} M_1\cdot \tag{4-91}$$

$$M_2\cdot + M_2 \xrightarrow{k_{22}} M_2\cdot \tag{4-92}$$

where M_1 is monomer 1 and M_2 is monomer 2. Assuming a steady-state condition, it follows that

$$k_{21}[M_2\cdot][M_1] = k_{12}[M_1\cdot][M_2] \tag{4-93}$$

$$-d[M_1]/d_t = k_{11}[M_1\cdot][M_1] + k_{21}[M_2\cdot][M_1] \tag{4-94}$$

$$-d[M_2]/d_t = k_{12}[M_1\cdot][M_2] + k_{22}[M_2\cdot][M_2] \tag{4-95}$$

Dividing Eqs. (4-94) and (4-95) gives

$$d[M_1]/d[M_2] = ([M_1]/[M_2])(r_1[M_1]/[M_2] + 1/[M_1]/[M_2] + r_2) \tag{4-96}$$

where $r_1 = k_{11}/k_{12}$ and $r_2 = k_{22}/k_{21}$; these are called the monomer reactivity ratios.

If the fraction of monomer M_1 that is formed at any one moment is F_1 and the fraction of unreacted monomer is f_1, then

$$F_1 = d[M_1]/d([M_1] + [M_2]) = 1 - F_2 \tag{4-97}$$

$$f_1 = [M_1]/[M_1] + [M_2] = 1 - f_2 \tag{4-98}$$

From Eqs. (4-96), (4-97), and (4-98) we obtain, then, the copolymerization equation:

$$F_1 = \frac{r_1 f_1^2 + f_1 f_2}{r_1 f_1^2 + 2f_1 f_2 + r_2 f_2^2} \tag{4-99}$$

By using Eq. (4-99) we can calculate instantaneous polymer compositions, provided the monomer compositions and the copolymerization parameters r_1 and r_2 (reactivity ratios) are known.

TABLE 4-46

Rate Constants for Chain Growth at 60°C[a] (352)

Monomer	Styrene	Radical Methyl methacrylate	Methyl acrylate	Vinyl acetate
Styrene	176	789	11,500	$\approx 370{,}000$
Methyl methacrylate	338	367		$\approx 250{,}000$
Methyl acrylate	235		2,100	$\approx 37{,}000$
Vinyl acetate	3.2	18.3	233	$\approx 3{,}700$

[a] In liters per mole per second.

Since the reactivity ratios are only ratios of rate constants, they offer no basis for comparing reactivities of different radicals with the same monomer. When the absolute propagation constant k_{11} is known, the rate constant k_{12} for the reaction of radical 1 with monomer 2 can be obtained by dividing k_{11} by r_1.

Only relatively few absolute propagation rate constants are known. Table 4-46 is taken from Mayo and Walling (352) and lists the known rate constants.

Alfrey and Price (15) attempted to describe the behavior of monomers in copolymerization on a quantitative basis. They used two parameters: Q, denoting a specific reactivity, and e, the polarity of the radical adduct. They devised the following equations:

$$r_1 = \frac{Q_1}{Q_2} \exp\left[-e_1(e_1 - e_2)\right]$$

$$r_2 = \frac{Q_2}{Q_1} \exp\left[-e_2(e_2 - e_1)\right]$$

Arbitrarily styrene was assigned $Q = 1.0$ and $e = -0.8$. On that basis it was calculated for vinyl acetate $Q = 0.03$ and $e = -0.3$.

A number of experimental methods of determining the reactivity ratios of two monomers exist. Low-conversion copolymerizations are made, and after composition analysis the reactivity ratios are calculated by the Fineman–Ross (137) or the Mayo–Lewis (351) methods. A complete summary of experimentally determined reactivity ratios of vinyl acetate with other monomers is given in Table 4-47.

The rate of copolymerization depends on, besides the four propagation reactions mentioned before, the initiation and termination steps (139). A strong alternating tendency ($r_1 \times r_2 \approx 0$) signifies a more rapid chain

TABLE 4-47

Copolymerization Parameters of Vinyl Acetate M_1 and Comonomers M_2

Comonomer M_2	r_1	$\pm$	r_2	$\pm$	Temp., °C	Ref.
1-Acetoxy-1,3-butadiene	0.0		Very large		70	199
N-Acetoxyethyl maleimide	0.25		0.85		60	587
Acrolein	0.1		3.33		20	496
1-Acrylamido-1-deoxy-D-glucitol	0.18		2.41		50	581
Acrylic acid	0.01	0.003	10	1	70	72
	0.1		2.0		70	14
Acrylonitrile	0.009		3.88		25	536
	0.061	0.013	4.05	0.3	60	353
	0.02	0.02	6	2	60	144
	0.061		4.05		60	584
	0.07	15%	6.0	15%	70	11
	0.07		6.0		70	584
	0.05		4.2			126
Allyl acetate	0.60	0.15	0.45	0.15	60	321
	1.0		0.7		60	489
Allyl benzoate	1.25		2.5		60	489
Allyl chloride	0.7		0.67		68	2
Allyl laurate	0.71		0.8		60	490
n-Butyl acrylate	0.0388		5.529		50	29
t-Butylamino ethyl methacrylate	0.027		30.3			470
Butyl methacrylate	0.127	0.015	62.1	3.8	60	366
n-Butyl vinyl ether	0.71	0.1	0.2	0.05		285
n-Butyl vinyl sulfonate	0.40	0.01	0.20	0.05	70	445
Carbon monoxide	0.24	0.05	0.33	0.05	60	369
Chloroprene	0.01		50		65	558
Chlorotrifluoroethylene	0.6		0.01		60	540
Crotonamide	0.01	0.01	2.0	0.5		559
Crotonic acid	0.33	0.05	0.01	0.01	60	100
Crotonic acid	0.3		0.01		70	555
1-Deoxy-1-methacrylamido-D-glucitol	0.16		0.56		50	581
Diallyl melamine	1.44	0.28	0.20	0.03	60	475
	1.41	0.06	0.19	0.004	60	475
Diallyl phthalate	0.72		2.0			524
Di-n-butyl itaconate	0.02		6.3			457
1,3-Dichloro-2-butene	4.8	0.9	0		80	131
1,1-Dichloro-2,2-difluoroethylene	0.6	15%	0	15%	70	11
cis-Dichloroethylene	6.3	0.2	0.018	0.003	60	320
	2.8		0		68	13

TABLE 4-47 (continued)

Comonomer M$_2$	r$_1$	±	r$_2$	±	Temp., °C	Ref.
trans-Dichloroethylene	0.99	0.02	0.086	0.01	60	320
	0.85		0		68	13
2,5-Dichloro styrene	0.04				70	232
Diethyl fumarate	0.011	0.001	0.444	0.003	60	320
Diethyl maleate	0.17	0.01	0.043	0.005	60	320
Diisopropyl maleate	0.17		0.043		60	584
Diketene	2.59	0.08	0.32	0.12	60	411
Dimethylaminoethyl methacrylate	0.035		15.6			471
Dimethyl maleate	0.12		0.028		60	586
N,N-Divinyl aniline	0.1		2.0		60	99
Divinyl butyral	1.005	0.015	1.06	0.01		338
Divinyl ethanal	1.005	0.08	0.99	0.08		338
Divinyl formal	1.012	0.107	1.005	0.105		338
Divinyl isoamylal	1.04	0.08	0.987	0.057		338
Divinyl isobutyral	1.002	0.047	0.985	0.05		338
Dodecyl vinyl ether	3.67	0.45	0	0.23	50	7
Ethyl-α-acetoxy acrylate	0.08	0.03	5.4	0.5	60	553
Ethylene	1.08	0.19	1.07	0.06	90 (15,00 psi)	598
	1.16	0.21	1.07	0.06	1000 atm	81
	1.02	0.02	0.77	0.04	70	537
	1.02	0.02	0.97	0.03	130	537
	1.0		1.01		150	80
Ethyl-1-acetoxy acrylate	0.08	0.03	5.4	0.5	60	552,553
dl-Ethyl-2-methyl-2-ethyl-1-butenoate	0.3	0.2	3.2	0.5	60	529
	0.1	0.1	2.2	0.4	60	529
Ethyl vinyl ether	3.0	0.1	0		60	353
N-Ethyl-N-vinylurea	0.45		0.63		75	212
Fumaryl chloride	0.14		0		70	199
Heptyl methacrylate	0.271	0.039	60.4	0.4	60	366
Hexadecyl methacrylate	0.135	0.055	68.3	3.2	60	366
Hexadecyl vinyl ether	4.50	0.58	0.0	0.35	50	7
Hydroxymethyl crotonamide	0.01	0.01	0.045	0.1	110	559
2-Hydroxypropyl methacrylate	0.033		23.83			472
Isobutyl methacrylate	0.025		29.8		60	394
Isopropenyl acetate	1.0		1.0		75	211
Isopropenyl chloride	0.22		1.84		60	444
Maleic anhydride	0.072		0.010			251
	0.055	0.015	0.003		75	122
Methacrylic acid	0.01		20		70	14
Methacrylonitrile	0.01	0.01	12	2	70	144
Methacryloxymethyl pentamethyl disiloxane	0.16	0.16	24	5	50	360

TABLE 4-47 (continued)

Comonomer M_2	r_1	$\pm$	r_2	$\pm$	Temp., °C	Ref.
Methallyl chloride	0.13		0		73–90	*373*
Methyl acrylate	0.1	0.1	9	2.5	60	*353*
	0.1		9.0		60	*584*
Methyl bicyclo-[2,2,1]- 2-heptene-5-carboxylate	1.5	0.25	0.45	0.07	60	*271*
Methyl cyanoacrylate	0.005		0.5		60	*291*
Methyl methacrylate	0.015	0.015	20	3	60	*353*
	0.4	0.2	3.2	1.1	− 30	*312*
	0.072	0.026	22.21	0.89	60	*366*
Methylol crotonamide	0.01	0.01	0.045	0.1	110	*559*
Methyl vinyl ketone	0.05		7.0		70	*199*
Methyl vinyl sulfone	0.3		0.4		60	*464*
	0.0	0.01	0.40	0.08	60	*125*
Monobutyl maleate	0.011		0.398		65	*586*
Monomethyl maleate	0.0345		0.522		65	*556*
	0.04681		0.4747		56	*556*
	0.09	0.005		0.007	60	*586*
	0.13	0.03	0.015	0.01	70	*586*
	0.1168		0.99		78	*556*
Octyl vinyl ether	3.47	0.51	0.0	0.31	50	*7*
Phenyl vinyl sulfone	0.28		0.35		60	*463*
Polybutylene glycol fumarate	0.15	0.07	0.2	0.2	60	*510*
Polyethylene glycol fumarate	0.020	0.02	0.2	0.1	60	*510*
cis-Propenyl chloride	7.0		0.01		60	*444*
trans-Propenyl chloride	3.56		0.08		60	*444*
Sodium acrylate	0.01		2.0		70	*72*
Sodium vinyl sulfonate						*284*
Styrene	0.01	0.01	55	10	60	*353*
Styrene (anionic)	0.1	0.1	0.01	0.01	− 30	*312*
Styrene (cationic)	0.30	0.15	2.64	0.35		*233*
	0.18	0.08	6.1	0.8		*233*
	0.015	0.015	8.25	0.05	20	*312*
Tetrachloroethylene	6.8	0.5	0		60	*124*
	5		0		68	*2*
trans-2,3,4,5-Tetrachloro- hexa-1,3,5-triene	0.013	0.013	32.0	2.0	70	*8*
Triallylcyanurate	0.71	0.02	0.62	0.05	60	*475*
	0.77	0.15	0.52	0.07	60	*475*
Triallylisocyanurate	0.91	0.03	0.75	0.06	60	*475*
	0.95	0.18	0.70	0.06	60	*475*
Trichloroethylene	0.66	0.04	0.01	0.01	60	*353*
	0.67		0		68	*2*
3,3,3,-Trichloropropene	0.19	0.04	0.19	0.03	60	*125*

TABLE 4-47 (continued)

Comonomer M_2	r_1	$\pm$	r_2	$\pm$	Temp., °C	Ref.
Bis(trimethylsiloxyl) vinylmethylsilane	0.99		0.01		70	459
Tris(trimethylsiloxyl) vinylsilane	0.99		0.01		70	459
B-Trivinyl-N-triphenyl borazine	0		0		80	455
Trimethylsiloxy vinyl dimethylsilane	0.99		0.01		70	459
N-Vinyl acetanilide	0.15	0.015	1.6	0.13	70	243
Vinyl benzoate	0.35	0.09	0.99	0.13	60	570
	0.6		1.3		60	248
	0.7		1.5		80	38
Vinyl bromide	0.35	0.09	4.5	1.2	60	353
N-Vinyl carbazole	0.126		6.05		65	205
9-Vinyl carbazole	0.126	0.032	2.680	0.1	65	557
Vinyl chloride	0.6	0.2	1.8	0.6	40	335
	0.65	0.04	1.35	0.05	40	290
	0.23	0.02	1.68	0.08	60	353
	0.033		3.74		−32	32
	0.3		2.1		68	2
Vinyl chloroacetate	0.73		1.20		60	142
	0.45	0.03	0.42	0.03		399
Vinylene carbonate	3.71		0.0579		55	333
	7.3	0.7	0.013	0.10	60	271
	4.00		0.15		70	200
	3.0		0.27		70	222
Vinylethyl oxalate	0.3		3			278
Vinylidene chloride	0.0	0.03	3.6	0.5	60	124
	0.1		6		68	2
Vinylidene cyanide	0.0054		0.11		45	185
Vinyl isocaproate	0.67		1.14		79.6	309
Vinyl 4-ketostearate	1.18	0.22	1.04	0.2		334
Vinyl-9(10)-ketostearate	1.49	0.25	1.03	0.05	60	334
Vinyl 12-ketostearate	1.26	0.08	1.07	0.02		334
Vinyl laurate	1.4		0.7		60	490
N-Vinyl-2-oxazolidone	0.52	0.08	1.90	0.1	50	71
N-Vinyl-2-oxazolidone	0.60		1.50		75	213
Vinyl palmitate	1.15	0.13	0.78	0.1	70	460
Vinyl phthalimide	0.07		2.4			402
2-Vinylpyridine	0.3		10.0			440
	0		30	15%	70	11
N-Vinylpyrrolidone	0.205	0.015	3.30	0.15	50	71
	0.38		0.44			75
N-Vinylpyrrolidone	0.38		0.44		70	222
	0.237	0.037	2.28	0.19	76	272

TABLE 4-47 (continued)

Comonomer M$_2$	r_1	$\pm$	r_2	$\pm$	Temp., °C	Ref.
Vinyl stearate	0.90		0.73		70	*584*
Vinyl stearate-vinyl palmitate (70:30)	0.97		1.00		50	*1*
N-Vinyl succinimide	0.18		6.05		60	*169*
	0.175		5.1		65	*401*
Vinyl trichloroacetate	0.32	0.15	0.36	0.15		*399*
Vinyl trifluoroacetate	0.6		0.32		60	*197*
Vinyl trimethylacetate	0.75	0.04	0.43	0.05	60	*257*
N-Vinylurethane	0.33		0.33		65	*181*

propagation due to higher rate constants for the cross-propagation steps. A good example of this is the rapid copolymerization of vinyl acetate and maleic anhydride, which is also due to favorable cross initiation. In general, at a fixed rate of initiation the copolymerization of monomers well separated from each other in the polarity series is likely to be lower than the mean of the rates of the separate polymerizations.

The copolymerization of vinyl chloride and vinyl acetate has recently been reviewed (*170*). Technically important copolymers containing from 3 to 40% vinyl acetate are being manufactured. Most of these are made by a suspension polymerization process with lauroyl peroxides or benzoyl peroxides as initiators. Solution copolymers of vinyl chloride and vinyl acetate are also made for surface-coating applications.

Since the reactivity ratios for vinyl acetate–vinyl chloride do not allow homogeneous copolymers to be made in a batch system, vinyl chloride must be added proportionally to its consumption during the reaction according to a schedule, which has been calculated (*538*).

For surface coatings copolymers of vinyl acetate and dialkyl maleates and dialkyl fumarates are important. The preparation of homogeneous copolymers is described by Reaville and Fallwell (*465*), and correlations of structure and property of these copolymers have been made by Cass and Raether (*96*). The latter found a correlation between the number of carbons in the side chain of the maleate ester and fumarate ester and the modulus of elasticity. The greatest plasticizing effect was noted at nine carbons in the side chain. Also important for surface coatings are vinyl acetate–acrylic ester copolymers. Again, for homogeneous copolymers the acrylic ester should be added proportionally to its consumption during the polymerization reaction.

Vinyl acetate–ethylene copolymers have become important recently. Copolymers having high ethylene contents are being used in hot melts (*311*) as specialty rubbers (*45*) and in molding compounds (*304*). Copolymers having high vinyl acetate contents are being used in surface-coating applications as emulsions (*3*).

Vinyl acetate is a minor component of acrylonitrile polymers for fiber applications. It contributes to better spinning and dyeing properties.

C. Graft and Block Copolymerization

Although industrially not yet important, the synthesis of graft and block copolymers of vinyl acetate has advanced considerably, as shown in the numerous papers and patents published during the last few years (*82,97*).

1. GRAFT COPOLYMERS

Graft copolymers are typically represented as

$$\begin{array}{ccccccc} \dashv A-(A)_n-A-(A)_n-A\vdash \\ | & & | & & | \\ (B)_n & & (B)_n & & (B)_n \\ | & & | & & | \\ B & & B & & B \end{array}$$

where A denotes the backbone and B the side branches. The mechanical properties that can be obtained by graft copolymerization often combine the desirable properties of both copolymers and mechanical polymer blends. Figure 4-35 shows the modulus of a vinyl acetate–ethylene copolymer and

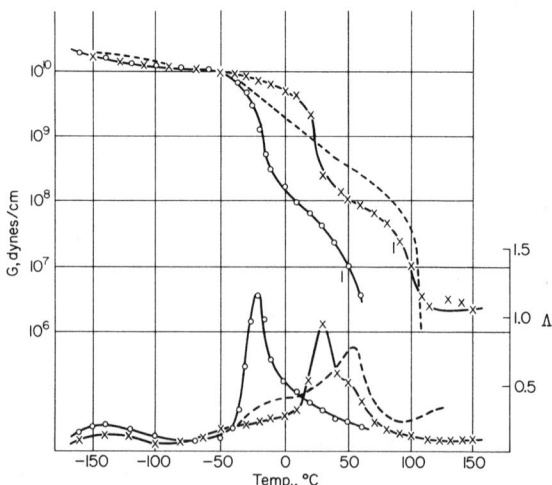

Fig. 4-35. Modulus temperature and damping temperature curves: ○, 30:70 VAc/ethylene copolymer; ×, 30:70 copolymer of VAc grafted on polyethylene; - - -, branched polyethylene (*585*).

of a graft copolymer (585). Obviously, it is difficult to obtain good mechanical properties at all from a blend of polyethylene and polyvinyl acetate. The figure shows that the copolymer has a fairly sharp second-order transition range but that the graft copolymer has two second-order transition points and no undesirable properties which are normally associated with the incompatibility of two polymers.

The two general methods of preparing graft copolymers are the polymerization of a monomer in the presence of the polymer, relying on chain transfer to the polymer to give branches and the polymerization of a monomer in the presence of a polymer having reactive groups that can initiate the polymerization of the monomer.

2. INITIATION BY CHAIN TRANSFER

Chain transfer to polymer and branching in vinyl acetate polymerization have been treated (pages 227 and 230). A graft copolymer will be formed when polymer, monomer, and initiator are present. The nature of the initiator is very important (361). For example, azo compounds are poor initiators (190) of graft copolymerizations, because carbon radicals are usually inefficient hydrogen abstractors, whereas oxy and thiyl radicals are fairly efficient. Sakurada and Sakaguchi (487) found that when vinyl acetate was polymerized in the presence of polyvinyl alcohol fibers, no grafting took place if AIBN or BPO was catalyst, but if potassium persulfate was catalyst, grafting took place smoothly.

The structure of the polymer will determine whether a radical formed on the backbone is stable (not reactive) or unstable (reactive). Only the latter will initiate polymerization of the monomer and induce grafting.

Table 4-48 is a compilation of the polymer backbones used with vinyl acetate and the polyvinyl acetate backbone used with other monomer for graft copolymerization. The relative amounts of graft copolymer and homopolymer are dependent upon concentrations, initiator, etc. The site of attack will vary from polymer to polymer. It has been shown earlier that the methyl group in the acetyl group is a favored place of attack in the case of polyvinyl acetate or partially hydrolyzed polyvinyl alcohol. This has also been found when ethylene was polymerized in the presence of polyvinyl acetate: after hydrolysis long-chain fatty acids were found (473). Chlorine is always a site that yields graft copolymers easily; for example, when polyvinyl chloride was used as backbone and vinyl acetate as monomer, a high yield of graft copolymer was found (288). The phenyl group in polyvinyl benzoate has shown a strong transfer activity (203) and was used for preparing graft copolymers with vinyl acetate (505). Many more examples of this type of graft copolymerization may be found in the literature; they are summarized in reviews (82,97,172,303,504).

TABLE 4-48

Graft Copolymers of Vinyl Acetate

Polymer backbone	Monomer	Ref.
Polyvinyl alcohol	Vinyl acetate	*214,323,324* *438,441,442* *405,487*
Polyethyl-α-chloroacrylate	Vinyl acetate	*503,506*
Polyethylene	Vinyl acetate	*240,461*
Polymethyl methacrylate	Vinyl acetate	*506,545*
Polyvinyl benzoate	Vinyl acetate	*505*
Polyvinyl chloride emulsion	Vinyl acetate	*224*
Polyvinyl acetate	Acrylonitrile	*390*
	Ethylene	*473*
Polyvinyl chloride	Vinyl acetate	*288*
Polytetrafluoro ethylene	Vinyl acetate	*187,392* *246,486*
Cellulose	Vinyl acetate	*497,498*
Polystyrene (*t*-BuOO end group)	Vinyl acetate	*77*
Polyvinyl pyrrolidone	Vinyl acetate	*132*
Vinyl acetate–vinyl chloride copolymer	Vinyl acetate	*255*

3. INITIATION BY ACTIVATION

Photochemical or radiochemical methods can be used for activating sites on a polymer chain to induce graft copolymerization. Two effects of gamma irradiation on a polymer chain are as follows.

1. Free radical is formed through loss of hydrogen:

$$\sim\!CH_2\!-\!CH_2\!-\!CH_2\!\sim \xrightarrow{\gamma-} \sim\!CH_2\!-\!\underset{\cdot}{C}H\!-\!CH_2\!\sim$$

2. Two free radicals are formed through degradation:

$$\sim\!CH_2\!-\!\underset{\underset{CH_3}{\overset{\displaystyle |}{\underset{|}{C=O}}}}{\overset{\overset{\displaystyle CH_3}{\displaystyle |}}{CH}}\!-\!CH_2\!\sim \xrightarrow{\gamma-} \sim\!CH_2\!-\!\underset{\underset{CH_3}{\overset{\displaystyle |}{\underset{|}{C=O}}}}{\overset{\overset{\displaystyle CH_3}{\displaystyle |}}{C}}\!\cdot + \cdot CH_2\!\sim$$

At low temperature and in the absence of oxygen trapped radicals are formed. These can initiate a graft copolymerization.

Restaino and Reed (*466*) studied the kinetics of gamma-ray-induced graft copolymerization of vinyl acetate and polytetrafluorethylene. Hydroquinone acted as a retarder until it was used up, after which a normal rate of grafting was achieved. Confirming the surface effect, they found that the amount of vinyl acetate bound was independent of the film thickness of the Teflon.

The rate of graft copolymerization, R_g, was found to be

$$R_g \approx [M]^{3/2}[I]^{1/2}T$$

with an activation energy of 4.78 kcal/mole, where M is monomer concentration, [I] is radiation dose, and T is temperature.

Restaino and Reed determined the chain-transfer constant of carbon tetrachloride in order to prove a free-radical mechanism. They found the expected chain-transfer constant $C_s = 0.47$, indicating a free-radical mechanism.

Geacintov and co-workers (*173*) studied the reaction of grafting of acrylonitrile, vinyl acetate, styrene, and methyl methacrylate to cellulose by means of a photosensitizer. Acrylonitrile gave the most grafting and vinyl acetate the least.

4. GRAFTING BY REDOX INITIATOR

Certain ceric salts react with alcohols, thiols, aldehydes, and amines as follows:

$$Ce^{4+} + RCH_2OH \rightarrow Ce^{4+} + H^+ + RCH_2O\cdot$$

If a polymeric reducing agent such as polyvinyl alcohol or cellulose is employed, an activated polymer molecule results and can initiate graft copolymerization.

Ide (*246*) found that the graft efficiency when $CeNH_4(NO_3)_4$ was activator of the cellulose–vinyl acetate reaction was inversely proportional to nitric acid concentration, polymerization temperature, and catalyst concentration. It was independent of monomer concentration up to a limiting concentration. The amount of homopolymer produced was high compared with the methyl methacrylate–cellulose reaction.

Arthur and Demint (*23*) found that acrylonitrile reacted to the extent of 92.5 % within a relatively short time but that vinyl acetate gave only negligible results with cellulose as substrate and Ce^{4+} as redox agent. The same low activity of vinyl acetate was found by Richards (*467*). Schwab and co-workers (*497*) found that vinyl acetate failed to graft to paper when the ceric ion method was used.

5. BLOCK COPOLYMERS

Copolymers in which monomer units of a given type occur in long sequences are called block copolymers. There are a number of ways of preparing block copolymers:

1. A polymeric peroxide can initiate the polymerization of a monomer in which it is dissolved. A block copolymer a vinyl acetate and ethyl chloroacrylate was prepared by this method (*503*).

2. A monomer may be polymerized in the presence of 4,4'-azobis(4-cyano-*n*-valeric acid) as initiator (*36*). In the case of polyvinyl acetate, which

terminates by disproportionation, one carboxyl group per molecule permits further reaction (for example, with a diol) after converting the carboxyl groups to acid chlorides.

3. A third block copolymerization mechanism takes advantage of the fact that polymeric radicals are formed by mechanical means such as by high shear. These polymer radicals can then initiate polymerization. It was found that the rate of polymerization was proportional to the square root of the initial concentration of polymer (*188*).

ACKNOWLEDGMENTS

The author wishes to express his thanks to Dr. M. T. Chiang for his invaluable help in reading the extensive Japanese literature on vinyl acetate. Thanks are also due Dr. M. Matsumoto, Dr. S. Imoto of the Kurashiki Rayon Company, Prof. I. Sakurada, and Prof. J. Furukawa, both of Kyoto University, and Prof. V. Stannett of the Camille Dreyfus Laboratory for providing reprints of papers and a copy of a thesis, Mrs. S. Lindemann for help in the literature searching and for typing the manuscript, and Dr. C. E. Blades for his encouragement in the writing of this chapter.

LIST OF SYMBOLS

A_E	area occupied by 1 g of emulsifier
C	chain-transfer constant
C_i	chain-transfer constant for initiator
C_m	chain-transfer constant for monomer
CMC	critical micelle concentration
C_s	chain-transfer constant for solvent
C_p	chain-transfer constant for polymer
$\bar{D}$	radical regeneration ratio
D	particle diameter
d	particle radius
$\overline{DP}$	average degree of polymerization
$\overline{DP}_A$	average degree of polymerization of polyvinyl alcohol
$\overline{DP}_{Ac}$	average degree of polymerization of polyvinyl acetate
E	emulsifier or soap
$\bar{E}$	energy of activation
$\bar{E}_p$	energy of activation of propagation
$\bar{E}_{tr}$	energy of activation of transfer
f	initiator efficiency constant
I	initiator
I·	initiator radical
k_d	rate constant for radical formation
k_p	rate constant for propagation
k_{pm}	rate constant for reinitiation (monomer)
k_{ps}	rate constant for reinitiation (solvent)
k_t	rate constant for termination (polymer, polymer)
$k_{t'}$	rate constant for termination (polymer, polymer by disproportionation)

k_{tri}	rate constant for transfer to initiator
k_{trm}	rate constant for transfer to monomer
k_{trs}	rate constant for transfer to solvent
k_{ts}	rate constant for termination (polymer, solvent)
k_{tss}	rate constant for termination (solvent, solvent)
k_{tzz}	rate constant for termination (inhibitor, inhibitor)
λ	retardation coefficient
M	monomer
M·	monomer radical
μ	rate of particle growth
M_n	polymer radical
N	number of particles
N·	monomer radical produced by transfer
n_B	number of branches per molecule
ϕ	mutual termination constant
R·	primary radical
R_i	rate of initiation
ρ	rate of radical formation
R_p	rate of propagation
S	solvent
S^*	entropy
T	temperature
t	time
V	volume of particle
Z	inhibitor or retarder

REFERENCES

1. A. Adicoff and A. J. Buselli, *J. Polymer Sci.,* **21**, 340 (1956).
2. P. Agron, T. Alfrey, Jr., J. Bohrer, H. Haas, and H. Wechsler, *J. Polymer Sci.,* **3**, 157 (1948).
3. Airco Chemical Div., Cumberland Chemical Corp., Aircoflex 100 and Aircoflex 500, *Product Literature EVA 1 and 2,* 1965.
4. Air Reduction Co., Inc., Brit. Pat. 880,544 (1961).
5. Air Reduction Co., Inc., Brit. Pat. 852,593 (1960).
6. G. Akazome, *Kogyo Kagaku Zasshi,* **63**, 592 (1960).
7. G. Akazome, S. Sakai, Y. Choshi, and K. Murai, *Kobunshi Kagaku,* **17**, 627 (1960).
8. A. N. Akopyan and G. E. Krbekyan, *Vysokomolekul. Soedin.,* **5**, 201 (1963).
9. M. G. Alder and J. E. Leffler, *J. Am. Chem. Soc.,* **76**, 1425 (1954).
10. L. Alexandru and M. Opris, *Vysokomolekul. Soedin.,* **3**, 306 (1961).
11. T. Alfrey, Jr., J. Bohrer, H. Haas, and C. Lewis, *J. Polymer Sci.,* **5**, 719 (1950).
12. T. Alfrey, Jr., J. Bohrer, and H. Mark, *Copolymerization,* Wiley (Interscience), New York, 1952.
13. T. Alfrey, Jr., and S. Greenberg, *J. Polymer Sci.,* **3**, 297 (1948).
14. T. Alfrey, Jr., and B. Magel, in *Copolymerization* (T. Alfrey, Jr., J. Bohrer, and H. Mark, eds.), Wiley (Interscience), New York, 1952, pp. 34, 35, 38, 39, 40.
15. T. Alfrey, Jr., and C. C. Price, *J. Polymer Sci.,* **2**, 101 (1947).
16. J. K. Allen and J. C. Bevington, *Polymer,* **2**, 265 (1961).
17. P. E. M. Allen, G. M. Burnett, J. M. Downer, and H. W. Melville, *Makromol. Chem.,* **38**, 72 (1960); **58**, 169 (1962).
18. P. E. M. Allen, R. Hardy, and J. R. Majer, *Makromol. Chem.,* **67**, 157 (1963).

19. P. W. Allen, F. M. Merrett, and J. Scanlan, *Trans. Faraday Soc.,* **51**, 95 (1955).
20. D. B. Anderson, G. M. Burnett, and A. C. Gowan, *J. Polymer Sci.,* **A1**, 1465 (1963).
21. L. M. Arnett, *J. Am. Chem. Soc.,* **74**, 2027 (1952).
22. L. M. Arnett and J. H. Peterson, *J. Am. Chem. Soc.,* **74**, 2031 (1952).
23. J. C. Arthur and R. J. Demint, *Textile Res. J.,* **31**, 988 (1961).
24. Asahi Kasei Co., Japan. Pat. 6136 (1959).
25. N. Ashikari, *J. Polymer Sci.,* **28**, 250 (1958).
26. N. Ashikari, *J. Polymer Sci.,* **28**, 641 (1958).
27. N. Ashikari and A. Nishimura, *J. Polymer Sci.,* **31**, 249 (1958).
28. R. Autrata and J. Mueller, *Collection Czech. Chem. Commun.,* **24**, 3442 (1959).
29. I. S. Avetisyan, K. A. Pospelova, K. E. Onikul, and P. I. Zubov, *Lakokrasochnye Materialy i ikh Primenenie,* **1964**(2), 13; *CA,* **61**, 9677a (1964).
30. K. S. Bagdasaryan, *Symp. on Rad. Chem., Acad. Soc. U.S.S.R., Moscow,* 1955, as reported in Ref. *480,* p. 92.
31. K. S. Bagdasaryan, *Acta Phys. Chim. USSR,* **19**, 226 (1944).
32. W. P. Baker, *J. Polymer Sci.,* **42**, 578 (1960).
33. C. H. Bamford, W. G. Barb, A. D. Jenkins, and P. F. Onyon, *The Kinetics of Vinyl Polymerization by Radical Mechanism,* Academic, New York, 1958, p. 227.
34. C. H. Bamford and M. J. S. Dewar, *Nature,* **158**, 361 (1946).
35. C. H. Bamford and M. J. S. Dewar, *Proc. Roy. Soc. (London),* **A192**, 309 (1948).
36. C. H. Bamford and A. D. Jenkins, *Nature,* **176**, 78 (1955).
37. C. H. Bamford and E. F. T. White, *Trans. Faraday Soc.,* **52**, 716 (1956).
38. S. Banerjee and M. S. Muthana, *J. Polymer Sci.,* **35**, 292 (1959).
39. I. M. Barkalov, V. I. Goldanskii, N. S. Yenikolopyan, S. F. Terekhova, and G. M. Trofimova, *J. Polymer Sci.,* **C4**, 909 (1963); *Vysokomolekul. Soedin.,* **6**, 98 (1964).
40. C. E. Barnes, *J. Am. Chem. Soc.,* **67**, 217 (1945).
41. C. A. Barson, J. C. Bevington, and D. E. Eaves, *Trans. Faraday Soc.,* **54**, 1678 (1958).
42. E. Bartholome, H. Gerrens, R. Herbeck, and H. M. Weitz, *Z. Elektrochem.,* **60**, 334 (1956).
43. H. Bartl, Ger. Pat. 1,115,459 (1960) to Farbenf. Bayer AG.
44. H. Bartl, U.S. Pat. 2,947,735 (1960) to Farbenf. Bayer AG.
45. H. Bartl and J. Peter, *Kautschuk Gummi,* **14**, WT 23 (1961).
46. P. D. Bartlett and R. Altschul, *J. Am. Chem. Soc.,* **67**, 816 (1945).
47. P. D. Bartlett, G. S. Hammond, and H. Kwart, *Dicussions Faraday Soc.,* **2**, 342 (1947).
48. P. D. Bartlett and H. Kwart, *J. Am. Chem. Soc.,* **72**, 1051 (1950).
49. P. D. Bartlett and H. Kwart, *J. Am. Chem. Soc.,* **74**, 3969 (1952).
50. P. D. Bartlett and K. Nozaki, *J. Polymer Sci.,* **3**, 216 (1948).
51. P. D. Bartlett and C. G. Swain, *J. Am. Chem. Soc.,* **68**, 2381 (1946).
52. B. Baysal and A. V. Tobolsky, *J. Polymer Sci.,* **8**, 529 (1952).
53. W. I. Bengough, *Trans. Faraday Soc.,* **54**, 54 (1958).
54. W. I. Bengough, *Trans. Faraday Soc.,* **54**, 1560 (1958).
55. W. I. Bengough and H. W. Melville, *Proc. Roy. Soc. (London),* **A225**, 330 (1954).
56. W. I. Bengough and H. W. Melville, *Proc. Roy. Soc. (London),* **A230**, 429 (1955).
57. W. I. Bengough and R. A. M. Thomson, *Trans. Faraday Soc.,* **56**, 407 (1960).
58. C. J. Benning, U.S. Pat. 3,052,661 (1962) to W. R. Grace Co.
59. G. Benson and R. L. Perks, U.S. Pat. 2,535,189 (1950) to Shawinigan Chemical Co.
60. G. D. Berezhnoi, P. M. Khomikovskii, and S. S. Medvedev, *Vysokomolekul. Soedin.,* **3**, 1839 (1961).
61. H. Berg, U.S. Pat. 2,279,436 (1940) to Chem. Forsch. Ges.
62. G. C. Berry, Ph.D. thesis, Univ. Michigan, Ann Arbor, 1960.
63. G. C. Berry and R. G. Craig, *Polymer,* **5**, 19 (1964).

64. J. C. Bevington, *Proc. Roy. Soc. (London)*, **A221**, 437 (1954).
65. J. C. Bevington, *Makromol. Chem.*, **34**, 152 (1959).
66. J. C. Bevington, G. M. Guzman, and H. W. Melville, *Proc. Roy. Soc. (London)*, **A221**, 437 (1954).
67. J. C. Bevington and H. G. Troth, *Trans. Faraday Soc.*, **59**, 127 (1963).
68. J. C. Bevington and H. G. Troth, *Trans. Faraday Soc.*, **59**, 1348 (1963).
69. R. A. Bird and K. E. Russell, *Can. J. Chem.*, **43**, 2123 (1965).
70. C. E. Blades and P. L. Foote, *Gas Chromatographic Analysis of Vinyl Acetate, Air Reduction Chemical and Carbide Co. Bull. V-2*, 1965.
71. J. F. Bork and L. E. Coleman, *J. Polymer Sci.*, **43**, 413 (1960).
72. J. Bourdais, *Bull. Soc. Chim. France*, **1955**, 485.
73. F. A. Bovey, I. M. Kolthoff, A. I. Medalia, and E. J. Meehan, *Emulsion Polymerization*, Wiley (Interscience), New York, 1955.
74. J. W. Breitenbach, G. Billek, G. Faltlhausl, and E. Weber, *Monatsh.*, **92**, 1100 (1961).
75. J. W. Breitenbach and H. Edelhauser, *Ric. Sci.*, **25**, 242 (1955).
76. J. W. Breitenbach and A. Maschin, *Z. Physik. Chem. Leipzig*, **A187**, 175 (1940).
77. J. E. Brepoels and G. Smets, *J. Polymer Sci.*, **56**, 359 (1962).
78. J. E. Bristol, E. P. Czerwin, and N. Turnbull, U.S. Pat. 2,782,173 (1957) to DuPont.
79. J. G. Brodnyan, J. A. Cala, T. Konen, and E. L. Kelley, *J. Colloid Sci.*, **18**, 73 (1963).
80. F. E. Brown and G. E. Ham, *J. Polymer Sci.*, **A2**, 2623 (1964).
81. R. D. Burkhart and N. L. Zutty, *J. Polymer Sci.*, **A1**, 1137 (1963).
82. W. J. Burlant and A. S. Hoffmann, *Block and Graft Polymers*, Reinhold, New York, 1960.
83. P. H. Burleigh, *J. Am. Chem. Soc.*, **82**, 749 (1960).
84. G. M. Burnett, *Discussions Faraday Soc.*, **2**, 322 (1947).
85. G. M. Burnett, *Trans. Faraday Soc.*, **51**, 219 (1955).
86. G. M. Burnett, M. H. George, and H. W. Melville, *J. Polymer Sci.*, **16**, 31 (1955).
87. G. M. Burnett and L. D. Loan, *Trans. Faraday Soc.*, **51**, 214 (1955).
88. G. M. Burnett and H. W. Melville, *Nature*, **156**, 661 (1945).
89. G. M. Burnett and H. W. Melville, *Proc. Roy. Soc. (London)*, **A189**, 456, 481, 494 (1947).
90. G. M. Burnett and H. W. Melville, *Discussions Faraday Soc.*, **2**, 322 (1947).
91. G. M. Burnett, L. Valentine, and H. W. Melville, *Trans. Faraday Soc.*, **45**, 960 (1949).
92. A. J. Buselli, M. K. Lindemann, and C. E. Blades, *J. Polymer Sci.*, **28**, 485 (1958).
93. S. Bywater, *Fortschr. Hochpolymer.-Forsch.*, **4**, 66 (1965).
94. J. A. Cala, *Kinetics of Emulsion Polymerization*, in *Advanced Polymer Course*, Rohm & Haas Co., Philadelphia, 1959, p. 74.
95. C. Capitani and P. Imperiale, *Chim. Ind. (Milan)*, **37**, 622 (1955); through *CA*, **49**, 16512 (1955).
96. R. A. Cass and L. O. Raether, *Offic. Dig. Federation Soc. Paint Technol.*, **36**, 947 (1964).
97. R. J. Ceresa, *Block and Graft Co-polymers*, Butterworth, London, 1962.
98. R. N. Chadra and G. S. Misra, *Trans. Faraday Soc.*, **54**, 1227 (1958).
99. E. Y. Chang and C. C. Price, *J. Am. Chem. Soc.*, **83**, 4650 (1961).
100. E. C. Chapin, G. E. Ham, and C. L. Mills, *J. Polymer Sci.*, **4**, 597 (1949).
101. A. Chapiro, *J. Chim. Phys.*, **47**, 747 (1947); **50**, 689 (1953); **54**, 276 (1957).
102. A. Chapiro, *Radiation Chemistry of Polymeric Systems*, Wiley (Interscience), New York, 1962.
103. A. Chapiro, C. Cousin, Y. Landler, and M. Magat, *Rec. Trav. Chim.*, **68**, 1037 (1949).
104. A. Charlesby, *Atomic Radiations and Polymers*, Pergamon, London, 1959.
105. H. Cherdron, *Kunststoffe*, **50**, 568 (1960).
106. H. Cherdron, R. C. Schulz, and W. Kern, *Makromol. Chem.*, **32**, 197 (1959).
107. K. H. Chung and S. K. Han, *J. Korean Chem. Soc.*, **6**, 19 (1962).

108. J. T. Clarke, R. O. Howard, and W. H. Stockmayer, *Makromol. Chem.*, **44/46**, 427 (1961).
109. J. T. Clarke, *Kunststoffe-Plastics*, 3, 151 (1956).
110. M. D. Cohen, J. E. Leffler, and L. M. Barbato, *J. Am. Chem. Soc.*, **76**, 4169 (1954).
111. R. G. Collison and T. T. Jones, Brit. Pat. 767,417 (1957) to Bakelite Ltd.
112. A. Conix and G. Smets, *J. Polymer Sci.*, **10**, 525 (1953).
113. W. Cooper, *Nature*, **162**, 927 (1948).
114. Z. Csuros and I. Geczy, *Periodica Polytech.*, **2**, 65 (1958).
115. A. C. Cuthbertson, G. Gee, and E. K. Rideal, *Proc. Roy. Soc. (London)*, **A170**, 300 (1939).
116. F. S. Dainton, *J. Chem. Soc.*, **1952**, 1533.
117. F. S. Dainton and P. H. Seaman, *J. Polymer Sci.*, **39**, 279 (1959).
118. R. A. Darby and E. K. Ellingboe, U.S. Pat. 3,069,404 (1962) to DuPont.
119. S. K. Dass and S. R. Chatterjec, *Proc. Roy. Soc. (London)*, **A227**, 252 (1955).
120. Denki Kagaku Co., Japan. Pat. 16,446 (1961).
121. D. F. DeTar and C. S. Savat, *J. Am. Chem. Soc.*, **75**, 5116 (1953).
122. M. C. DeWilde and G. Smets, *J. Polymer Sci.*, **5**, 253 (1950).
123. G. Dixon-Lewis, *Proc. Roy. Soc. (London)*, **A198**, 510 (1949).
124. K. W. Doak, *J. Am. Chem. Soc.*, **70**, 1525 (1948).
125. K. W. Doak, through F. R. Mayo and C. Walling, *Chem. Rev.*, **46**, 191 (1950).
126. I. S. Dorokhina, A. D. Abkin, and V. S. Klimenkov, *Khim. Volokna*, **1962** (1), 49; through *CA*, **59**, 2956h (1963).
127. R. D. Dunlop and F. E. Reese, *Ind. Eng. Chem.*, **40**, 654 (1948).
128. A. S. Dunn and P. A. Taylor, *Makromol. Chem.*, **83**, 207 (1965).
129. DuPont Co., Brit. Pat. 599,762 (1948).
130. E. I. DuPont de Nemours Co., VAZO, Azobisisobutyronitrile, Product Literature (1964).
131. A. A. Durgaryan, A. S. Grigoryan, and O. A. Chaltykyan, *Izv. Akad. Nauk Arm. SSR, Khim. Nauk*, **15**, 455 (1962); through *CA*, **58**, 14104g (1963).
132. W. Ehrmann, Ger. Pat. 1,149,904 (1963) to Farbwerke Hoechst AG.
133. W. Ehrmann and K. H. Kahrs, U.S. Pat. 3,141,010 (1964) to Farbwerke Hoechst AG.
134. B. G. Elgood, E. U. Gulbekian, and D. Kinsler, *J. Polymer Sci.*, **B2**, 257 (1964).
135. R. H. Ewart and C. I. Carr, *J. Phys. Chem.*, **58**, 640 (1954).
136. H. Fikentscher, H. Gerrens, and H. Schuller, *Angew. Chem.*, **72**, 856 (1960).
137. M. Fineman and S. D. Ross, *J. Polymer Sci.*, **5**, 259 (1950).
138. P. J. Flory, *J. Am. Chem. Soc.*, **59**, 241 (1937).
139. P. J. Flory, *Principles of Polymer Chemistry*, Cornell Univ. Press, Ithaca, N.Y., 1953, pp. 169–203.
140. P. J. Flory, *Principles of Polymer Chemistry*, Cornell Univ. Press, Ithaca, N.Y., 1953, pp. 136–144.
141. P. J. Flory and F. S. Leutner, *J. Polymer Sci.*, **3**, 880 (1948); **5**, 267 (1950).
142. J. W. L. Fordham, G. H. McCain, and L. E. Alexander, *J. Polymer Sci.*, **39**, 335 (1959).
143. J. W. L. Fordham and C. L. Sturm, *J. Polymer Sci.*, **33**, 503 (1958).
144. R. G. Fordyce, E. C. Chapin, and G. E. Ham, *J. Am. Chem. Soc.*, **70**, 2489 (1948).
145. C. F. Foster, *J. Am. Chem. Soc.*, **74**, 2299 (1952).
146. R. B. Fox and D. E. Field, *Telomerization, a Review*, Naval Research Laboratory Rept. 5190, PB-131,930 (1958).
147. M. Frankel, A. Ottolenghi, M. Albeck, and A. Zilkha, *J. Chem. Soc.*, **1959**, 3858.
148. D. M. French, *J. Polymer Sci.*, **32**, 395 (1958).
149. N. Fuhrman and R. B. Mesrobian, *J. Am. Chem. Soc.*, **76**, 3281 (1954).
150. H. Fujii, *Kobunshi Kagaku*, **16**, 516 (1959).
151. H. Fujii, as reported in *Ref. 480*, p. 87.
152. B. L. Funt and W. Pasika, *Can. J. Chem.*, **38**, 1865 (1960).

153. J. Furukawa, *J. Polymer Sci.*, **31**, 247 (1958); *Kogyo Kagaku Zasshi*, **61**, 1631 (1958).
154. J. Furukawa, *Kogyo Kagaku Zasshi*, **62**, 1759 (1959).
155. J. Furukawa, *Kogyo Kagaku Zasshi*, **63**, 640 (1960).
156. J. Furukawa, as reported in *Ref. 480*, p. 87.
157. J. Furukawa and T. Fueno, *Bull. Inst. Chem. Res. Kyoto Univ.*, **37**, 260 (1959).
158. J. Furukawa and T. Tsuruta, *J. Polymer Sci.*, **28**, 227 (1958).
159. J. Furukawa, T. Tsuruta, and T. Fueno, *J. Polymer Sci.*, **28**, 234 (1958).
160. J. Furukawa, T. Tsuruta, and T. Imada, *Kogyo Kagaku Zasshi*, **65**, 74 (1962).
161. J. Furukawa, T. Tsuruta, T. Imada, and H. Fukutani, *Makromol. Chem.*, **31**, 122 (1959).
162. J. Furukawa, T. Tsuruta, and S. Inoue, *J. Polymer Sci.*, **26**, 234 (1957).
163. J. Furukawa, T. Tsuruta, and K. Ito, *Kogyo Kagaku Zasshi*, **64**, 1312 (1961).
164. J. Furukawa, T. Tsuruta, and Y. Nakayama, *Kogyo Kagaku Zasshi*, **63**, 876 (1960).
165. J. Furukawa, T. Tsuruta, A. Onishi, T. Miki, T. Fueno, H. Fukutani, and T. Imada, *Kogyo Kagaku Zasshi*, **61**, 728 (1958).
166. J. Furukawa, T. Tsuruta, A. Onishi, T. Saegusa, T. Fueno, S. Inoue, and N. Kawabata, *Kogyo Kagaku Zasshi*, **61**, 723 (1958).
167. J. Furukawa, T. Tsuruta, T. Saegusa, A. Onishi, A. Kwasaki, T. Fueno, S. Chen, N. Yamamoto, and T. Matsumoto, *Kogyo Kagaku Zasshi*, **61**, 1046 (1958).
168. J. Furukawa, T. Tsuruta, and Y. Takeda, *Kogyo Kagaku Zasshi*, **64**, 1307 (1961).
169. J. Furukawa, T. Tsuruta, N. Yamamoto, and H. Fukutani, *J. Polymer Sci.*, **37**, 215 (1959).
170. J. F. Gabbett and W. Smith, in *Copolymerization* (G. E. Ham, ed.), Wiley (Interscience), New York, 1964, pp. 587–594.
171. F. P. Gay, U.S. Pat. 3,047,514 (1962) to DuPont Co.
172. N. G. Gaylord and F. S. Ang, in *Chemical Reactions of Polymers* (E. M. Fettes, ed.), Wiley (Interscience), New York, 1964, pp. 831–892.
173. N. Geacintov, V. Stannett, and E. W. Abrahamson, *Makromol. Chem.*, **36**, 52 (1959).
174. K. K. Georgieff, *J. Polymer Sci.*, **14**, 589 (1954).
175. K. K. Georgieff, K. G. Blaikie, and R. C. White, *J. Appl. Polymer Sci.*, **8**, 889 (1964).
176. K. K. Georgieff and G. S. Shaw, *J. Appl. Polymer Sci.*, **5**, 212 (1961).
177. H. Gerrens, *Z. Elektrochem.*, **60**, 400 (1956).
178. H. Gerrens, *Fortschr. Hochpolymer.-Forsch.*, **1**, 288, 234 (1959).
179. H. Gerrens, *Dechema Monograph.*, **49**, 53 (1964).
180. H. Gerrens and E. Kohnlein, *Z. Elektrochem.*, **64**, 1199 (1960).
181. L. Ghosez and G. Smets, *J. Polymer Sci.*, **35**, 215 (1959).
182. P. Ghosh, S. C. Chadha, and S. R. Palit, *J. Polymer Sci.*, **A2**, 4441 (1964).
183. P. Ghosh, S. C. Chadha, A. R. Mukherjee, and S. R. Palit, *J. Polymer Sci.*, **A2**, 4433 (1964).
184. P. Ghosh and S. R. Palit, *Nature*, **195**, 1197 (1962).
185. H. Gilbert, F. F. Miller, S. J. Averill, E. J. Carlson, V. L. Folt, H. J. Heller, F. D. Stewart, R. F. Schmidt, and H. L. Trumbull, *J. Am. Chem. Soc.*, **78**, 1669 (1956).
186. G. Goldfinger, D. Josefowitz, and H. Mark, *J. Am. Chem. Soc.*, **65**, 1432 (1943).
187. J. A. Goodman, *Research London*, **6**, 428 (1953).
188. K. Goto and H. Fujiwara, *J. Polymer Sci.*, **B1**, 505 (1963).
189. N. Grassie and H. W. Melville, *Proc. Roy. Soc.* (*London*), **A207**, 285 (1951).
190. P. Gray and A. Williams, *Chem. Soc.* (*London*) *Spec. Publ.*, **9**, 97 (1957).
191. F. Gregor and V. Macho, *Chem. Prumysl*, **7**, 505 (1957).
192. F. Gregor and E. Pavlacka, *Chem. Prumysl*, **10**, 669 (1960).
193. G. G. Greth and J. E. Wilson, *J. Appl. Polymer Sci.*, **5**, 135 (1961).
194. T. Guha, M. Biswas, R. S. Konar, and S. R. Palit, *J. Polymer Sci.*, **A2**, 1471 (1964).
195. G. M. Guzman and L. Delgado, *Anales Real Soc. Espan. Fis. Quim.* (*Madrid*), **B55**, 119 (1959).

196. G. M. Guzman and L. Delgado, *Anales Real Soc. Espan. Fis. Quim. (Madrid)*, **B56**, 325 (1960).
197. H. C. Haas, E. S. Emerson, and N. W. Schuler, *J. Polymer Sci.*, **22**, 291 (1956).
198. H. C. Haas and H. Husek, *J. Polymer Sci.*, **A2**, 2297 (1964).
199. H. C. Haas and M. S. Simon, *J. Polymer Sci.*, **9**, 309 (1952).
200. H. C. Haas and N. W. Schuler, *J. Polymer Sci.*, **31**, 237 (1958).
201. H. J. Hahn and E. Braun, Ger. Pat. 879,315 (1953) to Farbwerke Hoechst AG.
202. G. E. Ham, ed., *Copolymerization*, Wiley (Interscience), New York, 1964.
203. G. E. Ham and E. L. Ringwald, *J. Polymer Sci.*, **8**, 91 (1952).
204. M. Hamashima, *Nippon Kagaku Zasshi*, **82**, 905, 910 (1961).
205. G. Hardy, J. Varga, K. Nytrai, I. Tsajlik, and L. Zubonyai, *Vysokomolekul. Soedin.*, **6**, 758 (1964).
206. R. Hardy and P. E. M. Allen, *Makromol. Chem.*, **42**, 33 (1960).
207. W. D. Harkins, *J. Am. Chem. Soc.*, **69**, 1428 (1947).
208. W. D. Harkins, *J. Polymer Sci.*, **5**, 217 (1950).
209. J. Harmon, U.S. Pat. 2,396,261 (1946) to DuPont Co.
210. R. Hart, *Makromol. Chem.*, **47**, 143 (1961).
211. R. Hart and G. Smets, *J. Polymer Sci.*, **5**, 55 (1950).
212. R. Hart and D. Timmerman, *Bull. Soc. Chim. Belge*, **67**, 123 (1958).
213. R. Hart and D. Timmerman, *Makromol. Chem.*, **31**, 223 (1959).
214. F. D. Hartley, *J. Polymer Sci.*, **34**, 397 (1959).
215. S. Hasegawa, *Bull. Chem. Soc. Japan*, **31**, 696 (1958).
216. K. Hashimoto and Y. Sakaguchi, *Kobunshi Kagaku*, **20**, 312 (1963).
217. K. Hashimoto and Y. Sakaguchi, *Kobunshi Kagaku*, **20**, 316 (1963).
218. K. Hashimoto and Y. Sakaguchi, *Kobunshi Kagaku*, **20**, 322 (1963).
219. K. Hashimoto and Y. Sakaguchi, *Kobunshi Kagaku*, **20**, 343 (1963).
220. R. N. Haward, *J. Polymer Sci.*, **4**, 273 (1949).
221. S. Hayashi and S. Okamura, *Kobunshi Kagaku*, **11**, 59 (1954).
222. K. Hayashi and G. Smets, *J. Polymer Sci.*, **27**, 275 (1958).
223. P. Hayden and H. W. Melville, *J. Polymer Sci.*, **43**, 201, 215 (1960).
224. R. A. Hayes, *J. Polymer Sci.*, **11**, 531 (1953).
225. J. Heckmaier, E. Bergmeister, and G. Beier, U.S. Pat. 3,145,194 (1964) to Wacker-Chemie.
226. G. Henrici-Olivé and S. Olivé, *Fortschr. Hochpolymer.-Forsch.*, **2**, 496 (1961).
227. G. Henrici-Olivé and S. Olivé, *Fortschr. Hochpolymer.-Forsch.*, **2**, 558 (1961).
228. G. Henrici-Olivé and S. Olivé, *Makromol. Chem.*, **48**, 237 (1961).
229. G. Henrici-Olivé and S. Olivé, *Makromol. Chem.*, **51**, 236 (1962).
230. Hercules Powder Co., Brit. Pat. 819,291 (1959).
231. W. D. Herrmann and H. W. Haehnel, *Angew. Chem.*, **71**, 324 (1959).
232. R. Hess, through T. Alfrey, Jr., J. Bohrer, and H. Mark, eds., *Copolymerization*, Wiley (Interscience), New York, 1952, pp. 36, 37.
233. T. Higashimura and S. Okamura, *Kobunshi Kagaku*, **17**, 635 (1960).
234. A. Hill, U.S. Pat. 2,673,192 (1954) to Diamond Alkali Co.
235. A. Hill and D. K. Hale, BIOS 2788, *U.S. Dept. Comm. Office Tech. Serv. PB Rept.*, 81,539, p.16.
236. R. B. Hodgdon, *J. Polymer Sci.*, **47**, 259 (1960).
237. W. P. Hohenstein and H. F. Mark, *J. Polymer Sci.*, **1**, 127 (1946).
238. H. Hopff, H. Luessi, and P. Gerspacher, *Makromol. Chem.*, **78**, 24 (1964); **78**, 37 (1964).
239. H. Hopff, H. Luessi, and E. Hammer, *Makromol. Chem.*, **82**, 175 (1965); **82**, 184 (1965); **84**, 282 (1965); **84**, 274 (1965); **84**, 286 (1965).
240. Houilleres du Bassin-du-Nord, French Pat. 1,222,417 (1959).

241. R. O. Howard, Ph.D. thesis, Massachusetts Institute of Technology, Cambridge, Mass., 1952.
242. F. Hrabak and L. Jiresova, *Collection Czech. Chem. Commun.*, **26**, 1283 (1961).
243. Y. W. Hsu, *Vysokomolekul. Soedin.*, **6**, 1291 (1964).
244. D. O. Hummel, *Angew. Chem.*, **75**, 330 (1963).
245. D. O. Hummel, G. Ley, and C. Schneider, *Advan. Chem. Ser.*, **34**, 60 (1962).
246. F. Ide, *Kogyo Kagaku Zasshi*, **64**, 925 (1961).
247. F. Ide and Y. Takeyama, *Kogyo Kagaku Zasshi*, **63**, 529, 533 (1960).
248. K. Imai, *Kobunshi Kagaku*, **16**, 229 (1959).
249. K. Imai and Y. Kazusa, *Kobunshi Kagaku*, **16**, 176 (1960).
250. K. Imai and M. Matsumoto, *Kogyo Kagaku Zasshi*, **58**, 670 (1955).
251. E. Imoto and H. Horiuchi, *Kobunshi Kagaku*, **8**, 463 (1951).
252. M. Imoto, *Kogyo Kagaku Zasshi*, **61**, 452 (1958).
253. M. Imoto and M. Kinoshita, *Mem. Fac. Eng. Osaka City Univ.*, **1**, 23 (1959).
254. S. Imoto and T. Kominami, *Kobunshi Kagaku*, **15**, 60 (1958).
255. S. Imoto and T. Kominami, *Kobunshi Kagaku*, **15**, 279 (1958).
256. S. Imoto and J. Ukida, *Kobunshi Kagaku*, **12**, 235 (1955).
257. S. Imoto, J. Ukida, and T. Kominami, *Kobunshi Kagaku*, **14**, 101 (1957).
258. S. Imoto, J. Ukida, and T. Kominami, *Kobunshi Kagaku*, **14**, 127 (1957).
259. S. Imoto, J. Ukida, and T. Kominami, *Kobunshi Kagaku*, **14**, 384 (1957).
260. S. Imoto, S. Usami, and T. Kominami, *Kogyo Kagaku Zasshi*, **61**, 764 (1958).
261. S. Inoue, J. Furukawa, and T. Tsuruta, *Kogyo Kagaku Zasshi*, **63**, 2046 (1960).
262. S. Inoue, T. Tsuruta, and J. Furukawa, *Makromol. Chem.*, **32**, 97 (1959).
263. S. Inoue, T. Tsuruta, and J. Furukawa, *Kogyo Kagaku Zasshi*, **64**, 492 (1961).
264. S. Inoue, T. Tsuruta, and J. Furukawa, *Makromol. Chem.*, **49**, 13 (1961).
265. S. Ishida, Japan. Pat. 3,135 (1962) to Asahi Kasei Co.; through *CA*, **58**, 11481 (1963).
266. M. Ishii, *Kogyo Kagaku Zasshi*, **65**, 807 (1962).
267. A. D. Jenkins, *Trans. Faraday Soc.*, **54**, 1885, 1895 (1958).
268. L. T. Jenkins, *J. Chem. Educ.*, **33**, 231 (1956).
269. D. H. Johnson and A. V. Tobolsky, *J. Am. Chem. Soc.*, **74**, 938 (1952).
270. R. M. Joshi, *Makromol. Chem.*, **66**, 114 (1963).
271. J. M. Judge and C. C. Price, *J. Polymer Sci.*, **41**, 435 (1959).
272. D. J. Kahn and H. H. Horowitz, *J. Polymer Sci.*, **54**, 363 (1961).
273. K. H. Kahrs, W. Stark, F. Winkler, and J. W. Zimmermann, U.S. Pat. 3,143,532 (1964) to Farbwerke Hoechst AG.
274. K. H. Kahrs and J. W. Zimmermann, *Makromol. Chem.*, **58**, 75 (1962).
275. T. Kajimoto, meeting Japanese Chem. Soc., 1956.
276. S. L. Kapur and R. M. Joshi, *J. Polymer Sci.*, **14**, 489 (1955); **22**, 508 (1956).
277. H. P. Kaufman and H. Bruening, *Fette, Seifen, Anstrichmittel*, **65**, 1031 (1963).
278. N. Kawabata, T. Tsuruta, and J. Furukawa, *Makromol. Chem.*, **48**, 106 (1961).
279. W. Kawai and S. Tsutsumi, *Nippon Kagaku Zasshi*, **80**, 776 (1959).
280. H. Kawakami, N. Mori, K. Kawashima, and M. Sumi, *Kogyo Kagaku Zasshi*, **66**, 88 (1963).
281. D. J. Kelley, *J. Polymer Sci.*, **59**, S6 (1962).
282. J. A. Kent, A. Winston, and W. R. Boyle, *Repts. ORO-600 ORO-612*, Office of Tech. Service, U.S. Dept. Commerce, Washington, D.C. (1963).
283. W. Kern, *Makromol Chem.*, **1**, 249 (1948); **4**, 216 (1951); **13**, 210 (1954).
284. W. Kern, V. V. Kale, and B. Schering, *Makromol. Chem.*, **32**, 37 (1959).
285. A. M. Khomutov, *Vysokomolekul. Soedin.*, **5**, 1121 (1963); through *CA*, **59**, 11670 (1963).

286. J. L. Kice, *J. Am. Chem. Soc.*, **76**, 6274 (1954).

287. J. L. Kice, *J. Polymer Sci.*, **19**, 123 (1956).

288. T. Kimura, I. Ishida, and K. Yoshida, *Kagaku To Kogyo (Tokyo)*, **36**, 13 (1962).

289. T. Kimura, I. Ishida, and K. Yoshida, *Kagaku To Kogyo (Tokyo)*, **36**, 129 (1962).

290. T. Kimura and K. Yoshida, *Kagaku To Kogyo (Tokyo)*, **32**, 223 (1958); through *CA*, **53**, 4806g (1959).

291. J. B. Kinsinger, J. R. Panchak, R. L. Kelso, J. S. Bartlett, and R. K. Graham, *J. Appl. Polymer Sci.*, **9**, 429 (1965).

292. I. M. Kolthoff and F. A. Bovey, *J. Am. Chem. Soc.*, **70**, 791 (1948).

293. I. M. Kolthoff and W. J. Dale, *J. Am. Chem. Soc.*, **69**, 441 (1947).

294. I. M. Kolthoff, P. R. O'Connor, and J. L. Hanson, *J. Polymer Sci.*, **15**, 459 (1955).

295. T. Kominami, *Kogyo Kagaku Zasshi*, **62**, 151 (1959).

296. T. Komuro, E. Togami, and A. Futami, *Kobunshi Kagaku*, **9**, 1 (1952).

297. R. S. Konar, T. Guha, and S. R. Palit, *J. Polymer Sci.*, **A2**, 1481 (1964).

298. H. Konishi, *Kobunshi Kagaku*, **17**, 249 (1960).

299. H. Konishi and T. Ishizuka, *Kobunshi Kagaku*, **17**, 125 (1960).

300. H. Konishi and T. Ishizuka, *Kobunshi Kagaku*, **17**, 169 (1960).

301. H. Konishi and T. Ishizuka, *Vortraege Original·Fassung Intern. Kongr.*, **1960**, 66; through *CA*, **57**, 6112 (1962).

302. M. M. Koton, *Dokl. Akad. Nauk SSSR*, **88**, 991 (1953).

303. H. A. Kraessig and V. Stannett, *Fortsch. Hochpolymer.-Forsch.*, **4**, 111 (1965).

304. B. H. Krevsky, *Techn. Papers, RETEC, Soc. Plastics Eng.*, Philadelphia, 1964.

305. C. Kuang-Fu, *Kobunshi Kagaku*, **16**, 456 (1959).

306. C. Kuang-Fu and I. Sakurada, *Kobunshi Kagaku*, **15**, 804 (1958).

307. Kurashiki Rayon Co. Ltd., Brit. Pat. 876,660 (1960).

308. Kurashiki Rayon Co. Ltd., Japan. Pat. 3,034 (1958).

309. C. J. Kurian and M. S. Muthana, *Makromol. Chem.*, **29**, 26 (1959).

310. H. Kwart, H. S. Broadbent, and P. D. Bartlett, *J. Am. Chem. Soc.*, **72**, 1060 (1950).

311. S. T. Lamar and A. A. D'Addieco, *Tappi*, **48**, 385 (1965).

312. Y. Landler, *J. Polymer Sci.*, **8**, 63 (1952).

313. Y. Landler, *Compt. Rend.*, **230**, 539 (1950).

314. E. S. Lane, Brit. Pat. 907,775 (1962) to United Kingdom Atom. Energ. Auth.

315. R. Lanthier, Can. Pat. 663,529 (1963) to Shawinigan Chemical Co.

316. M. Lazar, J. Paulinec, and Z. Manasek, *Collection Czech. Chem. Commun.*, **26**, 1380 (1961).

317. L. Leed, Brit. Pat. 837,486 (1960) to I.C.I.

318. J. E. Leffler and R. A. Hubbard, *J. Org. Chem.*, **19**, 1089 (1954).

319. F. M. Lewis and M. S. Matheson, *J. Am. Chem. Soc.*, **71**, 747 (1949).

320. F. M. Lewis and F. R. Mayo, *J. Am. Chem. Soc.*, **70**, 1533 (1948).

321. F. M. Lewis, C. Walling, W. Cummings, E. R. Briggs, and W. J. Wenisch, *J. Am. Chem. Soc.*, **70**, 1527 (1948).

322. L. Lim, unpublished result, through G. V. Schulz and D. J. Stein, *Makromol. Chem.*, **52**, 1 (1962).

323. C. C. Lin, *J. Chinese Chem. Soc. (Taiwan)*, **6**, 122, 154, 160 (1960).

324. C. C. Lin, *J. Chinese Chem. Soc. (Taiwan)*, **8**, 276 (1961).

325. L. D. Loan and G. M. Burnett, *Trans. Faraday Soc.*, **51**, 214, 219 (1955).

326. H. Logemann, in *Houben-Weyl, Methoden der Organischen Chemie*, 4th ed. Vol. 14/1, Georg Thieme Verlag, Stuttgart, 1961, pp. 406–429.

327. V. C. Long, Ph.D. thesis, Univ. Michigan, Ann Arbor, 1959.

328. H. Magaki, K. Yagi, S. Saeki, and S. Okamura, *Kobunshi Kagaku*, **17**, 37 (1960).

329. H. Magaki, K. Yagi, S. Saeki, and S. Okamura, *Kobunshi Kagaku*, **17**, 135 (1960).

330. H. Magaki, K. Yagi, S. Saeki, and S. Okamura, *Kobunshi Kagaku*, **17**, 139 (1960).
331. T. Makimoto, T. Tsuruta, and J. Furukawa, *Makromol. Chem.*, **52**, 239 (1962).
332. T. Manabe, T. Motoyama, and S. Okamura, *Kobunshi Kagaku*, **15**, 695 (1958).
333. H. L. Marder and C. Schuerch, *J. Polymer Sci.*, **44**, 129 (1960).
334. C. S. Marvel, T. K. Dykstra, and F. C. Magne, *J. Polymer Sci.*, **62**, 369 (1962).
335. C. S. Marvel, G. D. Jones, T. W. Mastin, and G. L. Schertz, *J. Am. Chem. Soc.*, **64**, 2356 (1942).
336. C. S. Marvel and R. G. Woodford, *J. Am. Chem. Soc.*, **80**, 830 (1958).
337. M. S. Matheson, E. E. Auer, E. B. Bevilacqua, and E. Hart, *J. Am. Chem. Soc.*, **71**, 2610 (1949).
338. S. G. Matsoyan, *Polymer Sci. USSR (English Transl.)*, **5**, 90 (1964).
339. M. Matsumoto, *Kobunshi Kagaku*, **12**, 441 (1955).
340. M. Matsumoto and K. Imai, in *Polyvinyl Alcohol Symposium Osaka*, 1955 (I. Sakurada, ed.), pp. 185–197.
341. M. Matsumoto and K. Imai, *Kogyo Kagaku Zasshi*, **62**, 1123 (1959).
342. M. Matsumoto and M. Maeda, *Kobunshi Kagaku*, **12**, 428 (1955).
343. M. Matsumoto and M. Maeda, *Kobunshi Kagaku*, **12**, 441 (1955); *J. Polymer Sci.*, **17**, 438 (1955).
344. M. Matsumoto and M. Maeda, *J. Polymer Sci.*, **17**, 435 (1955).
345. M. Matsumoto and M. Maeda, *Kobunshi Kagaku*, **14**, 551 (1957).
346. M. Matsumoto and M. Maeda, *Kobunshi Kagaku*, **14**, 582 (1957).
347. M. Matsumoto and Y. Ohyanagi, *J. Polymer Sci.*, **46**, 520 (1960).
348. M. Matsumoto, J. Ukida, and H. Iwasaki, *Kobunshi Kagaku*, **7**, 390 (1950).
349. M. Matsumoto, J. Ukida, G. Takayama, T. Eguchi, K. Mukumoto, K. Imai, Y. Kazusa, and M. Maeda, *Makromol. Chem.*, **32**, 13 (1959).
350. F. R. Mayo, *J. Am. Chem. Soc.*, **65**, 2324 (1943).
351. F. R. Mayo and F. M. Lewis, *J. Am. Chem. Soc.*, **66**, 1594 (1944).
352. F. R. Mayo and C. Walling, *Chem. Rev.*, **46**, 191 (1950).
353. F. R. Mayo, C. Walling, F. M. Lewis, and W. F. Hulse, *J. Am. Chem. Soc.*, **70**, 1523 (1948).
354. S. S. Medvedev, *International Symposium on Macromolecular Chemistry, Prague, 1957*, Pergamon, London, 1959, pp. 174–190.
355. H. W. Melville, *Proc. Roy. Soc. (London)*, **A237**, 149 (1956).
356. H. W. Melville, *Z. Elektrochem.*, **60**, 276 (1956).
357. H. W. Melville, F. W. Peaker, and R. L. Vale, *Makromol. Chem.*, **28**, 140 (1958).
358. H. W. Melville and P. R. Sewell, *Makromol. Chem.*, **32**, 139 (1959).
359. C. C. Menon and S. L. Kapur, *J. Polymer Sci.*, **54**, 45 (1961).
360. R. L. Merker and M. J. Scott, *J. Polymer Sci.*, **25**, 115 (1957).
361. F. M. Merrett, *Trans. Faraday Soc.*, **50**, 759 (1954).
362. Y. B. Milovskaya and P. I. Dolgopolskaya, *Vysokomolekul. Soedin.*, **5**, 151 (1963).
363. Y. B. Milovskaya and L. U. Zamoiskaya, *Vysokomolekul. Soekin.*, **7**, 670 (1965).
364. Y. B. Milovskaya and T. G. Zhuravleva, *Vysokomolekul. Soedin.*, **6**, 1035 (1964).
365. Y. B. Milovskaya, T. G. Zhuravleva, P. I. Dolgopolskaya, and L. I. Veselova, *Vysokomolekul. Soedin.*, **6**, 412 (1964).
366. S. K. Min and C. H. Chu, *Hua Hsueh Hsueh Pao*, **23**, 262 (1957).
367. L. M. Minsk and E. W. Talor, U.S. Pat. 2,582,055 (1952) to Eastman Kodak.
368. F. A. Mirabile and F. X. Werber, Brit. Pat. 891,566 (1962) to W. R. Grace Co.
369. A. Mitsutani and M. Yano, *Kogyo Kagaku Zasshi*, **67**, 935 (1964).
370. T. Miyake, *Kogyo Kagaku Zasshi*, **63**, 880 (1960).
371. T. Miyake and M. Matsumoto, *Kogyo Kagaku Zasshi*, **62**, 1101 (1959).

372. H. Miyama, *Bull. Chem. Soc. (Japan)*, **29**, 711, 715, 720 (1956); **30**, 10, 459 (1957).

373. E. W. Moffett and R. E. Smith, U.S. Pat. 2,356,871 (1944) to Pittsburgh Plate Glass Co.

374. H. W. Moll and W. J. LeFevre, through R. H. Boundy and R. F. Boyer, *Styrene*, Reinhold, New York, 1952, p. 281.

375. D. E. Moore and A. G. Parts, *Makromol. Chem.*, **37**, 108 (1960).

376. M. Morton, J. A. Cala, and M. W. Altier, *J. Polymer Sci.*, **19**, 547 (1956).

377. M. Morton, J. A. Cala, and I. Piirma, *J. Polymer Sci.*, **15**, 167 (1955).

378. M. Morton and I. Piirma, *J. Polymer Sci.*, **A1**, 3043 (1963).

379. M. Morton, P. P. Salatiello, and H. Landfield, *J. Polymer Sci.*, **8**, 215 (1952).

380. M. Morton, P. P. Salatiello, and H. Landfield, *J. Polymer Sci.*, **8**, 279 (1952).

381. M. Morton, P. P. Salatiello, and H. Landfield, *J. Polymer Sci.*, **8**, 111 (1952).

382. G. Morimoto, unpublished results, as reported in Ref. *480*, pp. 59, 77.

383. K. Morimoto, J. Furukawa, and T. Tsuruta, *Kogyo Kagaku Zasshi*, **60**, 1402 (1957).

384. K. Morimoto, J. Furukawa, and T. Tsuruta, *Kogyo Kagaku Zasshi*, **61**, 1359 (1958).

385. G. A. Mortimer and L. C. Arnold, *J. Am. Chem. Soc.*, **84**, 4986 (1962).

386. S. Motoda, unpublished results, as reported in *Ref. 480*, p. 74.

387. T. Motoyama, *Kobunshi Tembo*, **14**, 70 (1950), as reported in Ref. *480*, p. 89.

388. T. Motoyama, *Kogyo Kagaku Zasshi*, **61**, 348 (1958).

389. T. Motoyama and S. Okamura, as reported by I. Sakurada, *Kobunshi Kagaku*, **19**, 593 (1962).

390. T. Motoyama and S. Okamura, *Kobunshi Kagaku*, **15**, 359 (1958).

391. T. Motoyama, S. Yamamoto, and S. Okamura, *Kobunshi Kagaku*, **10**, 108 (1953).

392. M. Mozisek, *Jaderna Energie*, **9**, 293 (1963); through *CA*, **60**, 1857g (1964).

393. K. Mukumoto, *Kobunshi Kagaku*, **14**, 472 (1957).

394. A. S. Nair and M. S. Kuthana, *Makromol. Chem.*, **47**, 138 (1961).

395. Y. Nakayama, *Kogyo Kagaku Zasshi*, **63**, 1477 (1960).

396. Y. Nakayama, T. Tsuruta, and J. Furukawa, *Makromol. Chem.*, **40**, 79 (1960).

397. D. H. Napper and A. E. Alexander, *J. Polymer Sci.*, **61**, 127 (1962).

398. D. H. Napper and A. G. Parts, *J. Polymer Sci.*, **61**, 113 (1962).

399. K. L. Negishi, as reported in Ref. *480*, p. 98.

400. F. S. Nichols and R. G. Flowers, *Ind. Eng. Chem.*, **42**, 292 (1950).

401. A. F. Nikolaev, S. N. Ushakov, and L. S. Mishkileeva, *Vysokomolekul. Soedin.*, **6**, 287 (1964).

402. A. F. Nikolaev, S. N. Ushakov, L. P. Vishnevetskaya, N. A. Voronova, and E. I. Rodina, *Vysokomolekul. Soedin.*, **4**, 1053 (1962).

403. Y. Nishino, *Kogyo Kagaku Zasshi*, **64**, 1089, 1092 (1961).

404. K. Noma and K. Imai, *Kobunshi Kagaku*, **8**, 44 (1951).

405. K. Noma and C. C. Lin, *Doshisha Kogaku Kaishi*, **9**, 45 (1959).

406. K. Noma and O. Nishiura, *Kobunshi Kagaku*, **7**, 269 (1950); through *CA*, **46**, 4843b (1952).

407. K. Noma and O. Nishiura, *Kobunshi Kagaku*, **8**, 48 (1951).

408. K. Noma, O. Nishiura, and K. Kawai, *Kobunshi Kagaku*, **12**, 453 (1955).

409. F. F. Nord, M. Bier, and S. M. Timasheff, *J. Am. Chem. Soc.*, **73**, 289 (1951).

410. K. Noro, *Symposium High Molecular Chemistry*, Kobe, 1961, as reported in Ref. *480*, pp. 72, 73.

411. K. Noro, as reported in Ref. *480*, p. 99.

412. K. Noro, as reported in Ref. *480*, p. 87.

413. K. Noro and H. Kawazura, *J. Polymer Sci.*, **45**, 264 (1960).

414. K. Noro and H. Kawazura, *Kogyo Kagaku Zasshi*, **65**, 970 (1962).

415. K. Noro, H. Kawazura, and E. Vemura, *Kogyo Kagaku Zasshi*, **65**, 973 (1962).

416. K. Noro, G. Morimoto, and E. Vemura, *Kobunshi Kagaku*, **19**, 407 (1962).

417. K. Noro, G. Morimoto, and E. Vemura, Japan. Pat. 18,542 (1963) to Japan Synth. Chem. Co.; through *CA*, **60**, 687e (1964).

418. K. Noro and H. Takida, *Kobunshi Kagaku*, **19**, 239 (1962).

419. K. Noro and H. Takida, *Kobunshi Kagaku*, **19**, 245 (1962).

420. K. Noro and H. Takida, *Kobunshi Kagaku*, **19**, 251 (1962).

421. J. T. O'Donnell, R. B. Mesrobian, and A. E. Woodward, *J. Polymer Sci.*, **28**, 171 (1958).

422. S. Okamura, *Kobunshi Kagaku*, **7**, 289 (1950).

423. S. Okamura, *Kogyo Kagaku Zasshi*, **64**, 488 (1961).

424. S. Okamura, as reported in Ref. *480*, p. 94.

425. S. Okamura and H. Inagaki, *Kobunshi Kagaku*, **16**, 757 (1959).

426. S. Okamura, K. Katagiri, and T. Motoyama, *J. Polymer Sci.*, **43**, 509 (1960).

427. S. Okamura, Z. Koshimoto, and T. Yamagata, *Kobunshi Kagaku*, **7**, 285 (1950).

428. S. Okamura and T. Manabe, *Kobunshi Kagaku*, **15**, 688 (1958).

429. S. Okamura and T. Motoyama, *Bull. Inst. Chem. Res. Kyoto Univ.*, **31**, 142 (1953); through *CA*, **47**, 11921e (1953).

430. S. Okamura and T. Motoyama, *Kogyo Kagaku Zasshi*, **57**, 930 (1954).

431. S. Okamura and T. Motoyama, *Kobunshi Kagaku*, **12**, 109 (1955).

432. S. Okamura and T. Motoyama, *Mem. Fac. Eng. Kyoto Univ.*, **17**, 220 (1955).

433. S. Okamura and T. Motoyama, *Kogyo Kagaku Zasshi*, **60**, 850 (1957).

434. S. Okamura and T. Motoyama, *Kobunshi Kagaku*, **15**, 487 (1958).

435. S. Okamura and T. Motoyama, *Mem. Fac. Eng. Kyoto Univ.*, **21**, 312 (1959).

436. S. Okamura and T. Motoyama, *J. Polymer Sci.*, **58**, 221 (1962).

437. S. Okamura, T. Motoyama, T. Manabe, and H. Inagaki, *IAEA Conf. on Large Radiation Sources in Industry*, Vol. 1, Warshaw, 1959, p. 361.

438. S. Okamura, T. Motoyama, and T. Yamashita, *Kobunshi Kagaku*, **15**, 170 (1958).

439. S. Okamura, Y. Oshima, E. Toyama, and S. Yoshikawa, *Kogyo Kagaku Zasshi*, **49**, 20 (1946).

440. S. Okamura and K. Uno, *Kobunshi Kagaku*, **8**, 467 (1951); through *CA*, **47**, 9663i (1953).

441. S. Okamura and T. Yamashita, *Ann. Meeting Japan Chem. Soc.*, April 1954, as reported in *Polyvinyl Alcohol, Symposium at Osaka*, Nov. 1955, (I. Sakurada, ed.), High Polymer Associates, Tokyo, 1956, Chap. 7, p. 61.

442. S. Okamura and T. Yamashita, *Kobunshi Kagaku*, **15**, 165 (1958).

443. T. Otsu, K. Nayatani, I. Muto, and M. Imai, *Makromol. Chem.*, **27**, 142 (1958).

444. T. Otsu, A. Shimizu, and M. Imoto, *J. Polymer Sci.*, **A3**, 615 (1965).

445. C. G. Overberger, D. E. Baldwin, and H. P. Gregor, *J. Am. Chem. Soc.*, **72**, 4864 (1950).

446. C. G. Overberger and A. J. Rosenthal, *Am. Chem. Soc., Div. Polymer Chem. Preprints*, **1**(1), 159 (1960).

447. C. G. Overberger, M. T. O'Shaughnessy, and H. Thalit, *J. Am. Chem. Soc.*, **71**, 2661 (1949).

448. T. Ozawa, S. Sukegawa, and K. Masaki, *Kobunshi Kagaku*, **17**, 367 (1960).

449. S. R. Palit and S. K. Dass, *Proc. Roy. Soc. (London)*, **A226**, 82 (1954).

450. A. G. Parts and D. E. Moore, *J. Oil Colour Chemists Assoc.*, **45**, 648 (1962).

451. T. M. Patrick, U.S. Pat. 2,676,981 (1954) to Monsanto Co.

452. R. A. Patsiga, Ph.D. thesis, State Univ. College of Forestry at Syracuse Univ., Syracuse, N.Y., 1962.

453. R. A. Patsiga, M. Litt, and V. Stannett, *J. Phys. Chem.*, **64**, 801 (1960).

454. L. H. Peebles, J. T. Clarke, and W. H. Stockmayer, *J. Am. Chem. Soc.*, **82**, 4780 (1960).

455. J. Pellon, W. G. Deichert, and W. M. Thomas, *J. Polymer Sci.*, **55**, 153 (1961).

456. R. C. Petersen, J. H. Markgraf, and S. D. Ross, *J. Am. Chem. Soc.*, **83**, 3819 (1961).

457. Chas. Pfizer and Co., *Product News*, 1957.

458. I. Piirma, Ph.D. thesis Univ. of Akron, Akron, Ohio, 1960; through *Dissertation Abstr.*, **21**, 2129 (1961).

459. R. M. Pike and D. L. Bailey, *J. Polymer Sci.*, **22**, 55 (1956).

460. W. S. Port, E. F. Jordan, Jr., J. E. Hansen, and D. Swern, *J. Polymer Sci.*, **9**, 493 (1952).

461. J. Potts, *Am Chem. Soc. Meeting in Miniature*, 1957; as reported in Ref. *480*, p. 103.

462. C. C. Price, *J. Polymer Sci.*, **3**, 772 (1948).

463. C. C. Price and H. Morita, *J. Am. Chem. Soc.*, **75**, 4747 (1953).

464. C. C. Price and J. Zomlefer, *J. Am. Chem. Soc.*, **72**, 14 (1950).

465. E. T. Reaville and W. F. Fallwell, Jr., *Offic. Digest Federation Soc. Paint Technol.*, **36**, 625 (1964).

466. A. J. Restaino and W. N. Reed, *J. Polymer Sci.*, **36**, 499 (1959).

467. G. N. Richards, *J. Appl. Polymer Sci.*, **5**, 539 (1961).

468. J. A. Robertson, U.S. Pat. 2,468,111 (1949) to DuPont Co.

469. J. A. Robertson, U.S. Pat. 2,520,338 (1950) to DuPont Co.

470. Rohm and Haas Co., Prod. Lit., Special Products Dept., SP-206 (1960).

471. Rohm and Haas Co., Prod. Lit., Special Products Dept., SP-84 (1961).

472. Rohm and Haas Co., Prod. Lit., Special Products Dept., SP-216 (1961).

473. J. Roland and L. Richards, *J. Polymer Sci.*, **9**, 61 (1952).

474. J. Rosen, P. H. Burleigh, and J. F. Gillepsie, *J. Polymer Sci.*, **54**, 31 (1961).

475. R. W. Roth and R. F. Church, *J. Polymer Sci.*, **55**, 41 (1961).

476. A. Rysanek and D. Parizkova, *Chem. Prumysl*, **12**, 271 (1962).

477. T. Saegusa, M. Nozaki, and R. Oda, *Kogyo Kagaku Zasshi*, **57**, 333 (1954).

478. R. Sakata, as reported in Ref. *480*, p. 88.

479. R. Sakata, T. Tsuruta, T. Saegusa, and J. Furukawa, *Kogyo Kagaku Zasshi*, **63**, 1817 (1960).

480. I. Sakurada, ed., *Vinyl Acetate Resins*, Kobunshi Kagaku Publ., Kyoto, 1964.

481. I. Sakurada, K. Noma, and A. Kato, *Kobunshi Kagaku*, **15**, 797 (1958).

482. I. Sakurada, K. Noma, H. Konishi, and T. Ishizuka, *Kobunshi Kagaku*, **17**, 120 (1960).

483. I. Sakurada, Y. Sakaguchi, and K. Hashimoto, *Kobunshi Kagaku*, **18**, 694 (1961).

484. I. Sakurada, Y. Sakaguchi, and K. Hashimoto, *Kobunshi Kagaku*, **19**, 593 (1962).

485. I. Sakurada, Y. Sakaguchi, and K. Hashimoto, *Kobunshi Kagaku*, **19**, 597 (1962).

486. I. Sakurada and Y. Sakaguchi, *Seni-i Gakkaishi*, **20**, 463 (1964).

487. I. Sakurada and Y. Sakaguchi, *Seni-i Gakkaishi*, **20**, 555 (1964); through *CA*, **62**, 7925 (1965).

488. I. Sakurada, Y. Sakaguchi, and K. Yamaguchi, *Kobunshi Kagaku*, **20**, 491 (1963).

489. I. Sakurada and M. Takahashi, *Kobunshi Kagaku*, **11**, 295 (1954); through *CA*, **50**, 602a (1956).

490. I. Sakurada, M. Takahashi, and H. Mata, *Kobunshi Kagaku*, **12**, 362 (1955); through *Chem. Zentr.*, **131**, 7869 (1960).

491. I. Sakurada and O. Yoshizaki, *Kobunshi Kagaku*, **14**, 339 (1957).

492. C. J. Schoot, J. Bakker, and K. H. Klaassen, *J. Polymer Sci.*, **7**, 657 (1951).

493. H. Schuller, *Tenside*, **2**, 83 (1965).

494. G. V. Schulz and L. Roberts-Nowakowska, *Makromol. Chem.*, **80**, 36 (1964).

495. G. V. Schulz and D. J. Stein, *Makromol. Chem.*, **52**, 1 (1962).

496. R. C. Schulz, H. Cherdron, and W. Kern, *Makromol. Chem.*, **28**, 197 (1958).

497. E. Schwab, V. Stannett, D. H. Rakowitz, and J. K. Magrane, *Tappi*, **45**, 390 (1962).

498. R. F. Schwenker and E. Pascu, *Tappi*, **46**, 665 (1963).

499. A. Sheinker and S. S. Medvedev, *Dokl. Akad. Nauk SSSR*, **97**, 111 (1954).

500. J. S. Shim and S. J. Hong, *J. Korean Chem. Soc.*, **6**, 88 (1962): through *CA*, **58**, 11206g (1963).

501. V. G. Shlyk, *CA*, **52**, 8616 (1958).
502. A. R. Shultz, *J. Am. Chem. Soc.*, **76**, 3422 (1954).
503. G. Smets, L. Convent, and X. Van der Borght, *Makromol. Chem.*, **23**, 162 (1953).
504. G. Smets and R. Hart, *Fortschr. Hochpolymer.-Forsch.*, **2**, 173 (1960).
505. G. Smets and A. Hertoghe, *Makromol. Chem.*, **17**, 189 (1956).
506. G. Smets, J. Roovers, and W. Humbeck, *J. Appl. Polymer Sci.*, **5**, 149 (1961).
507. W. V. Smith, *J. Am. Chem. Soc.*, **70**, 3695 (1948).
508. W. V. Smith and R. H. Ewart, *J. Chem. Phys.*, **16**, 592 (1948).
509. J. A. Snelgrove, Brit. Pat. 900,571 (1962) to Shawinigan Chemicals Co.
510. S. S. Spasskii, *Zh. Obshch. Khim.*, **30**, 250 (1960).
511. R. D. Spencer, M. B. Fulton, and B. H. Beggs, *Am. Chem. Soc., Div. Polymer Chem. Preprints*, **1**(1), 126 (1960).
512. R. D. Spencer, M. B. Fulton, and B. H. Beggs, *U.S. Dept. Comm. Office Tech. Serv. PB Rept.*, 171,570 (1960).
513. K. A. Stacy and P. Alexander, *Ric. Sci. Suppl.*, **A25**, 889 (1955).
514. H. W. F. Starkweather and G. B. Taylor, *J. Am. Chem. Soc.*, **52**, 4708 (1930).
515. D. J. Stein, *Makromol. Chem.*, **76**, 170 (1964).
516. D. J. Stein and G. V. Schulz, *Makromol. Chem.*, **38**, 248 (1960).
517. D. J. Stein and G. V. Schulz, *Makromol. Chem.*, **52**, 249 (1962).
518. W. H. Stockmayer and M. Fixman, *Ann. N.Y. Acad. Sci.*, **57**, 334 (1953).
519. W. H. Stockmayer, R. O. Howard, and J. T. Clarke, *J. Am. Chem. Soc.*, **75**, 1756 (1953).
520. W. H. Stockmayer and L. H. Peebles, Jr., *J. Am. Chem. Soc.*, **75**, 2278 (1953).
521. Sumitomo Kagaku Co., Japan Pat. 10,839 (1961).
522. C. G. Swain and P. D. Bartlett, *J. Am. Chem. Soc.*, **68**, 2381 (1946).
523. Y. Takagi and T. Asahara, *Kogyo Kagaku Zasshi*, **64**, 1691 (1961).
524. M. Takahashi, *Kobunshi Kagaku*, **14**, 151 (1957); through *CA*, **52**, 1670c (1958).
525. G. Takayama, *Kobunshi Kagaku*, **15**, 89 (1958).
526. G. Takayama, *Kobunshi Kagaku*, **15**, 117 (1958).
527. G. Takayama, *Kobunshi Kagaku*, **15**, 124 (1958).
528. G. Takayama, *Kobunshi Kagaku*, **17**, 644 (1960).
529. M. Takebayashi and Y. Ito, *Bull. Chem. Soc. Japan*, **29**, 287 (1956).
530. H. Takida, unpublished results, as reported in Ref. *480*, p. 76.
531. H. Takida, unpublished results, as reported in Ref. *480*, p. 73.
532. B. Takigawa, *Kogyo Kagaku Zasshi*, **55**, 301 (1952).
533. B. Takigawa, *Kogyo Kagaku Zasshi*, **56**, 356 (1953).
534. B. Takigawa, *Kogyo Kagaku Zasshi*, **56**, 632 (1953).
535. M. Tanaka, *Kagaku (Kyoto)*, **16**, 151 (1961).
536. M. Taniyama and G. Oster, *Bull. Chem. Soc. Japan*, **30**, 856 (1957).
537. A. I. Terteryan, *Neftekhimiya*, **3**, 719 (1963).
538. C. M. Thomas and J. P. Hinds, *Brit. Plastics*, **31**, 522 (1958).
539. W. M. Thomas, E. H. Gleason, and G. J. Mino, *J. Polymer Sci.*, **24**, 43 (1957).
540. W. M. Thomas and M. T. O'Shaughnessy, *J. Polymer Sci.*, **11**, 455 (1953).
541. C. F. Thompson, W. S. Port, and L. P. Witnauer, *J. Am. Chem. Soc.*, **81**, 2552 (1959).
542. L. K. J. Tong and W. O. Kenyon, *J. Am. Chem. Soc.*, **69**, 2245 (1947).
543. E. Trommsdorff, H. Kohle, and P. Lagally, *Makromol. Chem.*, **1**, 169 (1948).
544. T. Tsuruta, *Kobunshi Kagaku*, **11**, 245 (1954).
545. E. Turska and S. Polowinsky, *J. Polymer Sci.*, **A1**, 2085 (1963).
546. J. Ukita, *Kobunshi Kagaku*, **10**, 466 (1953).
547. J. Ukita, *Kobunshi Kagaku*, **10**, 220, 352 (1953).
548. J. Ukita, *Kobunshi Kagaku*, **10**, 358 (1953).

549. J. Ukita, *Kobunshi Kagaku*, **10**, 371 (1953).
550. J. Ukita, *Kobunshi Kagaku*, **10**, 441, 447 (1953).
551. K. Uno and S. Okamura, *Kobunshi Kagaku*, **10**, 535 (1953).
552. C. C. Unruh and T. M. Laakso, *Ind. Eng. Chem.*, **50**, 1124 (1958).
553. C. C. Unruh and T. M. Laakso, *J. Polymer Sci.*, **33**, 87 (1958).
554. S. Usami, *Kobunshi*, **7**, 496 (1961).
555. S. N. Ushakov and E. M. Lavrenteva, *Zh. Prikl. Khim.*, **31**, 1686 (1958).
556. S. N. Ushakov, S. P. Mitsengendler, and B. M. Polyatskina, *Khim. i Fiz. Khim. Vysoko-molekul. Soedin. Dokl. K. po Vysokomolekul. Soedin. 7-ya*, **1952**, 59; through *CA*, **47**, 7820 (1953).
557. S. N. Ushakov and A. F. Nikolaev, *Bull. Acad. Sci. USSR, Div. Chem. Sci. English Transl.*, **1**, 79 (1956).
558. S. N. Ushakov and L. B. Trukhmanova, *Izv. Akad. Nauk SSSR, Otd. Khim. Nauk*, **1957**, 980; through *CA*, **52**, 4237i (1958).
559. S. N. Ushakov and L. B. Trukhmanova, *Vysokomolekul. Soedin.*, **1**, 1754 (1959).
560. R. L. Vale and W. G. P. Robertson, *J. Polymer Sci.*, **33**, 518 (1958).
561. E. J. Vandenberg, Ger. Pat. 1,031,515 (1958) to Hercules Powder Co.
562. B. M. E. Van der Hoff, *J. Phys. Chem.*, **60**, 1250 (1956).
563. B. M. E. Van der Hoff, *J. Polymer Sci.*, **44**, 241 (1960).
564. J. W. Vanderhoff, J. F. Vitkuske, E. B. Bradfors, and T. L. Alfrey, Jr., *J. Polymer Sci.*, **20**, 225 (1956).
565. A. A. Vansheidt and G. Hardy, *Acta Chim. Hung.*, **20**, 261 (1959); through *Resins, Rubbers, Plastics*, **1960**, 303.
566. A. A. Vansheidt and G. Hardy, *Acta Chim. Hung.*, **20**, 381 (1959); through *Resins, Rubbers, Plastics*, **1961**, 915.
567. E. Vanzo, Ph.D. thesis, State Univ. College of Forestry at Syracuse Univ., Syracuse, N.Y., 1963.
568. J. F. Voeks, *J. Polymer Sci.*, **18**, 123 (1955).
569. A. Voss and W. Heuer, Ger. Pat. 946,848 (1954) to Farbwerke Hoechst AG.
570. M. Vrancken and G. Smets, *Makromol. Chem.*, **30**, 197 (1959).
571. C. Walling, *J. Am. Chem. Soc.*, **70**, 2561 (1948).
572. E. G. Wastning, H. Naarmann, H. Reis, and C. Berding, *Angew. Chem.*, **77**, 313 (1965).
573. H. Wenning, *Makromol. Chem.*, **20**, 196 (1956).
574. H. Wenning, *Kunststoffe-Plastics*, **5**, 328 (1958).
575. H. Wexler, U.S. Pat. 3,099,645 (1963) to Air Reduction Co.
576. H. Wexler and J. A. Manson, *J. Polymer Sci.*, **A3**, 2903 (1965).
577. O. L. Wheeler, *Ann. N.Y. Acad. Sci.*, **57**, 367 (1953).
578. O. L. Wheeler, S. L. Ernst, and R. N. Crozier, *J. Polymer Sci.*, **8**, 409 (1952).
579. O. L. Wheeler, E. Lavin, and R. N. Crozier, *J. Polymer Sci.*, **9**, 157 (1952).
580. O. L. Wheeler and H. D. Smyser, U.S. Pat. 3,036,054 (1962) to Air Reduction Co.
581. R. L. Whistler and J. L. Goatley, *J. Polymer Sci.*, **50**, 127 (1961).
582. W. K. Wilson, U.S. Pat. 2,587,562 (1952) to Shawinigan Resins Corp.
583. M. Wishman, F. E. Detoro, M. C. Botty, C. Felton, and R. E. Anderson, *J. Appl. Polymer Sci.*, **7**, 833 (1963).
584. L. P. Witnauer, N. Watkins, and W. S. Port, *J. Polymer Sci.*, **20**, 213 (1956).
585. K. A. Wolf, through V. A. Kargin, *J. Polymer Sci.*, **C4**, 1601 (1964).
586. M. Yamada, *Kobunshi Kagaku*, **18**, 85 (1961).
587. M. Yamada and I. Takase, *Kobunshi Kagaku*, **22**, 626 (1965).
588. Y. Yamashita, *Kogakuin Daigaku Kenkyu Hokoku*, **1**, 90 (1954); through *CA*, **53**, 16944h (1959).

589. Y. Yamashita, T. Tsuda, and T. Ichikawa, *Kogyo Kagaku Zasshi*, **62**, 1274 (1959).

590. M. Yano, *Kogyo Kagaku Zasshi*, **60**, 932 (1957).

591. M. Yano and M. Matsumoto, *Kogyo Kagaku Zasshi*, **60**, 763 (1957).

592. S. Yoshioka, as reported in Ref. *480*, p. 54.

593. A. T. Yurzhenko and M. Kolechova, *Dokl. Akad. Nauk SSSR*, **47**, 354 (1945).

594. A. T. Yurzhenko, V. A. Puchin, and K. S. Grigoreva, *Dokl. Akad. Nauk SSSR*, **92**, 97 (1953); through *CA*, **48**, 400e (1954).

595. R. Zand, *Encyclopedia of Polymer Science and Technology*, Vol. 2 (N. B. Bikales, ed.), Wiley (Interscience), New York, 1965, pp. 278–295.

596. V. M. Zhulin, *Izv. Akad. Nauk SSSR*, **1962**, 716; through *CA*, **57**, 4850 (1962).

597. V. M. Zhulin, *Izv. Akad. Nauk SSSR*, **1965**, 432; through *CA*, **62**, 16388b (1965).

598. N. L. Zutty and R. D. Burkhart, *Advan. Chem. Ser.*, **34**, 52 (1962).

CHAPTER 5

Polymerization of Vinyl Chloride and Vinylidene Chloride

Gianpietro Talamini

Società Edison, Azienda chimica and Istituto di Chimica fisica Università di Padova, Padova, Italy

Evaristo Peggion

Centro di Chimica Macromolecolare del C.N.R., Istituto di Chimica organica, Università di Padova, Padova, Italy

5-1. INTRODUCTION

Polyvinyl chloride finds wide applications in plastics manufacturing.

For about fifty years German industry has been able to produce both vinyl chloride monomer and polyvinyl chloride, but the practical use of the polymer began only after 1930, when the benefits of mixing the polymer with plasticizers were realized.

The use of pure polyvinyl chloride to obtain rigid materials began later, when the thermal stability of the polymer was improved by the discovery of new and more effective stabilizing compounds.

Pure polyvinylidene chloride has a rather limited use because of its low thermal stability, high softening point, and incompatibility with plasticizers, but copolymers of vinylidene chloride and different monomers, especially vinyl chloride and acrylonitrile, are commonly used.

Owing to the practical importance of polyvinyl chloride and copolymers of vinylidene chloride they have been extensively studied both from a theoretical and from a practical point of view.

This chapter deals with the most important features of vinyl and vinylidene chloride homopolymerization and copolymerization with emphasis on mechanism studies. Information on the industrial production of the polymers is also reported.

5-2. VINYL CHLORIDE

A. Bulk Polymerization

1. GENERAL FEATURES

Most kinetic studies of vinyl chloride polymerization have been carried out in bulk with free-radical initiators. The most significant results of these studies are the following.

1. The reaction is heterogeneous, owing to the insolubility of the polymer in the monomer; polymer precipitates during polymerization.

2. Acceleration is present from the onset of the reaction (1–7); see Fig. 5-1.

3. The reaction order in initiator is between 0.5 and 0.6 (2,4,7,8).

4. The molecular weight of the polymer does not depend on the conversion or on the initiator concentration (2,3,6,7,9) in a wide range of the latter.

5. The molecular weight of the polymer increases with decreasing polymerization temperature to a minimal value of about $-30°C$. A further decrease in polymerization temperature decreases the molecular weight; that is, the curve of molecular weight versus temperature passes through a maximum at $-30°C$ (10).

According to Prat (1), the acceleration is due to the fact that the initiation reaction consists of two consecutive steps:

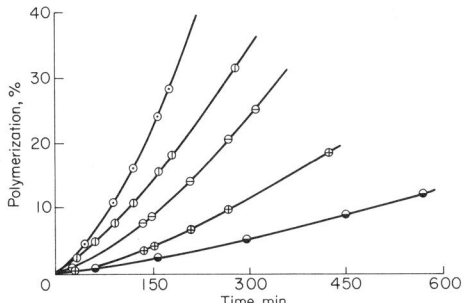

Fig. 5-1. Effect of benzoyl peroxide concentration on the polymerization of vinyl chloride at 47°C. ⊙, 1.15 mole-% Bz$_2$O$_2$; ①, 0.533 mole-% Bz$_2$O$_2$; ⊖, 0.281 mole-% Bz$_2$O$_2$; ⊕, 0.117 mole-% Bz$_2$O$_2$; ⊕, 0.0295 mole-% Bz$_2$O$_2$ (2).

$$\text{Monomer + initiator} \longrightarrow \text{addition complex}$$

$$\text{Addition complex} \longrightarrow \text{growing chain}$$

The acceleration operates until the rate of the second step equals the rate of the first.

Subsequently Bengough and Norrish (2) proved that the acceleration is to be attributed to the precipitated polymer. In fact, addition of preformed polymer to the system increases the polymerization rate. These investigators, moreover, showed that the catalytic effect of the polymer is approximately proportional to the amount of polymer to the power of two thirds. In the presence of a solvent for the polymer, no catalytic effect is observed.

According to Schindler and Breitenbach (4), the acceleration is due to the trapping of growing radicals in the precipitated polymer particles swollen by the monomer. This fact does not change the propagation rate but decreases the rate of the termination step more and more as the polymerization proceeds. The same workers observed that addition of a powerful chain-transfer agent to the system reduces autoacceleration and increases the initial rate of polymerization (5). They explained the decrease of the catalytic effect by assuming that the lowering in molecular weight decreases the occluding power of polymer particles. This effect was also observed by Bamford and co-workers in the bulk polymerization of acrylonitrile (11). On the other hand, the increase in the initial reaction rates produced by chain-transfer agents is attributed by Schindler and Breitenbach to the replacing of degradative chain transfer to the monomer with nondegradative chain transfer to the transfer agent (4). This suggestion was criticized by Bamford et al. (11), who claim that transfer to monomer and to transfer agent are independent and not competitive processes. Arlman and Wagner suggested that the autocatalytic behavior in the bulk polymerization of vinyl chloride also depends on the type of initiator (6). With benzoyl peroxide the autocatalytic range is up to 20% of conversion; with 2,2'-azoisobuty-ronitrile it is up to 80%.

According to Magat, the steady-state hypothesis is not applicable to all heterogeneous polymerization, including vinyl chloride bulk polymerization (12). He suggests a very simple reaction scheme consisting only of initiation, propagation, and termination; the integration of the system of differential equations derived from this scheme without the steady-state hypothesis gives a kinetic equation in fairly good agreement with the experimental results.

Mickley et al. in a recent work (10) on vinyl chloride polymerization observed that the autocatalytic effect depends on the polymer concentration to the first power in the first stages of reaction and to the 2/3 power at higher conversions. These results are interpreted as a mechanism of growing radicals trapped in the precipitated polymer particles. According to those workers, the radical activity involves the total volume of small initial particles, whereas polymerization is confined to a thin surface layer of larger particles present at higher conversion.

Bengough and Norrish (2) made an interesting remark on the shape of the conversion–time curves: when the polymerization is carried out in the presence of chalklike preformed polyvinyl chloride, a point of inflection appears in the curve, after which the reaction rate is lower and the catalytic effect is practically absent (Fig. 5-2). They suggest that the inflection point is due to a transformation of chalklike polymer to a polymer glass. The transformation would then be accompanied by a reduction in surface area, with a consequent reduction in the rate of polymerization.

In a recent kinetic study carried out at 25°C with the system

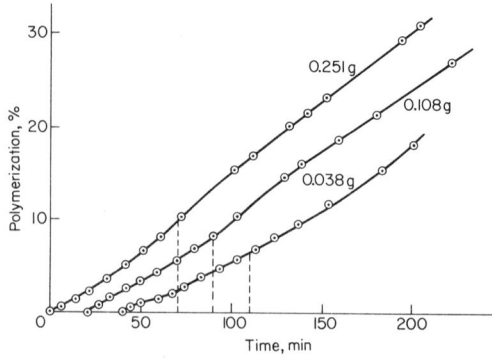

Fig. 5-2. Effect of addition of chalklike polyvinyl chloride to vinyl chloride catalyzed by 0.57 mole-% of benzoyl peroxide at 47°C. The origin has been moved to show more clearly the "added polymer effect" and also the points of inflection on the curves. The amounts of added polymer are indicated on the curves (2).

B(n-butyl)$_3$ + O$_2$ as initiator Talamini and Vidotto (*13*) found that conversion–time curves determined by dilatometry (also used by Bengough and
Norrish) show an inflection point in the range of conversion between 4 and
8% (Fig. 5-3). Beyond the inflection point autocatalysis disappears or
decreases considerably. The authors explain these results by a coagulation
of the polymer particles.

   With regard to the reaction order in initiator, Bengough and Norrish (*2*)
found a 0.5 value in polymerization carried out at 40°C with benzoyl peroxide
as initiator. Breitenbach and Schindler (*3*) with the same initiator found a
0.58 order at 30 to 60°C. Danusso (*8*), using 2,2'-azoisobutyronitrile, lauroyl
peroxide, benzoyl peroxide and *p*-Cl-benzoyl peroxide as initiators, by
determining the average value of polymerization rate between 2 and 8%
of conversion at various initiator concentrations found a reaction order of
0.46 to 0.52. On the other hand, using the time ratios at 30% conversion,
he found a reaction order in initiator between 0.50 and 0.54. With cyclohexanone peroxide

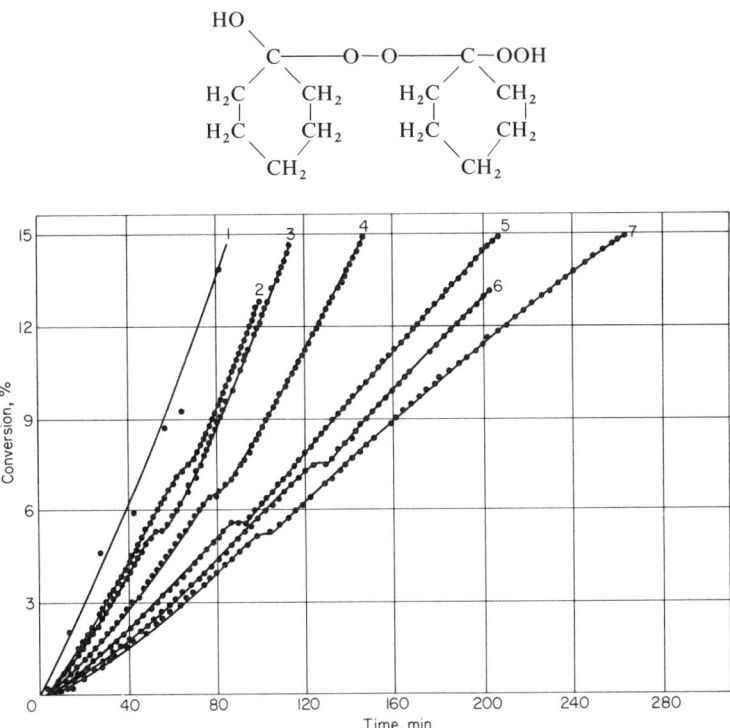

Fig. 5-3. Polymerization of vinyl chloride catalyzed by B(C$_4$H$_9$)$_3$ + O$_2$. 1, 3.33 × 10^{-3};
2, 1.71 × 10^{-3}; 3, 1.30 × 10^{-3}; 4, 10^{-3}; 5, 0.67 × 10^{-3}; 6, 0.52 × 10^{-3}; 7. 0.40 × 10^{-3}
mole-% B(C$_4$H$_9$)$_3$ per mole of VC; O$_2$ constant is 1.3 × 10^{-4} mole per mole of VC (*13*).

as initiator he (8,14) found a reaction order of 1. With this initiator, however, the polymerization shows special features; in fact, after an initial induction period the polymerization starts at a much higher rate than that observed with the usual initiators. The peculiarities observed are discussed by Danusso on the basis of a reaction mechanism in which the initiation process is a bimolecular reaction with free radicals among the reagents, as in an induced decomposition of the initiator.

Talamini and Vidotto (13,15) in polymerizations carried out at 25°C and at −50°C with B(n-butyl)$_3$ + O$_2$ system as initiator found a reaction order of 0.56 at both temperatures in tri-n-butyl borane.

Schindler and Breitenbach (4) suggest that the reaction order in initiator slightly higher than 0.5 is due to the presence of a portion of first-order termination arising from a strong occlusion of chain radicals in the polymer particles. According to them, this hypothesis is strongly supported by the fact that the reaction rate determined exactly at zero time depends on the initiator concentration to the theoretical power 0.50.

As mentioned above, the molecular weight of the polymer does not depend on the conversion or, in a wide range (0.008 to 2 mole-%), on the initiator concentration. This fact was explained by Bengough and Norrish (2) and by Schindler and Breitenbach (3) with a very important chain-transfer reaction to the monomer. Arlman and Wagner (6) suggest a chain-transfer reaction to the initiator. By application of the Mayo equation Danusso and Sianesi (9) determined the constant of chain transfer to the monomer in bulk polymerization of vinyl chloride: the value 1.48×10^{-3} was found at 60°C; that is, on the average one chain transfer to the monomer occurs for every 680 propagation acts. In a later work (16) they confirmed this result by using labelled 2,2′-azoisobutyronitrile as initiator. Talamini and Vidotto (17) in a recent work analyze the molecular-weight distribution curves of various polyvinyl chloride samples prepared in different conditions. They conclude, in disagreement with Danusso and Sianesi, that chain transfer to monomers does not play a very important role in vinyl chloride polymerization. According to Talamini and Vidotto, less than 20% of the molecules formed by disproportionation or by chain transfer are present in polyvinyl chloride, regardless of the type of polymerization (in bulk, in solution, in suspension, or in emulsion).

It is difficult to account for the disagreement between the results of the various workers. It is to be remarked that the Mayo equation for the determination of the chain-transfer constant is strictly valid only for homogeneous polymerizations and is of dubious value when applied to heterogeneous processes. Moreover, we must point out that the independence of the molecular weight of the polymer on the conversion and initiator concentration is not a sure proof of the presence of an important chain transfer to the monomer. In fact, in the case of the bulk polymerization of acrylonitrile (*18*) an independence of molecular weight of polymer on conversion and initiator concentration was observed in spite of the low constant of chain transfer to the monomer.

An anomalous effect of the polymerization temperature on the molecular weight of polyvinyl chloride was found by Talamini and Vidotto (*13*) for polymerizations carried out in the temperature range $-78 \pm 25°C$ with the system $B(n\text{-butyl})_3 + O_2$ as initiator. As we have seen, the molecular weight of the polymer increases with decreasing polymerization temperature, reaching a maximal value at about $-30°C$. A further decreasing of the polymerization temperature decreases the molecular weight (Fig. 5-4). A similar effect was observed by Bamford and Jenkins (*19*) in the heterogeneous bulk polymerization of acrylonitrile. In this case the maximal molecular weight of the polymer was obtained at about $60°C$. According to these workers, the observed behavior is due to occlusion of the chain radicals in the polymer particles; the occlusion rises as the polymerization temperature decreases. Below the temperature at which the maximal molecular weight occurs the occlusion would be strong enough to reduce the propagation step, too. The presence of a maximum in the curves of molecular weight versus temperature should, therefore, be peculiar to all heterogeneous polymerizations.

A later work of Talamini and Vidotto (*20*) showed that the molecular weights of polyvinylidene chloride samples prepared by bulk heterogeneous polymerization in the temperature range $-50°$ to $15°C$, continually increase on lowering of the temperature. In the same work the dissolution time in different solvents was determined for samples of polyvinyl chloride, poly-acrylonitrile, and polyvinylidene chloride prepared at various temperatures. In the cases of the first two the curves of dissolution time versus polymerization temperature increase on lowering of the temperature and sharply

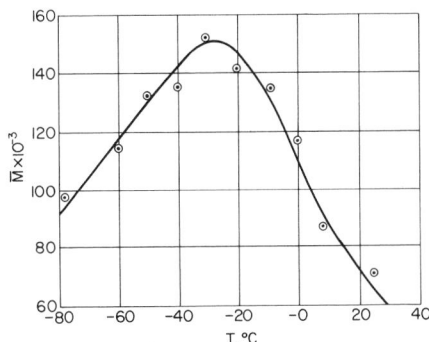

Fig. 5-4. Effect of polymerization temperature on molecular weight (*13*).

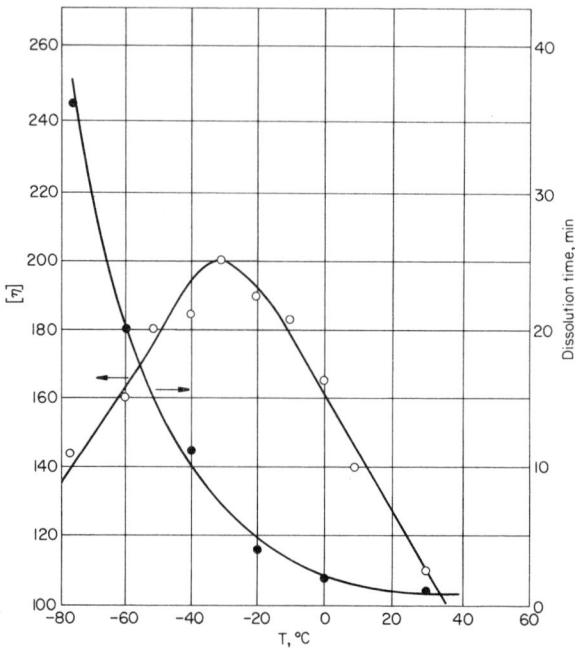

Fig. 5-5. Intrinsic viscosities and dissolution times of PVC samples prepared at different temperatures. The dissolution times were determined in *o*-dichlorobenzene at 120°C.

rise when the temperature at which maximal molecular weight occurs is reached (Fig. 5-5–5-6). In the case of the last no relation between dissolution time and the polymerization temperature is shown. These results seem to indicate that the maximum in molecular weights is associated with a structural change in the polymers. Stereoregularity (and therefore crystallinity), which

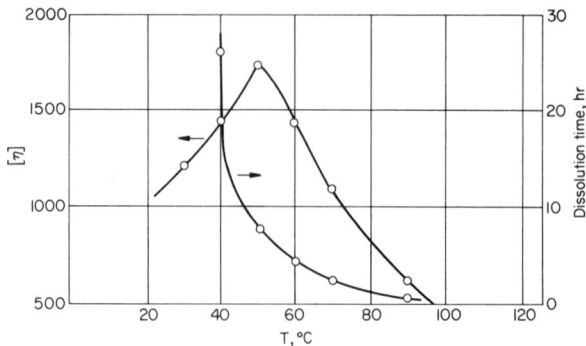

Fig. 5-6. Intrinsic viscosities and dissolution times of PAN samples prepared at different temperatures. The dissolution times were determined in dimethyl formamide at 90°C (*21*).

depends on the polymerization temperature, appears to be the most probable structural change. Polyvinyl chloride and polyacrylonitrile seem to show a sharp increase in long stereoregular sequences at polymerization temperatures below that of the maximal molecular weight; x-ray data on the first of these polymers support this hypothesis. Polyvinylidene chloride does not have asymmetric carbon atoms in its chain; thus, the structural regularity and, consequently, the crystallinity of this polymer do not depend on the polymerization temperature.

2. KINETICS AND MECHANISM

The following scheme gives all the possible reactions that have been proposed by various workers for the bulk polymerization of vinyl chloride.

Reaction in liquid phase:

(1)	$I \rightarrow R\cdot$	initiation	$R_i = f k_d[I]$
(2)	$R\cdot + M \rightarrow R\cdot$	propagation	$R_p = k_p[M][R\cdot]$
(3)	$R\cdot + M \rightarrow P$ (polymer) $+ M\cdot$	chain transfer to monomer	$R_{tr,M} = k_{tr,M}[M][R\cdot]$
(4)	$R\cdot + R\cdot \rightarrow R$	termination	$R_t = k_t[R\cdot]^2$

Reaction in the polymer particles:

(5)	$R\cdot + P \rightarrow T\cdot$ (trapped radical) $+ P$	trapping of radicals by polymer particles	$R_c = k_c[R\cdot]F([P])$
(6)	$T\cdot + M \rightarrow T\cdot$	propagation	$R'_p = k'_p[T\cdot][M]_p$
(7)	$T\cdot + M \rightarrow P + M\cdot$	chain transfer to monomer	$R'_{tr,M} = k'_{tr,M}[T\cdot][M]_p$
(8)	$T\cdot + T\cdot \rightarrow P$	termination	$R'_t = k'_t[T\cdot]^2$
	$T\cdot + M\cdot \rightarrow P$		$R''_t = k''_t[T\cdot][M\cdot]$

The monomeric radicals $M\cdot$ may undergo the following reactions:

(7')	$M\cdot + M \rightarrow T\cdot$	propagation	$R''_p = k''_p[M\cdot][M]_p$
(7")	$M\cdot + P \rightarrow T\cdot$	chain transfer to polymer	$R_{tr,P} = k_{tr,P}[M\cdot][P]$
(7‴)	$M\cdot \rightarrow R\cdot$	escape of monomeric radicals from the particles into the liquid phase	$R_{esc} = k_{esc}[M\cdot]$

Reactions 1 to 4 are typical of the homogeneous free-radical polymerization.

Reaction 5 indicates the formation of trapped free radicals in the polymer particles. Its rate is a function of the polymer concentration (i.e., of the conversion).

The trapped radicals may undergo propagation (6), chain transfer to the monomer (7), or termination (8) with rate constants that may be different from those of the corresponding homogeneous reactions.

Reactions 7' to 7''' represent the possible reactions of monomeric radicals M· in the polymer particles.

Bengough and Norrish (2) assume the steady-state condition for all the free radicals present in the system; that is,

$$d\frac{([R\cdot] + [T\cdot] + [M\cdot])}{dt} = 0$$

The trapping of the free radicals in the polymer particles is due, according to these workers, to a chain transfer of radicals R· to the polymer on the surface of the particles. Let A be the total surface area of the particles, which is proportional to the polymer concentration to the 2/3 power ($A = K[P]^{2/3}$); then

$$k_c F([P]) = k_{tr,p} A = K \cdot k_{tr,p}[P]^{2/3}$$

where $[P]$ is the concentration of suspended polymer. As the polymerization occurs on the surface of the particles, a radical escapes (reaction 7''') for each chain transfer to the monomer (reaction 7). Bengough and Norrish assume, moreover, that $k'_t = k''_t = 0$, $k_p = k'_p = k''_p$, $k_{tr,M} = k'_{tr,M}$, and $|M|$ (monomer concentration in the liquid phase) $= [M]_p$ (monomer concentration in the polymer particles). On the basis of these assumptions the following equation for the polymerization rate is derived:

$$-\frac{d[M]}{dt} = (k_p + k_{tr,M})\left(f\frac{k_d}{k_t}\right)^{1/2}\left([M] + \frac{k_{tr,p}}{k_{tr,M}}K[P]^{2/3}\right)[I]^{1/2} \quad (5\text{-}1)$$

The steady-state approximation for the radicals' concentration is also assumed by Schindler and Breitenbach (4). The presence of polymer radicals in the particles swollen from the monomer is due both to an initiation into the particles and to an entrance of chain radicals from the liquid monomeric phase. Moreover, it is assumed that $k'_t < k_t$ and that the over-all termination rate decreases during polymerization according to the equation:

$$(k_t)_{\text{over-all}} = \frac{k_t}{1 + ac} \quad (5\text{-}2)$$

where c is the degree of conversion and a is a constant. Moreover, it is assumed that $k_p = k'_p = k''_p$, $[M] = [M]_p$, and $k_{tr,M} = k'_{tr,M}$. The following equation is derived:

$$c = k_p[M]/[M]_0\left(f\frac{k_d[I]}{k_t}\right)^{1/2}\left[1 + \frac{a}{4}k_p[M]\left(f\frac{k_d[I]}{k_t}\right)^{1/2}t\right]t \quad (5\text{-}3)$$

which gives the degree of conversion as a function of the time. $[M]_0$ is the initial monomer concentration.

According to Schindler and Breitenbach, a fraction of chain radicals undergoes such a strong trapping that the latter corresponds to a first-order termination. This fact should account for the reaction order in initiator slightly higher than 0.5 found by different authors.

Magat (12) assumes that the steady-state approximation does not apply to the vinyl chloride bulk polymerization and that the termination constants are very low and all equal ($k_t' = k_t'' = k_t'''$) and moreover, that $k_{tr,M} = k_{tr,M}' = 0$, $k_{tr,P} = 0$, and $k_p = k_p'$. By integrating the system of differential equations under these conditions he obtains the following equation, in which the degree of conversion is a function of the time:

$$c = \frac{k_p}{k_t} \ln \cosh \left[(f k_d k_t [I])^{1/2} t \right] \tag{5-4}$$

In the early stages of the polymerization, by series expansion of the logarithm Eq. (5-4) gives

$$c = \tfrac{1}{2} f k_d k_p [I] t^2 \tag{5-4a}$$

Mickley et al. (10) assumed k_t' equal to $k_t'' = 0$ and $k_c F(|P|)$ (their Eq. 5) equal to $4\pi N_p D_L'$, where N_P is the number of polymer particles (spheres with average radius r) in a unitary volume of suspension, and D_L' is the diffusion coefficient of the chain radicals in the liquid phase. They also apply the steady-state hypothesis. According to them, the monomeric radicals formed in reaction 7 may undergo propagation (reaction 7') or chain transfer to the polymer (reaction 7'') or may escape from polymeric particles according to reaction 7'''. In the later case k_{esc} is equal to $4\pi r D_L$, where D_L is the diffusion coefficient of monomeric radicals in the liquid phase. The workers suggest the following equations:

$$-\frac{d[M]}{dt} = k_p \left(f \frac{k_d(I)}{k_t} \right)^{1/2} \left([M] + \frac{D_L' k_{tr,p}[T\cdot]V_p}{D_L \alpha k_{tr,M}} \right) \tag{5-5}$$

$$-\frac{d[M]}{dt} = k_p \left(f \frac{k_d[I]}{k_t} \right)^{1/2} \left([M] + \frac{D_L' k_{tr,p}[T\cdot]\delta S_p}{D_L \alpha k_{tr,M}} \right) \tag{5-5a}$$

where α is the ratio of the monomeric radical concentration at the surface of the particles to the average concentration of monomeric radicals in the active volume, S_p is the total area, V_p is the total volume of the particles in a unitary volume of suspension, and δ is the depth of radical penetration into the particles.

When $[P] < 30$ g/liter, the radical activity involves the total volume of the polymer particles, and Eq. (5-5) is applicable; when $[P] > 60$ g/liter, the radical activity is confined to a thin surface of thickness δ, and equation (5-5a) is applicable.

It must be remarked that the polymerization mechanisms proposed by Bengough and Norrish (2) and by Mickley et al. (10) require an important chain-transfer to the monomer due to the assumption that termination into the particles is absent. As was seen, some (2,3,9) suggest that the chain transfer to the monomer plays an important role in the vinyl chloride polymerization whereas other authors (17) consider this reaction unimportant.

The Bengough and Norrish mechanism, moreover, requires a chain transfer to the polymer. In consequence, long branches should be formed in the polymer.

Cotman (21) was the first to determine the extent of branching in polyvinyl chloride by replacing the chlorine atoms with hydrogen atoms, and he did so by treating the polymer with lithium aluminum hydride. From the study of the infrared spectrum he was able to detect the $-CH_3$ end groups. He concludes that commercial polyvinyl chloride can contain up to one branching per fifty monomeric units.

George et al. (22), using Cotman's method, demonstrate that polyvinyl chloride prepared at 45°C contains branching; no branching was detected in polymers prepared at -40°C.

Batzer and Nisch (23) observe a decrease in degree of polymerization by reducing polyvinyl chloride with $LiAlH_4$ in the presence of O_2. This discovery suggests that tertiary chlorine atoms are present and, consequently, that all the commercial polyvinyl chlorides are branched to some degree.

Staudinger (24) reports that commercial-grade polyvinyl chloride can contain as many as 16 branches per molecule.

By none of these investigators, however, is decisive experimental evidence given in favor of either short or long branches.

Hahn and Müller (25) determined the melting points of products obtained by polyvinyl chloride reduction and found that melting occurs in the temperature range 120 to 130°C. The melting range is between 106 and 110°C in low-density polyethylene. These findings suggest that the extent of short branching in polyvinyl chloride is lower than in conventional polyethylenes. The lower solubility in the solvents of the reduced polyvinyl chloride with respect to polyethylene would confirm these hypotheses.

Bovey and Tiers (26) suggest that the branching in polyvinyl chloride is probably of a "backbiting" type, as in low-density polyethylene. This type of branching would also be consistent with the results of the molecular-weight distribution analyses performed by Talamini and Vidotto (17).

The backbiting branching does not depend on the degree of conversion of the polymerization process. On the contrary Krozer and Czlonkowska (27) claim that the extent of branching in polyvinyl chloride depends on the conversion and that it decreases with increasing conversion. According to them the branching is produced by a chain transfer to the polymer, which should be proportional to the monomer–solid polymer interface area.

The evidence available up to this time seems to confirm the presence of branching in polyvinyl chloride, but it is hardly sufficient to confirm whether long or short branches are present and, in consequence, it is difficult to be sure of the presence of an important chain transfer to the polymer, required by the Bengough and Norrish mechanism.

An interesting observation on the kinetic equations proposed by the various workers is derived from the findings of Danusso (7). He observed that the conversion–time curves of experiments carried out at the same temperature with different initiator concentrations overlap when the conversion is reported as a function of $[I]^{1/2}t$ instead of t (Fig. 5-7). This fact suggests an interesting consideration of the kinetic equation proposed by the different workers. In fact, Danusso's observation leads one to conclude that the kinetic equation must have the form

$$c = f([I]^{1/2}t) \tag{5-6}$$

In the simplest case of the algebraic development of this function one obtains

$$c = \sum_i^n \alpha_i [I]^{i/2} t^i$$

At low conversion α_i can be considered constant, depending only on the temperature. In the particular case of $n = 2$ the following equation is obtained:

$$c = \alpha_1 [I]^{1/2}t + \alpha_2 ([I]^{1/2}t)^2 \tag{5-7}$$

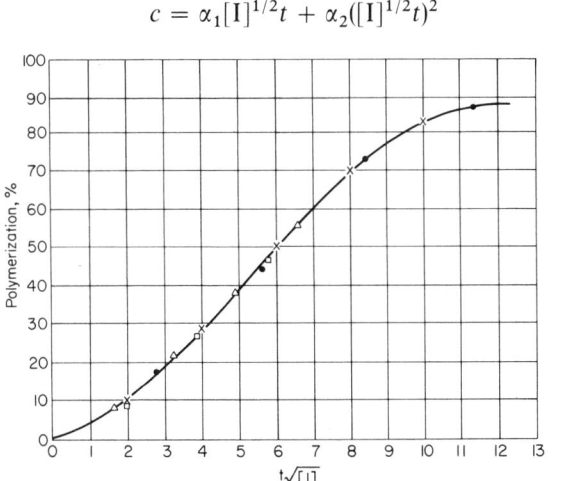

Fig. 5-7. Plot of percentage versus $t[I]^{1/2}$ for vinyl chloride bulk polymerization initiated by different amounts of benzoyl peroxide at 50°C. ●, $[I] = 2\%$; ×, $[I] = 1\%$; △, $[I] = 0.3\%$; □, $[I] = 0.15\%$ (7).

Among the various equations proposed the only one that is in this form is the equation of Schindler and Breitenbach, Eq. (5-3), and there is none in the form of Eq. (5-6) or (5-7).† Schindler and Breitenbach found (4) that the experimental conversion–time curves are consistent with Eq. (5-3) up to 20 % conversion.

This conclusion is a very interesting one, because these workers derived the equation from a very simple reaction scheme. In fact, the equation is obtained on the basis of a simple homogeneous polymerization mechanism, only by assuming the rate constant of the termination step to be a simple function [Eq. (5-2)] of the degree of conversion. The detailed polymerization process will probably be much more complicated, but thus far the simple scheme of Schindler and Breitenbach leads to an equation that gives the best correlation with the experimental results.

Moreover, Eq. (5-7) can explain the fact that the reaction order in initiator found by different authors was slightly above 0.5. In fact, two terms contribute to the reaction rate: the first is characteristic of homogeneous polymerization and gives rise to a 0.5 order in initiator, and the second may be ascribed to the heterogeneity. The latter is a function of time and depends on the initiator concentration to the power of 1. Therefore, the over-all reaction order in initiator will be between 0.5 and 1, the exact value being determined by the relative importance of the two terms. At zero time the reaction order in initiator is exactly 0.5 and increases with the polymerization time. It becomes unity theoretically only at $t = \infty$, when the heterogeneity term is the more important one. From the known data it seems possible to conclude that the importance of the second term is only relative, and in consequence the reaction order determined at moderate conversion is only slightly higher than 0.5.

B. Suspension Polymerization

Although numerous patents (28) in the literature deal with suspension polymerization of vinyl chloride, only a few works have been published in an attempt to clarify the polymerization mechanism.

Bankoff and Shreve (29) studied the influence of the type of suspending agents and of the initiator on the polymer properties. They conclude that the best initiator-suspending agent is the lauryl peroxide–polyvinyl alcohol system (obtained by 86 to 89 % hydrolysis of polyvinyl acetate). The con-

---

† Magat's equation (12), Eq. (5-4a), should be considered in the form of Eq. (5-7) by assuming $\alpha = 0$. Equation (5-4a), however, is inconsistent with the results of Schindler and Breitenbach (4), who showed that the plots of c/t versus t are, according to Eq. (5-7), straight lines with slope and intercept depending on initiator concentration. The intercept has always a finite value, whereas, according to the Magat's equation this value should be zero, i.e., all the straight lines should pass through the origin.

version–time curves were found very similar to those of the bulk polymerization, with an autocatalytic behavior from the onset of the process.
Within the limits of experimental error the molecular weight of the polymer
was independent of the suspending-agent concentration. The size of polymer
particles decreases with increase in suspending-agent concentration, as
shown in Fig. 5-8, where the percentage of polymer passing through screens
of various apertures is reported. Each curve corresponds to a suspending-
agent concentration.

As in the bulk polymerization, the molecular weight of the polymer is
independent of the degree of conversion and, to a great extent, of the initiator
concentration.

It is interesting to note that the conversion reached at a fixed time of
reaction and suspending-agent concentration is a linear function of the
initiator concentration. Thus, the average reaction rate calculated on polymerization time is proportional to the first power of the initiator concentration (Fig. 5-9). On the other hand, it may be seen from the data of Bankoff
and Shreve that the reciprocal of the time necessary to reach a fixed conversion (i.e., the average rate between zero and a fixed conversion) is directly
proportional to the initiator concentration to a 0.5 power. These observations give rise to the hypothesis that the kinetics of the suspension polymerization of vinyl chloride are consistent with an equation similar to the Eq.
(5-7) of bulk polymerization, in which, however, the first term on the right
hand is negligible compared with the second one. Unfortunately, data
available at this time are insufficient for any definitive conclusion to be
drawn.

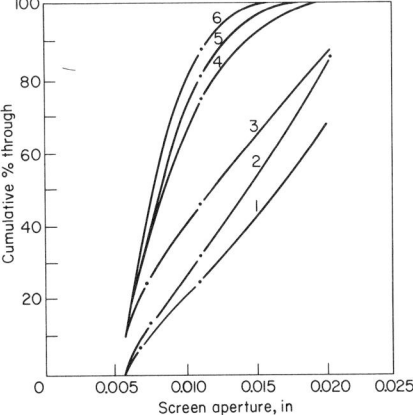

Fig. 5-8. Effect of polyvinyl alcohol concentration on polymer particle size at 50°C for 14.7 hr
with 0.15 part lauroyl peroxide. Parts PVA: 1, 0.65; 2, 0.74; 3, 1.02; 4, 1.57; 5. 1.85; 6, 2.12 (*30*).

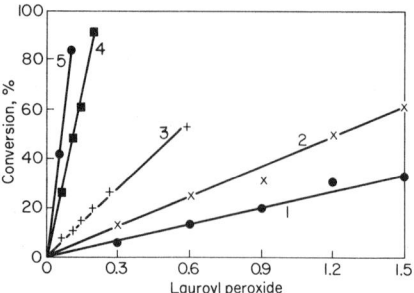

Fig. 5-9. Effect of lauroyl peroxide concentration on conversion at constant time of reaction and temperature, with 0.27 part polyvinyl alcohol. 1, 50°C and 3 hr; 2, 50°C and 5 hr; 3, 60°C and 3 hr; 4, 50°C and 14.7 hr; 5, 60°C and 8.7 hr (*30*).

Pezzin et al. (*30*) determined the molecular-weight distributions of six samples of polyvinyl chloride taken during a suspension polymerization at various degrees of conversion (between 4 and 94%). With the exception of the lower conversion sample the molecular weight distributions of the samples were very nearly the same (Fig. 5-10). This means that the molecular-weight distribution of polyvinyl chloride obtained in suspension does not change substantially in the course of the polymerization. The molecular-weight distribution of the sample taken at 4% conversion is shifted to the lower molecular weights. Pezzin and co-workers suggest that this fact is due to the presence of O_2 at the beginning of polymerization. The oxygen may strongly affect the polymerization process by reacting with the monomer to

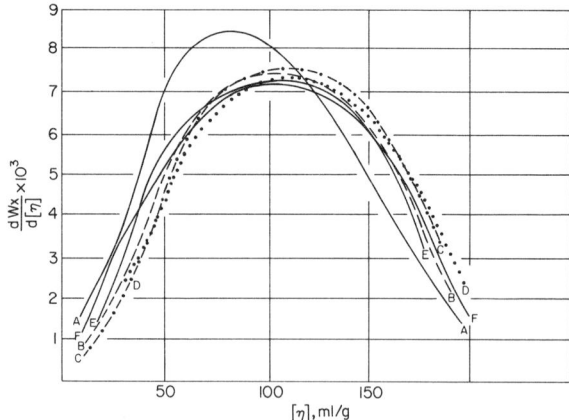

Fig. 5-10. Differential distribution curves of PVC samples taken during a suspension polymerization at various degrees of conversion. A, 4% conversion; B, 25%; C, 58%; D, 74%; E, 90%; F, 94% (*31*).

give peroxides or by terminating the chain radicals. The suggestion is supported by the lower chlorine content, by the appreciable infrared absorption at 1720 cm^{-1}, and by the low thermal stability of the 4% conversion sample.

Even though the experimental proofs are scarce, the suspension polymerization process seems to be similar to that of the bulk polymerization. Further work is necessary before one can come to any definite conclusion.

C. Emulsion Polymerization

In spite of the great technical importance of emulsion polymerization of vinyl chloride only a few works have been published on the kinetics and mechanism of this process.

Lazor (31) studied the effect of the emulsion polymerization of vinyl chloride initiated by the redox system $K_2S_2O_8-N_2HSO_3$. He found that the number of latex particles, N, in unit volume depends principally on the concentration of the emulsifier C_S and to a lesser extent on the persulfate and bisulfite concentrations, when C_S is below the CMC (critical micellar-concentration value). The effect of initiator concentration on N becomes negligible when C_S is very near to the CMC value: in this case N is affected principally by the emulsifier concentration.

Peggion et al. (32) made an extensive study of the effect of the type and concentration of emulsifier on the number N of latex particles produced at fixed temperature and initiator ($K_2S_2O_8$) concentrations. As may be seen

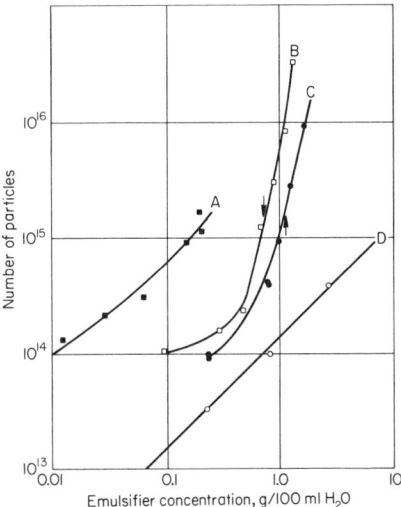

Fig. 5-11. Dependence of number of particles (in 1 ml of H_2O) on emulsifier concentration (arrows indicate CMC values). A, sodium lauryl sulfate; B, Aerosol MA; C, Aerosol AY; D, Aerosol DBM (33).

from Fig. 5-11, it was found that N increases considerably on an increase in soap concentration. All other conditions being equal, N depends on the type of emulsifier. In spite of the large influence on N, the emulsifier concentration affects the polymerization rate only to a very minor extent. With Na–dibutylsulfosuccinate as emulsifier Peggion and co-workers observed that the reaction rate is nearly independent of the emulsifier concentration C_S. With different emulsifiers the polymerization rate becomes practically independent of C_S when the latter is higher than the CMC (Fig. 5-12). From Figs. 5-11 and 5-12 it is possible to observe that a small change in reaction rate corresponds to a large change in N. In the same work the reaction order in initiator was also determined; a value between 0.6 and 0.7 was found. It is very interesting to note that, according to the findings of these workers, the number of latex particles does not change during polymerization after about 6% conversion. The conversion–time curves, moreover, present the same typical autocatalytic behavior as the bulk and suspension polymerization.

In a recent work Giskehaug (33) carried out extensive investigations into the influence of the number and size of latex particles on the reaction rate, using "seeded" polymerizations from which new latex particle formation was excluded. The results of his work are very interesting. He found a reaction order in initiator ($K_2S_2O_8$) of 0.5 to 0.6 in polymerization carried out with equal amounts of seed but with a particle diameter variable in the range 10 to 500 mμ. Some experiments carried out by varying the amounts of seed while maintaining the diameter of the particles constant showed that the polymerization rate does not depend on the number of particles. On the other hand, some experiments were performed with constant weights of seed and varying diameters and, therefore, varying numbers of particles; the results, shown in Table 5-1, indicate that the reaction rate is nearly constant in the particle diameter range of 600 to 100 mμ, that is, a range of

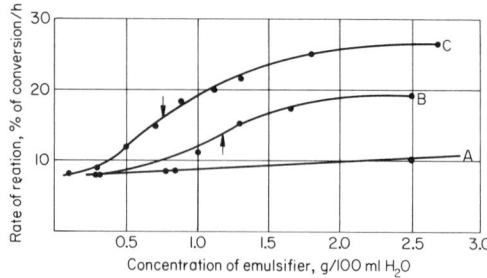

Fig. 5-12. Emulsion polymerization of vinyl chloride. Dependence of reaction rate on emulsifier concentration (arrows indicate CMC values). A, sodium dibutyl sulfosuccinate; B, sodium diamyl sulfosuccinate; C, sodium diesyl sulfosuccinate (33).

TABLE 5-1

Seed Polymerization of Vinyl Chloride at 50°C
(Water, 800 g; $K_2S_2O_8$, 0.1 %; vinyl chloride, 440 g)

Particle diam., $m\mu$	Seed PVC, g	N (particles per 800 ml of water)	Tot. particle surface, m^2	Rate of polymeriz., g of PVC/hr 800 ml
580	8	5.6×10^{13}	14.8	38.6, 32.6
358	8	2.4×10^{14}	24	27.1, 30.2
307	8	3.8×10^{14}	27.9	34.6
106	5.76	6.6×10^{15}	58.3	37.4
28	8	5.0×10^{17}	306	52.4, 48.5
15	8	3.24×10^{18}	573	72.5

N of 10^{13} to 10^{15} per 800 cm^3. The polymerization rate doubles only at lower particle diameters ($d < 100$ mμ) when N reaches the value 10^{18}. These results agree substantially with the observations of Peggion et al. to the effect that a very large change in the number of the particles scarcely affects the reaction rate.

Krasovec (*34*) determined the molecular-weight distribution curves of polyvinyl chloride samples taken during an emulsion polymerization process at various degrees of conversion. The distributions were about the same for the different samples, except for the one taken at lowest conversion, which had a distribution shifted to the lower molecular weights. These results are quite similar to those obtained by Pezzin et al. (*30*) from suspension polymerization (Fig. 5-10).

On the basis of the available literature it is possible to affirm that the Smith–Ewart (*35*) theory of emulsion polymerization does not apply to the emulsion polymerization of vinyl chloride. In fact, according to this theory the reaction rate should be proportional to the number of particles N, in disagreement with the experimental results.

It is to be noticed that vinyl chloride at 50°C at the saturation pressure is appreciably soluble in water (about 0.5 mole liter^{-1}). Therefore it is reasonable to suggest an initiation of polymerization in solution rather than in the monomer dissolved in the soap micelles, as in the emulsion polymerization of styrene. The occurrence of a solution polymerization was also suggested by Jacobi (*36*) on the basis of studies on the emulsion polymerization "in continuum" of vinyl chloride. This author claims that no micellar polymerization is operative in the case of vinyl chloride. The deviations from the Smith–Ewart theory in the case of vinyl chloride might be due to the presence of a solution polymerization competitive with the micellar polymerization. However, this hypothesis does not completely explain the anomalous behavior of the emulsion polymerization of vinyl chloride. In fact, the extensive investigations of Cherdron (37) on the emulsion polymerization of various vinyl monomers demonstrated that monomers more soluble in water than vinyl chloride show minor deviations from the Smith–Ewart theory.

In our opinion the anomalies of vinyl chloride emulsion polymerization can be imputed partially to the water solubility of monomer but especially to the heterogeneity of the monomer–polymer system.

The literature data are rather too meagre to draw definitive conclusions about the mechanism of the emulsion polymerization of vinyl chloride, but some hypotheses may be put forward. Owing to the appreciable water solubility of the monomer the polymerization starts in the aqueous phase. The radicals produced by decomposition of the water-soluble initiator may react with the monomer dissolved in water. The polymer radicals so formed separate from the solution at a very low polymerization degree, forming nuclei protected by the emulsifier, which can grow to latex particles on consuming the monomer at their surface. When the number of particles has become large enough to adsorb the emulsifier completely, the polymer radicals continuously produced in the aqueous phase precipitate on the preformed polymer particles, since they no longer have any emulsifier to be stabilized. From this stage on the number of particles does not change during the reaction, in agreement with experimental results. The polymerization proceeds at the interface of the liquid phase and polymer particles, and the monomer is continuously supplied by diffusion from the droplets throughout the aqueous solution.

Such an hypothesis requires an effect of the particles' surface on the polymerization rate. From Table 1 in the work of Giskehaug (33) it may be observed that at constant seed weight the reaction rate increases with decreasing particle diameter when the total surface of the particles is very large. The increase in the rate is greatest in the case of the small particles. This fact seems to indicate that the surface may participate in the total reaction. This idea is also supported by the data of Peggion et al. (32), who found, using Aerosol AY, a more marked increase in reaction rate with increasing emulsifier concentration (Fig. 5-12). Moreover, the increase in number of particles with increasing emulsifier concentration was more pronounced than with other emulsifiers (Fig. 5-11). Owing to the fact that Aerosol AY produces a very large number of particles, naturally of small diameters, it should be concluded that in this case the total surface affects the polymerization rate.

Drawing a conclusion from the data given above, it seems that the total surface may participate in some way in the reaction.

The polymerization scheme suggested on the basis of experimental results shows some analogies with the bulk polymerization of vinyl chloride.

We must point out that in the emulsion polymerization autocatalytic conversion–time curves (Fig. 5-13) were found with reaction orders in initiator equal to or slightly above 0.5. Likewise, this may be explained in the same way as for the bulk polymerization.

In conclusion, available evidence indicates that the emulsion polymerization of vinyl chloride does not resemble the true emulsion polymerization described by Smith and Ewart but shows the general behavior of the heterogeneous solution polymerization.

D. Solution Polymerization

Burnett and Wright (38) studied the photosensitized polymerization of vinyl chloride in tetrahydrofuran solution over the temperature range 25 to 55°C, using either 2,2′-azobisisobutyronitrile or 1,1′-azobis-1-cyclohexane nitrile as initiator. They found that the extent of reaction was linear with time up to approximately 10% conversion; thereafter the rate of polymerization gradually decreased.

According to these workers the decrease of the rate is due either to the consumption of monomer or to light-scattering by the polymer particles formed, since at 10% conversion the solution was quite turbid. They found that:

1. The rate is proportional to the 3/2 power of the monomer concentration (in the monomer concentration range 1 to 7 moles/liter).

2. The rate is proportional to the square root of the initiator concentration at 25°C and to the power of 0.63 at 55°C.

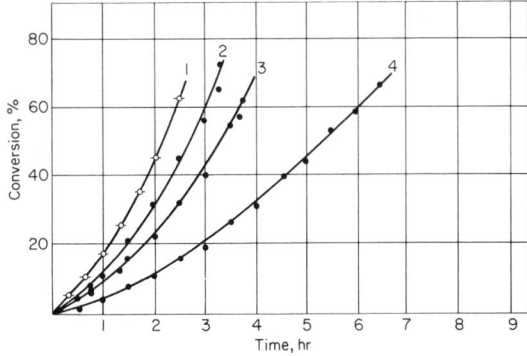

Fig. 5-13. Emulsion polymerization of vinyl chloride at different concentrations of initiator ($K_2S_2O_8$, mole per liter). 1, 12.2; 2, 9.15; 3, 6.1; 4, 1.22. Emulsifier, Aerosol MA (0.7 g per 100 ml of H_2O) (33).

3. Over the same temperature range the value of the intensity exponent increases from 0.62 to 0.86.

Burnett and Wright interpreted the results by assuming coexistence of mutual termination between free radicals and of termination by reaction of the chain radicals with the monomer. The last reaction occurs by chlorine transfer from monomer to chain radicals leading to $CH_2=CH$ radicals, which can terminate growing chains or dimerize, giving butadiene. Butadiene inhibits the polymerization owing to the formation of allylic free radicals by addition to the chain radicals. The mutual termination would predominate at 25°C, whereas the termination with the monomer is more and more important with increasing temperature.

Nevertheless, such a mechanism cannot explain the observed reaction orders in monomer and in initiator of the over-all polymerization rate. In fact, in a photosensitized polymerization a termination of chain radicals with the monomer leads to unit order in the intensity of the incident radiation and to zero order in monomer (and not unit order in both radiation intensity and monomer, as claimed by Burnett and Wright). On the other hand, a mutual termination between chain radicals leads to a 0.5 order with respect to the radiation intensity and to unit order in monomer (and not to reaction orders 1/2 and 2/3, respectively, as affirmed by Burnett and Wright).

Danusso et al. (39) studied vinyl chloride polymerization initiated by benzoyl peroxide at 50°C in the presence of chlorobenzene, which is a good solvent of the polymer. Increasing amounts of solvent depress the autoacceleration characteristic of the bulk reaction, until a complete suppression is obtained when about 40% (by weight) of solvent is present. Under such conditions the reaction is a homogeneous one with order 0.5 in initiator and 1 in monomer.

The solution polymerization in tetrahydrofuran initiated by 2-2'-azobis-isobutyronitrile at 40°C was investigated by Mickley et al. (10). They found that the physical nature of the reaction mixtures in the tetrahydrofuran depends on the monomer concentration. At monomer concentrations of less than 6 moles/liter a homogeneous solution results at low conversion; colloidal properties, however, appear after some time. The reaction orders in initiator and in the monomer are 0.7 and 2, respectively, and the molecular weight of the polymer is very low. A gelatinous polyvinyl chloride precipitate appears at $[M] = 9$ moles/liter but no rate acceleration is observed. The monomer order decreases, but the initiator order is still approximately 0.7. The molecular weight of the polymer is anyway very low. At very high monomer concentrations, $[M] = 13$ to 14 moles/liter, a granular precipitate forms, as in bulk, rate acceleration occurs, and the molecular weight of the polymer increases several fold. The initiator order decreases to 0.6. Mickley et al. suggest that tetrahydrofuran acts as a retarder by forming radicals less reactive to propagation by chain transfer or copolymerization reactions.

We mention, finally, some studies carried out in methanol (40) and cyclohexane (10) which are solvents of the monomer but nonsolvents of the polymer. The polymerization in such cases presents a behavior similar to that of bulk heterogeneous polymerization. In methanol with benzoyl peroxide as initiator at 50°C reaction orders of 1 in monomer and 0.7 in initiator were found.

E. Polymerization under Special Conditions

1. POLYMERIZATION BY METALLOORGANIC COMPOUNDS

The preparation of stereoregular polyvinyl chloride with the use of special initiating systems has been the object of many researches in the last few years. Various metalloorganic compounds were used, such as $M'''R_3$, $Al-R'R''R'''$, $M'M'''R_{3y+2x}$, $M'M'''R_4$, $M''R_2$, $B_nR_nH_p$, where M''' is a metal of the third group (such as B, Ga, In, and Tl), M'' is a metal of the second group (such as Mg, Be, Zn, Cd, and Hg), M' is an alkaline metal and R, R', R'', R''' are linear or branched alkyl groups (41,42). Moreover, some patents describe the use of such systems as SbR_3 + silver salt (43), $Pb(C_2H_5)_4$ + $TiCl_4$ (44), and $Pb(C_2H_5)_4$ + $AgNO_3$. In the last case AgC_2H_5 is formed in situ. Other patents describe the use of Ziegler–Natta types of catalyst complexed with Lewis bases such as tetrahydrofuran, ethyl ether, and triethylamine. The catalyst is obtained by reaction between alkyl aluminum or alkyl magnesium and a transition-metal compound, such as $TiCl_4$, VCl_4, $VOCl_2$, and $MoCl_5$ (45).

Up to the present no definite evidence exists that vinyl chloride is polymerized by these catalysts by an ionic mechanism. Polyvinyl chloride prepared with such initiators is normally more than usually crystalline. In most cases, however, the polymerizations are carried out at low temperatures; it is known that a lowering of the polymerization temperature increases the stereoregularity of this compound. The first workers (46,47) who described the use of boroalkyl compounds as initiators in the polymerization of vinyl chloride suggested that an anionic mechanism was operative in this case. Subsequently the radical character of these polymerizations was demonstrated by determining the reactivity ratios of copolymerizations of various monomer couples (48,49). Moreover, the presence of oxygen was found indispensable; this fact suggested that an alkyl–boron peroxide is the active species in the catalysis (50).

Giannini and Cesca (51) studied the polymerization of vinyl chloride by using initiators prepared with aluminum alkyls and vanadium compounds, in particular $AlCl(C_2H_5)OC_2H_5$ + $VO(C_5H_7O_2)$, in the absence of Lewis bases. Both kinetic data and reactivity ratios in copolymerizations of vinyl chloride and vinyl acetate are consistent with a radical polymerization mechanism. These workers, moreover, report that polyvinyl chloride as obtained with radical initiators at 70 to 80°C in the presence of powerful chain-transfer agents presents a degree of crystallinity of the same order of magnitude as that of samples prepared in the presence of aldehydes. It was suggested that aldehydes exercise a stereoregulating effect on the vinyl chloride polymerization (52,53). To the contrary, Giannini and Cesca suggest that all low-molecular-weight polyvinyl chloride is crystallizable and that the aldehydes act only as powerful transfer agents, lowering the molecular weight of the polymer.

In a recent work Yamazaki et al. (54) describe vinyl chloride polymerization by the initiating system n-butyltitanate–aluminum alkyls. They found that typical radical inhibitors have no effect on the polymerization rate. Moreover, the molecular weight of the polymer is unaffected by the addition of CCl_4, and the reactivity ratios in copolymerizations with styrene or vinylidene chloride depend on the type of the solvent and are different from the literature values for free-radical copolymerizations. On the basis of these results Yamazaki and his colleagues exclude a radical mechanism. An anionic mechanism in polymerizations initiated by tert-butylmagnesium chloride in tetrahydrofuran as solvent was suggested by Guyot et al. (55). According to them the polymerization consists only of initiation, propagation, and termination steps, and an anionic mechanism takes into account the kinetics of the process, the type of terminal group, the high crystallinity, and the low molecular weight of the polymer.

2. RADIATION POLYMERIZATION

The polymerization of gaseous vinyl chloride induced by alpha radiation was studied by Mund et al. (56,57). It was found that the reaction rate is proportional to the dose rate and to the monomer pressure to a power between 1 and 2 (the monomer pressure was varied in the range 100 to 700 mm Hg). The yield G, or monomer consumed per 100 eV of radiation, was found to be between 40 and 200, depending on the size of the reaction vessel, on the pressure, and on the temperature. These workers suggested a chain termination on the walls of the vessel, in order to explain the observed effects of the vessel size. The over-all activation energy determined in the range of temperature 0 to 55°C was found to be negative. Similar results were obtained by Puig and Bretton by gamma-radiation initiation (58). They studied the polymerization in the temperature range 20 to 100°C and in the pressure range 0.5 to 2 atm. A G value of 900 was found at 1.5 atm. The over-all activation energy was found to be -5.8 kcal/mole.

The polymerization in the gas phase was also studied by Herman and Hupin (59) with x-ray initiation in the temperature range 0.2 to 25.2°C and in the pressure range 189 to 788 mm Hg. A G value between 100 and 400 was found, depending on the temperature and pressure. The polymerization consists of three definite stages: a first one in which the reaction rate increases, a second one characterized by a constant reaction rate, and a third one occurring after the end of the irradiation. The latest stage lasts about 40 min at 0.2°C. The activation energies corresponding to the reaction rates of the three stages are 2.5, -2.1, and -4.9 kcal/mole, respectively. On the basis of these results the authors suggested a polymerization mechanism with a termination step strongly hindered owing to the trapping of chain radicals in the solid polymer. The activation energy of the termination would be quite high (7.4 kcal/mole), leading to a negative over-all activation energy.

Initiation by gamma radiation was also used in the bulk polymerization of vinyl chloride (60,61). Chapiro (60) found in this case that the reaction is quite similar to the bulk polymerization initiated by conventional initiators. However, in the radiation polymerization autoacceleration is present up to very high conversion ($\approx 80\%$), owing to the fact that both monomer and polymer form active radicals by interaction with the initiating radiation. The polymerization rate is proportional to a 0.59 power of the dose rate, and the molecular weight of the polymer is practically independent of the dose rate. An after-effect was observed but was less marked than in the case of acrylonitrile.

A method of obtaining syndiotactic polyvinyl chloride is reported by White and Brown (62), who irradiated adducts of vinyl chloride with urea. The molecular weight of the polymer so obtained is very low.

5-3. VINYLIDENE CHLORIDE

A. Bulk Polymerization

The bulk polymerization of vinylidene chloride is a heterogeneous reaction like the bulk polymerization of vinyl chloride, owing to the insolubility of the polymer in the monomer. One of the first kinetic studies of vinylidene chloride bulk polymerization was carried out by Burnett and Melville (63) by photochemical initiation in the range of temperature 13 to 35°C. In spite of the heterogeneity of the polymerizing system they found that no autoacceleration took place, and the reaction rate was proportional to the square root of the intensity of the initiating radiation. By determining the absolute rate constants of propagation and termination steps at different temperatures they were able to determine the activation energies and the frequency factors. It was found that

$$A_p = 10^{16} \text{ mole}^{-1} \text{ liter sec}^{-2} \qquad E_p = 25 \text{ kcal}$$
$$A_t = 10^{30} \text{ mole}^{-1} \text{ liter sec}^{-2} \qquad E_t = 40 \text{ kcal}$$

where the subscripts t and p indicate termination and propagation, respectively.

Although the k_p and k_t values are normal in a narrow range of temperature, from the high activation energies it appears that to a small rise in the polymerization temperature corresponds a large increase in the rate constants, which assume unusually high values. Moreover, the very high frequency factors are hardly interpretable in the light of the present theories on the reaction rates.

Bengough and Norrish (64) in more recent work studied the kinetics of the process initiated by benzoyl peroxide in the temperature range 47 to 75°C. In this case they found that the polymerization shows an auto-acceleration behavior quite similar to that in the corresponding heterogeneous polymerization of vinyl chloride and acrylonitrile.

The apparent disagreement between these results may be resolved by taking into account a discovery made by Bamford et al. (11), who found that the acrylonitrile bulk polymerization does not present autoacceleration when photoinitiation is used. According to these workers, the photochemical initiation is of less kinetic significance in heterogeneous systems. In fact, in photochemical polymerization scattering of the initiating radiation occurs from the polymer particles formed during the reaction, and the scattering increases with the amount of polymer. This leads to a reduction of the intensity of the initiating radiation and as a consequence to a reduction of the initiation rate, which opposes the tendency of the polymerization to accelerate.

In conclusion, under normal conditions—that is, with thermally catalyzed polymerization—the bulk polymerization of vinylidene chloride exhibits the usual features of heterogeneous polymerization.

Magat (12) tried to apply Eq. (5-3) to the data of Bengough and Norrish and found a poorer correlation than for vinyl chloride.

As we pointed out in Section 2-2-A-1, for polyvinylidene chloride the curve of molecular weight versus temperature does not show an anomalous behavior with a maximum, as in the case of polyvinyl chloride and poly-acrylonitrile (20). It was suggested that the anomalous behavior of the latter two polymers is due to the increasing stereoregularity and, therefore, crystallinity of the polymers as the polymerization temperature is lowered. Such changes in stereoregularity are not possible in polyvinylidene chloride, the chain of which is lacking in asymmetric carbon atoms.

Razuvaev and Minsker (65) studied the influence of oxygen on the bulk polymerization of vinylidene chloride. They observed an induction period, in which a stable peroxide is formed by reaction between monomer and oxygen. The presence of oxygen in the monomer leads to $-C-O-O-C-$ sequences in the polymer, which negatively influence the thermal stability of the polymer.

B. Emulsion Polymerization

The emulsion polymerization of vinylidene chloride shows interesting features. Unfortunately, relatively little experimental work has been carried out on this process.

One of the first to experiment in this field was Wiener (66), who found that the polymerization rate (determined dilatometrically) depends on the square root of the initiator concentration and on the 0.6 power of emulsifier concentration. These data were considered by Wiener to be in fairly good agreement with the Smith–Ewart theory.

Tkachenko and Khomikovskii (67) successfully showed that the polymerization does not extend into the polymer particles but only to their surface, owing to the insolubility of the polymer in the monomer. The most extensive studies on this subject were made by Hay et al. (68), Light et al. (69), and Evans et al. (70), in which was determined the influence of different factors, such as initiator and emulsifier concentration, coalescence of polymer particles, and rate of stirring, on the reaction rate.

The conversion–time curves show a characteristic behavior in which three definite reaction stages may be identified (Fig. 5-14). In stage I an apparently "normal" emulsion polymerization occurs with a nearly constant polymerization rate depending on the 0.6 power of emulsifier concentration and on the 0.5 power of initiator concentration. Stage II is characterized by a sharp decreasing of the polymerization rate; this stage occurs at an extent of reaction that depends on the emulsifier concentration. Just before the lowering of the reaction rate a strong coalescence of the monomer droplets is

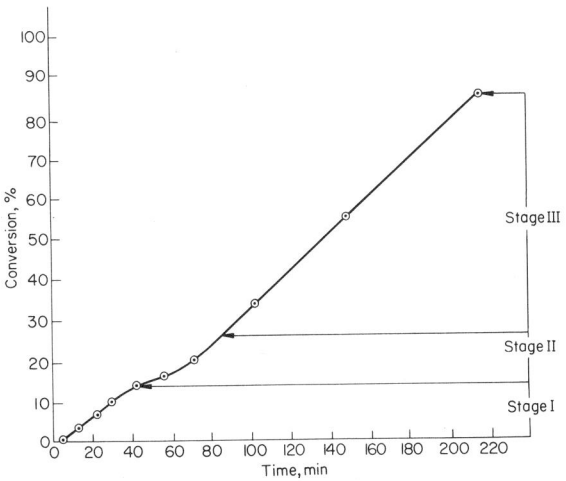

Fig. 5-14. Emulsion polymerization of vinylidene chloride. Typical three-stage curve; 2.0 % sodium lauryl sulfate, 0.15 % catalyst (47).

observed. Stage III shows an increase in the reaction rate, which reaches a value that depends on the first power of the initiator concentration and does not depend on the emulsifier concentration.

These results do not agree with what one would expect from the Smith–Ewart theory.

Hay et al. suggest that in the first stage of the polymerization the reaction occurs in the monomer dissolved into the emulsifier micelles and it almost obeys the Smith–Ewart theory. At the end of this stage noticeable separation of monomer occurs, because not enough emulsifier is present to stabilize both monomer droplets and polymer particles. The fall in the number of monomer droplets should be responsible for the decrease in reaction rate in stage II, owing to the decrease in the rate of diffusion of the monomer from the droplets to the surface of the polymer particles. In the stage III the increase in reaction rate to a value almost independent of the initial emulsifier concentration should be due to collision between polymer particles and monomer droplets, which assures monomer supply to the surface of the particles. This collision is allowed by the weak repulsion forces between particles and droplets in the system, owing to insufficient emulsifier for protection of the whole surface of the particles.

Hay et al. derived an equation on the basis of the experimental observations, taking into account both the coalescence of polymer particles and monomer droplets and the possibility that the average number of chain radicals in the polymer particles is higher than 0.5. The proposed equation agrees fairly well with the experimental results in the whole range of conversion.

From this reaction scheme it is difficult, however, to understand the reaction order of 1 with respect to the initiator observed in stage III.

It may be interesting to observe the formal analogy existing between the conversion–time curves found by these workers and the corresponding curves relative to the bulk polymerization of vinyl chloride initiated by the $B(n$-butyl$)_3 + O_2$ system at 25°C (Fig. 13) (13). In the last case the sharp fall in the reaction rate was attributed to a decrease in free polymer surface, due to coalescence of the polymer particles.

C. Anionic Polymerization

Regarding vinylidene chloride polymerization, Konishi (71) concludes from theoretical consideration of the Alfrey–Price polarity and resonance factors that an anionic polymerization of this monomer should be possible. In fact, he polymerized vinylidene chloride in n-hexane solution by using butyllithium as initiator. The kinetics of the process was interpreted as an anionic mechanism. In his opinion this interpretation is supported by the fact that hydroquinone, a typical radical scavenger, shows little effect on the reaction rate and that the reactivity ratios of copolymerizations with methylacrylate, methyl methacrylate, styrene, acrylonitrile, and vinyl chloride, are completely different from those of the corresponding free-radical copolymerizations.

5-4. VINYL CHLORIDE INDUSTRIAL POLYMERIZATION

A. Suspension Polymerization

The suspension polymerization process is the most important in the industrial production of polyvinyl chloride. A number of patents (28) have appeared in technical literature on this subject. The most common initiators are organic peroxides, of which the most frequently used are lauryl peroxide and benzoyl peroxide. In some patents the use of azo compounds such as 2-2'-azobisisobutyronitrile is suggested.

The polymerization temperature is generally in the range 40 to 60°C. In the most recent patents the use of a couple of suspending agents is decribed. The first agent, the primary suspending agent, generally consists of water-soluble polymers, such as polyvinyl alcohol, methyl ethers of cellulose, copolymers of vinyl acetate and maleic anhydride or of ethylene and maleic anhydride, gelatin, salts of polyacrylic acid, and condensation products of phenol aldehydes. The second agent, or secondary suspending agent, consists of vinyl acetate–allyl alcohol copolymers or glyceryl esters, etc.

The primary suspending agent acts as a protector colloid; it prevents the coagulation of the suspension and affects the size of polymer particles. The secondary suspending agent acts on the porosity of the polymer particles. Its mechanism of action is not completely understood. In a recent work Benetta and Cinque (72) demonstrated that, the greater the secondary suspending agent's action on the tension at the water–monomer interface, the greater the efficiency in increasing resin porosity. They correlated this efficiency with the hydrophilic–lyophilic balance number (HLB number) (73,74,93) and showed that the secondary suspending agent must have an HLB number in the range 3 to 13.

The suspension polyvinyl chloride normally is granular with high porosity and can readily be mixed with plasticizers to give dry blends, from which it is possible to obtain plastified films without the so-called fish-eyes, i.e., particles with a glasslike surface. A standard recipe of an industrial suspension polymerization, as reported in U.S. Patent 3,049,520, is the following:

Components	Parts by weight
Water	150
Vinyl chloride	100
1:1 vinyl acetate–maleic anhydride copolymer (primary suspending agent)	0.15
9:1 vinyl acetate–ally alcohol copolymer (secondary suspending agent)	0.20
Lauroyl peroxide	0.15

The components listed above are charged in a $15\text{-}m^3$ glass-lined steel kettle, from which oxygen is removed before the introduction of vinyl chloride. The polymerization is carried out at 52°C for about 12 hr under vigorous stirring. At the end of the process the residual monomer is vented; the polymer is recovered from the suspension by centrifugation, washed, and dried in hot air. The polyvinyl chloride so obtained is granular and fine, and the grains are highly porous, their surfaces not being glasslike.

B. Emulsion Polymerization

The industrial emulsion polymerization is described in a number of patents (75). Two types of polyvinyl chloride are produced: one for general use and one for "plastisols." The first is produced only in Europe and finds applications in the same fields as the suspension polymer. The second is produced throughout the world and appears as a very fine, nonporous chalklike powder. These properties constitute the most important difference between the suspension product and the emulsion product. The second type of emulsion product, when mixed with plasticizer, forms a plastisol; indeed, the suspension polymer forms a "dry blend." The plastisols are a dispersion of emulsion polymer in the plasticizer, which at room temperature is a poor solvent of the polymer. On a raising of the temperature the plasticizer swells the polymer (gelation), until a temperature is reached at which a tough gel is formed (fusion). The rheological properties of plastisols are of great importance in the practical applications of emulsion polyvinyl chloride. They depend on the polymer–plasticizer interactions. At a constant weight ratio of polymer to plasticizer small polymer particles give rise to viscous plastisols, owing to the large surface contact with the plasticizer. With large polymer particles very fluid plastisols are obtained.

Almost all polymerization processes are "seeded"; i.e., in the initial polymerization mixture a preformed latex with uniform particle size is introduced.

The numerous patents on this topic differ from one another in the type of emulsifier and operative conditions used. The most common emulsifiers are secondary alkyl sulfonates (such as mersolate), alkaline salts of alkyl sulfates, such as lauryl sulfate or acetyl sulfate, ether of alkaline salts of sulfosuccinic acid, such as Aerosol AY, and Aerosol MA. In most cases water-soluble redox systems, such as persulfate–bisulfite, are used as initiators. Polymerization processes in continuum (36,76), in which the monomer is continuously drawn, are also described.

An example of a standard procedure, as reported in a British Patent (75f), to produce polyvinyl chloride for plastisols is the following.

A mixture of 7.5 parts (by weight) of seed with 35% solids, with a particle diameter of about $0.3\ \mu$, 130 parts of deionized water, and 0.1 part of $NaHCO_3$, is introduced into a 15-m³ glass-lined steel kettle. After air-removing 0.1 part of NaHCO₃ and 20 parts of vinyl chloride are introduced, and the temperature is fixed at 50°C. The polymerization is initiated by adding a solution of $K_2S_2O_8$; this compound (in total 0.02 parts) is added in continuum during the whole process. After 1 hr the introduction of 80 parts of vinyl chloride, 0.25 part of sodium lauryl sulfate, and 0.5 part of Na–bistridecyl sulfosuccinate (these last in aqueous solution) is initiated. These components are fed continuously during the whole polymerization process, which is completed in 6 to 7 hr. At the end of the polymerization 0.2 part of Na–bistridecyl sulfosuccinate is quickly added, to stabilize the emulsion. The unreacted monomer is vented, and the latex is dried in a spray desiccator. During the drying the polymer particles agglomerate. The agglomerates are later eliminated by milling. When 100 parts of the polymer so obtained and and 60 parts of plasticizer as dioctyl phthalate are mixed, a very fluid plastisol, suitable for moulding processes, is obtained.

C. Bulk Polymerization

The bulk polymerization of vinyl chloride does not find a wide application in industrial practice, owing to the technological difficulty encountered, especially in the elimination of the reaction heat (≈ 20 kcal/mole of monomer polymerized). The St. Gobain Co. (77) was able to carry out a bulk process by using horizontal kettles revolving upon their axes; a constant polymerization temperature is assured by means of an appropriate apparatus that maintains the mass being polymerized in a fluid state. The St. Gobain Co. claims that the polymer so obtained presents high purity and high thermal stability. These properties enable products of great transparency to be manufactured. Moreover, the product presents low moisture absorption, easy manufacture, and good dielectrical properties.

The following is an example of bulk polymerization according to the St. Gobain patent.

The polymerization is carried out in a cylindrical kettle 60 cm in length and 50 cm in diameter revolving on its axis. The kettle contains 6, inox steel, balls 9 cm in diameter filled with small lead pellets to a 3-kg weight for each ball. Then 50 kg of vinyl chloride, 40 g of benzoyl peroxide, and 100 g of sodium phosphate are introduced into the kettle, and the polymerization is carried out at 58°C. After 17 hr the residual monomer is distilled. Finally 40 kg of polyvinyl chloride is obtained in the form a chalklike powder.

5-5. VINYLIDENE CHLORIDE INDUSTRIAL POLYMERIZATION

The emulsion and suspension processes are, as in the case of polyvinyl chloride, the most important in the industrial production of polyvinylidene chloride. Since the vinylidene chloride is easily oxidized, the polymerization process is best carried out at less than 50°C. For this reason in the emulsion processes redox systems such as ammonium persulfate as oxidizing agent and sulfite, bisulfite, or hydrazine sulfate as reducing agent are employed as initiators. Lead tetraethyl, nickel carbonyl, iron salts, and inorganic acids have also been suggested as promoters (78). Dicrotonyl peroxide, a monomer-soluble peroxide, has been employed for polymerizations in the temperature range 20 to 45°C (79).

The most commonly used emulsifiers are alkaline salts of aliphatic acids, alkyl sulfates, alkyl- or alkarylsulfonates, polythylene oxides, glyceryl monocaproate (80), polyglyceryl monostearate (81), polyalkylen glycols, with molecular weights of 300 to 9000 (82).

An example of emulsion polymerization is the following (83).

Under stirring in N_2 atmosphere 100 parts (by weight) of monomer, 300 parts of water, 3 parts of ammonium persulfate, 1.5 parts of hydrazine sulfate, 3 parts of the sodium salt of the sulfuric ester of oleic alcohol, and 1.8 parts of sodium hydroxide are polymerized. After only 1 hr the conversion is 90% and a very fluid emulsion is obtained.

As already noted, the pure polyvinylidene chloride owing to the low heat stability, high softening point, and incompatibility with plasticizers, is material of little commerical importance.

5-6. VINYL CHLORIDE–VINYLIDENE CHLORIDE COPOLYMERIZATION

When a mixture of vinyl chloride and vinylidene chloride is copolymerized, the final product obtained is a heterogeneous mixture of copolymers of different composition. This fact is due to the large difference between the reactivity ratios of the two monomers. Mayo et al. (84) report the values $r_{VDC} = 3.2$, $r_{VC} = 0.3$.

An homogeneous product can be obtained only by adding during the polymerization process the faster-polymerizing monomer, to maintain constant the composition of the monomeric mixture. Measurements of the copolymerization rates of vinyl chloride–vinylidene chloride in various composition ratios were carried out by Reinhardt (85) and Staudinger (86). The reaction was studied by Reinhardt in bulk at 45°C with benzoyl peroxide as initiator, and by Staudinger in emulsion at 40°C with ammonium persulfate as initiator. Both workers found that in spite of the comparable polymerization rates of each monomer alone the copolymerization rate can be as little as one fifth or less of the polymerization rate of either component.

Polyvinylidene chloride is a crystalline polymer and, as Havens (87) showed, the introduction of vinyl chloride units into the polymer chains reduces the crystallinity to some extent. Havens found that practically amorphous copolymer is obtained with a 3:1 vinylidene chloride–vinyl chloride mixture. Commercial products (Saran) were used by him in these measurements.

In a recent work Enomoto (88) prepared vinyl chloride–vinylidene chloride copolymers, starting with monomeric mixtures having different compositions and stopping the polymerizations at very low conversions. By infrared measurements he was able to determine the reactivity ratios, which were found to depend on the "feed ratios." The reactivity ratios (average values) were found to be $r_{VDC} = 3.15$ and $r_{VC} = 0.23$, in agreement with the values of Mayo et al.

Chujo et al. (89) determined from nuclear magnetic resonance the molar fraction of head-to-head structures $(-CCl_2-CH_2-CH_2-CCl_2-)$ present in the vinylidene chloride portions of vinyl chloride–vinylidene chloride copolymers of different composition. They found that the fraction of head-to-head structures decreases on an increase of vinylidene chloride content (Table 5-2).

The reactivity ratios determined by these workers are $r_{VDC} = 2.5$ and $r_{VC} = 0.4$. The discrepancy between these and the Enomoto values is to be attributed, according to Chujo, to the fact that the presence of head-to-head bonds was neglected in the infrared measurements.

It is interesting to note that the x-ray diffraction patterns of the copolymers, except the sample 1 of Table 5-2, are similar to that of polyvinylidene chloride but not to that of chlorinated poly-2,3-dichlorobutadiene. This means, according to Chujo, that the head-to-head structure cannot enter into the crystalline regions; in other words, the copolymer crystallinity is also reduced by the occurrence of the head-to-head structure.

Germar (90) determined by infrared measurements the reactivity ratios and the weight distribution of the vinyl chloride and vinylidene chloride sequences in copolymers of different composition. He found $r_{VDC} = 3.2 \pm 0.2$ and $r_{VC} = 0.2 \pm 0.05$. Regarding the sequences' length, he observed that with 75 % of vinylidene chloride in the monomer feed a copolymer is obtained

TABLE 5-2

Number (or Mole) Fraction of Skeletal Head Structures
in Vinylidene Chloride–Vinyl Chloride Copolymers

Sample	VDC/VC feed ratio	Fraction, %
1	5/95	
2	25/75	45.5
3	30/70	34.8
4	50/50	24.7
5	80/20	12.6
6	85/15	10.1
PVDC	100/00	0.0

almost completely consisting of polyvinylidene sequences with $n > 10$ (where n is the number of consecutive vinylidene chloride units). When the vinyl chloride content in the monomeric feed is increased the length of the vinylidene chloride sequences is obviously reduced. With 90% of vinyl chloride in the feed a distribution of vinyl chloride sequences of length between $n = 1$ and $n = 18$ is obtained, with a maximum at $n = 2$. The length of the corresponding vinylidene chloride sequences is always less than $n = 10$.

It should be pointed out that Germar assumes that all the vinylidene chloride sequences are in head-to-tail arrangement, neglecting the possibility of head-to-head structures suggested by Chujo et al.

Only vinyl chloride–vinylidene chloride copolymers with high vinyl chloride content (at least 80%) or with high vinylidene chloride content (at least 75%) have commerical interest. Copolymers with intermediate composition have little importance.

In the first type of copolymer (with high vinyl chloride content) the introduction of vinylidene chloride units makes the product more soluble in solvents and more easily manufactured than pure polyvinyl chloride.

In the second type of copolymer (with high vinylidene chloride content) the introduction of vinyl chloride units makes the product more suitable as a plastic material in the ordinary sense than pure polyvinylidene chloride. The last product shows a high softening range, a strong tendency to evolve HCl at the temperatures required for plastic working, and incompatibility with the usual plasticizers. The copolymers of high vinylidene chloride content find large application as fibers, monofilaments, pipes, and films. During manufacture the tendency of the product to crystallize is useful in improving strength properties by orienting the crystallites in one direction.

The emulsion and suspension techniques are the most commonly employed in the industrial preparation of these copolymers. The operating conditions are quite similar to these adopted in vinyl chloride homopolymerization (91).

An exhaustive review of this topic has recently been published (92).

REFERENCES

1. M. Prat Jean, *Mem. Serv. Chim. Etat* (*Paris*), **32**, 319 (1946).
2. W. I. Bengough and R. G. W. Norrish, *Proc. Roy. Soc.* (*London*), **A220**, 301 (1950).
3. J. W. Breitenbach and A. Schindler, *Mh. Chem.*, **80**, 429 (1949).
4. A. Schindler and J. W. Breitenbach, *Ric. Sci. Suppl.*, **25**, 34 (1955).
5. J. W. Breitenbach and A. Schindler, *Mh. Chem.*, **86**, 437 (1955); *J. Polymer Sci.*, **18**, 435 (1955).
6. E. J. Arlman and W. M. Wagner, *J. Polymer Sci.*, **9**, 581 (1951).
7. F. Danusso and G. Perugini, *Chim. Ind.* (*Milan*), **35**, 881 (1953).
8. F. Danusso, *Ric. Sci. Suppl.*, **25**, 46 (1955).
9. F. Danusso and D. Sianesi, *Chim. Ind.* (*Milan*) **37**, 695 (1955).

10. H. S. Mickley, A. S. Michaels, and A. L. Moore, *J. Polymer Sci., 60*, 121 (1962).
11. C. H. Bamford, W. G. Barb, A. D. Jenkins, and P. F. Onyon, *The Kinetics of Vinyl Polymerization by Radical Mechanisms*, Butterworth, London, 1958, Chap. 4.
12. M. Magat, *J. Polymer Sci., 16*, 491 (1955).
13. G. Talamini and G. Vidotto, *Makromolekul. Chem., 50*, 129 (1961).
14. F. Danusso and D. Sianesi, *Chim. Ind. (Milan), 37*, 278 (1955).
15. G. Talamini and G. Vidotto, *Makromolekul. Chem., 53*, 21 (1962).
16. F. Danusso, G. Pajaro, and D. Sianesi, *Chim. Ind. (Milan), 41*, 1170 (1959).
17. G. Talamini and G. Vidotto, *Chim. Ind. (Milan), 46*, 16 (1964).
18. W. M. Thomas, *Fortschr. Hochpolmer.-Forsch., 2*, 401 (1961).
19. C. H. Bamford and A. D. Jenkins, *Proc. Roy. Soc. (London), A216*, 515 (1953).
20. G. Talamini and G. Vidotto, *Chim. Ind. (Milan), 46*, 371 (1964).
21. J. D. Cotman, *J. Am. Chem. Soc., 77*, 2750 (1955); *Ann. N.Y. Acad. Sci., 57*, 417 (1953).
22. M. H. George, R. J. Grisenthwaite, and R. F. Hunter, *Chem. & Ind. (London), 1958*, 1114.
23. H. Batzer and A. Nisch, *Makromolekul. Chem., 22*, 131 (1957).
24. J. J. P. Staudinger, *Plastics Progress*, Iliffe Books Ltd., London, 1961, p. 65.
25. W. Hahn and W. Müller, *Makromolekul. Chem., 16*, 71 (1955).
26. F. A. Bovey and G. D. V. Tiers, *Chem. & Ind. (London), 42*, 1826 (1962).
27. Sz. Krozer and Z. Czlonkowska, *J. Appl. Polymer Sci., 8*, 1275 (1964).
28. See, for example:
    U.S. Pats.: 2,194,354; 2,322,309; 2,445,970; 2,470,909; 2,470,910; 2,470,911; 2,476,474; 2,483,959; 2,483,960; 2,492,087; 2,492,088; 2,492,089; 2,528,469; 2,538,050; 2,538,051; 2,511,811; 2,543,094; 2,564,291; 2,564,292; 2,580,277; 2,594,375; 2,772,257; 2,778,257; 2,812,318; 2,820,028; 2,823,200; 2,824,862; 2,833,754; 2,836,584; 2,840,549; 2,843,576; 2,875,186; 2,875,187; 2,957,857; 3,049,520
    Brit. Pats.: 548,682; 627,235; 637,995; 640,120; 646,969; 658,426; 670,197; 671,446; 712,442; 745,053; 791,894
    Germ. Pats.: 751,602; 813,459; 826,358; 888,172; 888,173; 912,022; 947,736; 1,076,374
    It. Pats.: 526,394; 532,304; 560,363; 562,180; 572,070; 643,255.
29. S. G. Bankoff and R. N. Shreve, *Ind. Eng. Chem., 45*, 270 (1953).
30. G. Pezzin, G. Talamini, and G. Vidotto, *Makromolekul. Chem., 43*, 12 (1961).
31. J. T. Lazor, *J. Appl. Polymer Sci., 1*, 11 (1959).
32. E. Peggion, F. Testa, and G. Talamini, *Makromolekul. Chem., 71*, 173 (1964).
33. K. Giskehaug, *Symposium on the Chemistry of Polymerization Processes*, London, April 1965.
34. F. Krasovec, *J. Stefan Inst. Rept. Ljubljana, 1956*, 203.
35. W. V. Smith and R. H. Ewart, *J. Chem. Phys., 16*, 592 (1948); W. V. Smith, *J. Am. Chem. Soc., 70*, 3695 (1948).
36. B. Jacobi, *Angew. Chem., 64*, 539 (1952).
37. H. Cherdron, *Kunststoffe, 50*, 568 (1960).
38. G. M. Burnett and W. W. Wright, *Proc. Roy. Soc. (London), A221*, 28 (1954).
39. F. Danusso, F. Sabbioni, and L. Siliprandi, *Chim. Ind. (Milan), 38*, 99 (1956).
40. F. Danusso and F. Sabbioni, *Chim. Ind. (Milan), 37*, 1032 (1955).
41. Belg. Pats. 566,530–566,532.
42. Belg. Pats. 566,533–566,535.
43. Belg. Pat. 566,356 (1958).
44. Belg. Pat. 545,968 (1956).
45. Australian Pat. Applications 26889-57.
46. G. S. Kolesnikov and L. S. Fedorova, *Izv. Akad. Nauk SSSR Otd. Khim. Nauk, 1957*, 236.
47. N. Ashikari, *J. Polymer Sci., 28*, 250 (1958).

48. I. W. Fordham and C. L. Sturm, *J. Polymer Sci.*, **33**, 503 (1958).
49. N. Ashikari and A. Nishimura, *J. Polymer Sci.*, **31**, 249 (1958).
50. J. Furukawa, T. Tsuruta, T. Imada, and H. Fukutani, *Makromolekul. Chem.*, **31**, 122 (1959).
51. U. Giannini and S. Cesca, *Chim. Ind. (Milan)*, **44**, 371 (1962).
52. P. H. Burleigh, *J. Am. Chem. Soc.*, **82**, 749 (1960).
53. J. F. Gillespie and P. H. Burleigh, *Abstracts ACS Meeting, Cleveland, 1960*, Vol. I, No. 1, p. 131.
54. N. Yamazaki, K. Sasaki, and S. Kambara, *Polymer Letters*, **2**, 487 (1964).
55. A. Guyot and Pham Quang Tho, *J. Polymer Sci.*, **C4**, 299 (1964); *Symposium on the Chemistry of Polymerization Processes, London*, April 1965.
56. W. Mund, J. A. Herman, and G. Verfaillie, *Bull. Acad. Roy. Belges*, **35**, 656 (1949).
57. W. Mund, M. Van Meerssche, and J. Momigny, *Bull. Soc. Chim. Belges*, **62**, 109, 645 (1953).
58. See A. Chapiro, *Radiation Chemistry of Polymeric Systems*, Wiley (Interscience), New York, 1962, p. 220.
59. J. A. Herman and P. M. Hupin, *Can. J. Chem.*, **41**, 1578 (1963).
60. A. Chapiro, *J. Chim. Phys.*, **47**, 764 (1950); **53**, 512 (1956).
61. Fr. Pat. 1,121,084 (1955).
62. D. M. White and J. F. Brown, *Abstracts 134th ACS Meeting, Chicago*, Sept. 1958; D. M. White, *J. Am. Chem. Soc.*, **82**, 5678 (1960).
63. J. D. Burnett and H. W. Melville, *Trans. Faraday Soc.*, **46**, 976 (1950).
64. W. I. Bengough and R. G. W. Norrish, *Proc. Roy. Soc. (London)*, **A218**, 149 (1953).
65. G. A. Rusavaiev and K. S. Minsker, *Zh. Obshthei Khim. Akad. Nauk SSSR*, **28**, 983 (1958).
66. H. Wiener, *J. Polymer Sci.*, **7**, 1 (1951).
67. G. V. Tkachenko and P. M. Khomikovskii, *Dokl. Akad. Nauk SSSR*, **72**, 543 (1950).
68. P. M. Hay, J. C. Light, L. Marker, R. W. Murray, A. T. Santonicola, O. S. Sweeting, and J. G. Wespic, *J. Appl. Polymer Sci.*, **5**, 23 (1961).
69. J. C. Light, L. Marker, A. T. Santonicola, and O. J. Sweeting, *J. Appl. Polymer Sci.*, **5**, 31 (1961).
70. C. P. Evans, P. M. Hay, L. Marker, R. W. Murray, and O. J. Sweeting *J. Appl. Polymer Sci.*, **5**, 39 (1961).
71. A. Konishi, *Bull. Chem. Soc. Japan*, **35**, 193, 197, 395 (1962).
72. G. Benetta and G. Cinque, *Chim. Ind. (Milan)*, **47**, 500 (1965).
73. W. C. Griffin, *J. Soc. Cosmetic Chemists*, **1**, 311 (1949); **5**, 249 (1954); *Offic. Dig. Federation Paint Varnish Prod. Clubs*, **28**, 466 (1956).
74. J. T. Davies, *Surface Activity* (J. H. Schulman, ed.), Butterworth, London, 1957, pp. 426–437.
75. See, for example:
    (*a*) H. Mark et al., U.S. Pat. 2,068,424;
    (*b*) D. D. Coffman and F. C. McGrew, U.S. Pat. 2,404,791;
    (*c*) R. G. R. Bacon and L. B. Morgan, Brit. Pat. 573,366; U.S. Pat. 2,404,781; U.S. Pat. 2,462,422; U.S. Pat. 2,168,808;
    (*d*) J. R. Powers, U.S. Pat. 2,520,959; Brit. Pat. 634,647;
    (*e*) G. Benetta, G. Gatta, and F Testa, It. Pat. 680,525;
    (*f*) G. Benetta, V. Bresquar, G. Gatta, and F. Testa, Brit. Pat. 984,487 (1965);
    (*g*) C. Corso and E. Ferrari, *Materie Plastiche*, **28**, 10 (1962).
76. F. K. Schoenfeld and W. L. Semon, U.S. Pat. 2,259,180; F. Fikentscher, *U.S. Dept. Comm. Office Tech. Serv. PB Rept.*, *40,908 and 949*, Pt. IIa; W. L. de Nie et al., U.S. Pat. 2,475,016.
77. *Plastics*, (1960) 225; Fr. Pat. 1,079,772; Brit. Pat. 940,245.
78. U.S. Pat. 2,160,933; U.S. Pat. 2,160,939; U.S. Pat. 2,333,633.
79. Brit. Pat. 594,717.

80. U.S. Pat. 640,120.
81. Brit. Pat. 711,355.
82. Ger. Pat. 946,087.
83. Brit. Pat. 573,369.
84. F. R. Mayo, F. M. Lewis, and C. Walling, *J. Am. Chem. Soc.,* **70**, 1529 (1948).
85. R. C. Reinhardt, *Ind. Eng. Chem.,* **35**, 422 (1943).
86. J. J. P. Staudinger, *Brit. Plastics,* **19**, 381 (1947).
87. C. B. Havens, *Ind. Eng. Chem.,* **42**, 315 (1950).
88. S. Enomoto, *J. Polymer Sci.,* **55**, 95 (1961).
89. R. Chujo, S. Satoh, and E. Nagai, *J. Polymer Sci.,* **A2**, 895 (1964).
90. H. Germar, *Makromolekul. Chem.,* **84**, 36 (1965).
91. See, for example, U.S. Pat. 2,640,050; U.S. Pat. 2,482,771; U.S. Pat. 2,160,931; Brit. Pat. 617,891; It. Pat. 393,311; Ger. Pat. 749,586; Fr. Pat. 950,947; U.S. Pats. 2,968,651, 3,033,812.
92. G. E. Ham, ed., *Copolymerization,* Wiley (Interscience), New York, 1964, Chap. X.
93. S. Ross, E. S. Chen, P. Becher, and H. J. Ranauto, *J. Phys. Chem.,* **63**, 1681 (1958).

CHAPTER 6

Occlusion Phenomena in the Polymerization of Acrylonitrile and Other Monomers

A. D. Jenkins

The Chemical Laboratory, University of Sussex, Sussex, England

6-1. INTRODUCTION

The reactivity of monomers in polymerization reactions is often discussed in terms of the chemical nature of the reacting species, but it is important to realize that in many systems physical factors also play a major part in determining the kinetic behavior. Among such reactions are the so-called heterogeneous polymerizations, which may be defined as those polymerizations in which the propagating free radicals pass from one phase to another. This behavior is usually a consequence of the separation of solid polymer from monomer initially present in either vapor or liquid state; in the latter case the monomer may be present in bulk (i.e., undiluted) or as a solution, emulsion, or suspension.

The numerous heterogeneous polymerizations include the reactions of acrylonitrile, vinyl chloride, vinylidene chloride, and trifluorochloroethylene. Reactions which are normally confined to a single phase can often be rendered heterogeneous by adding to the system a diluent that acts as a precipitant for the polymer. The polymerization of styrene in methanol affords an example of such systems.

It is legitimate to include among heterogeneous polymerizations the "popcorn" polymerizations, although they are certainly less well understood. They consist of the separation, from the vapor or liquid state, of small opaque nodules of polymer which proliferate rapidly, giving rise to a highly cross-linked and insoluble product. Owing to the intractability of the polymers structural examination is difficult, so that these polymers and their method of growth are the subject of much speculation. Apart from these rather special reactions, heterogeneous polymerizations also include reactions initiated in the monomer vapor phase, which were among the earliest vinyl polymerizations to receive attention.

Acrylonitrile is exceptional among common and commercially important vinyl monomers in having a relatively high solubility in water. The aqueous-solution reaction has been extensively studied and shown to be highly complex, having many features in common with the bulk reaction.

Although emulsion polymerization falls into the category of heterogeneous polymerizations, it will receive no attention here, another chapter being devoted entirely to this topic.

In homogeneous reactions simple kinetic relations are usually found to hold, at least at low conversions. One expects to find a square-root dependence on initiator concentration and a first-order behavior with respect to monomer. Further, photochemical after-effects are dependent upon the intensity but not the duration of the irradiation. When insoluble polymers are produced, any or all of these relationships may fail, even though in the presence of sufficient solvent normal behavior is observed. This proves that the abnormal behavior is not due to impurities present in the system but to the separation of polymer during reaction. A striking demonstration is provided by the experiments of Abere et al. (*1*) and of Chapiro (*2*), who added methanol as a precipitant to the polymerization of styrene. In such circumstances the characteristics of heterogeneous reactions are observed, although in the absence of the precipitant the reaction is normal.

Clear proof that the physical conditions govern the kinetic nature of the reaction is also provided by the copolymerization of maleic anhydride and styrene, in which the system is heterogeneous or homogeneous, depending only on the molar ratio of the monomers.

These and numerous other reactions have many features in common, and in recent years the basic reasons for such phenomena have been elucidated. Since acrylonitrile has received the most exhaustive study, it will be best to discuss this monomer in detail first and then review other systems with other monomers.

6-2. ACRYLONITRILE POLYMERIZATION

There are comparatively few simple solvents for polyacrylonitrile other than N,N-dimethyl formamide (DMF) and dimethyl sulfoxide; it is quite insoluble in acrylonitrile monomer and in most common organic solvents. As soon as polymerization commences in the bulk medium, precipitation of polymer in the form of a granular solid occurs without increase in the viscosity of the associated liquid. Unless the rate of polymerization is abnormally low, the precipitate remains dispersed, imparting a milky appearance to the reaction mixture. The commencement of reaction is easily observed on account of the opalescence and, especially in photochemical experiments, by the scattering of incident light by the polymer particles.

Purely thermal polymerization does not occur; direct photopolymerization is possible but very low rates are obtained. Great care is necessary in removing oxygen from the system, because this is a powerful inhibitor of acrylonitrile polymerization.

The progress of a typical reaction, in which benzoyl peroxide is employed as initiator, is shown in Fig. 6-1. This figure shows clearly the autocatalytic nature of the reaction, although a parallel reaction, with sufficient DMF to keep the polymer in solution, behaves in a kinetically normal manner (Fig. 6-2). Obviously, the acceleration in the first case is not due to the gradual elimination of a retarder; this conclusion is borne out by the use of residual monomer from a reaction that has been allowed to proceed to about 60% conversion, in which any retarder initially present would have been removed in the first stage.

For the reaction in DMF there is a square-root dependence of rate on initiator concentration. It is not very easy to make simple quantitative

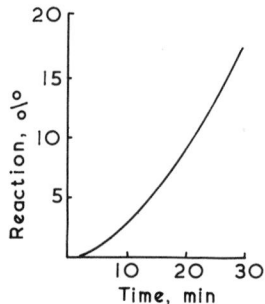

Fig. 6-1. Bulk polymerization of acrylonitrile at 60°C initiated by 2.7×10^{-2} mole-% benzoyl peroxide. [After Bamford and Jenkins (3).]

statements regarding the heterogeneous process because of the inconstancy of rate, but the initiator exponent is apparently approximately 0.9.

Anomalies also appear in the photochemical after-effect of the heterogeneous reaction. Normally, the after-effect in a homogeneous system is not dependent on the duration of the irradiation, provided this is not extremely short or long. With bulk acrylonitrile, however, the after-effect is greater the longer the period of irradiation. Moreover, successive irradiations of a given specimen give progressively longer after-effects for constant irradiation periods, unless there is a long intervening dark period between two consecutive irradiations. When the latter is the case, the next after-effect is similar to the first one observed with the given specimen. One can conclude from such observations that the precipitated polymer is endowed with an activity that decays only over a period of several hours at room temperature (3).

Unfortunately, it is not possible to study the apparent catalytic effect of the polymer directly by adding polyacrylonitrile to the reaction system, because polymer that has once been exposed to air inhibits polymerization, no doubt owing to the adsorption of oxygen. An attempt at overcoming this difficulty was made by Bamford and Jenkins (3), who prepared the poly-

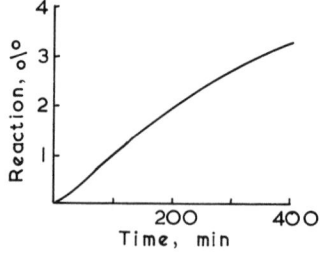

Fig. 6-2. Polymerization of acrylonitrile at 60°C in solution in DMF: $[M] = 2.88$ moles/liter^{-1}, benzoyl peroxide 2.7×10^{-2} mole-% based on the monomer. [After Bamford and Jenkins (3).]

mer in situ by photopolymerization at 25°C and subsequently raised the temperature to 60°C, which is normal for the thermally catalyzed reaction. This experiment gave a most unexpected result, as shown in Fig. 6-3. After a photochemical conversion of about 20% the mixture was allowed to stand in the dark for a while and then was transferred to the 60°C thermostat. As the temperature of the mixture approached 60°C, an extremely fast polymerization was observed, in which approximately 10% of the monomer was consumed within 2 min. Subsequently, the reaction rate fell and resumed its usual course with some autoacceleration. The very rapid phase was termed the "fast reaction."

It was found possible to isolate the fast reaction by employing a volatile initiator, such as di-t-butyl peroxide (4). At the end of the photopolymerization the initiator and monomer were removed by distillation (at low temperature) and replaced with monomer alone. No appreciable polymerization can then occur at 60°C except that arising from the influence of the photopolymer. In fact, the usual fast reaction is manifest on heating to 60°C, but the rate rapidly declines to a comparatively low value (Fig. 6-4).

Many aspects of the fast reaction have been examined. In summary one can say that it is unaffected by:

1. Allowing the photopolymer to remain in contact with monomer for long periods at low temperatures.

2. Heating the dry polymer to 60°C for 30 min.

3. Replacing the monomer after the photoreaction.

Nevertheless, admission of oxygen destroys it completely.

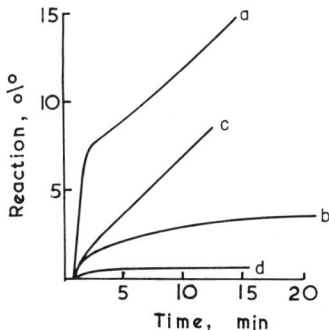

Fig. 6-3. The "fast reaction" in the polymerization of acrylonitrile at 60°C. Initiator, 2.7×10^{-2} mole-% benzoyl peroxide, except in (b). (a) after 45-min photopolymerization at 25°C to 18% conversion, (b) after photopolymerization to 18% conversion without initiator, (c) after photopolymerization to 18% conversion with initiator present but at the same rate of initiation as in (b), (d) as in (a) but monomer replaced with ethyl alcohol after photopolymerization. This experiment demonstrates that the fast reaction is not simply due to a volume change on heating of the photopolymer. [After Bamford and Jenkins (3).]

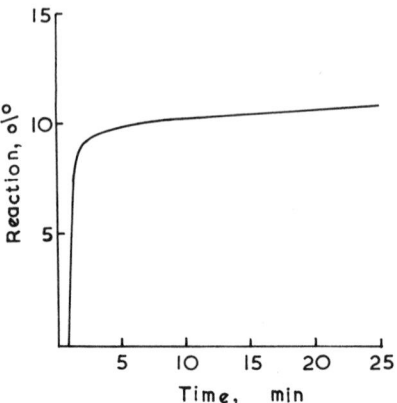

Fig. 6-4. The fast reaction in the polymerization of acrylonitrile at 60°C with di-*t*-butyl peroxide as photoinitiator. The initiator was removed by distillation before heating to 60°. [After Bamford and Jenkins (*4*).]

All these phenomena indicate that the agencies responsible for the fast reaction reside in the photopolymer and are consistent with the identification of the active species as free radicals, which must possess extraordinarily long lifetimes at temperatures below 60°C. It will be explained later that the radicals exist for these protracted periods because they are mechanically trapped in the precipitate, by which they are shielded from almost all reactions at low temperatures.

The existence of these trapped radicals has been established beyond doubt by electron spin resonance (ESR) studies and by chemical means (*5*). Thus, α,α-diphenyl-β-picryl hydrazyl (DPPH) has been found to undergo reaction with the radicals when heated in contact with the photopolymer under the conditions of the fast reaction, and it was shown that concentrations of trapped radicals as high as 10^{-4} mole liter^{-1} can be obtained. In a typical reaction (corresponding to Fig. 6-3) between 1 and 10% of the total radicals generated become trapped in the polymer, and it is evidently these which initiate the fast reaction.

The chemistry of DPPH is, in fact, more complex than was at one time supposed (*6,7*), but evidently the results obtained by using it in the present context are not misleading, because subsequent investigations of trapped radicals by ESR have confirmed that concentrations of 10^{-4} mole liter^{-1} are indeed obtained. By employing radical concentrations from ESR measurement (*8*) one can deduce that the mean value of the specific velocity coefficient for termination is only 200 mole^{-1} liter sec^{-1}, or about seven orders of magnitude lower than that for the homogeneous reaction in DMF. Clearly, the trapped radicals are far from free, even when heated to 60°C.

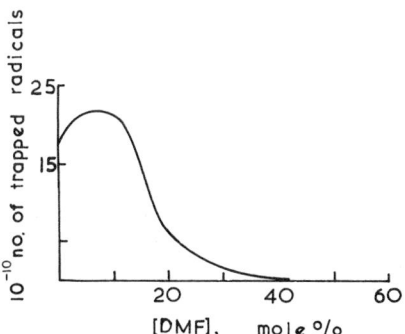

Fig. 6-5. Number of trapped polyacrylonitrile radicals as a function of DMF concentration after photopolymerization at 20°C to 20% conversion with di-*t*-butyl peroxide as initiator. [After Bamford et al. (9).]

ESR techniques have produced some interesting results concerning the effect of swelling agents (9), for example, DMF. As Fig. 6-5 shows, small amounts of DMF are conducive to an increase in the concentration of trapped radicals after 20% photopolymerization. This occurs up to about 8 mole-% of DMF, beyond which point the trapped-radical concentration decreases, becoming zero at about 50%; then the polymer formed is a very swollen, opaque gel.

A qualitatively similar state of affairs is found when methyl acrylate is copolymerized with acrylonitrile (9). The concentration of trapped radicals apparently increases with up to about 2% methyl acrylate and thereafter decreases.

It is interesting to consider the effect of the temperature of the photo-polymerization on the number of trapped radicals resulting; this is shown in Table 6-1, which demonstrates that a high concentration can be obtained only at temperatures below 60°C (9).

TABLE 6-1

Trapped-Radical Concentration as a Function of Temperature of Photopolymerization

Temp., °C	No. of trapped radicals, $\times 10^{-16}$
20	3.7
25	2.3
40	0.8
60	<0.1

Although these results show that permanent radical trapping cannot occur at 60°C, nevertheless the mean lifetimes of the radicals generated at this temperature may well be several orders of magnitude greater than in the homogeneous case, thereby vitiating the assumption of stationary-state conditions.

The fast reaction described above was observed on heating 25°C photo-polymer to 60°C in contact with monomer. Fast reactions are also observed if the photopolymer is heated to any other temperature above 25°C; Table 6-2 indicates the speed and extent of the process (5). One interesting feature is that, if the fast reaction is performed at 40°C, a further fast reaction occurs if the temperature is subsequently raised to 60°C and, moreover, it has been shown that virtually no diminution in trapped-radical concentration accompanies the 40°C fast reaction.

TABLE 6-2

Speed and Extent of Fast Reaction as a Function of Temperature

Temp. of final bath, °C	Half-life of fast reaction, min	Extent of fast reaction, mole liter^{-1}
40	40	0.38
50	12	0.95
55	4.5	1.01
60	2.3	1.46
70	1.5	1.91

There is an intimate connection between the rate of polymerization and the degree of polymerization of the product, which in a simple case enables details of the reaction to be established quantitatively. It is therefore of interest to examine the variation in $\bar{P}$ for polyacrylonitrile with conditions of preparation.

For constant initiator concentration one normally expects $\bar{P}$ to decrease with increasing temperature but, as Fig. 6-6 shows, for the heterogeneous polymerization of acrylonitrile there is a pronounced maximum at about 60°C.

Finally, there is an abnormal kinetic effect of transfer agents, such as n-butyl mercaptan, as shown in Fig. 6-7. The rate of polymerization not only decreases markedly as the concentration of mercaptan increases but the plots of conversion versus time become less curved and eventually linear. When the mercaptan concentration exceeds approximately 0.03 mole liter^{-1} the rate of polymerization becomes independent of mercaptan.

From these observations Bamford and Jenkins constructed a qualitative theory of the underlying processes, which is summarized in the next section.

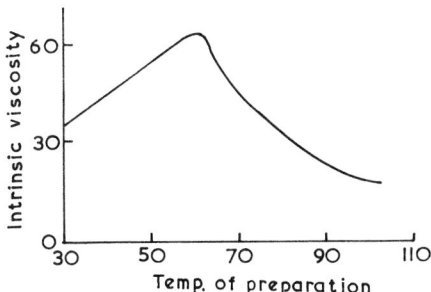

Fig. 6-6. Variation in intrinsic viscosities of acrylonitrile polymers as a function of temperature for the bulk reaction at 60°C with 2.7×10^{-2} mole-% benzoyl peroxide as initiator. Concentration units are base moles per liter. [After Bamford and Jenkins (3).]

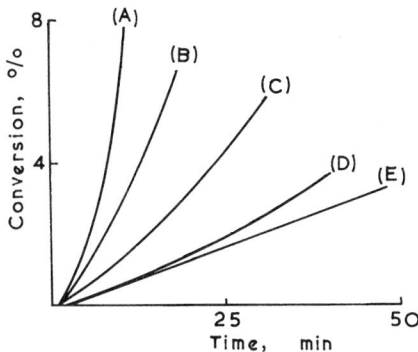

Fig. 6-7. Effect of n-butyl mercaptan on the bulk polymerization of acrylonitrile at 60°C with 1.6×10^{-2} mole-% azobisisobutyronitrile as initiator. Concentration of mercaptan in moles per liter. A, 0; B, 3.74×10^{-3}; C, 2.53×10^{-2}; D, 2.95×10^{-2}; E, 3.14×10^{-1}. [After Bamford and White (10).]

A. Occlusion Theory

When all the kinetic observations are considered together, it becomes clear that many, and in some cases perhaps all, of the polymer radicals precipitate from the liquid phase during growth and, in consideration of the behavior of polymer molecules in poor solvent environments, one supposes that such precipitated radicals will be tightly coiled. Coiling will in itself reduce the reactivity of the radicals since, if the radical end is shielded by the remainder of the molecule, any potential reactant may have to penetrate a diffusion barrier. This is not to say that the radical end will always be in an internal arrangement, but on a statistical basis it will be so accommodated for a fraction of its time. If the precipitated radical also undergoes coalescence with dead polymer particles, the average reactivity will be further reduced, and the relative kinetic importance of coiling and coalescence may vary according to conditions. Coiling would not be expected to be of great significance when the polymer is swollen, but in an unswollen state it may restrict reactivity very considerably. Nevertheless, it is believed that coalescence nearly always plays the major part.

In order to discuss the experimental results in more detail it is necessary to introduce the concept of "degree of occlusion" which, although lacking precise definition, is understood to indicate the size of the polymer barrier tending to obstruct the radical end from reaction.

B. Degree of Occlusion and Specific Velocity Coefficients

The term "coefficient" rather than "constant" is now employed, because it is implicit in this treatment that for given concentrations of reactants the rate of reaction is a function of the degree of occlusion.

In the light of what has been said above regarding coiling and coalescence one would expect all velocity coefficients for reactions of occluded radicals to be reduced in heterogeneous conditions, but it is immediately obvious that bimolecular radical termination will be most seriously affected, because this reaction depends on two radicals being able to bring their terminal carbon atoms into close proximity. If the radicals are occluded, this can happen only when both active ends are at the surface, which can only be for a small fraction of the time, if ever. Propagation and transfer reactions, on the other hand, are impeded only to the extent that monomer and transfer agent must diffuse into the precipitated particle in order to react with the radical.

Since the rate of reaction depends only on the ratio of the rates of propagation and termination steps, the net result of the occlusion will be an acceleration in the over-all rate of polymerization and an enhancement of the importance of transfer relative to bimolecular termination.

Although ordinary bimolecular radical termination may be enormously reduced by occlusion, other termination mechanisms are possible. Thus:

1. Two radicals that have not grown sufficiently to precipitate may react in solution.

2. A small radical may penetrate a particle containing an occluded radical. Although it may be difficult for such a radical to diffuse in, once there the probability of reaction will be high because of the concomitant difficulty of escaping.

3. The active end of the radical will (or may) occasionally appear at the surface and react with solution radicals. High temperature will, of course, favor such a process because of the tendency of coalesced particles to disperse under thermal agitation.

4. Chain transfer may take place internally, enabling a small radical to escape into the bulk solution, although egress of the small radical will be impeded if it undergoes growth on its way out.

The prolonged activity of the photopolymer shows that during reaction at 25°C extreme degrees of occlusion arise, preventing subsequent reactions even when the polymer is left in contact with the monomer for long periods. Even the formation of mobile radicals by transfer to monomer must be negligibly slow (3). The slight but definite increase in concentration of trapped radicals in the presence of a small quantity of swelling agent evidently demonstrates that the trapped radicals are able in those conditions to undergo some propagation within the polymer aggregate, which leads by a sort of self-plugging process to an even higher degree of occlusion than is normally the case, and this is substantiated by observations of the rate of photopolymerization at 25°C in the presence of a swelling agent, the rate passing through a maximum at approximately 8 mole-% of DMF. Greater quantities of DMF inevitably result in swelling of the polymer, a reduction in both coiling and coalescence and, hence, a reduction in all the peculiarly heterogeneous characteristics.

The main result of moderate degrees of occlusion, then, is a reduction principally in the velocity of the termination process, giving rise to an increase in the over-all rate of reaction. Extreme degrees of occlusion that cause complete trapping of radicals can reduce the velocity of propagation to a point where the polymerization is virtually prevented. In the chemical sense the intrinsic reactivity of the trapped radicals is unaltered; nevertheless, on account of physical restraints the apparent velocity coefficients become very small, even tending to zero.

C. Over-All Kinetic Effects of Occlusion

It follows that the behavior characteristic of heterogeneous polymerization systems is determined inter alia by both the number of polymer particles present and their total weight. The former will essentially determine the probability of any given radical's becoming occluded by coalescence, and the latter will determine the efficiency of the polymer barrier in the aggregate (that is, the degree of occlusion). Since both the number of particles present and their average size will increase during a reaction, the termination velocity coefficient will progressively fall, leading to the acceleration which is observed, and the progressive increase in photochemical after-effect with the duration of irradiation can be ascribed to the same cause.

In a situation in which all the velocity coefficients are changing with extent of reaction no simple kinetic relationships whatever can be expected to hold. The effect being particularly marked with the termination process, it is qualitatively in order to expect the initiator exponent to be greater than 1/2, particularly since extreme occlusion can be regarded as a first-order termination process.

It seems that the explanation of the dependence of molecular weight on temperature is that an increase in temperature, starting from 25°C, encourages swelling, or at least agitation, of the aggregates, which permits propagation to occur more readily without facilitating termination. However, when the temperature reaches 60°C or above, the occlusion is so diminished that bimolecular termination becomes increasingly important with progressive reduction in molecular weight. The result of these opposing influences is the observed maximum near 40°C.

The effect of transfer agent on rate can be explained in terms of the escape from polymer particles of the small mobile radicals formed by the act of transfer. There is also, of course, the reduction in molecular weight arising from transfer, which will reduce the degree of self-occlusion of individual radicals. When transfer is abundant, the reaction then loses its heterogeneous character, in agreement with the results in Fig. 6-7.

These arguments are supported by observations of the polymerization in the presence of ferric chloride, when under appropriate conditions the first-order (in radicals) termination process

$$R\cdot + FeCl_3 \rightarrow RCl + FeCl_2$$

completely dominates the bimolecular reaction (11). In such a case the relative rates of diffusion of monomer and ferric chloride into the polymer particles determine the balance between acceleration or retardation when the reaction becomes heterogeneous, as it does on an increase in monomer concentration beyond about 6 moles liter^{-1}. As Fig. 6-8 shows, in fact, the rate falls somewhat, and we deduce that propagation to monomer is rather more adversely affected than is termination by ferric chloride. When propagation competes with the bimolecular termination, on the other hand, the onset of heterogeneous conditions is made strikingly manifest by a very marked acceleration.

D. The Fast Reaction

This discussion assumes that trapped radicals have been prepared by photopolymerization at 25°C. If the mixture is gently heated to, say, 40°C, the propagation process is obviously enhanced, because reaction occurs, although ESR measurements show that no radicals are destroyed. There must, then, be propagation inside the aggregates, which must increase the degree of occlusion of the contained radical to a point where no further reaction is possible. As stated above, heating to 60°C destroys all the radicals, but those which have had an intermediate treatment at 40°C will undergo more reaction at 60°C than those which have not, because of the higher degree of occlusion.

Although we know that after 3 min at 60°C no trapped radicals remain, it is not immediately obvious whether the particles disintegrate instantaneously or whether reaction occurs at least partly within swollen aggregates. If the former were the case, the magnitude of the fast reaction could be

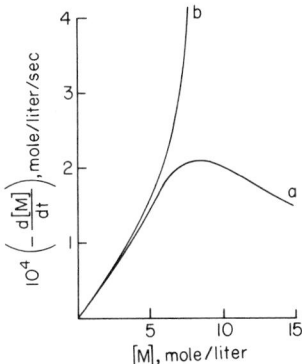

Fig. 6-8. Rate of polymerization of acrylonitrile in DMF at 60°C as a function of monomer concentration. (a) $[FeCl_36H_2O] = 6.8 \times 10^{-3}$ mole liter^{-1}, [azobisisobutyronitrile] = 6.20 $\times 10^{-2}$ mole liter^{-1} (b) $[FeCl_36H_2O] = 0$, [azobisisobutyronitrile] = 7.90 $\times 10^{-3}$ mole liter^{-1}. [After Bamford et al. (*11*).]

calculated by treating it as an ordinary after-effect according to the equation

$$\Delta M = \frac{k_p[M]}{k_t} \log \frac{\theta + 1}{2}$$

where θ is the ratio of the initial and final rates in the fast reaction. If the aggregates disperse instantaneously, k_p and k_t will have their values in homogeneous solution, equal to 2458 and 9.8×10^8 liters mole^{-1} sec^{-1}, respectively (*12*). On this basis one calculates $\Delta M = 6 \times 10^{-5}$ mole liter^{-1} approximately, which contrasts sharply with the observed value 1.4 moles-liter. One, if not both, of the velocity coefficients must be very different from its solution value, and the only reasonable explanation is that k_t is very low. The fast reaction can, therefore, be regarded as taking place largely within the polymer particles.

The trapped radicals have been used to bring about the initiation of other reactions by removing the residual monomer after photoreaction and replacing it with another (*13*). On heating to 60°C, then, unless rapid transfer takes place, a block copolymer is formed through continued growth of the trapped radicals utilizing the new monomer. Once a single such propagation step has occurred, new radicals X will continue to propagate with their own monomer M, which will exist at a mean concentration $[\overline{M}]$ at the site of reaction. Hence, the rate of reaction during the fast period is given by

$$\omega = k_p[X][\overline{M}]$$
$$\frac{d\omega}{dt} = k_p[\overline{M}]\frac{d[X]}{dt} + k_p[X]\frac{d[\overline{M}]}{dt}$$

382   A. D. JENKINS

From the latter equation we can describe, with certain reservations, a number of limiting cases of fast reaction behavior.

Case 1. If $d[X]/dt = d[\overline{M}]/dt = 0$, that is, if $[X]$ and $[\overline{M}]$ are constant, the rate will be constant, so that the conversion Δ will be linear in time, corresponding to (a) in Fig. 6-9.

Case 2. If the diffusion barrier does not remain constant during the period of reaction, autoocclusion will develop, and $d[\overline{M}]/dt$ will diminish as $[\overline{M}]$ tends to zero. This will give a curve of the form of (b) in Fig. 6-9. If the new polymer is able to encourage an enhancement of swelling, it is possible to visualize an increase in rate with time, as shown in Fig. 6-9, curve (c).

Case 3. If $[\overline{M}]$ remains constant, but some destruction of radicals takes place, there will be no single kinetic form, unless an assumption is made regarding the rate of radical termination, which may in these circumstances be first-order. This corresponds to a higher degree of swelling of the polymer than in cases 1 and 2, but it would give a relation similar to curve (b) in Fig. 6-9.

Case 4. If bimolecular radical termination occurs with constant $[\overline{M}]$, the progress of the fast reaction amounts to a simple after-effect with a constant rate coefficient for termination having a much lower value than in solution. One thus arrives at curve (d) of Fig. 6-9.

Case 5. In the more complicated case in which the period required to produce swelling is comparable to the length of the experiment the concentration of radicals will decrease slowly, and the concentration of monomer at the reaction may decrease steadily, or it may rise as swelling occurs. It is not easy to predict the kinetic behavior in such cases, although extreme examples would correspond to (e) and (d) in Fig. 6-9.

The results obtained with a variety of monomers are shown in Fig. 6-10, in which the relative radical concentration (initial concentration = 1.0) is indicated. With n-propyl acrylate and n-butyl acrylate a slow steady reaction occurs with no decrease in trapped radical concentration, suggesting

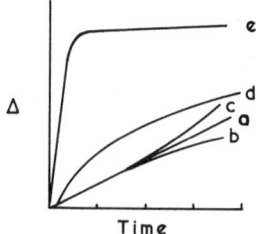

Fig. 6-9. Form of kinetic behavior of reactions initiated by trapped radicals. (a) case 1; (b) case 2 with autoocclusion; (c) case 3 with increasing swelling; (d) case 4; (e) case 5. [After Bamford and Jenkins (*13*).]

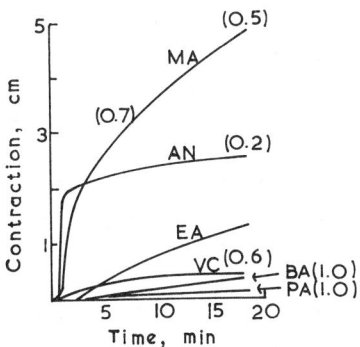

Fig. 6-10. Polymerization of monomers initiated by trapped polyacrylonitrile radicals. MA, methyl acrylate; EA, ethyl acrylate; PA, n-propyl acrylate; BA, n-butyl acrylate; AN, acrylonitrile; VC, vinylidene chloride, Numbers in brackets denote the concentration of the trapped radicals which have survived at the time indicated as a fraction of the number of initial polyacrylonitrile radicals. [After Bamford and Jenkins (*13*).]

case 1 behavior. With ethyl acrylate there is again no radical consumption, but the rate decreases, indicating case 2. The fast reaction with acrylonitrile at 40°C also, it will be recalled, falls into this category. With vinylidene chloride the radical concentration decreases, as does the rate, the latter following the bimolecular law. In view of the small decrease in radical concentration this presumably arises fortuitously as a result of a combination of effects; the reaction probably belongs to case 5 with self-occlusion.

The course of the reaction with acrylonitrile itself is accompanied by the destruction of most of the trapped radicals, and the form of the curve resembles (e) in Fig. 6-9. This reaction is then assigned to case 5.

The reaction with methyl acrylate is especially interesting, because it shows a very high degree of conversion with slow radical decay; in fact, almost complete conversion occurs after several hours. Evidently, this is another case 5 with a complicated interplay of radical and monomer concentrations. The final polymer in this case is insoluble in DMF, which is a good solvent for both polyacrylonitrile and polymethyl acrylate, and this suggests that the fast reaction has some of the character of "popcorn" polymerizations, which are discussed below.

6-3. OTHER BULK POLYMERIZATIONS

A. Vinyl Chloride

Before the acrylonitrile polymerization had been studied, Prat (*14*) reported an investigation of the polymerization of vinyl chloride, which showed the autocatalytic effect. This result was subsequently confirmed by several workers (15–17), and in particular Bengough and Norrish (18) showed that the precipitated polymer acts as a cocatalyst for polymerization, the increase in rate being proportional to the $\frac{2}{3}$ power of the weight of added polymer, a result which prompted the suggestion that the activity is a function of the surface area of the polymer particles. The suggestion was made that chain transfer to the polymer surface occurred, producing radicals that were immobilized and therefore less likely to participate in bimolecular termination. This idea was certainly not in conflict with the chain-transfer potential of the vinyl chloride system, because it was known that the degree of polymerization for bulk reaction is almost independent of the initiator concentration. However, the immobilization process would hardly give rise to radicals of very long life, since by the same token transfer from surface radical to monomer could destroy the immobilized radical. In any case the same mechanism cannot account for reactions of other monomers, e.g. acrylonitrile, which do not undergo rapid transfer reactions; neither will it explain the fast reaction.

Magat (19) offered a quantitative treatment of the reaction by regarding the acceleration as an extended pre-effect due to an abnormally low termination coefficient. This treatment regarded the individual specific velocity coefficients as constant, in contrast to the occlusion theory, but was able to fit the results fairly well, although an extension to vinylidene chloride was much less successful. A criticism on the grounds that the calculations predicted impossibly long radical lifetimes was answered by reference to the very extended after-effects in the radiation-induced polymerization of this monomer.

In the light of occlusion theory there are no special features of this reaction which cannot be explained when the degree of transfer occurring is taken into account, as has been shown by Mickley et al. (20). These workers showed that the rate of polymerization of vinyl chloride in bulk and in cyclohexane is given by the equation

$$w = K[M][C]^{1/2} + f([P])[C]^{1/2}$$

where [M], [P], and [C] are respectively the monomer, polymer, and initiator concentrations. The first term on the right of this equation represents the homogeneous reaction, taking place side by side with the heterogeneous process, represented by the second term. The most interesting point is that $f([P])$ is proportional to [P] at low conversions and to $[P]^{2/3}$ at high conversions, the latter observation being in agreement with the work of Bengough and Norrish. Mickley and co-workers were able to explain their observations in the following manner.

The homogeneous component arises from reaction of polymer radicals before they reach a critical size for coiling into primary polymer particles.

Such particles will be very small and will flocculate with others very rapidly, judging by the speed with which gross turbidity develops in the mixture. By application of Von Smoluchowski's treatment of particle flocculation it was shown that virtually every primary particle is incorporated into an aggregate almost as soon as it is formed. There are two further points to note: the aggregates will sediment extremely slowly, and the frequency of collision between aggregates of very different sizes is much higher than that between aggregates of similar size. Large particle clusters thus tend to scavenge the primary particles as they are produced.

With little sacrifice of rigor, then, the system may be regarded as a precipitation process in which the primary polymer particles, as they are formed, deposit immediately on the large aggregates present, which remain constant in number but increase in size. If radicals are trapped in the primary particles and thence transferred into the aggregates, one will expect to find a contribution to the polymerization which will be dependent in some way on the polymer concentration. While the aggregates remain small enough for species in solution to be quite accessible to the trapped radicals, the nature of the dependence will be to the first power; when the aggregates reach dimensions such that only the regions in the outer shell have effective access to the solution, a two-thirds power dependence—that is, a proportionality to the surface area—will be found.

B. Vinylidene Chloride

The photopolymerization of vinylidene chloride was studied in the temperature range 13 to 35°C by Burnett and Melville (21). Many of the results were consistent with normal homogeneous kinetics, there being no autoacceleration or unusual relationship to incident intensity. Radical lifetimes in the range 1 to 12 sec, depending on temperature, were observed and absolute rate constants were deduced from determinations of the rate of initiation by an inhibitor method. However, the activation energies for propagation and for termination were found to have the extraordinarily high values $E_p = 25$ kcal mole^{-1} and $E_t = 40$ kcal mole^{-1} with associated frequency factors $A_p = 10^{16}$ and $A_t = 10^{30}$ mole^{-1} liter sec^{-1}. This being so, it is obvious that at a temperature only slightly different from the range employed very unusual values for rate coefficients would be obtained. The frequency factors, of course, cannot be interpreted on any reasonable kinetic basis. Analysis of the data by Magat's method (19) was not very satisfactory and gave very high values for the activation energies of the component reactions.

Burnett and Melville advanced the possible explanation that the tendency of the polymer to become crystalline might result in radicals' becoming embedded in a crystalline region, requiring a high activation energy for further reaction. They also made the point, consistent with the occlusion approach, that the concentration of monomer would be much lower near the embedded radical than in the bulk phase.

The reaction initiated by benzoyl peroxide was examined by Bengough and Norrish (22), who found an autoacceleration very similar to those exhibited by acrylonitrile and vinyl chloride, and this apparent contrast between thermal and photo reactions is entirely in agreement with Bamford and Jenkins' observations of acrylonitrile (3), where little acceleration was found in the photopolymerization, which also showed a nearly square-root dependence on intensity. This apparently is because the tendency to accelerate is offset by the polymer's scattering of light, which progressively reduces the rate of initiation in the system.

Altogether, it seems valid to conclude that Burnett and Melville's results with vinylidene chloride are entirely consistent with occlusion phenomena, which lead to great sensitivity of rate coefficients to changes in temperature.

C. Vinyl Bromide

Blauer et al. (23) examined the polymerization of vinyl bromide in solution in 1,2-dibromethane. Although the mixture is not obviously heterogeneous, the rate of reaction showed a dependence on the first power of the initiator concentration and the second power of the monomer concentration. The first of these might be ascribed to retardation arising out of transfer, but no satisfactory kinetic explanation of the high monomer dependence could be found. Although there is no acceleration, it was concluded that some radical burial may be occurring because there is evidence that the reaction mixture is very close to phase separation. Light-scattering studies indicated that polymer association takes place in the solvent medium employed.

D. Chlorotrifluoroethylene

This monomer has received little detailed attention, but the general kinetic character is similar to that shown by the monomers discussed above. Thomas and O'Shaughnessey (24) showed that the reaction is apparently zero order in monomer up to 80% conversion, the autoacceleration tendency presumably being compensated by the depletion of monomer. Further, the initiator exponent is between 0.7 and 0.8. Experiments carried out in some diluents, which had no solvent power for the polymer, were qualitatively similar.

Lazár (25) has found that the diluent has an effect upon the kind of kinetics obtained. With benzoyl peroxide initiation, benzene and 1,1,2-trifluorochloroethane behave as inert diluents whereas 1,3,5-trimethylbenzene is an inhibitor, and with chlorinated hydrocarbons a maximal rate occurs at a certain ratio of diluent to monomer. No doubt occlusion phenomena are, at least in part, responsible for behavior of the latter kind.

E. Copolymerization of Styrene and Maleic Anhydride

In the foregoing it has been seen that a change from heterogeneous to homogeneous kinetics results from the addition of sufficient solvent or swelling agent to the reaction mixture. Likewise, we shall see below that the addition of a polymer precipitant to an otherwise homogeneous system can effect the reverse transition. In both cases the presence of a foreign substance constitutes an undesirable uncertainty because chemical participation, however unlikely, cannot be entirely ruled out. It is fortunate, therefore, that a system exists in which the homogeneous–heterogeneous transition can be observed merely by an adjustment of the ratio of the reactants, and this reaction is the copolymerization of maleic anhydride (A) with styrene (M). This occurs with bulk monomers or in diluents such as o-dichlorobenzene. If $[A]/[M] < 10^{-2}$, approximately, on a molar basis, the polymer remains in solution, but at higher ratios it precipitates in a somewhat swollen form. At the critical value of $[A]/[M]$ a discontinuity in the kinetic behavior is observed (26,27).

Figure 6-11 shows how the rate, measured as the rate of consumption of the anhydride, depends upon the initial anhydride concentration in the reaction in o-dichlorobenzene at 60°C. If the copolymerization follows the normal course, and if the A· + A propagation is omitted (since maleic anhydride does not readily homopolymerize) the order of reaction with respect to $[A]$ should change from unity to zero as $[A]$ increases. The early part of the curve, where the polymer remains soluble, corresponds to this expectation but, when $[A]$ exceeds the critical value, there is a sharp increase in rate, following which the order of reaction with respect to $[A]$ again

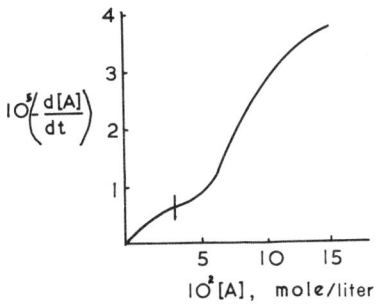

Fig. 6-11. Dependence of rate of reaction of maleic anhydride on its concentration in copolymerization with styrene at 60°C in o-dichlorobenzene. Initiator 2.5×10^{-2} w/v azobisisobutyronitrile. Transition from homogeneous to heterogeneous systems occurs at the vertical bar. [After Bamford and Barb (27).]

diminishes. This is readily attributed to a reduction in the effective k_t values, occurring when the polymer fails to remain dissolved in the reaction medium.

It was also found that in the heterogeneous region the reaction exhibits autoacceleration. This was shown by experiments in which slightly differing initial values of [A] were employed in order to assure that the same mean value obtained over the varying reaction periods. This is illustrated in Table 6-3. Similar experiments were carried out with identical reagents but at [A] values such that the polymer remained in solution; no acceleration was then observed.

TABLE 6-3

Dependence of Rate of Copolymerization of Maleic Anhydride and Styrene on Extent of Reaction[a]

Reaction time, min	Initial concn. 10^2[A] mole liter^{-1}	Mean concn. 10^2[A], mole liter^{-1}	Convsn., %	A in polymer, %	Mean rate $-10^5 (d[A]/dt)$, mole liter^{-1} sec^{-1}
Polymer precipitates during reaction; catalyst, 0.014% azobisisobutyronitrile					
7	29.1	28.3	0.4	36.5	3.62
10	29.8	28.4	0.7	37.1	4.37
15	30.9	28.5	1.2	37.0	5.15
20	32.0	28.2	2.0	36.8	6.40
Polymer remains in solution; catalyst, 0.025% azobisisobutyronitrile					
8	9.3	8.92	0.35	22.1	1.53
15	9.65	8.95	0.6	22.9	1.55
30	10.15	8.88	1.1	22.7	1.44

[a] All experiments in undiluted styrene at 60°C.'

A large variation in initiator concentration was used, the reaction times being so chosen as to give the same final conversion in each case. In the homogeneous region the initiator exponent is 0.5, but it rises in the heterogeneous range to 0.67.

An interesting contrast is the lack of effect which the change to precipitating conditions has on the composition of the copolymer that is formed. This is seen in Fig. 6-12, which shows that no observable discontinuity in composition follows the change in reaction conditions. In this figure n, the mole ratio of M to A in the polymer, is shown as a function of the anhydride concentration. Assuming, to a good approximation, a reactivity ratio of zero for maleic anhydride radicals, standard copolymerization theory predicts the following relationship, where r_m is the reactivity ratio for styryl

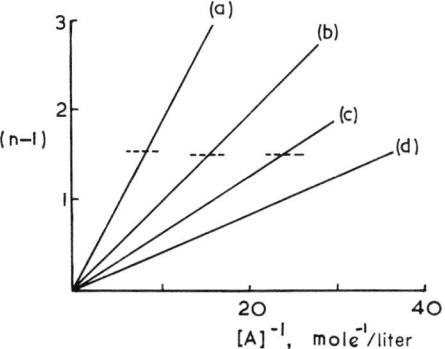

Fig. 6-12. Dependence of copolymer composition on monomer concentrations for the copolymerization of maleic anhydride and styrene at 60°C. Solvent: (a) bulk styrene; (b) 50% styrene, 50% o-dichlorobenzene, (c) 25% styrene, 75% o-dichlorobenzene, (d) 50% styrene, 50% decane. The horizontal bars indicate approximately the points at which the systems become heterogeneous with increasing [A]. [After Bamford and Barb (27).]

radicals:

$$n - 1 = r_m[\text{M}]/[\text{A}]$$

The plots of $(n - 1)$ versus $[\text{A}]^{-1}$ are linear throughout the range for reactions in both the presence and the absence of o-dichlorobenzene, although the value of r_m differs in the two cases.

The explanation of these phenomena is readily available in terms of occlusion. Evidently, since the polymer is somewhat swollen, the degree of occlusion is only moderate. The termination coefficients will be reduced, leading to acceleration, but the accessibility of monomer will be only slightly impaired. Since, in any event, the composition is dependent only upon the relative rates of the various propagation processes, a change in composition will not result if there is no differential in the availability of the two monomers within the polymer particles, that is to say, if the ratio of the monomer concentrations in the precipitated phase is similar to that in solution.

6-4. POLYMERIZATION IN THE PRESENCE OF PRECIPITANTS

A. Styrene

If a diluent that causes precipitation of the polymer is added to a polymerization system, increased rates and molecular weights are frequently found to result. Norrish and Smith (28) observed this behavior with methyl methacrylate, as did White and Haward (29) with methyl vinyl ketone, and Haward (30) with methyl isopropenyl ketone. The best-documented case is the polymerization of styrene in methanol.

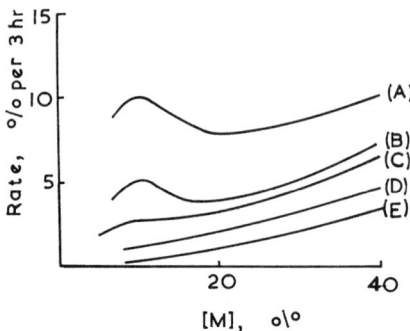

Fig. 6-13. Dependence of the rate of polymerization of styrene at 60°C on monomer concentration in methanol solution. Concentrations of benzoyl peroxide in per cent are: A, 0.32; B, 0.16; C, 0.10; D, 0.08; E, 0.04. [After Abere et al. (*1*).]

Abere et al. (*1*), using benzoyl peroxide as initiator, obtained the results shown in Fig. 6-13. According to their observations, as the initial monomer concentration is reduced by the addition of methanol, the rate at first declines, until 20% monomer is reached, when the rate increases as the monomer concentration diminishes to 10%. During the initial decrease in rate the polymer remains in solution, but at the point where the rise in rate occurs the polymer begins to separate as a gelatinous precipitate, and the enhancement of rate is no doubt due to the accompanying reduction in the

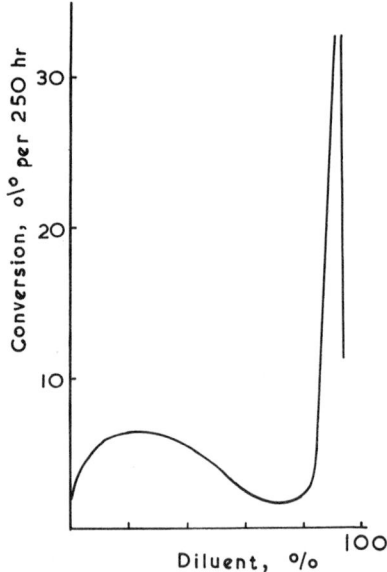

Fig. 6-14. Dependence of rate on monomer concentration for the gamma-ray-initiated polymerization of styrene in methanol at 15°C approximately. [After Chapiro (*2*).]

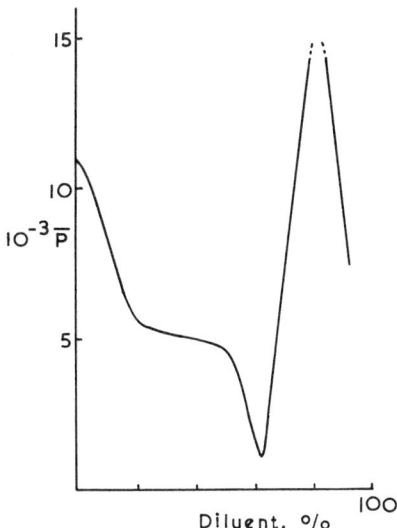

Fig. 6-15. Dependence of $\bar{P}$ on monomer concentration for the gamma-ray-initiated polymerization of styrene in methanol at 15°C approximately. [After Chapiro (2).]

velocity coefficient for termination. This is supported by the concomitant increase in the degree of polymerization.

Chapiro's experiments (2) in initiation by gamma radiation are complicated by the different rates of initiation that will arise from the differential disruptive effects of the radiation on styrene and methanol. Typical results are shown in Figs. 6-14 and 6-15.

In the first range, up to 30% methanol concentration, the rate increases rapidly with dilution, owing to the increased rate of initiation, which arises from the higher efficiency of radical production from methanol than from styrene, under the influence of gamma rays. At the same time the degree of polymerization diminishes, owing to enhanced initiation.

Between 20 and 70% methanol the rate passes first through a maximum and then decreases, while the degree of polymerization continues to decrease throughout. This behavior suggests a decrease in k_p or an increase in k_t superimposed upon the increasing rate of initiation. There is no evident reason for the former, but the latter is supported by the fact that in this concentration range the polymer separates as a transparent gel, in which the local concentration of growing chains will be much higher than if the polymer remained dispersed in solution.

Beyond 70% precipitant both rate and $\bar{P}$ increase very sharply with dilution, and in this region a granular precipitate is formed, so that all aspects of this phase of reaction suggests that typical occlusion phenomena

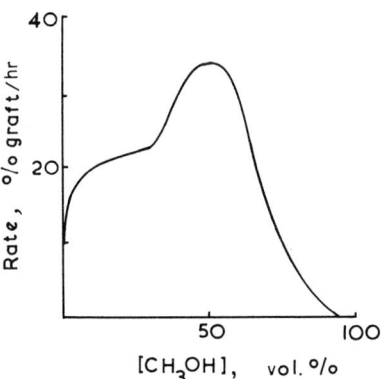

Fig. 6-16. Rate of grafting of styrene on polyethylene as a function of monomer concentration in methanol solution. [After Odian et al. (*31*).]

are operative, a reduction in the rate of termination being the dominant feature. In support of this, individual runs in this region show autoacceleration, and the intensity exponent increases above 0.5; further, there is a prolonged after-effect.

A related phenomenon is found when styrene is radiochemically grafted onto polyethylene in the presence of methanol (*31*). As Fig. 6-16 shows, there is an acceleration, which cannot entirely be attributed to the participation of methanol in the initiation step. Generally, this figure shows a resemblance to Chapiro's data in Fig. 6-14, but the quantitative differences are presumably due to the fact that the adsorbed concentration of methanol and styrene on the polyethylene film are different from those in the bulk solution. Undoubtedly, the methanol is responsible for a reduction in the rate of termination of the polystyrene graft by inducing coiling and precipitation.

B. Methyl Methacrylate

In the bulk polymerization of methyl methacrylate at high conversions the kinetics resemble those found with heterogeneous reactions at low conversions, although precipitation does not actually take place (*32*). The polymer must be in a state of incipient precipitation, and the increasing coiling and immobilization of the radicals reduces the probability of termination to such a point that it does not occur.

In the presence of sufficient cyclohexane the system becomes heterogeneous; autoacceleration occurs and the intensity exponent exceeds 0.5. The calculated apparent velocity coefficients of both propagation and termination decrease; the results were held to indicate that the process depends upon the occlusion of radicals by flocculated polymer and upon the form of the adsorption isotherm for monomer upon the particles.

6-5. POLYMERIZATION IN AQUEOUS SOLUTION

We are here concerned with the special case, technologically important, in which the monomer is dissolved in water, a medium from which the polymer precipitates. The reaction of acrylonitrile has been studied in considerable detail, especially by Dainton and his colleagues (*33–36*), as will appear from the account below.

A. Acrylonitrile

The early papers on the polymerization of acrylonitrile in aqueous solution reported conflicting results concerning a number of basic features. The monomer exponent in the rate equation was found in some cases to be 1, in other 2, and in yet others something intermediate. The intensity exponent for radiation-induced reactions was similarly found to vary from 0.2 to 0.9. Even when some of the less well substantiated data were discounted, there still remained a serious measure of disagreement between the results of various teams.

Since the studies of heterogeneous bulk polymerizations had been published previously, it was also of interest to analyze the kinetics of the aqueous system, to determine to what extent radical occlusion or trapping played a part and further to establish, if possible, the magnitudes of the velocity coefficients for propagation and termination in the aqueous medium.

Initiation was effected by two different means: by the Fenton reaction,

$$Fe^{2+} + H_2O_2 \rightarrow Fe^{3+} + OH^- + \cdot OH$$

at 25°C with variation of $[Fe^{2+}]$ and $[H_2O_2]$ over wide ranges, and photochemically with Fe^{2+}, Fe^{3+}, or I^- at 15 to 50°C.

A specially designed dilatometer was used in the work with Fenton's reagent in order that the reaction might be followed continuously in deaerated conditions having the reagents completely mixed without mechanical stirring, since this proved to have an important influence on the course of polymerization.

The plots of contraction versus time showed a brief period of acceleration followed by a prolonged period of constant rate, which persisted for as much as 5% conversion, provided care was taken to remove (by sequestration with fluoride) the ferric ions produced in the initiation step which give rise to a linear termination process parallel to that occurring in dimethyl formamide. The linear period was followed by a deceleration, which was never as rapid as would have been expected from the known decline in the

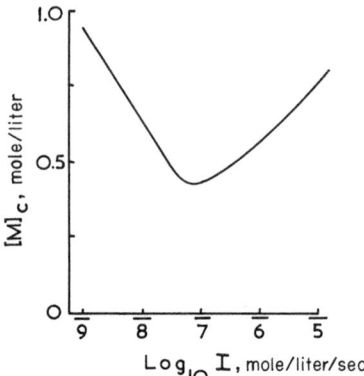

Fig. 6-17. Critical monomer concentration in the aqueous-solution polymerization of acrylonitrile as a function of rate of initiation. [after Dainton et al. *(33).*]

rate of initiation due to consumption of the reactants. Moreover, mechanical agitation resulted in a very rapid reduction of the rate to zero.

When Fenton's reagent is used, the reaction

$$R\cdot + Fe^{3+} \rightarrow Fe^{2+} + polymer$$

would be expected to become a progressively greater complicating factor as the ferric ion is accumulated through initiation, even to such a point that it might constitute the principal termination process. This was indeed found to be the case. Increasing the concentration of ferrous ion increased the rate during the steady period but also increased the subsequent rate of deceleration. If the ferric ion is removed by complexing with fluoride the effect disappears.

A striking result obtained with the photoinitiated reaction is that the after-effect corresponds to a slow bimolecular decay of chain centers with a mean lifetime of 150 to 800 sec, depending on the temperature. This lifetime is constant and (not as in the bulk reaction) independent of the duration of the illumination, provided the latter is long enough to enter the linear period. This phenomenon was attributed by Dainton and colleagues *(33)* to reaction propagated by chain centers present in minute suspended polymer particles, the concentration of which remains constant once the steady state has been reached.

The essential clue to the nature of the processes involved in the polymerization and responsible for the confused results reported in the literature came to light when the rate of reaction was measured as a function of the monomer concentration and the rate of initiation over a wide range of values of these parameters. Two striking observations were made. First, at low monomer concentrations the steady rate was found to be proportional to $[M]^2$, whereas at high monomer concentrations the first-order law was obeyed. Second, this transition from second-order to first-order behavior was seen to take place over a relatively narrow concentration range, the mean of which, $[M]_c$, is strongly dependent on the rate of initiation I. Figure 6-17 shows the form of this relationship. In the two regions different dependencies on initiator concentration also obtained. In the first-order range the rate was proportional to $([Fe^{2+}][H_2O_2])^{0.5}$, but in the second-order range the exponent was not equal to 0.5 but varied from 0.9 at low I to 0.2 at high I. Without advancing any precise explanation of these facts it was at once apparent that the results in the literature failed to agree because different groups of workers had used different concentration conditions.

Finally, it should be recorded that in photoinitiated reactions use of the rotating sector indicated a long-lived species with a mean life of about 250 sec, similar to the value obtained from the after-effect measurements.

It was realized that many of these observations indicated that two concurrent processes are operative; in one of them rapid propagation ensues through the agency of species that undergo ready termination either bimolecularly or by reaction with Fe^{3+}, whereas in the other chain carriers have a reduced rate of propagation and a very low rate of bimolecular termination. Clearly, the latter are responsible for the extended after-effects, and the influence of mechanical agitation suggests that the centers are located in insoluble, suspended, minute polymer particles.

Since the after-effect is independent of the duration of the period of illumination, it was thought that, once the steady rate period has been reached, the concentration of long-lived chain carriers remains constant. Thomas et al. (37) had previously observed that in the aqueous polymerization of acrylonitrile a constant number of polymer particles is formed before 10 % of the redox initiator has reacted. Electron microscope examination showed the particles to be uniform, initially about 50 A in diameter, and only coagulating when their volumes have increased 10^4 or 10^5 times. As a result of all these observations Dainton and colleagues suggested the following reaction mechanism (33).

The primary radicals will be captured by monomer molecules in aqueous solution, yielding small radicals that will initially grow in solution although tightly coiled. Both these radicals and the polymer molecules to which they give rise will be liable to coalesce with other small particles, until they reach a critical size of approximately 50-A diameter, when they will become stabilized by surface change. Radicals smaller and larger than this size are herein denoted by S· and P· respectively; any large polymer particle, by P. In the early stages the concentration of S· will increase rapidly and reach a stationary value; most of the polymer particles formed during this time will be subcritical and will coalesce together to form P-type particles at a rate that presumably will be greater the higher the degree of polymerization of the

S· before it is terminated. Since $\bar{P}$ is proportional to [M], this argument leads to the conclusion that the initial rate of formation of P is proportional to [M]·at low concentrations.

With progressing reaction the increasing number of P particles will result in an increase in the number of subcritical particles that coalesce with P rather than with each other (see the argument on p. 384). When self-coalescence of subcritical particles becomes negligible [P] becomes constant, and some of the particles are no doubt actually the radicals P· responsible for the photochemical after-effect. Therefore [P·] is presumed constant in the steady state and capable of only slow bimolecular decay. Since it is postulated that the large particles can capture small polymer particles, presumably they can also accrete small radicals S·, leading to the two reactions

$$S\cdot + P \rightarrow P\cdot$$

$$S\cdot + P\cdot \rightarrow P$$

which are, of course, the characteristic reactions involved in emulsion polymerization. In this system, however, they appear to play only a minor role. Together with a reaction of equilibrium adsorption of monomer on polymer particles, this mechanism was shown to lead to a kinetic scheme consistent with the observations, but it is important to note that the form assumed for the adsorption isotherms is critical. Well below saturation $[M]_{ads}$ is assumed to be proportional to [M] but at saturation independent thereof.

If the steady rate ω is taken to be sum of the two terms corresponding to propagation from S· and P· radicals, respectively,

$$\omega_s + \omega_p = k_p[M][S\cdot] + k_p'[M]_{ads}[P\cdot]$$

then the discussion above leads to the conclusion that ω_p will be proportional to $[M]^2$ at low monomer concentrations and independent of [M] at the higher concentrations, the changeover occurring at a value of [M] to be identified with $[M]_c$ and dependent upon I. The quantity ω_s will always be proportional to [M].

It is not easy to predict the dependence of $[M]_c$ on I, although at low I the number of particles is smaller and their average size larger, so that the limiting monomer concentrations for adsorption saturation and for particle number limitation may both be larger.

B. Vinyl Acetate

In contrast to the polymerization of acrylonitrile, vinyl acetate monomer and polymer are compatible, and so the locus of reaction is the swollen polymer particle. Napper and Parts (38) investigated this reaction and found the expected resemblance to emulsion systems. In the present case there should be little or no obstacle to propagation, monomer being readily available to the growing radicals, and it was found that k_p has a value similar to that in complete solution. The rate constant for termination, however, was by the same comparison reduced by a factor of 25.

C. Methyl Methacrylate

Atkinson and Cotton (*39*) studied the photopolymerization of methyl methacrylate in aqueous solution, and they attempted to analyze the after-effect to determine the individual rate constants. No simple treatment was possible, however, and they concluded that radicals of at least two types, judged by reactivity, are present. By assuming that ordinary and occluded radicals had values of k_t differing by a factor of 5 they were able to fit the after-effect curve, but it is much more likely that there is a continuous variation in k_t over at least that range. The k_p values were not reliably determined, but indications were that they were a little lower than in bulk.

D. Acrylamide

Polyacrylamide is soluble in water, so the aqueous solution reaction of this monomer is not expected to fall kinetically into the class of heterogeneous polymerization. Nevertheless, the kinetics of the process have a marked similarity to those of the others included in this section, although apparently for a different reason—which merits brief discussion.

Dainton and Tordoff (*40*) believe that the after-effect demonstrates that radicals are in some way "buried," under which conditions they have a lifetime of several hours. They consider and reject the hypothesis that this is due to self-burial by coiling, on the grounds that the experimental lifetimes are much longer than those which could reasonably be expected on this basis. Their hypothesis is that slow imidization occurs, especially at low pH values, so that for long periods the radical has the glutarimide structure (I) rather than the acetamide structure (II). These would not *per se*

differ greatly in reactivity, but (I) would exist in equilibrium with the tautomer (III), which might well resemble in stability the well-known succinimidyl radical.

According to this view the specific velocity constant for burial is that for the unimolecular tautomerization (I) → (III), and re-emergence will have the specific velocity constant for the reverse process. The detailed kinetics observed were shown to be consistent with the behavior expected from tautomerization. In particular, it is interesting to note that no after-effect is observed in alkaline solution, in agreement with the observation that tautomerism of the type proposed does not occur at high pH.

E. Methacrylamide

Polymethacrylamide has a limited solubility in water, and the reaction of this monomer is therefore expected to show a character intermediate between that of acrylonitrile and that of acrylamide. In practice this character is indeed encountered (41); thus, the photoreaction shows a negligible after-effect if illumination ceases before any precipitation occurs but, if polymer begins to separate, after-effects due to reduced termination coefficients arising from occlusion are observed.

6-6. POPCORN POLYMERIZATION

Although little detailed reproducible data on the kinetics of popcorn polymerization processes have been reported, the reactions almost certainly involve occlusion phenomena and present several interesting features, which will be dealt with very briefly in this chapter.

Popcorn polymers are tough, translucent materials, which arise as heterogeneous growths in liquid monomer or in the associated vapor phase. They are very light and therefore occupy a much larger volume than the liquid monomers from which they are derived. This expansion sometimes is responsible for the distortion and even fracture of the containing vessels, even when the latter are of steel. The popcorns are insoluble, have limited swelling properties, and are clearly cross-linked. They usually occur in the case of divinyl monomers, particularly butadiene, but some other cases are known.

When popcorn polymerization occurs, small nodules appear, known as "seeds," which apparently arise only when traces of oxygen are present in the system. Seed formation can be accelerated by addition of a free-radical generator (42) or irradiation with ultraviolet light (43). Moreover, a strange assortment of materials have been reported to catalyze seed formation, among them moist rusty iron (42,44,45), tin, nickel, aluminum, zinc, magnesium, barium, silver, and gold (45).

The induction periods normally observed can be reduced, but not eliminated, by adding to the monomer a seed of preformed popcorn. In many cases it seems that oxygen is necessary (46,47) and that it functions through the formation of hydroperoxides in the position α to a double bond. However, opinion is not unanimous on this point (48), and it has been shown that seeds of styrene–divinylbenzene popcorn do not lose their activity even when heated for 20 hr at 260°C (49). A recent infrared examination (50) of popcorn butadiene polymer has been found consistent with the following reaction scheme, which may apply to the peroxide-induced cases:

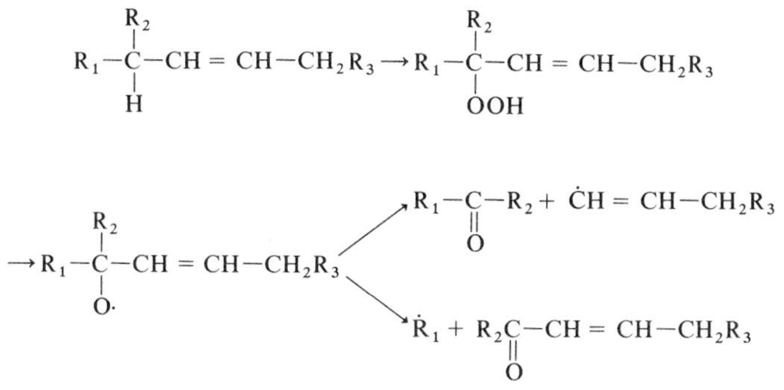

$$R_1-\underset{\underset{H}{|}}{\overset{\overset{R_2}{|}}{C}}-CH = CH-CH_2R_3 \rightarrow R_1-\underset{\underset{OOH}{|}}{\overset{\overset{R_2}{|}}{C}}-CH = CH-CH_2R_3$$

$$\rightarrow R_1-\underset{\underset{O\cdot}{|}}{\overset{\overset{R_2}{|}}{C}}-CH = CH-CH_2R_3 \begin{cases} \nearrow R_1-\underset{\underset{O}{||}}{C}-R_2 + \dot{C}H = CH-CH_2R_3 \\ \\ \searrow \dot{R}_1 + R_2\underset{\underset{O}{||}}{C}-CH = CH-CH_2R_3 \end{cases}$$

In summary, the kinetic evidence is that the growth of popcorns is a particular type of heterogeneous free-radical reaction, in which very little bimolecular termination can occur, because of the low mobility of the radicals. This is, of course, the case with other insoluble polymers, and with popcorns there is also cross-linking to restrict molecular motion.

Little is known in detail about the structure of popcorn polymers. With methyl methacrylate there is evidence that the cross-link density is as low as 1 in 10^3 or 10^4 units (51). Only limited swelling occurs in the presence of solvents for the linear polymer, but the structures are highly porous and propagation within the popcorn from the vapor phase may occur.

Infrared studies (50) with butadiene popcorns have shown that they contain a high proportion of $RCH=CH_2-$ groups, indicating that much 1,2 addition has taken place. Moreover, a significant concentration of methyl groups is present, which suggests that hydrogen atom transfer is common. Information was also obtained regarding the ketone groups, which are thought to be formed in the position α to double bonds, as in the scheme above. These conjugated bonds may be responsible for the yellow-orange color seen in some cases.

Chloroprene polymerization has recently been examined in some detail by Banbrook et al. (52). The popcorns seem to arise from the heterogeneous polymerization of chloroprene vapor absorbed on the walls of the vessel. The effective concentration of monomer is evidently proportional to the pressure of gaseous monomer, and reaction continues in the dark after irradiation.

6-7. VAPOR-PHASE POLYMERIZATION

Vapor-phase polymerizations fall within the scope of this chapter because growth initiated in vapor-phase monomer leads to the separation of polymer radicals and molecules as a mist which, incidentally, vitiates attempts to study the reactions photochemically to any extended degree of conversion. Moreover, the monomer becomes absorbed on the polymer, so that no real indication of the true rate of reaction is obtained by measurements of decrease in pressure (53,54).

In general, these reactions show a dependence on the square root of the incident-light intensity (55,56) and are retarded or inhibited by oxygen. Often a negative activation energy is found for the photoreaction, indicating that adsorption of monomer constitutes a rate-determining step in the reaction. The magnitude of this energy barrier, about -9 kcal/mole, is in line with sorption processes generally. In the case of vinyl acetate a remarkable effect of added inert gas was found, which is evidently associated with the initiation step (56).

The mechanism must involve growth of radicals in the vapor state initially and in the condensed state with absorbed monomer subsequently. The termination reaction will be highly restricted and, where transfer is facile (as with methyl acrylate), branching or cross-linking results.

REFERENCES

1. J. Abere, G. Goldfinger, H. Naidus, and H. F. Mark, *J. Phys. Chem.*, **49**, 211 (1945).
2. A. Chapiro, *J. Chim. Phys.*, **47**, 747, 764 (1950).
3. C. H. Bamford and A. D. Jenkins, *Proc. Roy. Soc. (London)*, **A216**, 515 (1953).
4. C. H. Bamford and A. D. Jenkins, *J. Polymer Sci.*, **20**, 405 (1956).
5. C. H. Bamford and A. D. Jenkins, *Proc. Roy. Soc. (London)*, **A228**, 220 (1955).
6. G. S. Hammond, J. N. Sen, and C. E. Boozer, *J. Am. Chem. Soc.*, **77**, 3244 (1955).
7. J. C. Bevington, *J. Chem. Soc.*, **1956**, 1127.
8. C. H. Bamford, D. J. E. Ingram, A. D. Jenkins, and M. C. R. Symons, *Nature*, **175**, 894 (1955).
9. C. H. Bamford, A. D. Jenkins, M. C. R. Symons, and M. G. Townsend, *J. Polymer Sci.*, **34**, 181 (1959).
10. C. H. Bamford and E. F. T. White, unpublished results.
11. C. H. Bamford, A. D. Jenkins, and R. Johnston, *Proc. Roy. Soc. (London)*, **A239**, 214 (1957).
12. C. H. Bamford, A. D. Jenkins, and R. Johnston, *Trans. Faraday Soc.*, **55**, 418 (1959).
13. C. H. Bamford and A. D. Jenkins, *J. Chim. Phys.*, **56**, 798 (1959).
14. J. Prat, *Compt. Rend., J. Inst. Plast.*, **1949**, 58.
15. W. I. Bengough and R. G. W. Norrish, *Nature*, **163**, 325 (1949).
16. E. Jenckel, H. Eckmans, and B. Rumbach, *Makromolekul. Chem.*, **4**, 15 (1949).
17. J. W. Breitenbach and A. Schindler, *Monatsh*, **80**, 429 (1949).
18. W. I. Bengough and R. G. W. Norrish, *Proc. Roy. Soc. (London)*, **A200**, 301 (1950).
19. M. Magat, *J. Polymer Sci.*, **16**, 491 (1955).
20. H. S. Mickley, A. S. Michaels, and A. L. Moore, *J. Polymer Sci.*, **60**, 121 (1962).
21. J. D. Burnett and H. W. Melville, *Trans. Faraday Soc.*, **46**, 976 (1950).

22. W. I. Bengough and R. G. W. Norrish, *Proc. Roy. Soc. (London)*, **A218**, 149 (1953).
23. G. Blauer, M. Shenblat, and A. Katchalsky, *J. Polymer Sci.*, **38**, 189 (1959).
24. W. M. Thomas and M. T. O'Shaughnessy, *J. Polymer Sci.*, **11**, 455 (1953).
25. M. Lazár, *J. Polymer Sci.*, **29**, 573 (1958).
26. C. H. Bamford, W. G. Barb, and A. D. Jenkins, *Nature*, **169**, 1044 (1952).
27. C. H. Bamford and W. G. Barb, *Discussions Faraday Soc.*, **14**, 208 (1953).
28. R. G. W. Norrish and R. R. Smith, *Nature*, **150**, 336 (1942).
29. T. White and R. N. Haward, *J. Chem. Soc.*, **1953**, 25.
30. R. N. Haward, *J. Polymer Sci.*, **3**, 10 (1948).
31. G. G. Odian, A. Rossi, and E. N. Trachtenberg, *J. Polymer Sci.*, **42**, 575 (1960).
32. P. Hayden and H. W. Melville, *J. Polymer Sci.*, **43**, 201, 215 (1960).
33. F. S. Dainton and (in part) P. H. Seaman, D. G. L. James, and R. S. Eaton, *J. Polymer Sci.*, **34**, 209 (1959).
34. F. S. Dainton and P. H. Seaman, *J. Polymer Sci.*, **39**, 279 (1959).
35. F. S. Dainton and D. G. L. James, *J. Polymer Sci.*, **39**, 299 (1959).
36. F. S. Dainton and R. S. Eaton, *J. Polymer Sci.*, **39**, 313 (1959).
37. W. M. Thomas, E. H. Gleason, and G. Mino, *J. Polymer Sci.*, **24**, 43 (1957).
38. D. H. Napper and A. G. Parts, *J. Polymer Sci.*, **61**, 113 (1962).
39. B. Atkinson and G. R. Cotten, *Trans. Faraday Soc.*, **54**, 877 (1958).
40. F. S. Dainton and M. Tordoff, *Trans. Faraday Soc.*, **53**, 499, 666 (1957).
41. F. S. Dainton and W. D. Sisley, *Trans. Faraday Soc.*, **59**, 1369 (1963).
42. J. C. Devins and C. A. Winkler, *Can. J. Res.*, **B26**, 356 (1948).
43. W. H. Carothers, *J. Am. Chem. Soc.*, **53**, 4203 (1931).
44. L. M. Welch, M. W. Swaney, A. H. Gleason, R. K. Beckwith, and R. F. Howe, *Ind. Eng. Chem.*, **39**, 826 (1947).
45. K. B. Piotrowsky, *Zh. Prikl. Khim.*, **22**, 518 (1949).
46. M. S. Kharasch, W. Nudenberg, E. V. Jensen, P. E. Fischer, and D. L. Mayfield, *Ind. Eng. Chem.*, **39**, 830 (1947).
47. W. Graham and C. A. Winkler, *Can. J. Res.*, **B26**, 564 (1948).
48. G. H. Miller, R. L. Alumbaugh, and R. J. Brotherton, *J. Polymer Sci.*, **9**, 453 (1952).
49. J. W. Breitenbach, H. Preussler, and H. Karlinger, *Monatsh.*, **80**, 150 (1948).
50. G. H. Miller, V. R. Lanson, and G. O. Pritchard, *J. Polymer Sci.*, **61**, 475 (1962).
51. J. R. Panchak, T. T. Kryza, and T. G. Fox, A.C.S. meeting, Sept. 1952.
52. A. K. Banbrook, R. S. Lehrle, and J. C. Robb, *J. Polymer Sci.*, **C4**, 1161 (1966).
53. H. W. Melville, *Proc. Roy. Soc. (London)*, **A163**, 511 (1937).
54. C. H. Bamford and M. J. S. Dewar, *Proc. Roy. Soc. (London)*, **A197**, 356 (1949).
55. H. W. Melville, *Proc. Roy. Soc. (London)*, **A167**, 99 (1938).
56. H. W. Melville and R. F. Tuckett, *J. Chem. Soc.*, **1947**, 1201, 1211.

CHAPTER 7

Polymerization of Acrolein

Rolf C. Schulz

Institute of Organic Chemistry, Universität Mainz, Mainz, West Germany

7-1. INTRODUCTION

Many monomers contain only one group in the molecule capable of polymerizing. It may be a C—C double bond (e.g., in ethylene, propylene, styrene, vinyl halides, methacrylates, vinyl esters), a C=O group (e.g., in formaldehyde), or an epoxide ring (e.g., in ethylene oxide, bis(chloromethyl)-oxacyclobutane, tetrahydrofuran). For these monomers the conditions of polymerization influence the molecular weight, the number of branches, the end groups, and the tacticity of the resulting polymers. The catalysts, however, have no effect on the structure of the repeating unit and the chemical nature of the macromolecule.

Exceptions to this behavior are found in a few monomers, such as acrylamide (*1*) and 3-methyl-1-butene (*2*), which undergo isomerization under the influence of some catalysts, thereby giving repeating units of a different kind (see Chapter 2).

If the monomer contains two double bonds capable of polymerizing, more possibilities exist in the structure of the resulting macromolecule. The best-known example is butadiene which, depending on the catalyst, polymerizes either in a 1,2 or a 1,4 fashion or with both kinds of units in the same molecule. If the two double bonds are isolated (nonconjugated, as in acrylic anhydride), an intra-intermolecular propagation may take place, yielding cyclic repeating units (see Chapter 2).

A large number of possibilities exist when a monomer is used that contains two polymerizable groups, with different reactivities, in the same molecule. Examples of this type of compound are the following:

$$CH_3$$

Glycidyl methacrylate (*3,4*) $CH_2{=}\overset{CH_3}{\underset{\parallel}{C}}{-}\overset{\parallel}{\underset{O}{C}}{-}O{-}CH_2{-}CH{-}CH_2$

Vinyl glycidyl ether (*5,6*) $CH_2{=}CH{-}O{-}CH_2{-}CH{-}CH_2$

Dimethylketene (*7*) $(CH_3)_2C{=}C{=}O$

Vinyl isocyanate (*8*) $CH_2{=}CH{-}N{=}C{=}O$

Acrolein $CH_2{=}CH{-}CH{=}O$

Certain cycloolefins, such as cyclobutene (*9*) and norbornene (*10*), may be cited here as well, since they can polymerize either at the $C{-}C$ double bond or with opening of the ring.

In contrast to the monomers first cited above, it is possible in these cases to induce polymerization at will either in one or in the other group, or even in both, depending on the choice of catalyst. In this way a single monomer may yield entirely different polymers, depending on the conditions of polymerization. The products differ, not only in their physical properties, but also in their chemical constitution. Special analytical methods must, of course, be utilized, to determine the effect of the catalyst on the structure and constitution of the resulting polymers.

A particularly versatile monomer of the bifunctional type is acrolein. Being the simplest α,β-unsaturated aldehyde, it contains a conjugated-double-bond system and may, therefore, be considered to have a formal analogy to butadiene:

$$\underset{1}{CH_2}{=}\underset{2}{CH}{-}\underset{3}{CH}{=}\underset{4}{O}$$
$$CH_2{=}CH{-}CH{=}CH_2$$

In contrast to butadiene, however, the two double bonds of acrolein exhibit greatly different reactivities and polymerizabilities. From these considerations one may immediately conclude that there will be different possibilities in building up the acrolein polymer structure:

$$-C-C- \quad \longleftarrow \quad \overset{C=C-C=O}{\underset{-C-C=C-O-}{\downarrow}} \quad \longrightarrow \quad -C-O-$$

$$\underset{C=O}{|} \qquad\qquad\qquad\qquad\qquad\qquad\qquad \underset{C=C}{|}$$

It goes without saying that one may also obtain acrolein polymers having two different structural units.

Since only one functional group is required for polymerization, the other remains in the polymer and may subsequently be made to react (see Section 7-3F). Alternatively, one may make the monomer's vinyl or aldehyde group react and then polymerize the remaining functional group (see Section 7-6).

This chapter will deal with the preparation of acrolein polymers of various structures and the subsequent chemical modifications that they may undergo (11).

7-2. MONOMERIC ACROLEIN

A. Preparation

Various synthetic methods are known for the preparation of monomeric acrolein. The oldest method (12), which is still used today in laboratories, consists of splitting out water from glycerin. The yield may be as high as 50% (13).

$$\underset{\underset{OH}{|}}{CH_2}-\underset{\underset{OH}{|}}{CH}-\underset{\underset{OH}{|}}{CH_2} \xrightarrow[190°C]{KHSO_4} CH_2{=}CH{-}CHO + 2H_2O \qquad (7\text{-}1)$$

Acrolein may also be obtained in good yield by thermal cleavage of 2,3-dihydropyran (14):

$$\xrightarrow{540°C} CH_2{=}CH_2 + CH_2{=}CH{-}CHO \qquad (7\text{-}2)$$

The first commercially usable process was developed by the Degussa company in Frankfurt/Main (15). It consists of the condensation of formaldehyde with acetaldehyde at 280 to 330°C in the gas phase. The catalyst is alkaline silica gel, and yields of up to 82% based on acetaldehyde may be obtained:

$$CH_2O + CH_3{-}CHO \rightarrow CH_2{=}CH{-}CHO + H_2O \qquad (7\text{-}3)$$

This procedure is also suitable for the preparation of ^{14}C-labelled acrolein (16).

The most favorable starting material is propylene. Denigès observed as early as in 1898 that acrolein results when propylene is introduced into an acidic aqueous suspension of mercury(II) sulfate (*17*). The reaction conditions have since been studied more closely and improved. Presumably, an intermediate complex is formed, which disproportionates with the formation of acrolein and mercury(I) sulfate. The yield may be as high as 75%. However, 4 moles of mercury(II) sulfate are required per mole of acrolein. Of greatest importance by far is the gas-phase oxidation of propylene with air or oxygen:

$$CH_2{=}CH{-}CH_3 + O_2 \rightarrow CH_2{=}CH{-}CHO + H_2O \qquad (7\text{-}4)$$

The necessary catalysts have been described in numerous patents; examples are copper oxide (*18*), copper compounds of boric acid or phosphoric acid (*19*), phosphomolybdate or bismuth molybdate on silica gel (*20*), and molybdenum oxide–cobalt oxide (*21*).

The mechanism of this gas-phase oxidation was studied with the aid of propylene labelled with ^{14}C and ^{13}C or deuterated (*22*). Presumably, a hydrogen atom of the methyl group is first removed, an allyl radical being formed whose double bond is, however, not fixed:

$$\underset{1}{CH_2}{=}\underset{2}{CH}{-}\underset{3}{CH_3} \rightarrow \left[\underset{1}{CH_2}{=}\underset{2}{CH}{-}\underset{3}{CH_2} \cdot \leftrightarrow \cdot \underset{1}{CH_2}{-}\underset{2}{CH}{=}\underset{3}{CH_2} \right] \qquad (7\text{-}5)$$

Because of this, the carbonyl group may be formed either at the C-1 or at the C-3 atom of the propylene molecule. The formation of acrylonitrile from propylene, oxygen, and ammonia evidently proceeds by way of the same intermediate.

Since acrolein became available in large quantities it has aroused increasing interest as a starting material in chemical synthesis and in polymer chemistry (*15*).

B. Physical Properties

Acrolein is a colorless, lachrymatory liquid with a strong, pungent odor. The flash point is below $-29°C$, and the explosion limits in air are between 2.8 and 31 vol-% acrolein.

Investigation of the molecular structure gave the following bond lengths and bond angles (*23*):

C=O,	1.21 A	C=C—C,	122°5′
C=C,	1.36 A	C—C=O,	122°5′
C—C,	1.46 A	C=C—H,	120°
C—H,	1.09 A		

TABLE 7-1

Physical Properties of Monomeric Acrolein

Molecular weight	56.06
Melting point	$-86.95°C$
Boiling point (760 mm Hg)	52.7°C
Vapor pressure at:	
5°C	108.9 mm Hg
20°C	215.4 mm Hg
100°C	4.04 atm
Density at:	
0°C	0.8620 g/ml
10°C	0.8506 g/ml
15°C	0.8447 g/ml
20°C	0.8389 g/ml
Index of refraction at 20°C	1.4013
Solubility of acrolein in water at:	
0°C	20 wt-%, 7.4 mole-%
20°C	21 wt-%, 8.0 mole-%
40°C	24 wt-%, 9.2 mole-%
Solubility of water in acrolein at 20°C	6.8 vol-%

Because of partially hindered rotation around the C—C bond, two con-formers are possible. At room temperature the molecule is 90% in the *s-trans* isomeric form:

$$H_2C \diagdown \overset{H}{\underset{\underset{H}{C}}{C}} \diagup \overset{}{\underset{O}{}} \rightleftharpoons H_2C \diagdown \overset{\overset{O}{\|}}{\underset{\underset{H}{C}}{C}} \diagup \overset{}{\underset{H}{}} \tag{7-6}$$

Some of the most important physical properties are presented in Table 7-1. Numerous other data, including infrared, ultraviolet, and Raman spectra, may be found in a recently published monograph on acrolein (24). It suffices, therefore, to point out here a few of the latest spectroscopic investigations (25).

According to Joshi (26), the heat of free-radical polymerization is $-\Delta H = 19.1$ kcal/mole at 74.5°C.

C. Chemical Properties

Monomeric acrolein is an extremely reactive compound that can, under certain conditions, react explosively. It should be handled in the laboratory only in small amounts and with good ventilation. Being an unsaturated aldehyde, it can react at the carbonyl group as well as at the double bond. In some reactions it behaves like a conjugated diene. A few typical reactions will be cited.

The catalytic hydrogenation of acrolein yields, depending on catalyst and conditions, allyl alcohol, propionaldehyde, or propanol (27):

$$CH_2{=}CH{-}CH{=}O \nearrow \quad CH_2{=}CH{-}CH_2OH \qquad (7\text{-}7)$$
$$\longrightarrow CH_3{-}CH_2{-}CH{=}O \qquad (7\text{-}8)$$
$$\searrow CH_3{-}CH_2{-}CH_2OH \qquad (7\text{-}9)$$

The reduction with lithium aluminum hydride affords allyl alcohol in 70% yield.

The oxidation of the aldehyde group to acrylic acid has been described by Redtenbacher (12). Very thorough investigations were necessary to increase the yield (28). Smith and Holm (29) used hydrogen peroxide in the presence of selenium dioxide; t-butyl alcohol is a useful solvent.

$$CH_2{=}CH{-}CH{=}O \xrightarrow[H_2O_2]{SeO_2} CH_2{=}CH{-}COOH \qquad (7\text{-}10)$$

With hydrogen peroxide in the presence of osmium tetroxide the C—C double bond reacts and glyceraldehyde forms (28):

$$CH_2{=}CH{-}CH{=}O \xrightarrow[H_2O_2]{OsO_4} \underset{\overset{|}{OH}\ \ \overset{|}{OH}}{CH_2{-}CH{-}CHO} \qquad (7\text{-}11)$$

In weakly alkaline medium reaction with hydrogen peroxide produces glycidaldehyde (30):

$$CH_2{=}CH{-}CH{=}O \xrightarrow[H_2O_2]{OH^-} \underset{O}{CH_2{-}CH{-}CH{=}O} \qquad (7\text{-}12)$$

Acrolein reacts with hydroxylamine to give an oxime (boiling point, 108°C at 200 mm Hg) and with semicarbazide to give the corresponding semicarbazone (melting point, 171°C):

$$CH_2{=}CH{-}CH{=}O + NH_2OH \rightarrow CH_2{=}CH{-}CH{=}NOH + H_2O$$

$$(7\text{-}13)$$

With hydrazine or phenylhydrazine a cyclization to pyrazoline or phenyl-pyrazoline, respectively, takes place (31,32):

$$CH_2{=}CH{-}CH{=}O + H_2N{-}NHR \longrightarrow \underset{\underset{N}{R{-}N}}{CH_2{-}CH_2} \quad R{=}H \text{ or phenyl} \quad (7\text{-}14)$$

In these cases both the aldehyde group and the vinyl double bond undergo reaction.

On reaction with alcohols and depending on experimental conditions either of the two or both groups may participate (*33*):

$$CH_2=CH-CH=O \xrightarrow[ROH]{H^+} \begin{cases} CH_2=CH-CH(OR)_2 & (7\text{-}15) \\ R-O-CH_2-CH_2-CH=O & (7\text{-}16) \\ R-O-CH_2-CH_2-CH(OR)_2 & (7\text{-}17) \end{cases}$$

The products are acrolein acetals [Eq. (7-15)], alkoxypropionaldehydes [Eq. (7-16)], or alkoxypropionaldehyde acetals [Eq. (7-17)]. These reactions have been examined in numerous cases. In the reaction with sodium bisulfite, likewise, both the aldehyde group and the vinyl group participate (*34*).

Heating of acrolein to 170°C in the presence of a polymerization inhibitor produces, through the Diels–Alder reaction, a dimer, 2-formyldihydropyran (*35*):

$$(7\text{-}18)$$

Here acrolein acts both as diene and dienophile. With butadiene the compound tetrahydrobenzaldehyde is formed in 90% yield (*36*); only the vinyl group reacts in this case:

$$(7\text{-}19)$$

By contrast, acrolein acts as diene in the presence of vinyl ethers (*15,37,38*):

$$(7\text{-}20)$$

These few examples already illustrate the variety of reactions possible. Many other reactions are described in a very comprehensive monograph (*24*). A few reactions are used industrially; for example, in the production of glycerol or methionine.

Depending on the method of preparation, monomeric acrolein is contaminated with various quantities of impurities. It may contain, for example, water, lower alcohols, higher aldehydes, and ketones. For the prevention of

polymerization and condensation reactions it may contain added hydroquinone or derivatives of phenol besides small amounts of acids. These
substances do not generally interfere in the synthetic reactions described
above. If acrolein is to be used in polymerization, however, the most pains-
taking purification and special methods are necessary (39). For ionic polymerizations the water content must be as low as possible. All drying and
purification operations are hindered by the high reactivity and polymerizability of acrolein. Very soon after removal of the stabilizers a spontaneous
polymerization sets in, which may be recognized by the formation of a
colorless precipitate.

In fact, the extraordinarily high tendency to polymerize is a most significant
property of monomeric acrolein. Numerous substances capable of initiating
the formation of polymer exist; they may be grouped as follows.

1. Free-radical initiators (40,41): peroxides, aliphatic azo compounds,
redox systems.

2. Cationic initiators (40,42–44): boron fluoride etherate, sulfuric acid
etherate, tin(IV) chloride, aluminum chloride, titanium(IV) chloride.

3. Anionic initiators (40,42,45–47,82): sodium naphthalene, tritylsodium,
potassium benzophenone, alkali alcoholates, complex alkali hydrides,
phosphines, ammonia, piperidine, alkali cyanides.

In addition, polymerization catalysts whose method of action is not yet
known are described in the patent literature: for example, thiourea, heavy
metal oxides, sulfur dioxide, alkali-earth and alkaline-earth nitrites.

It will now be shown that the different catalysts yield polyacroleins of
different structures. The following three chapters are organized according
to the type of catalyst used.

7-3. FREE-RADICAL POLYMERIZATION

A. Polymerization in Bulk and in Organic Medium

Redtenbacher observed the formation of a precipitate on storage of
acrolein, which he named "disacryl" (12). This phenomenon was later more
closely investigated by various authors (48,49) and led to the discovery of
the stabilizing action of hydroquinone. Presumably, the formation of disacryl
involves a radical chain polymerization which, however, is poorly reproducible both in its course and in the nature of the product. This procedure is
therefore wholly unsuited to the preparation of polyacrolein.

Irradiation of undiluted acrolein with ultraviolet light induces polymerization (50). The gamma-ray-initiated polymerization has been particularly well studied (51–53). Both the structure of the polymer and the
over-all activation energy (3.1 kcal/mole) point to a radical propagation
mechanism in the range of $+20°C$ to $-78°C$. At low temperatures and low

conversions polymers are produced that are partially soluble in pyridine (52).

Polymerization in the presence of an organic solvent is generally preferred because of the high heat of reaction. The monomer is readily dissolved, but the polymer produced by the free-radical mechanism is insoluble in the usable reaction media, and the process is, therefore, a precipitative polymerization.

The rate of gamma-ray-induced polymerization of acrolein is strongly dependent on the solvent used (51). For 15% solutions at a dose rate of 1.4×10^5 r/hr the following order was established: dioxane $\approx$ acetone < chloroform = methanol < isopropyl alcohol < water. The relative rate of polymerization in aqueous solution is some 10 times as great as without solvent. The kinetic chain length was about 10^3.

Polymerizations catalyzed with peroxides or azobisisobutyronitrile are also preferably carried out in an organic solvent, since they would be too vigorous otherwise (40,54). Dimethyl formamide is particularly desirable, because the polymer, when produced up to about 15% conversion, does not precipitate. The reaction mixture then turns into a gel, and it may be assumed that the polymerization in the early stages proceeds already in the microgel state. To as much as 0.10 mole/liter of azobisisobutyronitrile the total rate is proportional to the square root of the concentration of initiator. The polymers are insoluble in all cases, even when polymerization is stopped at low conversions. According to the patent literature, soluble polyacroleins are obtained with azobisisobutyronitrile when the reaction medium contains at least 1 mole of a primary alcohol per mole of acrolein (55).

B. Polymerization in Aqueous Medium

The most favorable method is the polymerization of acrolein in aqueous medium with water-soluble initiators or redox systems (41). The monomer is soluble in water to 20 vol-% at 20°C; the polymer is insoluble, however. At higher concentrations one may use emulsion or bead polymerization. The preferred emulsifier is the adduct of sulfurous acid to polyacrolein, to be described below; in addition to emulsification it has reducing properties and may act as a component of a redox system (56–58,162).

The medium must in all cases be acidic during polymerization, since competing condensation reactions take place even at a pH of 8; these lead to polyacroleins having different properties.

Only certain combinations of oxidizers and reductants are useful. The potassium persulfate–silver nitrate system is particularly effective (41). Preferably, the oxidizer is added to the aqueous solution or emulsion of the acrolein, and the solution of silver nitrate is added thereto dropwise.

Although several mechanisms for this redox system have been proposed, it is certain that the polymerization is free-radical in nature (59). As in the case of redox polymerization of other vinyl compounds, the highest conversion is obtained at a mole ratio of $K_2S_2O_8$ to $AgNO_3$ of 1:1. The rate of polymerization in the absence of emulsifier is proportional to the square root of $[S_2O_8^{2-}][Ag^+]$ (41).

In emulsion polymerization the over-all rate, V_{br}, was proportional to $[I]^{2/5}$, in agreement with the Smith–Ewart theory (60). The dependence of rate on the concentration of emulsifier [S] differed from the theory (57) and was found to be

$$V_{br} \propto [S]^{0.2}$$

Entirely similar observations, made by Okamura et al. (61) in the case of vinyl acetate, were explained as being due to the solubility of the monomer in water. It is likely that this explanation holds as well for the emulsion polymerization of acrolein.

Since significant quantities of acrolein are in true solution in the water, the polymerization takes place not only in the micelles but also in the aqueous solution. Accordingly, the polymers produced have a very broad distribution of particle size. Electron microscope observations show particle diameters as low as 200 A (62). The polyacroleins produced by emulsion polymerization exhibit a particularly high reactivity, which will be discussed further in Section 7-3F.

Acrolein can also be polymerized in "inverse emulsion," that is, in a water-in-oil emulsion (63). For this purpose a 1:1 mixture of water and acrolein is dispersed in 2 to 5 times the quantity of heptane, benzene, or ether with addition of a detergent, and polymerization is brought about by a free-radical initiator or a redox system.

C. Copolymerization and Graft Copolymerization

The free-radical copolymerization of acrolein with vinyl or acrylic compounds, such as the following, has been described in several patents: styrene (55,64), acrylonitrile (55), methyl methacrylate (55), vinyl acetate (55), or methyl acrylate (65). The copolymers contain only small numbers of aldehyde groups, which may subsequently react. At higher acrolein contents the copolymers are frequently insoluble.

The reactivity behavior was determined by copolymerization of acrolein with a few selected monomers in aqueous and in organic media (66,67). Whereas all copolymers precipitated in the aqueous system during reaction, they stayed in solution in dimethyl formamide or dioxane up to a 20% conversion. After isolation most copolymers were found to be insoluble in organic media when the acrolein content exceeded 20 mole-%. Only the

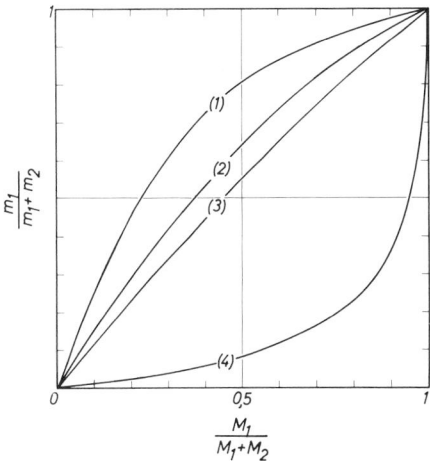

Fig. 7-1. Free-radical copolymerization of acrolein (subscript 1) with vinyl acetate (1), acryl-amide (2), acrylonitrile (3), and methyl acrylate (4) at 20°C in aqueous medium; redox system, $K_2S_2O_8–AgNO_3$.

copolymers with methacrylonitrile or methacrolein are soluble, even when the acrolein content is as high as 70% mole-$\%$.

The copolymerization diagrams are given in Figs. 7-1 and 7-2. In Table 7-2 the monomer reactivity behavior is summarized. From these data the $Q–e$ values were obtained according to Alfrey and Price (69) and the $q–\varepsilon$ values

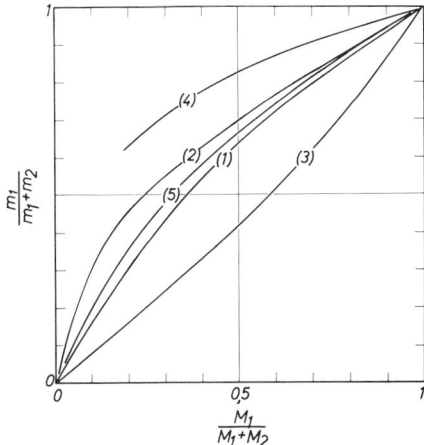

Fig. 7-2. Free-radical copolymerization of acrolein (subscript 1) with acrylonitrile in dimethyl formamide (1), acrylamide in DMF (2), methacrylonitrile in dioxane (3), 2-vinylpyridine in DMF (4), and methacrolein with methacrylonitrile in DMF (5) at 50°C; catalyst, azobisiso-butyronitrile.

TABLE 7-2

Some Copolymerization Parameters for Free-Radical Copolymerization of Acrolein and Methacrolein (66,67)

M_1	M_2	Polymeriz. medium	Temp., °C	r_1	r_2	Q_1	e_1	q_1, kcal/mole	ε_1, 10^{-10} esu
Acrolein	Acrylonitrile	DMF	50	1.60 ± 0.04	0.52 ± 0.02	0.69	0.67	−2.86	0.20
Acrolein	Acrylamide	DMF	50	1.69 ± 0.1	0.21 ± 0.02	0.99	0.05	−3.1	0.02
Acrolein	Methacrylonitrile	Dioxane	50	0.72 ± 0.06	1.20 ± 0.08	0.64	0.56	−2.8	0.17
Acrolein	2-Vinylpyridine	DMF	50	≈ 4	≈ 0				
Methacrolein	Methacrylonitrile	DMF	50	1.78 ± 0.06	0.4 ± 0.04	1.59	0.36	−3.4	0.11
Acrolein	Acrylonitrile	H_2O	20	1.09 ± 0.05	0.77 ± 0.1	0.47	0.69	−2.66	0.20
Acrolein	Acrylamide	H_2O	20	2.0 ± 0.05	0.76 ± 0.02				
Acrolein	Vinyl acetate	H_2O	20	3.3 ± 0.1	0.1 ± 0.05	0.20	0.69	−2.16	0.20
Acrolein	Methyl acrylate	H_2O	20	≈ 0	7.7 ± 0.2				
Methacrolein	Acrylonitrile	None	70	2 (68)	0.6 (68)				

according to Schwan and Price (70), provided that the r_1 and r_2 values were experimentally determined with sufficient accuracy.

The parameters for any given monomer pair (e.g., acrolein–acrylonitrile and acrolein–acrylamide) depend on the solvent used. This effect was already observed in the case of other monomer pairs, in which the copolymers precipitate during reaction [e.g., acrylonitrile–ethyl acrylate (71) and itaconic anhydride–styrene (72)]. This unexpected result may be explained by greatly different behavior of the monomers in the liquid and the precipitated phases as compared with the original mixture. The assumptions on which the copolymerization equation is based are, therefore, no longer fulfilled.

The homogeneous copolymerization of acrolein with acrylonitrile or with methacrylonitrile yields parameters that correspond to approximately equal Q and e values for acrolein, although different solvents were used. These values are therefore to be considered most reliable. The e value is positive, as expected, since the carbonyl group is an electron acceptor and imparts a net positive charge to the vinyl group. Similar values are found for methyl vinyl ketone or methacrylic acid. The Q value of acrolein may be compared with that of acrylic acid derivatives (such as acrylonitrile or ethyl methacryl-ate) (73,74).

The aldehyde groups in acrolein copolymers show a reactivity similar to that in polyacrolein (see Section 7-3F). In some cases it suffices to have a few acrolein repeating units to alter greatly the properties of the copolymer; for example, acrylonitrile–acrolein copolymers form bisulfite adducts and are, therefore, soluble in aqueous sulfur dioxide solutions. Films may be cast or fibers spun from these aqueous solutions (75).

In infrared spectra of copolymers the intensity of the carbonyl band increases with decreasing acrolein content. This, at first surprising, observa-tion may be explained on the basis of the special structure of the aldehyde groups in the polyacroleins (see section 7-3E). Neighboring aldehyde groups form hemiacetals, which behave chemically like aldehyde groups but show no carbonyl absorption. With increasing content of the comonomer the number of isolated acrolein units increases. The intensity of the carbonyl absorption then increases in like measure:

$$-CH_2-CH-CH_2-CH- \qquad\qquad -CH_2-CH-CH_2-CH-CH_2-CH-$$

In this way arises the possibility of measuring spectroscopically the number of isolated acrolein units and also the length of acrolein unit sequences. These results agree with statistically calculated values (76,77).

In addition to statistical copolymerization, the graft copolymerization of acrolein has been described. Particularly suitable for this purpose is initiation with gamma rays (51). If one immerses, for example, a sheet of polymethyl methacrylate in a methanolic solution of acrolein, the monomer diffuses into the polymer. The depth of penetration may be adjusted at will by means of the length of exposure. Upon subsequent irradiation a graft copolymerization sets in, which proceeds much more rapidly than with the pure monomer. The acrolein–methacrylate graft copolymers are insoluble in all solvents and react similarly to polyacrolein. The interior of the sheets, into which no acrolein had diffused, was unreacted polymethyl methacrylate and was soluble.

The grafting of acrolein onto cellulose (viscose rayon or cotton) was recently described (78). The fibers were first immersed in sodium thiosulfate solution, dried, and then treated at 20°C with an aqueous solution of potassium persulfate and acrolein. The weight increase was as much as 15%. It was shown that cross-linking of the cellulose took place by formation of hemiacetal structures. Chemical reactions may be carried out on the grafted polyacrolein.

Another method of preparing graft copolymers, which consists of reactions of polyacrolein, will be described in Section 7-3F.

D. Properties of the Polymers

The polymer disacryl, obtained spontaneously from acrolein, and the polymer resulting from radical initiation or redox systems are colorless powders. They discolor, upon being heated in the presence of air at about 170°C, to yellow or brown and sinter without melting at about 220°C (79). Since profound changes take place, polyacrolein cannot be reversibly processed as a normal thermoplastic material. At room temperature pressures of 18,000 kg/cm^2 are required for clear, transparent, but brittle moldings or sheets. Objects formed in this way were tested for torsional modulus and dynamic mechanical properties as a function of temperature (80,82). At 140°C an irreversible transformation takes place, which presumably consists of a cross-linking reaction. Other useful properties were also determined and compared with those of polyacrolein acetals, polystyrenes, and polymethyl methacrylates (81).

The index of refraction of the powder, measured by the immersion method, was found to be $n_D = 1.529$. Moldings had values of 1.527 to 1.529. The heat of combustion is 6 kcal/g. The density of the polymers lies between 1.32 and 1.37, corresponding to an increase of more than 60%, as compared to the monomer, which has an extraordinarily high contraction on polymerization (79). All polyacroleins obtained thus far are amorphous by x-ray determination.

The free-radical polyacrolein is insoluble at room temperature in the common organic solvents, provided no reaction occurs, as it does in the case of sodium hydroxide solution or sulfurous acid (see Section 7-3F). The redox polymers with degrees of polymerization less than 1,000 are soluble above 60°C in a mixture of 65 vol-% pyridine and 35 vol-% water (83). According to the investigations of Hank (84), the polyacroleins are also soluble in glycol carbonate, divinyl sulfone, tetramethylene sulfone, and dimethyl formamide, although only above 170°C. A significant decrease in viscosity results therefrom.

The solvents named above are not suitable for molecular-weight determination. As in the case of cellulose, the insoluble polyacrolein must first be converted to soluble derivatives. For osmotic measurements the thiophenol mercaptals have been useful (85); for viscometry the water-soluble adducts of sulfurous acid are better suited, because they are more conveniently prepared (86). One must caution, however, that polyelectrolytes are formed thereby and that standardized experimental conditions must be adhered to for reproducible results.

The relationship of intrinsic viscosity, thus determined, with molecular weight has not yet been definitely established. Viscometry does yield, however, values useful in the characterization of the polyacroleins (87). Ultraviolet spectrometry may be carried out on the polyacrolein–sulfurous acid solutions (88).

E. Structure of the Polymers

The elucidation of the structure of the polyacroleins is rendered extremely difficult by their lack of solubility. It was even long doubtful whether these were, in fact, macromolecular substances, since no molecular-weight determinations were possible. The older literature has some proposed structures (15,89,90); these need not be discussed here, since they are now obsolete. When it was recognized that, in contrast to other vinyl polymers, the structure of the polymer is dependent on the conditions of polymerization, the first step toward structural determination was to prepare polyacrolein reproducibly. Systematic investigations toward this goal were first undertaken with free-radical polymer (91). These are described in this section; for polymers prepared by cationic and anionic routes, see Sections 7-4C and 7-5C.

One may assume at first that the free-radical polymerization of acrolein, in analogy to other vinyl monomers, yields the following structure:

$$CH_2=CH \qquad \longrightarrow \quad \cdots-CH_2-CH-\cdots \qquad (7\text{-}21)$$
$$\underset{CH=O}{|} \qquad\qquad\qquad \underset{CHO}{|}$$

The experimental results do not agree, however, with this simple formula.

Polyacroleins always contain variable amounts of water; in spite of long drying at high vacuum over phosphorus pentoxide at room temperature the theoretically calculated amounts of carbon (64.27%) and of hydrogen

(7.19%) are never attained. One finds carbon contents of between 61.2 and 61.8% and hydrogen contents of between 7.4 and 8.0%. These correspond to a water content of between 4 and 5 wt-% (40). One portion of the water is reversibly bound, whereas another may not be removed without structural changes in the polymer. These facts must always be considered in any structural assignment. As will be shown below, a stepwise "pyrolysis" permits a fractional dehydration (93); one may distinguish and determine in this way the various types of bound water (structurally bound water, water of hydration, and free water).

Infrared spectroscopy plays an important role in structural elucidation. The groups so recognized were also identified by chemical methods and, wherever possible, quantitatively determined. For this purpose, it was necessary to make use of low-molecular-weight model compounds that contain the corresponding groups once or twice in the molecule (92); see Section 7-3F.

Figure 7-3 shows the infrared spectrum of free-radical-produced poly-acrolein. It agrees largely with the polymers obtained by redox polymerization in aqueous medium [see the infrared spectra in (40,45,76,79,82,84,94)]. The technique of sample preparation has no influence, as may be seen by a comparison with an infrared spectrum obtained with a transparent film (80).

The bands may be assigned as follows (in microns):

2.9	OH bond vibration
3.4 to 3.5	CH bond vibration
3.65	CH bond vibration of aldehyde group
5.85	C=O bond vibration of aldehyde group
6.1	Water
6.85 to 6.90	CH deformation vibration
8.5 to 11	Superposition of various C—O—C and O—C—O—C vibrations
12 to 12.3	Ring vibration of pyran ring (95).

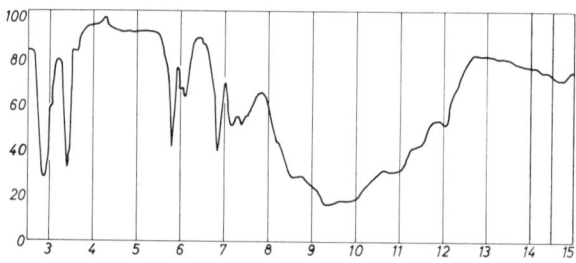

Fig. 7-3. Infrared spectrum of polyacrolein (KBr pellet); polymerization in dimethyl formamide with azobisisobutyronitrile at 50°C.

As the basis of this assignment free-radical-produced polyacroleins must contain the following monomeric units:

$$-CH_2-CH- \qquad -CH_2-CH- \qquad -CH_2-CH-CH_2-CH-$$

There is, therefore, a C—C main chain, which consists of heavily hydrated acrolein units. The molar ratio of acrolein to water amounts to 1:1 in the hydrate, 2:1 in the simple cyclic hemiacetal (dihydroxytetrahydropyran rings), and 3:1 or more in the joined, cyclic tetrahydropyran structure. On the basis of statistical and steric considerations sequences longer than 4 joined tetrahydropyran rings are unlikely. One must assume, however, that the various hydrate forms are in reversible equilibria and are readily interconverted. Hemiacetal linkages may also form between neighboring macromolecules, whereby reversible cross-linking results.

The content of free aldehyde groups and the degree of hydration depend, of course, on prior treatment. In normally dried polyacrolein one may determine by various methods 10 to 20 mole-% free aldehyde groups (96). Independent of this, all other monomeric units may react like free aldehyde groups under certain conditions; that is, one aldehyde group may react chemically per monomeric unit.

The structure described above is in agreement with all known physical and chemical properties of radical-produced polyacroleins and has been repeatedly confirmed. The unexpectedly high thermal stability may be ascribed to the partial ladder structure.

The structure of the free-radical homopolymer, described above, is also valid for the free-radical-produced copolymers with vinyl and acrylic compounds. As already mentioned, the tetrahydropyran rings do not form, or do so only in limited numbers, because of the insufficient length of acrolein sequences (76,77).

After the chemical structure of the macromolecule was elucidated, the question of the average molecular weight arose. If the usual methods were to be used, soluble polymers of polyacrolein had to be prepared without chain degradation. Fractions of thiophenol mercaptals in various solvents gave osmotic pressures corresponding to molecular weights of between 50,000 and 220,000 (85). In this way it was first unequivocally established that the polyacroleins are true macromolecular substances and that they are essentially linear. It is possible today to prepare polyacroleins having molecular weights ranging from 1000 to more than 1,000,000.

F. Chemical Reactions

As was shown in the previous section, the free-radical-produced polyacroleins contain one aldehyde group per monomeric unit. These may be masked, however, by more or less hydration but are accessible to the usual carbonyl reactions. Moreover, the main chain has hydrogen atoms activated by the aldehyde groups. Polyacroleins are, therefore, among the most reactive polymers (97) and may be transformed into a variety of derivatives. The reactions proceed in most cases under mild conditions and yield, usually without much degradation, polymeric derivatives that are soluble in various media, in contrast to the starting material. Consequently, all reactions begin at first as a heterogeneous system. One preferably chooses such experimental conditions as will result in solution of the product as reaction proceeds. The limitations of solubility of the reaction components and the increasing viscosities of the solutions place significant limitations on the maximum degree of conversion that may be reached. Furthermore, the degree of conversion (i.e., the number of reacted monomeric units per 100 monomeric units) depends on the type of reaction involved. In any event, it is advantageous to start with a finely divided polyacrolein. The emulsion polymers are particularly suitable, and in many cases one may use the aqueous emulsion directly for reaction. Sometimes it is preferable to dry the polyacroleins carefully at elevated temperatures in order to activate them (93).

Model reactions with low-molecular-weight compounds having an analogy to the monomeric units of polyacrolein were studied in order to establish starting points for the optimal reaction conditions and maximal degrees of conversion to be expected (92). The following model compounds were selected:

$$CH_3-CH-CH_3 \qquad CH_2-CH_2-CH_2 \qquad$$
$$CH=O \qquad CH=O \qquad CH=O$$

On the basis of these model reactions the reactions of polyacroleins may be classified into several groups, depending on the degree to which the pyran rings are cleaved (11).

1. In some reactions all pyran rings are opened, and every monomeric unit, regardless of extent of hydration, forms the corresponding aldehyde

derivative. Polyacrolein reacts in this case like a polymeric monoaldehyde; that is, each monomeric unit reacts independently of its neighbor. One obtains, therefore, essentially complete conversion. These reactions may be used, in principle, for the quantitative determination of the aldehyde groups, provided no other disturbing influences are present (such as poor solubility or blocking substituents). Examples of this type of reaction are reduction, oxidation, oximation, and formation of hydrazones.

2. Reactions in which two aldehyde groups participate may be favored by the presence of tetrahydropyran rings in polyacrolein. The latter then behaves as a polymeric dicarbonyl compound. The conversion is limited to 86 mole-% by statistical considerations. The best-studied example is disproportionation.

3. There are some reactions that only proceed on the hydroxyl groups of hemiacetals without opening thereby the pyran rings. Since there is an average of two OH groups per two to four acrolein monomeric units, the conversions per one hundred aldehyde groups range from 50 to 25 mole-% in this case. Examples of such reactions are acetalization, mercaptalization, reaction with ammonia and amines, Knoevenagel condensation.

4. Finally, there are reactions that proceed smoothly with low-molecular-weight aldehydes, yet could not be carried out with polyacroleins; for example, autoxidation has not yet succeeded (88). It could not be established whether the insolubility of the polymer, the hydration of the aldehyde groups, or the cyclic structure is responsible for this failure. In any event, polyacrolein is completely stable to molecular oxygen up to temperatures of 100°C. It is, therefore, easy to handle and may be stored indefinitely at room temperature. This is particularly remarkable because of its otherwise high reactivity.

1. REDUCTION

Treatment of polyacrolein suspended in water with potassium borohydride causes reduction of over 90% of all monomeric units and results in the formation of high-molecular-weight polyallyl alcohol. As is well known, polymerization of monomeric allyl alcohol yields only oligomers:

$$-CH_2-CH- \xrightarrow{KBH_4} -CH_2-CH- \qquad (7\text{-}22)$$

The primary hydroxyl groups may be esterified, etherified, or xanthogenated (98,99).

2. OXIDATION

Polyacroleins dissolve at higher temperatures in dilute peracetic acid, resulting in the formation of a polymeric acid that has largely the composition and properties of polyacrylic acid (100):

$$-CH_2-CH- \quad \xrightarrow{CH_3COOOH} \quad -CH_2-CH- \qquad (7\text{-}23)$$

Practically all aldehyde groups are oxidized; unfortunately, a marked degradation accompanies the reaction.

3. OXIMATION

The reaction with hydroxylamine hydrochloride or formate gives a practically quantitative formation of the oxime (101):

$$-CH_2-CH- \quad \xrightarrow{NH_2OH} \quad -CH_2-CH- \qquad (7\text{-}24)$$

This reaction may, therefore, be used for the identification of polyacrolein or the determination of the aldehyde groups. One may measure either the consumption of reagent titrimetrically (102) or the nitrogen content of the product in order to calculate the conversion. It must be said that the reaction is distinctly slower than with low-molecular-weight compounds.

4. FORMATION OF HYDRAZONES

Phenylhydrazine or its derivatives convert 70 to 90 mole-% of the aldehyde groups, depending on the conditions used, to the corresponding phenylhydrazone:

$$-CH_2-CH- \quad \xrightarrow{R-NH-NH_2} \quad -CH_2-CH- \qquad (7\text{-}25)$$

This reaction, too, is suited for the determination of the reactive aldehyde groups.

Unsubstituted hydrazine forms insoluble products (62). A portion of the phenylhydrazone groups may react with diazonium salts to form formazans. The latter may be dehydrated reversibly to tetrazolium salts (103):

$$\rightleftharpoons \qquad (7\text{-}26)$$

Hydrazones of polyacrolein may also be formed with hydrazides of acids (62). Kauffmann and Boettcher (104) used this reaction for the separation of amino acid hydrazides obtained by hydrazinolysis of proteins. The

Girard reagents yield water-soluble polyacrolein derivatives (*62*), but it is doubtful that the tetrahydropyran rings are opened, since the conversion amounts to only about 30 mole-%.

5. DISPROPORTIONATION

$$-CH_2-CH-CH_2-CH- \quad \xrightarrow{\text{NaOH}} \quad -CH_2-CH-CH_2-CH- \quad (7\text{-}27)$$

(structures: left — CH, CH, HO, O, OH ring system; right — CH$_2$OH, COONa)

Disproportionation (*105*) proceeds under very mild conditions and yields a water-soluble salt of a polyhydroxy polycarboxylic acid. Upon acidification the acid precipitates and is rapidly cross-linked by intermolecular esterification. Thiele and Jentsch (*106*) studied the electrochemical behavior of this polyelectrolyte.

Bäder et al. described the formation of gels by reaction of polyacrolein with alkali (*162*).

6. ACETALIZATION

Polyacroleins dissolve in primary alcohols at somewhat elevated temperatures and in the presence of an acidic catalyst, acetals forming: (*107*):

$$-CH_2-CH-CH_2-CH- \quad \xrightarrow{\text{ROH}} \quad -CH_2-CH-CH_2-CH- \quad (7\text{-}28)$$

(structures: left — CH, CH, O, O, OH ring system; right — CH, CH, O, O, OR)

The conversions depend on the alcohol but barely exceed 40 mole-%, although the infrared spectrum does not reveal any residual aldehyde groups. The polymeric hemiacetals are quite soluble in organic solvents but become insoluble upon standing because of cleavage of alcohol. A number of alcohols thus reacted. With the isomeric butyl alcohols the rate of acetalization decreases in the order normal, iso, secondary, tertiary (*108*). Osmotic measurements could be carried out on the polymeric hemiacetals from β-chloroethanol (*107*). Diols also yield soluble derivatives, presumably because only one alcohol group reacts.

7. MERCAPTILIZATION

The reaction of polyacrolein with mercaptans proceeds under conditions similar to those useful with alcohols and yields, likewise, soluble derivatives (*85*):

$$-CH_2-CH-CH_2-CH- \quad \xrightarrow{\text{RSH}} \quad -CH_2-CH-CH_2-CH- \quad (7\text{-}29)$$

(structures: left — CH, CH, O, O, OH ring system; right — CH, CH, O, O, SR)

The degree of conversion may be obtained from the sulfur content and amounts to 35 to 45 mole-%. The mercaptals from thiophenol are much more stable than the acetals and are suitable for fractionation and osmotic measurements. The spontaneously formed disacryls have a very broad mass distribution, in contrast to redox polymers.

8. REACTION WITH AMMONIA AND AMINES

Polyacrolein reacts exothermically with gaseous or dissolved ammonia. The reaction products are yellow to brown but completely insoluble. The nitrogen content amounts to 15 to 17% (109).

Soluble, colored derivatives are produced from aliphatic and aromatic amines as well as from piperidine (92,103). The conversion calculated from the nitrogen content is between 20 and 50 mole-%. The infrared spectra indicate that, in addition to azomethine groups, there are N-acetal groups and tetrahydropyran rings:

$$
\begin{array}{c}
-CH_2-CH-CH_2-CH- \\
\diagdown CH \diagdown CH \\
O \quad O \quad OH
\end{array}
\longrightarrow
\begin{array}{c}
-CH_2-CH-CH_2-CH- \\
\diagdown CH \diagdown CH \quad H \\
O \quad O \quad N \\
R
\end{array}
$$

$$+$$

$$
\begin{array}{c}
-CH_2-CH-CH_2-CH- \\
\diagdown CH \diagdown CH \\
O \quad OH \quad N-R
\end{array}
\qquad (7\text{-}30)
$$

9. KNOEVENAGEL CONDENSATION

Under the catalytic influence of potassium fluoride or piperidine in glacial acetic acid polyacrolein reacts with active methylene compounds, such as malononitrile, ethyl cyanoacetate, benzyl cyanide, phenylnitromethane, and acetoacetate (92,94). Soluble derivatives are thereby obtained. The conversions are between 20 and 50 mole-%. Hünig's reactivity series for substituents on CH_2 groups also holds for these reactions. Structural elucidation is difficult since, as for the Schiff's bases, various groupings are present side by side.

10. COLOR REACTIONS

The qualitative analysis of polyacrolein may be carried out by means of color reactions (88). The reaction with fuchsin sulfurous acid gives a dark blue-violet color; upon conversion into the hydroxamic acid by the Angeli-Rimini reaction a red-brown color forms with Fe(III) salts. The color reactions may be carried out with powdered polyacrolein or with moldings (110); they are particularly sensitive when the polymers are present as the water-soluble hydrate. In this case one may also carry out successfully the reactions with Fehling's or Feder's solution or with ammoniacal silver nitrate.

Carr and Gordon made a quantitative determination of polyacrolein, using polymers labeled with tritium or ^{14}C (*111*).

11. ALDOL CONDENSATION

The reactions of the free-radical-produced polymers described above involved only the carbonyl groups. The α hydrogen atom, which is present in each monomeric unit, is also capable of undergoing reaction. The most studied reaction has been that with formaldehyde (*112,113,161*):

$$-CH_2-\underset{\underset{CHO}{|}}{CH}- + 2CH_2O + H_2O \rightarrow -CH_2-\underset{\underset{CH_2OH}{|}}{\overset{\overset{CH_2OH}{|}}{C}}- + HCOOH \qquad (7\text{-}31)$$

Since intra- and intermolecular disproportionation may also take place under the same conditions, the polymers contain also a certain amount of carboxyl groups. It is particularly desirable to work with a pyridine–water mixture (*83,112*).

12. BISULFITE ADDUCTS

The polyacrolein–bisulfite adducts are particularly noteworthy because of their versatile reactivity (*88,114,115*). If polyacrolein is suspended in a 10% aqueous sulfur dioxide solution—as noted above, it is insoluble in nearly all organic solvents—a clear colorless solution results in several hours at room temperature. Polyacrolein is also soluble in aqueous sodium bisulfite solution (*116*). In agreement with the behavior of the corresponding low-molecular-weight compounds, the reaction may be formulated as follows:

$$\underset{\text{insoluble in water}}{-CH_2-\underset{\underset{O}{\diagdown\diagup}}{\underset{CH}{|}}-} + H_2O + SO_2 \rightarrow \underset{\text{soluble in water}}{-CH_2-\underset{\underset{HO}{\diagup}\underset{SO_3H}{\diagdown}}{\underset{CH}{|}}-} \qquad (7\text{-}32)$$

A water-soluble polyacrolein derivative is thus produced by formation of the adduct resulting from cleavage of the hemiacetal groups and, possibly, of the cross-linkages. It may be pointed out, however, that polymethacrolein does not form such an adduct. The polyacrolein–sulfurous acid adduct is in equilibrium with its components; apparently a hydrated form of the polymer is generated thereby since, in contrast to the starting polyacrolein, it is soluble in water (*88*):

$$\underset{\text{soluble}}{-CH_2-\underset{\underset{HO}{\diagup}\underset{SO_3H}{\diagdown}}{\underset{CH}{|}}-} \rightleftharpoons \underset{\text{soluble}}{-CH_2-\underset{\underset{HO}{\diagup}\underset{OH}{\diagdown}}{\underset{CH}{|}}-} + SO_2 \rightarrow \underset{\text{insoluble}}{-CH_2-\underset{\underset{O}{\diagdown\diagup}}{\underset{CH}{|}}-} + H_2O \qquad (7\text{-}33)$$

Water elimination with reversion to the insoluble state takes place only upon the addition of strong acids or by precipitation. The sulfurous acid may be removed by dialysis, ion exchange, or autoxidation, without any precipitation of the polyacrolein. In this way a SO_2-free aqueous solution of polyacrolein results (88). The position of the equilibrium and the equilibration conditions were thoroughly examined by Dawson and Welch (117). A few notable properties of the polyacrolein adducts will be described.

Since the solution of polyacrolein in sulfurous acid may be readily formed under mild conditions, it is particularly suitable for characterization of the polymers by means of viscosity measurements. It must be noted in this connection that the adduct is a polyelectrolyte and that a salt, such as sodium chloride or sulfate, must be added in these measurements (118,119). The polymer solutions form complexes with certain heavy metal salts (120).

The polyacrolein–SO_2 solution may be used as an emulsifier and has been particularly suitable for emulsion polymerization of acrolein (121–123). In the presence of these emulsifiers exceptionally high-molecular-weight polyacroleins are formed; furthermore, very small particle size and, therefore, high reactivity of the polymers may be achieved (62).

The bisulfite adduct and also the SO_2-free solutions of hydrated polymers permit a number of reactions to take place in homogeneous aqueous medium, which would not occur with insoluble polyacrolein or would do so only under extreme conditions.

The polyacrolein–SO_2 adducts have especially the property of reacting with the functional groups of other polymers. There results, thereby, a particular kind of cross-linked polymer that consists of two different kinds of macromolecule; this may, therefore, be called a "composite polymer" (124,125). In the following schematic equation A represents the hydrated aldehyde groups of polyacrolein, B the functional groups of another polymer (such as OH, NH_2, SH), and C the groups resulting from the condensation of A with B (such as acetals, azomethines, mercaptals). These groups form the cross-links between the macromolecules:

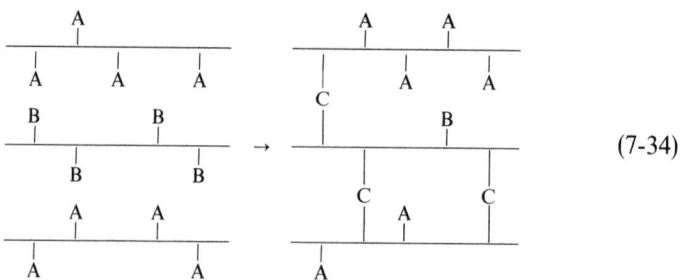

$$(7\text{-}34)$$

Since not all aldehyde groups of the polyacrolein are reacted, there remain in the "composite polymers" some free aldehyde groups, which may be detected by color reactions or may react in other reactions. Polyacrolein–SO_2 solutions may react with, for example, polyvinyl alcohol, polyvinylamine, polyethylenimine, polyacrylic hydrazide, polysilicic acid, cellulose, collagen, gelatin, catgut, casein, serum albumin, catalase, insulin. All reactions take place at room temperature. Agar-agar and sodium alginate do not react under these conditions (124).

The reactions may be carried out in various ways. If one mixes, for example, the aqueous solutions of both polymers there results either an immediate precipitation of the "composite polymer" or the formation of a clear gel. It is also possible to make the aqueous polyacrolein–SO_2 solution react with polymer B in the form of a powder, fiber, or film. In that case, reaction takes place only at the surface, and the result is similar to surface grafting. The properties of polymer B may be greatly modified in this way (e.g., surface modification of gelatin layers, collagen, catgut fibers, skin, cotton, paper). The extent of reaction and the depth of penetration may be established, here as well, by subsequent color reactions that are typical for the remaining aldehyde groups. The proportion of bound polymer may also be determined by the use of ^{14}C-labeled polyacrolein (111,126).

7-4. CATIONIC POLYMERIZATION

A. Homopolymerization in Bulk and in Organic Medium

It is well known that the strictest requirements of purity of the monomer and the solvent must be met for cationic polymerization. The purification and drying of monomeric acrolein is extremely difficult and does not succeed as well as with, for example, styrene or isobutylene (127). Presumably, the varying purity of the acrolein used is the cause of some of the contradictory statements in the literature in regard to ionic polymerization.

The cationic initiators used successfully thus far for the polymerization of acrolein are boron fluoride, boron fluoride etherate, sulfuric acid etherate, tin(IV) chloride, aluminum chloride, titanium(IV) chloride (40,42–44). In newer investigations the following compounds were tested for catalytic activity (62,128): zinc chloride, iron(III) chloride, antimony(III) chloride, antimony(V) fluoride, perchloric acid, lithium perchlorate, magnesium perchlorate, acetyl perchlorate, benzoyl perchlorate, t-butyl perchlorate, trityl perchlorate, and triethyloxonium tetrafluoroborate. The activity of these initiators is extremely variable; by far the most effective are acetyl perchlorate and boron fluoride etherate. For bulk polymerization the preferred temperatures are from 0°C to −87°C, the melting point of the monomer.

TABLE 7-3

Examples of Cationic Polymerization of Acrolein

Solvent	Catalyst	Mole-% based on monomer	Temp., °C	Time, min.	Yield, %
None	$BF_3 \cdot (C_2H_5)_2O$	1.6	-30	145	30
None	$BF_3 \cdot (C_2H_5)_2O$	0.8	0	120	45
Nitrobenzene	$H_2SO_4 \cdot (C_2H_5)_2O$	1.5	18	100	22
Nitrobenzene	$SnCl_4$	1.5	18	96	14
1,2-Dichloroethane	$SnCl_4$	1.5	18	220	15
None	$O(C_2H_5)_3BF_4$	1.2	0	95	40
Methylene chloride	$O(C_2H_5)_3BF_4$	1.2	0	185	16
Nitromethane	$O(C_2H_5)_3BF_4$	2.0	-20	2800	85
None	CH_3COClO_4	0.2	-50	720	41
Nitromethane	CH_3COClO_4	0.2	-20	300	20

Excellent agitation is required because of the frequently very vigorous polymerization and the possible precipitation of polymer. The solvent used has a great influence on the rate of polymerization; for example, the highest yields are found in nitromethane and nitrobenzene, and under the same conditions the yields in 1,2-dichloroethane, chloroform, carbon tetrachloride, or toluene are distinctly lower (*128*). A few examples of cationic polymerization of acrolein are presented in Table 7-3.

In contrast to radical polymerization, cationic polymerization is homogeneous up to about 40% conversion; at higher conversions gelation or precipitation of the polymers takes place. A typical infrared spectrum of a polyacrolein prepared by cationic polymerization is shown in Fig. 7-4.

B. Copolymerization

As with free-radical initiators, acrolein may be copolymerized with other monomers (*128*). Of course, the copolymerization parameters have different

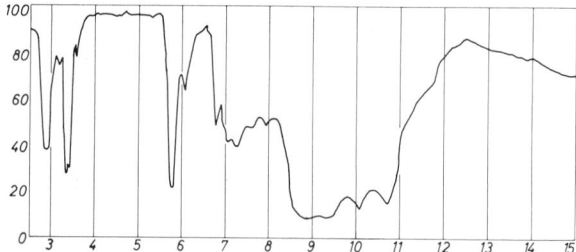

Fig. 7-4. Infrared spectrum of polyacrolein (KBr pellet); bulk polymerization with boron fluoride etherate at $-30°C$.

values in such case, and the properties of the copolymers are also expected to be different. Furthermore, some monomer pairs may be polymerized that do not copolymerize with radicals. However, only a few such experiments have been reported.

The most complete study has been that of the copolymerization of acrolein with styrene and boron fluoride etherate (42,128). The over-all rate of polymerization decreases sharply with increasing acrolein content in the monomer mixture. As Fig. 7-5 shows, the copolymer will be richer in acrolein. Surprisingly, cationic acrolein–styrene copolymers are soluble in organic solvents, in contrast to radical copolymers. The copolymer composition may therefore be determined with reliability.

The differences in solubility must be ascribed to differences in chemical structure; these are, however, not reflected in the numerical values of the copolymerization parameters. Statements regarding the latter must be considered dubious to the extent that the structure of the resulting polymers and the mechanism of the individual steps are not clarified. In these cases they may serve only to describe the over-all composition as a function of the composition of the monomer mixture; it must be remembered that this information is valid only under the specific experimental conditions used and does not possess the more general applicability that it has in radical copolymerization.

Acrolein may also be copolymerized cationically with indene (128). The maximal rate is observed at an acrolein content of about 25 mole-% in the mixture. The copolymers are soluble under all conditions in benzene,

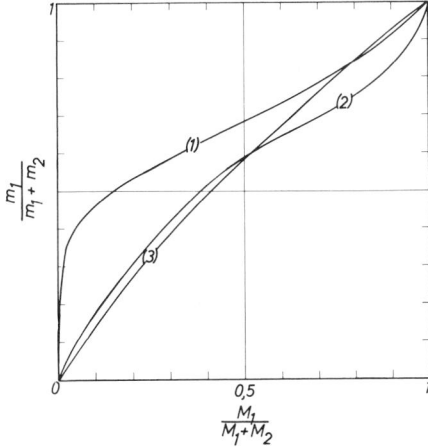

Fig. 7-5. Cationic copolymerization of acrolein (subscript 1) with styrene in bulk at $-30°C$ (1), epichlorohydrin in bulk at $0°C$ (2), bis(chloromethyl)oxetane in bulk at $0°C$ (3); catalyst, boron fluoride etherate.

tetrahydrofuran, or pyridine, but become insoluble on long standing. They soften at temperatures between 150 and 190°C depending on composition.

Copolymers are also possible with epoxides (*128*). With boron fluoride etherate copolymers may be prepared from acrolein and epichlorohydrin, styrene oxide, and bis(chloromethyl)oxetane. The copolymers are soluble in all cases and may, therefore, be purified by reprecipitation. The composition may be obtained from the carbon or chlorine content. Whereas the bis(chloromethyl)oxetane copolymers soften at 110 to 190°C, the epichlorohydrin copolymers of low acrolein content are tough pastes, and with increasing acrolein content the softening range extends to 130°C.

A copolymerization of acrolein and phenyl vinyl ether has recently been reported (*160*).

Figure 7-5 shows the composition of copolymers as a function of the monomer mixture for a few systems. Here too, it must be noted that the diagrams are valid only for the given experimental conditions; they describe only over-all composition and do not specify particular structures in the copolymers.

C. Properties and Structure of the Polymers

The cationically prepared polyacroleins are different in many respects from the radical polymers. They are, for example, easily dissolved in some organic solvents (such as dioxane, chloroform, tetrahydrofuran, or pyridine) if isolated at low conversions; upon being dried or stored they more or less rapidly become insoluble. These changes may be avoided if the polymer solutions are kept cold. Many studies have been hindered by this instability; for example, there have yet been no reported molecular-weight determinations.

Polyacrolein prepared by cationic polymerization softens between 80 and 110°C, depending on the conditions of preparation, and is, therefore, different from the free-radical polymers.

The infrared spectra of all homopolymers, prepared with the catalysts enumerated above, show bands at 3.25, 10.2, and 10.8 μ, which are missing in radical polymers (see Figs. 7-3 and 7-4); they show the presence of vinyl groups. In fact, chemical methods may also be used to demonstrate the presence of double bonds, in addition to aldehyde groups, and to measure these quantitatively (*42,44*). The structure of the polymers may, therefore, be described as

$$\left[\begin{matrix} -CH_2-CH- \\ | \\ CHO \end{matrix}\right]_x \cdots \left[\begin{matrix} -CH-O- \\ | \\ CH=CH_2 \end{matrix}\right]_y$$

Branching and cross-linking, undoubtedly present in these polymers, are neglected in this formulation. The ratio $x:y$ may be varied within certain limits; however, with the cationic catalysts mentioned above it has not been possible to prepare polymers in which $x = 0$ or $y = 0$. In a formal sense these acrolein polymers may be considered copolymers, since the macro-molecules consist of two different repeating units. These are actually isomeric, but the chemical structure of the backbone and the substituents depends on the manner in which the monomer is incorporated in the polymer.

For the cationic acrolein copolymers spectroscopic and chemical methods may be employed as well, to demonstrate the presence of carbonyl and vinyl groups and of the comonomer. These copolymers contain, therefore, not two, but three different repeating units. Presumably, the differences in properties, as compared with the radical copolymers, are due to this special structure. The elucidation of structure and the analytical determination of the composition are therefore greatly hindered; in particular, it is doubtful whether the copolymerization equation is applicable in this case. It is an advantage, however, that the cationic copolymers are soluble in many cases.

7-5. ANIONIC POLYMERIZATION

A. Homopolymerization with Various Catalysts

It has long been known that acrolein forms oily or resinous products under the influence of alkali hydroxides or organic bases (129). They are easily distinguished from the products prepared by free-radical polymeriza-tion, in that they are readily dissolved in organic solvents. In spite of extensive studies the method of formation, the structure, and the molecular weight of the substance were not clear. It was assumed at first that polycondensations were taking place. The work of Gilbert and Donleavy (130) permitted the conclusion that stepwise Michael addition was involved:

$$CH_2{=}CH{-}CHO \xrightarrow[OH^-]{H_2O} HO{-}CH_2{-}CH_2{-}CHO$$

$$\downarrow$$

$$\underset{\substack{|\\CHO}}{HO{-}CH_2{-}CH}{-}(\underset{\substack{|\\CHO}}{CH_2{-}CH})_n{-}\underset{\substack{|\\CHO}}{CH_2{-}CH_2} \qquad (7\text{-}35)$$

Presumably, there were also concurrent side reactions, and the molecular weight was undoubtedly not high. Besides aqueous sodium hydroxide (130), the compounds potassium carbonate (15), oxides or hydroxides of copper, silver, or lead (131), alkali nitrites or alkaline-earth nitrites (132) and, most recently, ammonia (133) have been employed. Considering the conditions used, it appears doubtful whether an anionic polymerization is truly involved. Only recently have experimental conditions been used that may be said to be typical for anionic polymerizations (40,42,45–47,134–136). Suitable catalysts were sodium naphthalene, triphenylmethylsodium, potassium benzophenone, sodium methoxide, sodamide, n-butyllithium, piperidine, triethylamine,

TABLE 7-4

Examples of Anionic Polymerization of Acrolein

Solvent[a]	Initiator	Mole-% based on monomer	Temp., °C	Time, min	Yield, %
THF	Sodium naphthalene	0.5	−50	285	79
THF	Tritylsodium	1.0	−35	180	93
THF	Tributylphosphine	0.1	−60	30	62
THF	Sodium cyanide	0.1	−60	240	43
THF	Potassium benzophenone	0.5	−55	150	55
DMF	Triphenylphosphine	0.1	−40	45	24
DMF	Sodium cyanide	0.02	−40	60	55
DMF	Lithium cyanide	0.08	0	2	50
Toluene	n-Butyllithium	1	+20	600	91[b]
Toluene	Sodium cyanide	0.08	−40	300	30
Acetonitrile	Sodium methoxide	1.0	−35	25	48
Diethyl ether	Sodium methoxide	1.0	−30	240	46[b]
Formaldehyde dimethylacetal	Potassium benzophenone	0.5	−30	150	33[b]

[a] THF = tetrahydrofuran, DMF = dimethyl formamide.

[b] The polymer precipitated during polymerization and was insoluble.

aliphatic and aromatic *tert* phosphines, alkali cyanides, potassium and lithium borohydrides, Grignard reagents, calcium–zinc tetraethyl. Less effective or ineffective were diethylzinc, phosphites, phosphine oxides, amine oxides, triphenylamine, and triphenylarsine.

The effectiveness of the phosphines decreased in the following order under comparable conditions (*134*): tripropyl-, tributyl-, diphenylmethyl-, triphenyl-. The catalytic activity is therefore related not only to basicity or dipole moment but also to size.

The polymerization may be carried out between −60 and +20°C in bulk or in solution. In bulk it is frequently too vigorous and cannot be controlled. Solution polymerization is, therefore, preferred. The nature and amount of the solvent has a great influence, not only on the course of polymerization, but also on the properties of the products.

Suitable reaction media are toluene, diethyl ether, methylal, methyl acetate, tetrahydrofuran, ethylene glycol dimethyl ether, acetonitrile, and dimethyl formamide. Some typical examples of anionic polymerization of acrolein are shown in Table 7-4. Depending on conditions, the polymerization either is homogeneous or has separation of the polymer. Gel formation frequently takes place at high conversions.

The polyacroleins prepared by anionic polymerization are frequently altered during workup or on standing. The secondary reactions mostly render them insoluble.

The most advantageous method is the polymerization of acrolein in tetrahydrofuran at $-50°C$, initiated with a solution of sodium cyanide in dimethyl formamide (47,137). As will be described in Section 7-5C, the polymers formed in this way have structural regularity, are soluble, and may be stored for long periods of time without change. Other cyanides may also be used, but they give polymers with somewhat different properties (137).

α-Methacrolein and other α-alkylacroleins have been polymerized anionically (138). Suitable catalysts have been metallic sodium, sodium naphthalene, or tritylsodium, and the reaction is conveniently carried out in tetrahydrofuran at temperatures of $+20$ to $-20°C$.

B. Initiation Step

The initiation step of anionic polymerization depends largely on the system used and cannot be formulated as generally as that of free-radical polymerization. This is particularly so in the case of acrolein, in which there are several possible modes of attack by the initiator.

In the case of organometallic compounds with acrolein, the initiation should consist of a nucleophilic attack of the base on the carbon atom of the carbonyl group and resulting formulation of an alkoxide anion:

$$Me^{(+)}B^{(-)} + \underset{\underset{CH=CH_2}{|}}{HC}=O \longrightarrow B-\underset{\underset{CH=CH_2}{|}}{HC}-\overline{O}|^{(-)} + Me^{(+)} \qquad (7\text{-}36)$$

This reaction should also hold, according to the knowledge of synthetic chemistry, for polymerization induced by alkali borohydrides or cyanides.

For reactions initiated by phosphines several possibilities must be considered:

$$(C_6H_5)_3^{(+)}P-CH_2-\underset{\underset{CHO}{|}}{CH}^{(-)} \xrightarrow{HBr} (C_6H_5)_3^{(+)}P-CH_2-\underset{\underset{CHO}{|}}{CH_2} Br^{(-)} \qquad (7\text{-}37)$$

(a)

$$(C_6H_5)_3P + CH_2=CH-CH=O \xrightarrow{(b)} (C_6H_5)_3^{(+)}P-CH_2-CH=CH-O^{(-)} \xrightarrow{HBr} \qquad (7\text{-}38)$$
$$(C_6H_5)_3^{(+)}P-CH_2-CH=CH-OH \ Br^{(-)}$$

$$(C_6H_5)_3^{(+)}P-\underset{\underset{CH=CH_2}{|}}{CH}-O^{(-)} \xrightarrow{HBr} (C_6H_5)_3^{(+)}P-\underset{\underset{CH=CH_2}{|}}{CH}-OH \ Br^{(-)} \qquad (7\text{-}39)$$

(c)

One may assume at first that an addition of phosphine to the $C=C$ double bond takes place [Eq. (7-37), step (a)]; such reactions are well known and have been formulated by Horner et al. (46) for the initiation of acrolein polymerization and by Koral (*139*) for the case of crotonaldehyde. On the other hand, attack may be on the C=O double bond (*140*) [Eq. (7-39), step (c)]. Finally, there can also be a 1,4 addition to the conjugated-double-bond system [Eq. (7-38), step (b)]. Although there are many examples of the first two reactions cited above, there had been no investigations of the reaction of phosphines with α,β-unsaturated aldehydes. Consequently, triphenylphosphine was reacted with acrolein under polymerization conditions and the primary adduct trapped by addition of hydrogen bromide (*42*). Only triphenyl-α-hydroxyallylphosphonium bromide could be isolated. Therefore, the initiation step must proceed according to Eq. (7-39), that is, by addition to the carbonyl group. Although the initiation step has thus been ascertained, it is not possible to draw any conclusions about propagation. These may be inferred from the structure of the polymers.

C. Properties and Structure of the Polymers

The properties of polyacrolein prepared by anionic polymerization depend, within limits, on the conditions of preparation, because the choice of reaction medium, catalyst, and temperature affects the structure of the resulting polymer. This hitherto insufficiently considered fact accounts for the many contradictory statements in the literature regarding the properties of polyacrolein. The following description holds for polyacrolein prepared according to the conditions of Table 7-4. These polymers differ fundamentally from those prepared by free-radical polymerization, in that they are soluble (at least when freshly prepared) in a variety of organic solvents but are insoluble in aqueous sulfurous acid. They melt or soften between 90 and 180°C, the lowest softening points being obtained at low temperatures of polymerization (*137*).

The anionic polymers have certain similarities to the cationic polymers. Infrared spectra indicate that both types of polyacrolein contain aldehyde as well as vinyl groups. They are, therefore, built up of two repeating units:

$$\left[\begin{array}{c} CH_2-CH- \\ | \\ CH=O \end{array}\right]_x \left[\begin{array}{c} CH-O- \\ | \\ CH=CH_2 \end{array}\right]_y$$

Catalytic hydrogenation shows the presence of up to 80 mole-% of C=C double bonds. They also form polymeric derivatives with phenylhydrazine, the nitrogen content of which may be used to calculate the aldehyde content (*45*).

Halogens may be added to the double bonds. The latter may also be used for a subsequent polymerization, a fact that may explain the already mentioned cross-linking on standing. This property may be used, for example, to obtain gels by illumination (*141*). The copolymerization of these vinyl side groups with other monomers will be described in Section 7-5D.

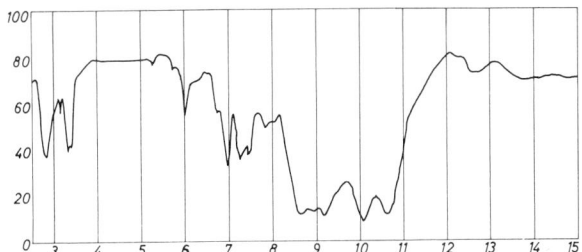

Fig. 7-6. Infrared spectrum of polyacrolein (KBr pellet); polymerization in tetrahydrofuran with sodium cyanide at $-48°C$.

An exception are the polymers prepared with sodium or sodium cyanide in tetrahydrofuran or toluene at -50 to $-40°C$ (*45,47,137*). They soften at 80°C and contain no aldehyde groups with the vinyl groups. A typical infrared spectrum is shown in Fig. 7-6. These polymers have, therefore, a uniform structure and contain exclusively the following repeating unit:

$$\left[\begin{array}{c} -CH-O- \\ | \\ CH=CH_2 \end{array}\right]_n$$

They may therefore be designated 3,4 polyacroleins. The free-radical polymers would, according to this designation, be considered 1,2 polyacroleins since, in this case, only the vinyl groups participate in the propagation. The structure, given above, of anionic polyacrolein was confirmed by chemical reactions and degradative processes.

For those polymers not uniformly constructed, it was necessary to establish whether in addition to 1,2 and 3,4 repeating units any 1,4 polymerization had taken place. Accordingly, the double bonds of these polyacroleins were first catalytically hydrogenated and then hydrolyzed. According to the following equations,

$$-CH-O-CH-O-CH_2-CH=CH-O-CH-O-$$
$$CH \quad CH \qquad\qquad CH \qquad\qquad (7\text{-}40)$$
$$CH_2 \quad CH_2 \quad \Big\downarrow H_2 \quad CH_2$$

$$-CH-O-CH-O-CH_2-CH_2-CH_2-O-CH-O-$$
$$CH_2 \quad CH_2 \qquad\qquad\qquad CH_2$$
$$CH_3 \quad CH_3 \quad \Big\downarrow H_2O \quad CH_3 \qquad (7\text{-}41)$$

$$CHO + CHO + HOCH_2-CH_2-CH_2-OH + CHO$$
$$CH_2 \quad CH_2 \qquad\qquad\qquad\qquad CH_2$$
$$CH_3 \quad CH_3 \qquad\qquad\qquad\qquad CH_3$$

propionaldehyde is formed from 3,4 units. Since no propanediol could be found, it must be concluded that, at least under the polymerization conditions cited above, no significant amount of 1,4 polymerization takes place. This conclusion was confirmed by nuclear magnetic resonance studies (134).

Judged from these results, the following reactions must be involved in propagation (137):

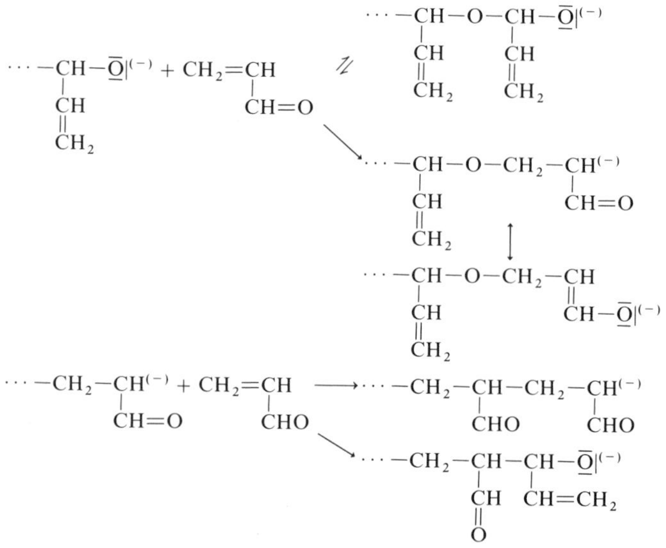

$$
\cdots-CH-\overline{\underline{O}}|^{(-)} + CH_2=CH \quad \nearrow
\begin{array}{cc}
\cdots-CH-O-CH-\overline{\underline{O}}|^{(-)} \\
| \qquad\qquad | \\
CH \qquad\quad CH \\
\| \qquad\quad \| \\
CH_2 \qquad\quad CH_2
\end{array}
\qquad (7\text{-}42)
$$

with left side:
$$
\cdots-CH-\overline{\underline{O}}|^{(-)} + CH_2=CH
$$
$$
| \qquad\qquad\qquad |
$$
$$
CH \qquad\qquad\qquad CH=O
$$
$$
\|
$$
$$
CH_2
$$

$$
\searrow
\begin{array}{cc}
\cdots-CH-O-CH_2-CH^{(-)} \\
| \qquad\qquad\quad | \\
CH \qquad\qquad CH=O \\
\| \\
CH_2
\end{array}
\qquad (7\text{-}43)
$$

$$
\downarrow
$$

$$
\begin{array}{cc}
\cdots-CH-O-CH_2-CH \\
| \qquad\qquad\quad \| \\
CH \qquad\qquad CH-\overline{\underline{O}}|^{(-)} \\
\| \\
CH_2
\end{array}
$$

$$
\cdots-CH_2-CH^{(-)} + CH_2=CH \longrightarrow \cdots-CH_2-CH-CH_2-CH^{(-)}
$$
$$
| \qquad\qquad\quad | \qquad\qquad\qquad | \qquad\quad |
$$
$$
CH=O \qquad\quad CHO \qquad\qquad CHO \qquad CHO \qquad (7\text{-}44)
$$

$$
\searrow \cdots-CH_2-CH-CH-\overline{\underline{O}}|^{(-)}
$$
$$
| \qquad |
$$
$$
CH \quad CH=CH_2 \qquad (7\text{-}45)
$$
$$
\|
$$
$$
O
$$

Therefore there are two different kinds of growing chain ends, namely alkoxide anions and carbanions. The counterions of the two chain ends may exist in equilibrium (not indicated here) with free ions or as ion pairs. The propagating form of both kinds may add acrolein either on the vinyl group [Eqs. (7-43), (7-44)] or on the carbonyl group [Eqs. (7-42), (7-45)]. There are thus four different propagation reactions. The positions of the various equilibria and the rates of the various propagation reactions depend very much on the medium of reaction and on the temperature. It may be understood that these parameters have a significant influence, not only on the over-all rate of reaction, but also on the structure of the polymers. Although the end products may be formally considered to be copolymers, since they have two different repeating units, the usual copolymerization equation does not apply to this system, because one of the propagation steps [Eq. (7-42)] is reversible (142).

D. Two-Step Copolymerization

Nothing has yet been reported on the anionic copolymerization of acrolein with other monomers. The particular structure of anionic polyacrolein offers, however, a new method of copolymerization in two separate reactions, distinct in time. The principle of this procedure, called "two-step copolymerization," is illustrated in the following equations (143):

$$\text{CH}_2=\underset{\underset{\text{CH}=O}{|}}{\text{CH}} + \text{CH}_2=\underset{\underset{C_6H_5}{|}}{\text{CH}} \begin{array}{l} \xrightarrow{\text{rad.}} \cdots \left[\text{CH}_2-\underset{\underset{\text{CH}=O}{|}}{\text{CH}}\right]_x\left[\text{CH}_2-\underset{\underset{C_6H_5}{|}}{\text{CH}-}\right]_z \cdots \quad (7\text{-}46) \\ \xrightarrow{\text{anion.(a)}} \cdots -\underset{\underset{\text{CH}_2=\text{CH}}{|}}{\text{CH}-O}- \cdots + \text{CH}_2=\underset{\underset{C_6H_5}{|}}{\text{CH}} \xrightarrow{\text{rad.(b)}} \cdots -\underset{\underset{\cdots-\text{CH}_2\text{CHCH}_2\text{CH}-\cdots}{|}}{\text{CH}-O}- \cdots \\ \hspace{17em} \underset{C_6H_5}{|} \\ \hspace{20em} (7\text{-}47) \end{array}$$

A normal copolymerization [Eq. (7-46)] consists of the addition of only *one* catalyst to the mixture of two different monomers (in this particular case acrolein and styrene). Propagation is thereby initiated, in which both monomers participate according to their respective reactivities. There results a copolymer built up more or less statistically.

In the two-step copolymerization a catalyst is added to the monomer mixture, which polymerizes the acrolein exclusively [Eq. (7-47a)]; an alkali alkoxide is suitable in this case. There results a polyacrolein that has a certain amount of vinyl substituents but no styrene. Styrene is a solvent only for the unsaturated polyacrolein formed in this first step of the process. After the anionic polymerization is either completed or interrupted by the addition of an acid, a radical donor is added. In this way is started a copolymerization between the vinyl groups of polyacrolein and the styrene [Eq. (7-47b)]. Graft copolymers are formed at first and, finally, cross-linking produces cured objects.

The two-step copolymerization described here may be varied in a number of ways (144) and utilize certain other monomer pairs (145). It differs from the known curing of unsaturated polyesters as follows:

1. Both reaction steps are polymerizations: one is anionic and the other free-radical.

2. The monomer (styrene) required for the second step (curing) is present from the beginning in the reaction mixture.

7-6. POLYMERIZATION OF ACROLEIN DERIVATIVES

As was described in Section 7-3-F, polyacrolein prepared by free-radical processes can be converted to polymeric derivatives. It was therefore obvious to attempt the preparation of acrolein derivatives and to subject these to polymerization. Many investigations have already been carried out with this goal in mind, but few have been successful.

Acrolein forms with acetic anhydride, for example, allylidene diacetate,

$$CH_2{=}CH{-}CH(OOCCH_3)_2$$

which may be polymerized by radical initiators or by gamma rays (147). Molecular weights have, however, not been high. Free-radical copolymerizations are also possible with vinyl compounds (148), such as styrene, methyl methacrylate, and vinyl acetate.

Acrolein acetals,

$$CH_2{=}CH{-}CH(OR)_2$$

such as the diethyl acetal and the di-β-chloroethyl acetal, which are readily prepared, may not be homopolymerized either with free-radical or ionic initiators. Copolymerization may be carried out between acrolein acetals and acrylonitrile, acrylamide, vinyl acetate, or methyl methacrylate (149). The cationic polymerization of cyclic acetals, such as 2-vinyl-1,3-dioxolane,

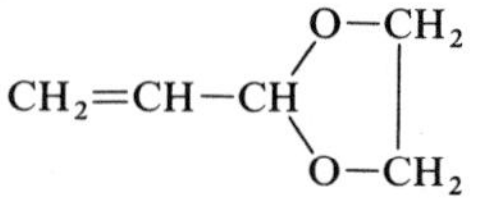

$$CH_2{=}CH{-}CH \begin{array}{c} O{-}CH_2 \\ | \\ O{-}CH_2 \end{array}$$

produces complications, because ring-opening reactions take place (163). Copolymerizations of this acrolein derivative have also been described (150).

Diallylidene pentaerythritol, the bisacrolein acetal of pentaerythritol, has been particularly well studied (15):

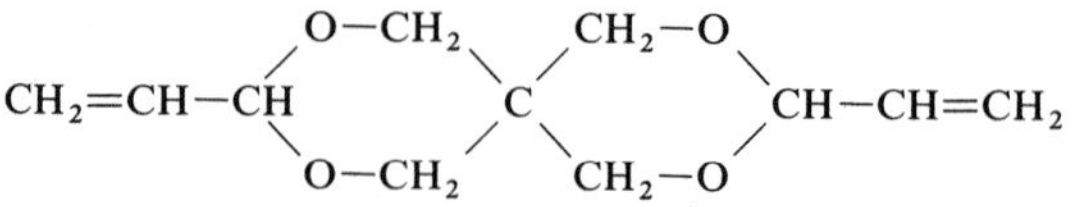

$$CH_2{=}CH{-}CH \begin{array}{c} O{-}CH_2 \\ O{-}CH_2 \end{array} C \begin{array}{c} CH_2{-}O \\ CH_2{-}O \end{array} CH{-}CH{=}CH_2$$

Radical homopolymerization and copolymerization result in the formation of cross-linked polymers of unknown structure. Addition reactions to the double bonds produce polymers (15,151–154).

Acrolein oxime,

$$CH_2{=}CH{-}CH{=}N{-}OH$$

may be polymerized by radical or cationic initiators, and also by gamma rays (147,155,156). The polymer is soluble in various organic solvents and softens at 70 to 100°C. Hydrogenation with Raney nickel produces a polymeric amine with about 80% of the theoretical quantity of amino groups.

Finally, the diene adducts of acrolein should be mentioned, since they must be considered acrolein derivatives. 2-Formyldihydropyran, obtained by dimerization (*35*), contains also two groups,

$$\text{[structure: dihydropyran ring with O and CHO substituents]}$$

capable of polymerization. On standing the polymerization of the carbonyl groups produces a solid resin, which has almost exclusively the following repeating unit (*157*):

$$-\text{CH}-\text{O}-$$
$$\text{[dihydropyran ring structure]}$$

Upon being heated, depolymerization sets in. Polymers that are very high in molecular weight and thermally stable are obtained with the use of diethylaluminum chloride as polymerization catalyst (*158*).

With certain cationic catalysts 2-formyldihydropyran reacts like a vinyl ether:

$$\text{[tetrahydropyran ring with O and CHO substituents]}$$

The aldehyde substituents may be determined from the infrared spectra and chemical reactions. They undergo side reactions already during the polymerization, with consequent cross-linking and disturbance of the regular structure.

The unsubstituted dihydropyran may also be polymerized cationically (*154*):

$$\text{[dihydropyran ring with O]}$$

The molecular weights are not very high. The products contain carbonyl groups, which indicate a ring-opening mechanism. The diene adduct of acrolein with vinyl ethers may also be polymerized.

$$\text{[dihydropyran ring with O and O—R substituents]}$$

7-7. CONCLUSION

Acrolein is a compound with versatile reactivity. It contains two different groups capable of undergoing polymerization, which may be effected with various kinds of catalysts. Because of this, and in contrast to most other monomers, the chemical structure of the resulting polymers depends largely on the conditions of polymerization. The polymers contain either aldehyde or vinyl groups as substituents, or both functional groups together. Because of differences in structure the polymers prepared by different methods have entirely different properties. Numerous reactions may be carried out with the substituent groups, whereby chemically modified polyacroleins are formed. An important derivative is the water-soluble adduct resulting from the reaction of sulfurous acid with polyacrolein prepared by free-radical polymerization. It exhibits special reactivity, even with other polymers. Various addition reactions may be carried out on the vinyl substituents of anionic polymers. Even polymerization is possible at these double bonds, giving branched or cross-linked polymers.

Finally, it should be remarked that acrolein as well as some of its derivatives may undergo polycondensation and polyaddition reactions, which have not been described here.

The multiplicity of reactions possible both with the monomer and the polymers makes the study of acrolein polymers a particularly rich and interesting field to the chemist, but is also the cause of many unexpected difficulties.

REFERENCES

1. D. S. Breslow, G. E. Hulse, and A. S. Matlack, *J. Am. Chem. Soc.*, **79**, 3760 (1957).
2. J. P. Kennedy and A. W. Langer, Jr., *Fortschr. Hochpolymer.-Forsch.*, **3**, 523 (1964).
3. Y. Iwakura, T. Kurosaki, and N. Nakabayashi, *Makromolekul. Chem.*, **44-46**, 570 (1961).
4. J. A. Simms, *J. Appl. Polymer Sci.*, **5**, 58 (1961).
5. W. Kawai and Sh. Tsutsumi, *J. Chem. Soc. Japan Pure Chem. Sect.*, **80**, 88 (1959); *CA*, **55**, 4466b (1961).
6. For other monomers with C=C double bonds and epoxide groups, see F. C. Frostick, B. Phillips, and P. S. Starcher, *J. Am. Chem. Soc.*, **81**, 3350 (1959).
7. G. Natta et al., *Makromolekul. Chem.* **44-46**, 546 (1961); **51**, 148 (1962).
8. R. C. Schulz and R. Stenner, *Makromolekul. Chem.*, **72**, 202 (1964); C. G. Overberger, S. Ozaki, and H. Mukamal, *J. Polymer Sci.*, **B2**, 627 (1964).
9. G. Dall'Asta et al., *Makromolekul. Chem.*, **56**, 224 (1962); **69**, 163 (1963).
10. W. L. Truett et al., *J. Am. Chem. Soc.*, **82**, 2337 (1960).
11. Previous reviews:
    R. C. Schulz, H. Cherdron, and W. Kern, in *Methoden der organischen Chemie*, 4th ed., Vol. 14-1 (E. Müller, ed.), Thieme-Verlag, Stuttgart, 1961, p. 1080.
    R. C. Schulz, *Angew. Chem.*, **76**, 357 (1964); *Angew. Chem. Intern. Ed. Engl.*, **3**, 416 (1964).
    R. C. Schulz, in *Encyclopedia of Polymer Science and Technology*, Vol. 1 (H. F. Mark, N. G. Gaylord, N. M. B. Kales, eds.), Wiley (Interscience), New York, 1964, p. 160.
    E. Bergman, W. T. Tsatsos, and R. F. Fischer, *J. Polymer Sci.*, **A3**, 3485 (1965).
12. J. Redtenbacher, *Liebigs Ann. Chem.*, **47**, 113 (1843).
13. H. Adkins and W. H. Hartung, *Org. Synth. Coll. Vol.* **1**, 15 (1964).

14. J. G. M. Bremner, D. G. Jones, and S. Beaumont, *J. Chem. Soc.*, **1946**, 1018.

15. H. Schulz and H. Wagner, *Angew. Chem.*, **62**, 105 (1950).

16. F. Weygand and G. Schaefer, *Ber.*, **85**, 311 (1952).

17. G. Denigès, *Compt. Rend.*, **126**, 1145 (1898); O. Bayer in *Methoden der organischen Chemie*, 4th ed., Vol. 7/1 (E. Müller, ed.), Thieme-Verlag, Stuttgart, 1954, p. 157.

18. G. W. Hearne and M. L. Adams, U.S. Pat. 2,451,485 (1948).

19. A. Hausweiler, K. Schwarzer, and R. Stroh, Ger. Pat. 1,079,615 (1960).

20. J. L. Callahan, R. W. Foreman, and F. Vaetsch, U.S. Pat. 2,941,007 (1960).

21. Belg. Pat. 587,684 (1960).

22. H. H. Voge, C. D. Wagner, and D. P. Stevenson, *J. Catalysis*, **2**, 58 (1963); C. R. Adams and T. J. Jennings, *ibid.*, **2**, 63 (1963); W. M. H. Sachtler, *Rec. Trav. Chim.*, **82**, 243 (1963); F. L. J. Sixma, *ibid.*, **82**, 901 (1963); C. C. McCain, *Nature*, **198**, 989 (1963); E. R. White, H. G. Davis, and E. S. Hammack, *J. Am. Chem. Soc.*, **87**, 1175 (1965).

23. H. Mackle and L. E. Sutton, *Trans. Faraday Soc.*, **47**, 691 (1951); J. Fine et al., *J. Chem. Phys.*, **23**, 601 (1955); R. Wagner et al., *ibid.*, **26**, 634 (1957).

24. C. W. Smith, (ed.), *Acrolein*, Wiley, New York, 1962.

25. S. Nagakura, *Mol. Phys.*, **3**, 105 (1960); K. Inuzuka, *Bull. Chem. Soc. Japan*, **34**, 729 (1961); *CA*, **56**, 5547g (1962); J. M. Hollas, *Spectrochim. Acta*, **19**, 1425 (1963); R. K. Harris, *ibid.*, **20**, 1129 (1964); R. K. Harris and R. E. Witkowski, *ibid.*, **20**, 1651 (1964); A. V. Krishna Rao, *J. Sci. Ind. Res. India*, **B21**, 446 (1962); *Chem. Zentr.*, **1966**, 9–769.

26. R. M. Joshi, *Makromolekul. Chem.*, **55**, 48 (1962).

27. H. D. Finch, see Ref. *24*, p. 88.

28. P. H. Williams, see Ref. *24*, p. 51.

29. C. W. Smith and R. T. Holm, *J. Org. Chem.*, **22**, 746 (1957).

30. G. B. Payne, *J. Am. Chem. Soc.*, **80**, 6461 (1958); **81**, 4901 (1959).

31. T. Curtius and F. Wirsing, *J. Prakt. Chem.*, **50**, 531 (1894).

32. E. Fischer, *Ber.*, **19**, 1563 (1886); *Liebigs Ann. Chem.*, **239**, 194 (1887); K. Auwers and A. Kreuder, *Ber.*, **58**, 1974 (1925).

33. R. C. Morris, see Ref. *24*, p. 110.

34. H. D. Finch, *J. Org. Chem.*, **27**, 649 (1962).

35. K. Alder and E. Rüden, *Ber.*, **74**, 920 (1941).

36. O. Diels and K. Alder, *Liebigs Ann. Chem.*, **460**, 98 (1928).

37. R. J. Longley and W. S. Emerson, *J. Am. Chem. Soc.*, **72**, 3079 (1950).

38. C. W. Smith, see Ref. *24*, p. 211.

39. R. C. Schulz and W. Passmann, *Makromolekul. Chem.*, **60**, 152 (1963).

40. R. C. Schulz, *Makromolekul. Chem.*, **17**, 62 (1955).

41. R. C. Schulz, H. Cherdron, and W. Kern, *Makromolekul. Chem.*, **24**, 141 (1957).

42. R. C. Schulz, *Chimia (Aarau)*, **19**, 143 (1965).

43. I. V. Andreeva, M. M. Koton et al., *Vysokomolekul. Soedin.*, **4**, 528 1537 (1962).

44. Y. Toi and Y. Hachihama, *Bull. Chem. Soc. Japan*, **37**, 302 (1964).

45. R. C. Schulz and W. Passmann, *Makromolekul. Chem.*, **60**, 139 (1963).

46. L. Horner, W. Jurgeleit, and K. Klüpfel, *Liebigs Ann. Chem.*, **591**, 116 (1955).

47. R. C. Schulz, G. Wegner, and W. Kern, *J. Polymer Sci.*, **C**, in press; *IUPAC Symposium, Prague, 1965, Preprint 140*.

48. C. Moureu and C. Dufraisse, *Compt. Rend.*, **169**, 621 (1919); **175**, 127 (1922); **176**, 797 (1923); **191**, 1126 (1930).

49. A. Wöhlk, *J. Prakt. Chem.*, **61**(2), 200 (1900); J. U. Nef, *Liebigs Ann. Chem.*, **335**, 221 (1904); G. Lockemann and O. Liesche, *J. Prakt. Chem.* **71**(2), 483 (1905).

50. F. E. Blacet, G. H. Fielding, and J. G. Roof, *J. Am. Chem. Soc.*, **59**, 2375 (1937).

51. A. Henglein, W. Schnabel, and R. C. Schulz, *Makromolekul. Chem.*, **31**, 181 (1959).

52. Y. Toi and Y. Hachihama, *J. Chem. Soc. Japan. Ind. Chem. Sect.*, **62**, 1924 (1959); *Bull. Chem. Soc. Japan*, **37**, 307 (1964).
53. E. I. Finkelstein and A. D. Abkin, *Dokl. Akad. Nauk SSSR*, **161**, 1098 (1965).
54. R. C. Schulz, S. Suzuki, H. Cherdron, and W. Kern, *Makromolekul. Chem.*, **53**, 145 (1962).
55. H. C. Miller and H. S. Rothrock, U.S. Pat. 2,657,192 (1951).
56. H. Cherdron, R. C. Schulz, and W. Kern, *Makromolekul. Chem.*, **32**, 197 (1959).
57. H. Cherdron, *Kunststoffe*, **50**, 568 (1960).
58. E. E. Ryder and P. Pezzaglia, *J. Polymer Sci.*, **A3**, 3459 (1965).
59. D. M. Yost, *J. Am. Chem. Soc.*, **48**, 152 (1926); R. G. R. Bacon, *Quart. Rev. (London)*, **9**, 287 (1955).
60. W. V. Smith and R. H. Ewart, *J. Chem. Phys.*, **16**, 592 (1948); H. Gerrens, *Fortschr. Hochpolymer.-Forsch.*, **1**, 234 (1959).
61. S. Okamura et al., *J. Polymer Sci.*, **58**, 221 (1962).
62. R. C. Schulz, unpublished work, 1962–1966.
63. F. J. Welch, Fr. Pat. 1,325,213 (1962).
64. H. Wolz and W. Bock, Ger. Pat. 855,162 (1944).
65. H. T. Neher and C. F. Woodward, U.S. Pat. 2,416,536 (1942).
66. R. C. Schulz, H. Cherdron, and W. Kern, *Makromolekul. Chem.*, **28**, 197 (1958).
67. R. C. Schulz, E. Kaiser, and W. Kern, *Makromolekul. Chem.*, **58**, 160 (1962).
68. H. C. Haas and M. S. Simon, *J. Polymer Sci.*, **9**, 309 (1952).
69. T. Alfrey, Jr. and C. C. Price, *J. Polymer Sci.*, **2**, 101 (1947).
70. T. C. Schwan and C. C. Price, *J. Polymer Sci.*, **40**, 457 (1959).
71. J. Brandrup, *Faserforsch. Textiltech.*, **12**, 133, 208 (1961).
72. J. Drougas and R. L. Guile, *J. Polymer Sci.*, **55**, 297 (1961).
73. L. J. Young, *J. Polymer Sci.*, **54**, 411 (1961).
74. G. E. Ham, ed., *Copolymerization, High Polymers*, Vol. 18, Wiley (Interscience), New York, 1964.
75. W. Kern, R. C. Schulz, and H. Cherdron, Ger. Pat. 1,019,825; U.S. Pat. 3,036,978 (1958); W. Göltner and P. Schlack, Ger. Pat. Application 1,104,183 (1959); Belg. Pat. 593,116.
76. R. C. Schulz, H. Cherdron, and W. Kern, *Makromolekul. Chem.*, **29**, 190 (1959).
77. R. C. Schulz, E. Kaiser, and W. Kern, *Makromolekul. Chem.*, **76**, 99 (1964).
78. S. Haworth and J. R. Holker, *J. Soc. Dyers Colourists*, **81**, 212 (1965).
79. R. C. Schulz, *Kunststoffe*, **48**, 257 (1958).
80. H. Schilling, *Kolloid-Z.*, **175**, 110 (1961).
81. R. F. Fischer and A. T. Stewart, Jr., *J. Polymer Sci.*, **A3**, 3495 (1965).
82. R. Hank and H. Schilling, *Makromolekul. Chem.*, **76**, 134 (1964).
83. R. C. Schulz, J. Kovacs, and W. Kern, *Makromolekul. Chem.*, **52**, 236 (1962).
84. R. Hank, *Makromolekul. Chem.*, **52**, 108 (1962).
85. R. C. Schulz, E. Müller, and W. Kern, *Makromolekul. Chem.*, **30**, 39 (1959).
86. R. C. Schulz, H. Cherdron, and W. Kern, *Makromolekul. Chem.*, **24**, 151 (1957).
87. E. E. Seibert, *J. Polymer Sci.*, **C8**, 87 (1965).
88. R. C. Schulz, I. Löflund, and W. Kern, *Makromolekul. Chem.*, **32**, 209 (1959).
89. M. S. Scherlin et al., *Chem. Zentr.*, **1939**, 1, 1971.
90. E. E. Gilbert and J. J. Donleavy, *J. Am. Chem. Soc.*, **60**, 1911 (1938).
91. R. C. Schulz, *Kunststoffe*, **47**, 303 (1957).
92. R. C. Schulz, K. Meyersen, and W. Kern, *Makromolekul. Chem.*, **54**, 156 (1962); **59**, 123 (1962).
93. L. Hunter and J. W. Forbes, *J. Polymer Sci.*, **A3**, 3471 (1965).
94. R. C. Schulz, K. Meyersen, and W. Kern, *Makromolekul. Chem.*, **53**, 58 (1962).
95. K. Meyersen, R. C. Schulz, and W. Kern, *Makromolekul. Chem.*, **58**, 204 (1962).

96. An IR spectroscopic method for the determination of carbonyl groups and unbound water was recently reported: J. W. Forbes and D. O. Schissler, *J. Polymer Sci.*, **C8**, 61 (1965).

97. W. Kern, R. C. Schulz, and D. Braun, *J. Polymer Sci.*, **48**, 91 (1960); *Chemiker Ztg.*, **84**, 385 (1960).

98. R. C. Schulz and P. Elzer, *Makromolekul. Chem.*, **42**, 205 (1961).

99. R. C. Schulz, J. Kovacs, and W. Kern, *Makromolekul. Chem.*, **54**, 146 (1962).

100. R. C. Schulz, I. Löflund, and W. Kern, *Makromolekul. Chem.*, **28**, 58 (1958).

101. R. C. Schulz, H. Fauth, and W. Kern, *Makromolekul. Chem.*, **20**, 161 (1956).

102. M. Marx and J. Kovacs, unpublished work, 1961, 1963.

103. R. C. Schulz, R. Holländer, and W. Kern, *Makromolekul. Chem.*, **40**, 16 (1960).

104. Th. Kauffmann and F. P. Boettcher, *Liebigs Ann. Chem.*, **625**, 123 (1959).

105. R. C. Schulz, E. Müller, and W. Kern, *Naturwiss.*, **45**, 440 (1958).

106. H. Thiele and F. Jentsch, *Kolloid-Z.*, **190**, 99 (1963).

107. R. C. Schulz, H. Fauth, and W. Kern, *Makromolekul. Chem.*, **21**, 227 (1956).

108. R. Neeb, unpublished work, Mainz, 1964.

109. K. Meyersen, unpublished work, Mainz, 1962.

110. R. C. Schulz, *Kolloid-Z.*, **182**, 99 (1962).

111. R. J. Carr and B. E. Gordon, *J. Polymer Sci.*, **C8**, 71 (1965).

112. R. C. Schulz, J. Kovacs, and W. Kern, *Makromolekul. Chem.*, **67**, 187 (1963).

113. W. H. Houff, W. Creck, and W. T. Tsatsos, U.S. Pat. 3,079,280 (1963).

114. R. C. Schulz, *Kunststoffe-Plastics*, **6**, 32 (1959).

115. W. Kern and R. C. Schulz, Ger. Pat. 1,016,020 (1955); O. Schweitzer, W. Kern, R. C. Schulz, and R. Holländer, Ger. Pat. 1,019,825 (1956); W. Kern, R. C. Schulz, and I. Löflund, Ger. Pat. 1,083,051 (1958).

116. R. C. Schulz and W. Kern, *Makromolekul. Chem.*, **18/19**, 4 (1956).

117. T. L. Dawson and F. J. Welch, *J. Am. Chem. Soc.*, **86**, 4791 (1964).

118. R. C. Schulz, H. Cherdron, and W. Kern, *Makromolekul. Chem.*, **24**, 151 (1957).

119. E. E. Seibert, *J. Polymer Sci.*, **C8**, 87 (1965).

120. J. V. Andreeva et al., *Soviet Radiochem.*, **6**, 76 (1964).

121. W. Kern, R. C. Schulz, and H. Cherdron, Ger. Pat. 1,062,937 (1958); U.S. Pat. 3,206,422.

122. H. Cherdron, R. C. Schulz, and W. Kern, *Makromolekul. Chem.*, **32**, 197 (1959); H. Cherdron, *Kunststoffe*, **50**, 568 (1960).

123. E. E. Ryder and P. Pezzaglia, *J. Polymer Sci.*, **A3**, 3459 (1965).

124. R. C. Schulz and I. Löflund, *Angew. Chem.*, **72**, 771 (1960).

125. R. C. Schulz, *Kolloid-Z.*, **182**, 99 (1962).

126. P. Pezzaglia et al., *Tappi*, **48**, 314 (1965).

127. P. H. Plesch, ed., *The Chemistry of Cationic Polymerization*, Pergamon, London, 1963.

128. R. Schaaf, unpublished work, Mainz, 1964–1966.

129. C. Moureu and C. Dufraisse, *Compt. Rend.*, **169**, 621 (1919); **175**, 127 (1922); **176**, 797 (1923).

130. E. E. Gilbert and J. J. Donleavy, *J. Am. Chem. Soc.*, **60**, 1911 (1938).

131. E. C. Shokal, U.S. Pat. 2,819,252 (1954) Shell Development.

132. G. W. Hearne et al., U.S. Pat. 2,809,185 (1954) Shell Development.

133. R. Hank and H. Schilling, *Makromolekul. Chem.*, **76**, 134 (1964).

134. G. Wegner, unpublished work, Mainz, 1963–1966.

135. M. M. Koton, I. V. Andreeva, and Y. P. Getmanchuk, *Vysokomolekul. Soedin.*, **4**, 1537 (1962).

136. J. Furukawa et al., *Makromolekul. Chem.*, **32**, 102 (1959).

137. R. C. Schulz, G. Wegner, and W. Kern, *Makromolekul. Chem.*, in press.

138. M. M. Koton et al., *Dokl. Akad. Nauk SSSR*, **155**, 836 (1964); *Vysokomolekul. Soedin.*, **7**, 2039 (1965); I. V. Andreeva and M. M. Koton, *IUPAC Symposium, Prague, 1965, Preprint 173.*

139. J. N. Koral, *Makromolekul. Chem.*, **62**, 148 (1963).

140. H. Hoffmann, *Angew. Chem.*, **72**, 77 (1960).

141. J. Golé and H. Calvayrac, *Compt. Rend.*, **260**, 163, 552 (1965).

142. P. Wittmer, *Bunsen Discussions, Ludwigshafen*, 1965; *Ber. Bunsen-Ges.*, **70**, 245 (1966).

143. R. C. Schulz and W. Passmann, *Makromolekul. Chem.*, **72**, 198 (1964).

144. J. Kovacs, unpublished work, Mainz, 1964.

145. R. C. Schulz and R. Stenner, *Makromolekul. Chem.*, **72**, 202 (1964).

146. Th. W. Evans, U.S. Pat. 2,478,154 (1949); *CA*, **43**, 8741i (1949).

147. Y. Hachihama and Y. Toi, *Technol. Rept. Osaka Univ.*, **13**, 237 (1963); *CA*, **59**, 10244c (1963); Y. Toi and Y. Hachihama, *J. Chem. Soc. Japan Ind. Chem. Sect.*, **63**, 1654 (1960).

148. E. F. Izard, *Ind. Eng. Chem.*, **42**, 2108 (1950); T. Saigusa and R. Oda, *Bull. Inst. Chem. Research Kyoto Univ.*, **34**, 56 (1956); *CA*, **51**, 4753h (1957); *CA*, **52**, 8617a (1958); L. M. Minsk et al., Brit. Pat. 571,635 (1945); *CA*, **41**, 2935 (1947).

149. E. F. Izard, U.S. Pat. 2,467,430 (1949); *CA*, **43**, 5635i (1949).

150. R. H. Wiley, U.S. Pat. 2,432,601 (1947); *CA*, **42**, 2994i (1948).

151. H. Stansburg and R. Guest, U.S. Pat. 2,960,495 (1960); *CA*, **55**, 7885e (1961).

152. J. G. Noltes and G. J. M. van der Kerk, *Rec. Trav. Chim.*, **80**, 623 (1961).

153. F. Brown, D. E. Hudgin, and R. J. Kray, *J. Chem. Eng. Data*, **4**, 182 (1959).

154. H. Orth, Ger. Pats. 852,301; 855,162 (1952).

155. Y. Toi and Y. Hachihama, *Kogyo Kagaku Zasshi*, **64**, 595 (1961); *CA*, **57**, 4857i (1962).

156. K. H. W. Tuerck, Brit. Pat. 578,598 (1946); *CA*, **41**, 1882g (1947).

157. S. Potnis, K. Shohara, R. C. Schulz, and W. Kern, *Makromolekul. Chem.*, **63**, 78 (1963).

158. H. Ohse, H. Cherdron, and F. Korte, *Makromolekul. Chem.*, **76**, 147 (1964).

159. K. Kamio, K. Meyersen, R. C. Schulz, and W. Kern, *Makromolekul. Chem.*, **90**, 187 (1966).

160. M. F. Schosstakowski et al., *Vysokomolekul. Soedin.*, **5**, 767 (1963); *Chem. Zentr.*, **1965**, 44–13917.

161. G. Bier, H. Hartel, and I. U. Nebel, *Makromolekul. Chem.*, **92**, 240 (1966).

162. E. Bäder, K. H. Rink, and H. Trautwein, *Makromolekul. Chem.*, **92**, 198 (1966).

163. K. Tada et al., *Makromolekul. Chem.*, **95**, 168 (1966).

CHAPTER 8

Heats of Polymerization and Their Structural and Mechanistic Implications

R. M. Joshi†

B. J. Zwolinski‡

Thermodynamics Research Center, Department of Chemistry
Texas A & M University, College Station, Texas

8-1. INTRODUCTION

Since the remarkable conquest of the polymerization of propylene and other α olefins in the 1950's the frontiers of polymer chemistry have been

† Robert A. Welch Foundation Postdoctoral Research Fellow.
‡ Director, Thermodynamics Research Center.

widening rapidly by virtue of the new powerful catalysts (1) of Ziegler and Natta. Many common solvents, such as acetone, benzene, and acetonitrile, may now be renamed "monomers" in view of their polymerizations (2), achieved in recent years through the organometallic catalysts. The role of thermochemistry in these developments was primarily to predict these polymerizations and to indicate such possibilities to the synthetic organic chemists. In many cases, however, the lack of precise and accurate thermochemical data, particularly in borderline cases involving small enthalpy changes in polymerizations, required clarification. For example, acetone, a most stable substance, has been polymerized by means of these new catalysts to a high-molecular-weight polymer by Furukawa and co-workers (2b). The enthalpies of formation for the monomeric acetone and its polymer [calculated by Bryant (3) on the basis of the bond energy scheme of Anderson, Bayer, and Watson] show that the polymerization

$$CH_3COCH_3 \rightarrow 1/n[-O-C(CH_3)_2-]_n - 2.8 \, kcal$$

would be slightly endothermic in the hypothetical gaseous phases† (ΔH_{gg}) and more endothermic (with the estimated heat of polymerization, $\Delta H_{lc} = +5.7 \pm 2$ kcal/mole, where "lc" signifies "liquid monomer to amorphous or partially crystalline polymer") in the liquid phase of acetone. With a similar theoretical estimate of the entropy of polymerization $\Delta S_{lc} = -28$ eu, which is a reasonable value for any polymerization process, the Gibbs energy change (ΔG_{lc}) turns out to be about $+11$ kcal/mole at $178°K$ and positive down to $0°K$. No amount of change in the ΔC_p (difference between the specific heats of monomer and polymer) can reverse the sign of the enthalpy and Gibbs energy in the right direction to account for the polymerization in any temperature range. The inadequacy of thermodynamic analysis is borne out by the ready polymerization of acetone with the use of these new catalysts. The experimental thermochemistry, rather than the theoretical schemes, has here a great role to play, and the paradox may become quite easy to explain some day, when the heat of formation of the poly(acetone) is obtained from direct-combustion calorimetry. The capacity of the various semiempirical bond-energy schemes for predicting thermochemical data on simple saturated hydrocarbons is rather limited (5), and their extension to hydrocarbon polymers is only partially successful in some cases and fails completely when the steric repulsions in the polymer chains are large. It is therefore not surprising that the application of these schemes to nonhydrocarbons, especially to the borderline polymerizations (with

---

† Throughout the text we have followed the phase specification for various thermodynamic quantities of Dainton and Ivin (4a).

marginal Gibbs energy change around zero), such as that of acetone, is unsatisfactory.

Cyclopropane, on the other hand, represents an exactly opposite thermodynamic situation. The very accurate data on the heats of combustion and formation of cyclopropane and polymethylenes indicate a strongly exothermic theoretical polymerization of cyclopropane (or of a few other cycloalkanes) (4) to linear polymethylene ($\Delta H_{1c} = -27$ kcal for cyclopropane) and an extremely easily effected reaction showing a Gibbs energy change of $\Delta G_{1c} = -22.1$ kcal. Thus far the polymerization of cyclopropane has not been achieved with any of the usual polymerization initiators, including ^{60}Co and ^{90}Sr irradiation, or the new organometallic catalysts.

Considering the predicted endothermicity of acetone and acetaldehyde polymerizations and the marginally small Gibbs energy changes associated with many similar polymerizations, such as that of sulfur, acetonitrile, and formaldehyde (in contrast to the unexpected stability of its industrial polymer, Delrin), one would doubt whether the heat of polymerization has any role at all in the mechanism and kinetics of the reaction. This chapter will show however, that even the existing provisional and nondefinitive data on the heats of polymerization not only afford excellent correlation with the monomer and polymer structures but also display a close parallelism with the "polymerizability" of monomers, owing to the profound influence of the heats on the main propagation reaction, whether the mechanism of polymerization is free-radical or ionic or of the coordinated-complex type. Data on standard heats of combustion and formation of monomers and polymers are badly needed for future thermochemical work.

8-2. PREDICTION OF THE ENTHALPY OF POLYMERIZATION

In recent years systematic study of the heats of atomization of certain groups of compounds has resulted in the development of semiempirical bond-energy schemes (5a) for the prediction of heats of atomization and, in turn, heats of formation of new compounds with an accuracy of 0.2 kcal/mole or better, particularly for saturated hydrocarbon isomers of homologous series. Some of these schemes have also been extended to olefins with some success. They fall into two broad categories of seemingly different approach.

In the first, the generalized bond-energy model (5b), it is assumed that each bond of a certain type has a constant characteristic energy, transferable from one molecule to another, and that the bond energy terms are additive. This is supplemented by certain corrective terms arising from different kinds and degrees of nonbonding interaction of bonded atoms, to be added to the basic values of the realistic bond energies. The higher the desired accuracy, the more numerous the corrective terms representing interactions of the second, third, or fourth order due to steric effects (repulsive) of adjacent bonds.

In the second scheme, that of Laidler, Mackle, Cox (6), and others, the number of basic, primary bond-energy terms is larger, because each bond is distinguished by the state of hybridization of the carbon and its association with other adjoining atoms. The bond (or group) energy terms are constructed from the few simple lower members of a class of compounds for which accurate data on the heats of formation are experimentally available. This second type of scheme is the more extensive, though less accurate, and is available for several classes of compounds beyond hydrocarbons.

A prediction of the enthalpy of polymerization would require the heat of atomization and formation of both monomer and polymer. The schemes of the first category, which are very precisely applicable to paraffinic hydrocarbons, should in principle be applicable to hydrocarbon polymers such as polyethylene and polypropylene, which represent a set of chains with the same repeating units of the respective monomers. A vinyl polymer derived from a substituted ethylene, $CH_2=C(RR')$, may, for the purpose of computing the heats of atomization and formation, be represented as

$$
\begin{array}{ccc}
\begin{array}{cc} H & R \\ | & | \\ C=C \\ | & | \\ H & R' \end{array}
& \longrightarrow &
\begin{array}{cc} H & R \\ | & | \\ -C-C- \\ | & | \\ H & R' \end{array}
\end{array}
$$

In addition to the usual single bonds of the ethylene-type polymer the repeating segment has one C—C bond, which is indicated by the dotted girdle, which makes a cyclic two-membered ring (but without strain), and allows the bond-energy terms and the nonbonding interactions to be calculated. On the basis of the ring model, the best-developed Allen–Skinner scheme (5b), or other similar schemes, in which the skeletal ("effective") C—H and C—C bond energy terms have been derived from methane and ethane, respectively, can be applied without any difficulty, even though the individual magnitudes of the steric repulsive interaction terms are not known (and not required, either). Such application, however, must be limited to only a few saturated hydrocarbon polymers, because the basic bond-energy terms and the non-bonded repulsion terms beyond those of the C—H and C—C bonds are at present not very precisely known.

Of the other categories of empirical schemes, in which there are more numerous individual bond-energy terms but no corrective terms for non-bonded interactions, we prefer the most developed one of Cox (6) for the easiness of its application to both hydrocarbon and other polymers, this scheme, like that of Benson and Buss (8), providing for nonhydrocarbon substituents. For the empirical calculation of the heat of polymerization the heats of formation for both monomer and polymer are required. Such calculation for a monomer, based on the Cox scheme, would be rather superfluous, however, since the very bond (or group) energy terms of the scheme have been derived from such lower vinyl compounds. The calculations for a polymer would be significant, and these, based on the model of the repeating polymer segment as represented by the two-membered strain-free ring for several vinyl polymers and interesting new polymers, are shown in Table 8-1, column 4. These values are for the hypothetical gaseous phase of a polymer segment and may be compared with the available experimental heats of formation of polymers, column 3, only after allowance is made for the heat of vaporization (sublimation) of the polymer segment, which may be reasonably taken as roughly the heat of vaporization of monomer shown in column 2. Alternatively, the heat of polymerization ΔH_{gg} (both monomer and polymer in gas phase) may be obtained from the well-established experimental values of $\Delta H_f^{\circ}(g)$, column 1, available for certain monomers and the calculated heats of formation of the polymer. These are shown in column 5. Approximately, these ΔH_{gg} values should compare closely with the experimental heats of polymerization, ΔH_{1c} (liquid monomer to amorphous or slightly crystalline polymer), given in the last column, if the scheme has any success in predicting the heat of formation of a long-chain polymer molecule.

The results of comparing the observed and predicted values of heats of polymerization by means of one of the best-developed bond-energy schemes may be summarized as follows: for the unsubstituted hydrocarbon monomers or those with single methyl group substitution, the predicted values of the heats of formation of polymers and the heats of polymerization are satisfactory; when the bond-energy terms or group contributions in the scheme are correctly known as, for example, the $-Cl$, $-CH_3$, $-COOH$ groups, the values of $\Delta H_f^{\circ}(g)$ predicted for polymers of such monosubstituted ethylenes are fairly accurate; the scheme fails totally in predicting for the 1:1-disubstituted ethylenes, such as isobutylene or vinylidene chloride, and for ring compounds with heteroatoms, such as tetrahydrofuran and, in general, for polymers involving any special structural features such as resonance and strongly polar or bulky substitutions.

When the scheme is applied to benzenoid compounds and small rings with special structural features such as conjugation or strain, it should be clear that no bond energy scheme can predict the individuality of various bonds in each and every molecule and that the usefulness of such calculations is limited to merely a semiquantitative estimation, in terms of energy, of the stabilization due to conjugation or of the destabilization due to strain. In

TABLE 8-1

Selected Thermodynamic Data on Monomers, Polymers and Polymerization reaction

No.	Compound	Monomer State, kcal/mole		Polymer State, kcal/monomole		Heat of Polymeriz., kcal/mole	
		$\Delta H^{\circ}_f(g)$ obsvd.	$\Delta H_v(25°)$ obsvd.	$\Delta H^{\circ}_f(c)$ obsvd.	$\Delta H_f(g)^a$	$-\Delta H_{gg}{}^a$	$-\Delta H_{lc}$ obsvd.
1	Ethylene (82,83,56)	12.5	3.2	−13.4	−9.8	22.3	22.7
2	Propylene (56)	4.9	4.4	−20.0	−16.2	21.1	20.5
3	Butene-1 (159)	−0.0	5.0		−21.1	21.1	
4	Isobutylene (56)	−4.0	4.9	−21.2	−24.5	20.5	12.3
5	Butadiene (88)	26.3	5.0	3.9	8.1	18.2	17.4
6	Isoprene (89)	17.9	6.1	−6.0	−0.8	18.7	17.8
7	Styrene (91)	35.6	10.7	8.2	16.1	20.5	16.7
8	α-methyl styrene (92)	28.2	11.4	8.4	7.9	20.3	8.4
9	Vinyl chloride (85)	5.2[b]	4.9	−22.6	−17.1	22.3	22.9
10	Vinylidene chloride (85)	0.5	6.5	−24.0	−26.1	26.6	18.0
11	Vinylidene fluoride (86a)	−79	4.1	−113.3	−99.3	20.3	30
12	Tetrafluoroethylene (5,87)	−152	4.3	−193.5	−188.8	36.8	37.2
13	Nitroethylene (15)	10.7	9.0	−20.0	−8.9	19.6	21.7
14	Acrylic acid (160)	−79.7[b]	11.0		−94.8	15.1	18.5
15	Acrolein (160)	−17.8	7.3		−35.5	17.7	19.1
16	Acrylonitrile (160)	44	7.8		21.5	22.5	18.4
17	Ethyl vinyl ether (7)	−33.5			−53.9	20.4	
18	Vinyl acetate (160)	−78	7.8		−97.0	19.0	21.0

19 Methyl acrylate	−77.1[b]	7.9		−94.4	17.3	18.8
20 Methyl methacrylate (161)	−81.5[b]	8.6	−103.6	−102.5	21.0	13.5
21 Maleic anhydride (162)	−98.6	10.5		−121.6	23.0	14
22 Formaldehyde (159)	−27.7	5.9	−40.9	−39.5	11.8	7.3
23 Acetaldehyde (163)	−37.4	6.5		−48.0	10.6	
24 Ethylene oxide (163)	−12.6	6.2		−40.0	27.4	22.6 (old data)
25 Styrene oxide	10.5[b]	13		−11.3	21.8	
26 Tetrahydrofuran (163)	−44.0	7.7		−49.8	5.8	5.3
27 Cyclopropene (121)	66.6	4.5	−20.1	25.4	41.2	
28 Cyclopropane (122)	12.6	5.0	−40.2	−15.7	28.3	27.7[c]
29 Cyclohexane (122)	−29.4	7.9	−53.6	−31.4	2.0	−0.7[c]
30 Cyclooctane (122)	−29.7	10.7		−39.2	9.5	8.3[c]
31 Allene (159)	45.9	4.4		9.2[d]	36.7	
				11.5	34.4	
32 Acetylene (159)	54.2	4.2		14.0	40.2	
33 Hydrogen cyanide (159)	31.2			25.3	5.9 + R[e]	
34 Acetonitrile (159)	21.0	8.4		16.4	4.6 + R[e]	
35 Acetone (163)	−51.7	7.6		−58.5	6.8	
36 Carbon monoxide (159)	−26.4	1.7		−30.8	4.4	
37 Cyclooctatetraene (100)	71.1	11	+8.2[f]	15.1	56	

[a] Values predicted from Cox scheme (6).
[b] Estimated by the present writers, J. Polymer Sci., B3, 779 (1965).
[c] Theoretical.
[d] Conjugated.
[e] Where R = resonance energy ≈ 10 kcal/mole per (CH=CH)- or (CH=N)-conjugated long-chain unit; see Orr (96).
[f] Fictitious polymerization to polystyrene $(C_8H_8)_n$, which is resonance-induced (resonance energy of benzene, 36 kcal), supplementing the energy of ethylenic double-bond-opening; see text.

extending such a scheme to polymers the advantage of eliminating the conjugation factor is completely offset by one special, important steric factor
in the long-chain molecules. This has been earlier demonstrated by Evans
and Polanyi (9) and Flory (10) in their treatment of the well-known case
of polyisobutylenes, which is, in fact, a structural isomer of polyethylene
or polypropylene that would be expected, from similar considerations of
corresponding unhindered, small hydrocarbon molecules, to be more stable.
The steric hindrance from the third and subsequent additions of monomer
segments in a polymer chain becomes very predominant owing to the
increasingly hindered rotations, forbidding the low-energy trans conformation of a segment with respect to both its adjacent neighboring
segments.

For other unhindered polymers the predicted heats of polymerization
are all about 20 ± 2 kcal, which is the normal difference between the average
bond energy of a $C=C$ bond (146 kcal) in a monomer and the sum of the two
$C-C$ single bonds ($83 \times 2 = 166$ kcal) formed in the polymer. This is the
simplest way of judging the heat of polymerization of an unsaturated compound, but it sometimes creates an inexplicable situation, as in account-
ing for the experimentally realized polymerizations of acetone, acetonitrile,
acetaldehyde, etc., namely that the predicted polymerization turns out to be
endothermic and becomes thermodynamically impossible because of the
obvious negative entropy involved in any association process. It may be
seen that the predicted values of ΔH_{gg}, based on the more refined Cox scheme
for the three compounds mentioned above and other similar "borderline
monomers," are definitely about 5 kcal negative (as also for tetrahydrofuran)
and, when combined with the appropriate entropies, should indicate these
polymerizations to be almost feasible at lower temperatures. Thus one may
expect in the future the polymerization of hydrogen cyanide and even of
carbon monoxide. The hydrocarbons with excessive unsaturation, such as
acetylene, allene, and cyclooctatetraene, and the ring compounds with strain
energies, such as the lower cycloalkanes, cyclopropene, and ethylene oxide,
do show the high values predicted for their heats of polymerization. As
emphatically mentioned (4), however, the mere exothermicity or thermodynamic feasibility of polymerization is no guarantee of a polymer obtained
from energy-rich lower cycloalkanes, unless a mechanism of opening these
rings without side reactions is found.

Heats of polymerization (assuming no steric hindrance in the polymer)
may also be predicted from the parallel reaction of hydrogenation, which
involves a change from trigonal to tetrahedral hybridization of the carbon
atoms, as in polymerization. In the former reaction, however, two additional
$C-H$ bonds contribute to the heat of formation of the product (and, hence,
to the heat of reaction), rendering the heat of hydrogenation of an ethylenic

compound higher than that of the corresponding polymerization by varying magnitudes. Flory (*10*) has shown that for the unsubstituted ethylene this value of the hypothetical dehydrogenation (ΔH_e) is 10.4 kcal and that for monosubstitution and 1:1 disubstitution with an alkyl group it should be 9.6 and 9.2 kcal, respectively. The heats of polymerization of the various hydrocarbon monomers would therefore be about 9 to 11 kcal less (negative) than of the corresponding hydrogenation. In the Cox scheme, covering various other substitutions, the bond contribution from different types of C_{sp^3}—H bond to the heat of formation vary broadly, from $+0.42$ to -3.48 kcal. The maximal variation in ΔH_e arising from two such C_{sp^3}—H bonds in other substitutions should range from about $+1$ to -7 kcal, which means that there is little correspondence between the heat of hydrogenation and the heat of polymerization in widely substituted ethylinic monomers. The differences in the two heat changes can vary broadly and unpredictably from $+1$ to -7 kcal, and Flory's original treatment and Roberts' extension of it (*11*) to other ethylinic monomers, for which the heats of hydrogenation were available, has limited significance and no independent status in any way for predicting heats of polymerization.

8-3. EXPERIMENTAL CALORIMETRY OF POLYMERIZATION

The experimental techniques adopted for the measurement of heats of polymerization by direct-reaction calorimetry are the adiabatic, the isothermal, and the thermodynamic-equilibrium techniques and differential-combustion calorimetry.

A. Adiabatic Methods

1. DEWAR-VESSEL CALORIMETERS

One of the earliest reports (*12*) on the directly measured heat of polymerization in a simple Dewar-vessel calorimeter (DVC) with a stirrer and a thermometer comes from Mark and his collaborators, who measured styrene and gave the first direct estimate (15 kcal/mole) of the exothermicity of vinyl polymerization. Shostakovski and Bogdanov (*13*) had also estimated the heat of polymerization of vinyl butyl ether (about 14.4 kcal/mole) polymerized with alcoholic $FeCl_3$, presumably in a DVC, and this value remains the only one available (though unconfirmed and rather too low) for a vinyl ether type of monomer. A low value, about 10 kcal/mole, was found for isobutylene polymerization at low temperature ($-78°C$), which was later confirmed at 12.8 kcal/mole in a DVC by Evans and Polanyi (*9*), establishing the very important concept (*10*) of steric hindrance in polymer.

Evans and Tyrrall (*14*) measured heats of polymerization of acrylic acid, methacrylic acid, and their two methyl esters, using a redox initiating system (the Fenton reagent), with which they were able to polymerize the monomers partially at the working temperature of, presumably, 20°C in their DVC. The two acids were polymerized in aqueous solution, the methyl methacrylate in emulsion, and the methyl acrylate as solution in ethanol. The polymer formed was determined both by residual-monomer estimation through bromination and by alkali titration and gravimetric assay of the precipitated polymers. The times of these partial ("dead end") polymerizations ranged from 2 to 15 min, and the temperature rise was reported to be as much as 67°C in some runs. The apparatus was calibrated by means of an electric heater, and the time–temperature curves were corrected for cooling. The values taken as ΔH_{ss} for acrylic acid (18.5 kcal/mole) and methacrylic acid (15.8 kcal/mole) may be considered accurate, but the estimates for the two esters appear to be somewhat in error in the light of many calorimetric measurements subsequently made by other workers (18,46,47,58). The rather low value for the methacrylate may be ascribed to the inaccuracy generally associated with the gravimetric assay of a polymer, and a possible over-estimation of the unreacted monomer in the bromination method may account for the high estimate (20.2 kcal/mole) for methyl acrylate, in view of the known substitution reaction of bromine with the α hydrogen, which accompanies the usual addition at the double bond. Grodzinski et al. (15) have measured the heat of polymerization of nitroethylene by using a DVC equipped with a thermistor bridge for measuring the adiabatic temperature rise and calibrating with electric energy. The simple DVC's of this type working at room temperature are, perhaps, not quite adequate for the radical polymerization that is abruptly retarded by traces of oxygen or that requires a higher temperature for a polymerization rate and conversion to be achieved in a short period so as to minimize the radiation losses. This shortcoming of the simple adiabatic calorimetry can be overcome by means of a differential twin calorimeter of higher sensitivity. Skuratov et al. (16) employed a differential calorimeter operating at 230°C and measured the heat of polymerization of 6-hexanolactam.

2. DIFFERENTIAL MICROCALORIMETER

Laidler and his co-workers (17,18) used an elaborate differential microcalorimeter of the Tian–Calvert type for measuring the heats of vinyl polymerization (18) and of another polymer-forming reaction of isocyanates with alcohols (17). This versatile apparatus can be employed for both exothermic and endothermic processes, such as heat of solution and of dilution and also heat of vaporization, with an ingenious recent adaptation (18). These associated thermodynamic measurements are very valuable for reducing the main polymerization data to standard states. The differential microcalorimeter consisted essentially of a large block of metal held at constant temperature (within 10^{-3}°C or better) with two metal reaction cells mounted in it. The reaction to be measured was carried out in one cell and a suitable blank reaction in the other. Each cell had one of the two identical thermopiles (with as many as 500 to 1000 elements and the "hot" junctions mounted evenly on the cell and the "cold" ones on the metal block), which served to measure the difference in temperature between the block and the reaction cell. The two thermopiles are connected in opposition, so that the "output" measures continuously the pure thermal difference between the reaction cell and the blank reference cell, freed from any background temperature fluctuations in the thermostated metal block. The output is fed to a d-c breaker-type amplifier and recorded as the emf–time curve. The total area under such a curve has been shown by Tian to be proportional to the heat released (or absorbed) in the reaction cell, which may be measured graphically or with an additional electronic integrating circuit, such as that incorporated in Laidler's apparatus which allows the heat of reaction to be read directly. The analog integrator also cancels out the effect of random noise from thermopiles and amplifier and renders the calorimeter remarkably stable, sensitive, and free from drift for long periods. The sensitivity of the instrument is such as to allow measurements in the range of 0.01 to 2 cal with a precision of 1 % or better; and under ideal conditions 0.002 cal is measurable, with a standard deviation of 0.1 %.

Reliable values of heats of polymerization at 25°C of acrylic and methacrylic acids and their several esters have been obtained by Lovering and Laidler (17) on the microcalorimeter; these are given in Table 8-2. The standard deviations average about 0.5 % and do not exceed 1 % for any of the monomers. These polymerizations have been performed in emulsion systems, and factors such as heats of emulsification [which seem to be generally about 2 to 5 kcal/mole of the surface-active agent micellized (19)] might additionally interfere† with the absolute significance of the polymerization data, as do the heats of solvation of monomers and polymers and of the primary and secondary-phase transitions. These side effects, however, generally compensating each other, are all estimated to be within 0.5 kcal/mole except for strongly polar monomers. In another thermochemical study with the same calorimeter Lovering and Laidler (17) determined the heats of the urethane reaction at 25°C of phenyl diisocyanates and o-tolyl, m-tolyl, p-tolyl, and 2,4-tolylene diisocyanates with isomeric butyl alcohols. The values range from 18.5 to 25.1 kcal/mole for the monoisocyanates forming urethanes in the excess alcohol in the order n-butyl > isobutyl > sec-butyl and, for the isocyanates, in the order phenyl > p-tolyl >

---

† In an emulsion polymerization the quantity of the detergent is generally about 3 to 5 % and, even if all this emulsifier should exist in the truly micellized form, this contribution should not exceed 0.25 kcal/mole in the measured heat of polymerization from an emulsion system.

o-tolyl > m-tolyl. For the 2,4-tolylene diisocyanate the values are 44.0, 42.6, and 41.3 kcal/mole of the diurethanes formed with the primary, iso, and secondary butyl alcohols, respectively. These valuable data on the basic reaction underlying the "polyurethanes" have been obtained for the first time and are of practical importance in modern plastics technology.

3. DIFFERENTIAL THERMAL ANALYSIS

A less sophisticated version of the twin microcalorimeter method is the differential thermal analysis (DTA) technique (20). The DTA technique, originally designed for inorganic minerals, has now been well developed (20) and is used for organic substances and for the approximate measurement of the heat of reaction. The apparatus is in principle a differential adiabatic calorimeter consisting of a metal block with two small, identical cavities, each fitted with a thermocouple. The substance to be studied is mixed uniformly with a large amount of inert filler (such as calcined alumina or KBr) of a standard mesh size, and one of the cavities is filled with it, while the other contains the same filler as a reference blank. The metal block is heated slowly at a constant rate of about 10°C/min, and both the differential temperature and the reference temperature are recorded by an X-Y function plotter. As in the differential microcalorimeter, the area under the thermogram (ΔT versus T time) combined with the appropriate data on the specific heats of the reactants, filler, construction material of the cells, etc. gives the enthalpy change of a transition or of a reaction, as the case may be. The apparatus is calibrated with some standard substance, such as stearic acid, having a known heat of fusion. Clampitt et al. (21) measured the heat of polymerization of triallyl cyanurate by DTA and then confirmed the resulting value of 18.5 kcal/mole per allyl group independently by differential combustion of the monomer and the polymer. The DTA technique was also employed by Klute and Viehmann (22) for studying the heat of polymerization (curing) of the epoxy resins with primary and secondary amines; values of about 26 kcal/mole were obtained, respectively, within a standard deviation of 0.37 kcal. The vulcanization of natural rubber with sulfur (68:32 mixture) was followed on a DTA apparatus and yielded a value of 147 cal/g of the mix (23). More detailed study of this important technological reaction was done by Hock and Schröter (24) on a differential calorimeter of high sensitivity; a range of values of 1.7 to 6.83 kcal/g-atom of sulfur for mixtures of low sulfur content (2 to 5%) was obtained. The DTA also gives reasonably accurate values of the heats of fusion and first-order transition of polymers (25) as measured by the area of the thermograms. Although not commonly used for fundamental studies, the DTA represents a simple, convenient, and rapid calorimetric technique particularly suited to polymeric reactions at elevated temperatures of complex mixed reactants in the polymer technology.

Recently the DTA apparatus has been fortified with an entirely new principle, the "thermal servo system." The new control system detects instantaneously (during the course of a heating cycle) any difference between sample and reference temperatures and simultaneously changes the amount of heat applied to either of the cells in such a manner as to maintain both cells always at the same temperature. What the instrument actually measures is not the temperature difference but the electrical power required to counter-act the exothermic or endothermic effect of the reaction, which is a more direct measurement. The new Differential Scanning Calorimeter (26), capable of measuring (isothermally) in the range of 2 to 32 mcal/sec with a precision of ±0.04 mcal/sec, is likely to find much application in polymeriza-tion calorimetry in the future.

4. LOW-TEMPERATURE RECORDING CALORIMETER

The special, interesting features of ionic polymerization and of the newly developed organometallic-catalyst systems, which render many unusual compounds polymerizable at low temperatures, call for an apparatus capable of measuring the rates as well as simultaneously performing as a reaction calorimeter. Such an adiabatic low-temperature calorimeter is that developed by Biddulph and Plesch (27), which is suitable for the study of ionic polymerization or any other reasonably fast reaction for which the heat liberation is of the order of 5 to 30 kcal/mole. In this calorimeter the temperature change due to the exothermicity of the polymerization in a Dewar-type vessel has been used for following the progress of reaction and also calculating the heat of polymerization from the total temperature change, the energy equivalent of the system, and the extent of reaction. Other important features of the apparatus are that the quantity of residual moisture critical for cationic polymerizations with a cocatalyst can be reduced to less than 10^{-5} mole, reaction can be started virtually instan-taneously, fast reactions with half-lives as short as 3 sec can be followed, and monomer concentrations as low as 0.01 molar can be used without loss of precision.

The essential parts of the calorimeter are the reaction vessel assembly and the temperature recorder; see Fig. 8-1. The reaction chamber with an evacuable outer jacket has a capacity of about 250 ml and is connected through a high-vacuum manifold to the solvent and monomer reservoirs with their metering systems (not shown). The required amounts of monomer and solvent are distilled into the reaction vessel by appropriate temperature and vacuum adjustments. The apparatus has a high-speed (500 rpm) mag-netically driven two-bladed propeller stirrer mounted on a Teflon gland and bearings (TB & I). The catalyst is contained in a phial (at H), which may be broken with the help of a phial breaker (K), for introducing the catalyst into

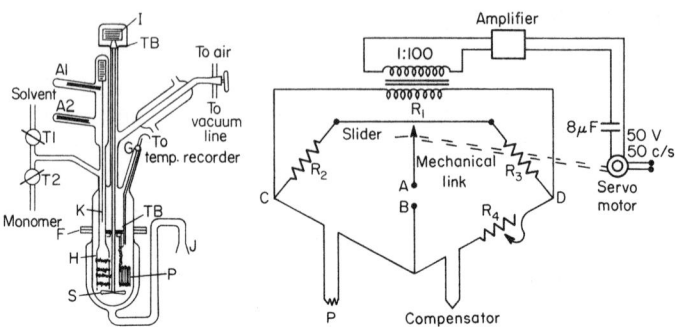

Fig. 8-1. Low-temperature adiabatic calorimeter.

the reactor. The temperature-sensing element is the platinum resistance thermometer (P), which forms one arm of the automatic self-balancing Wheatstone bridge (also shown). Bridge balance is established by the movement of a sliding contact (variable resistor), which is moved across a moving chart by a servo mechanism with a pen attached to it. The movement of the slider accompanying the temperature changes in the reaction vessel causes the pen to draw the curve of polymerization versus time automatically. The energy equivalent of the calorimeter is determined by calibration with electrical energy. With appropriate adjustments of the fixed resistances (decade boxes) in the other arms of the Wheatstone bridge one can shift the balance point (i.e. the working temperature of the calorimeter) anywhere in the range $+30$ to $-120°C$. The temperature sensitivity of the apparatus has been reported to be about 0.05 of a degree only (measured in terms of a full-scale deflection on an 11-inch-wide chart equivalent to 8 to 10°C). However, since the temperature rise in the usual polymerization runs was as much as 10°C, the apparatus worked with a precision of about 1 % and gave good reproducibility for the styrene polymerization. The heat of polymerization of this monomer in methylene chloride as solvent and with $TiCl_4 + H_2O$ as cationic initiator was found to be $16.0 \pm 0.5 \, kcal/mole$. This value appears to be somewhat low compared with the more standard value (*11*) of $16.7 \, kcal/mole$ available from differential combustion data. In a more recent study Plesch and collaborators (*28*) made a large number of calorimetric runs of the polymerization of two monomers, isobutene (52 experiments) and styrene (33 experiments). The polymerizations were carried out to almost complete conversion, in methylene dichloride, initiated by $TiCl_4$ at various temperatures in the interval 0 to $-95°C$. No significant variation of ΔH_p with temperature was observed for either of the monomers. The molecular weights of polystyrene ranged from 5×10^3 to 35×10^3 and of polyisobutylene from 10^4 to 10^5, so that the end-group effect is negligible, but the data are seriously affected by the heats of solution of monomer and polymer in such a powerful solvent as methylene dichloride. This may account for the apparently low value of styrene polymerization.

5. THERMOCOUPLE-DILATOMETER CALORIMETER

The principle of adiabatic calorimetry was ingeniously employed in the thermocouple method of Bengough and Melville (29) for following the non-stationary-state kinetics of radical polymerization and has since been extended by Bengough (30) to the measurement of the heat of reaction. The method is based on the fact that the heat generated by a polymerization reaction is not dissipated in the surroundings immediately, even when the reaction vessel stands in the thermostat bath, and that the conditions at the center of the dilatometer bulb, in which the polymerization reaction is initiated photochemically, remain truly adiabatic sufficiently long after the illumination has been turned on. The apparatus consists of a thermostated vacuum-filled capillary dilatometer, which is commonly used for following polymerization rates. The dilatometer has a capacity of about 15 to 20 ml and contains a fine copper–constantan thermocouple at the center and another identical reference thermocouple in the evacuated sidearm. The out-of-balance voltage between the two thermocouples is amplified with a d-c breaker-type amplifier and fed to a pen recorder. With a dilatometer of the size described by Bengough the thermally isolated condition would prevail for at least 10 sec and in some cases for 30 sec. The rate of temperature rise during this initial period of 10 to 30 sec resembles that in an ideal adiabatic calorimeter and can therefore be correlated with the heat of reaction (for a known rate of reaction) in terms of a single calorimetric constant, namely the specific heat of the reacting mixture. Since the specific heat of the polymer is normally less than that of the monomer, the reaction mixture would have a continually changing specific heat, which may be calculated accurately at any conversion. When a steady temperature gradient is attained in a polymerization bulk of the reaction mixture, the centrally located thermocouple measures the rate of temperature rise, while the rate of polymerization is followed dilatometrically and is calculated from the yield–contraction relationship, either based on the densities of monomer and polymer or obtained by direct calibration. In a modification of this method (31) the thermocouple has been eliminated and, instead, the dilatometer acts as its own thermometer, requiring, however, that the coefficients of expansion of monomer and polymer (polymerizing mixture) be known. The net volume change in a polymerization dilatometer is composed of three concurrent effects: the expansion e, due to heat, the contraction p, due to polymerization, and the contraction c, due to heat lost to the surroundings. The initial rate of expansion under adiabatic condition, $c = 0$, at the commencement of the photoillumination, and the initial rate of contraction immediately after the cessation of irradiation, when both $c = 0$ and $p = 0$, are measured. The rate of generation of heat is obtained from either of these two separate measurements. The rate of polymerization is measured, as in the original method (30), from the rate of contraction during the thermal steady state, in which the rate of self-heating due to polymerization is balanced by the rate of loss to the surroundings; that is, $e = c$. The method was successfully applied to vinyl acetate, and values of 21.2 and 21.6 kcal/mole were obtained for the heats of polymerization, which are in very good agreement with those obtained by other methods, as Table 8-2 shows. The modified method is limited to radiation-induced polymerizations, because it is necessary to be able to stop (or start) the reaction instantaneously.

The general self-heating method with a thermocouple, dilatometer, and a rotating-sector irradiation apparatus has been very recently applied to the complete kinetics of polymerization of 2-vinyl pyridine (32), and the heat of polymerization obtained (17.2 kcal/mole) was in excellent agreement with another, independent, earlier measurement made by an isothermal method (50). Miyama and co-workers (33) have introduced a thermistor in place of the thermocouple and studied the heats of some copolymerizations. For a successful extension of the self-heating methods the following conditions should be fulfilled.

1. For the exothermic polymerization reaction to be stopped within the shortest possible period after the interruption of irradiation the lifetime of the kinetic chain should not exceed a period of about 1 sec, which is quite short in comparison with the time for which adiabatic conditions are maintained around the thermocouple. Such polymerization conditions can be chosen without difficulty for most vinyl monomers.

2. The existence of a "thermal" rate of polymerization would interfere with the simplicity of this technique and, if it were appreciable, corrections would have to be made for it.

3. As polymerization proceeds, the over-all density, specific heat, and coefficient of expansion of the reaction mixture change, owing to polymer formation, and such correction factors would have to be applied if the reaction were taken beyond a few per cent conversion.

4. The polymerizing system must remain "fluid" throughout, and any gel effect irregularly altering the thermal convectivity is not tolerated. For this reason, too, the polymerization must be restricted to the initial few per cent conversion, especially that of such monomers as methyl acrylate, and the value of the heat of polymerization is in the form ΔH_{ls}, including the heat of solution of the polymer in the monomer solvent.

TABLE 8-2

Experimental Data on Heats of Polymerization

Compound	No. of expts.[a]	Temp., °C	Phys. states xy	$-\Delta H_{xy}$, kcal/mole	Method, ref., and notes[b]	Selected value of $-\Delta H_{lc}$ at 25°C
Ethylene	9[c]	25	gc	25.4 ± 0.1	DC, 82	21.2[d]
	−14[e]	25	gc	25.88 ± 0.1	DC, 56	
	−10[e]	25	gc	25.5 ± 0.1	DC, 83	
Propylene	6	−78	sc	16.5	IV, 84, in butane	19.5[d]
	7[a], 10[e]	25	gc	24.89 ± 0.1	DC, 56	
Isobutene		low	ss	12.8	DVC, 9, in hexane	12.9[d]
		25	lc	12.61	DC, 83	
	5, 9	25	gc	17.20 ± 0.1	DC, 56	
	34	−50	ss	12.96 ± 0.35	LTA, 28 in MeCl	
Vinyl chloride	−6[e]	25	gc	31.5 ± 0.6	DC, 85	
	10	74.5	ls	22.9 ± 0.3	IV, 53	18.0[d]
Vinylidene chloride		76.8	lc	14.4	IV, 44	
	5, 5	25	gc	24.0 ± 0.4	DC, 85	
	2	74.5	lc	17.7 ± 0.2	IV, 50	
Vinylidene fluoride	5, 10	25	gc	35 ± 2	DC, 86	31 ± 2
Tetrafluoroethylene	−11[e]	25	gc	41.5	DC, 5, 87	37 ± 2
Nitroethylene		25	lc	21.7	DC, 15	21.7[d]
			ss	21.78 ± 0.12	DVC, 15, in dimethyl formamide	
Butadiene	−4[e]	25	lc	17.6	DC, 88	17.6[d]
Isoprene		25	lc	17.9	DC, 89	17.9[d]
	5	74.5	ls	17[f]	IV, 50	
Chloroprene	3	35	ls	15.7 ± 0.4	IV, 41	
				16.2 ± 0.3	IV, 46	13.0[d]
Nitroisoprene	10	25	lc	13.0	DC, 90	

TABLE 8-2 (continued)

Compound	No. of expts.[a]	Temp., °C	Phys. states xy	$-\Delta H_{xy}$, kcal/mole	Method, ref, and notes[b]	Selected value of $-\Delta H_{lc}$ at 25°C
Styrene	7, 11	25	lc	16.68 ± 0.16	DC, 91	16.7
	18	76.8	lc	16.1[f] + 0.2	IV, 43	
	2	24	ls	16.8	TTD, 33	
	6	26.9	ls	17.7 ± 0.7	IF, 35	
	14	74.5	lc	16.4 ± 0.3[f]	IV, 47	
	6	127	lc	17.4	TE, 67	
	21	−60	ls	16.1 ± 0.1	LTA, 27, 28	
α-Methyl styrene	6, 24	25	lc	8.42 ± 0.2	DC, 92	8.4[d]
	5	−20	lc	8.15	TE, 64a	
	11	−20	ss	6.96	TE, 64b	
o-Chlorostyrene	9	76.8	lc	16.4 ± 0.2[f]	IV, 43	
p-Chlorostyrene	10	76.8	lc	16.0[f] ± 0.2	IV, 43	
2,5-Dichlorostyrene	12	76.8	lc	16.5[f] ± 0.2	IV, 43	
Ethyl styrene (isomer mixture)	6	76.8	lc	16.3 ± 0.2	IV, 43	
2,4,6-Trimethyl styrene (vinyl mesitylene)	9	26.9	lc	16.7 ± 0.3	IF, 35	
Acrylic acid	7	20	ss	18.5 ± 0.3	DVC, 14, in water	
	5	74.5	lc	16.0 ± 0.2	IV, 48	
	5	74.5	ss	17.7 ± 0.2	IV, 50, in hexane or benzene	
	6	25	ss[g]	18.4 ± 0.04	DMC, 18, in aqueous emulsion	
Acrolein	4	74.5	lc	19.1 ± 0.4	IV, 50	
Methyl vinyl ketone	5	74.5	lc	17.7 ± 0.1	IV, 43	
Acrylonitrile	5	76.8	lc	17.3 ± 0.5	IV, 44	18.4[d]
	2	25	ss[g]	18.3	DVC, 93	
Acrylamide	8	74.5	lc	18.4 ± 0.2	IV, 47	
	5	26.9	ss	19.8 ± 0.7	IF, 35, in water	

Monomer		Temp.		ΔH	Reference	Selected
Acrylamide	3	74.5	ss	19.6 ± 0.2	IV, 47, in water	
	6	74.5	ss	14.4	IV, 47, in benzene	
	6	74.5	ss	13.8	IV, 47, in hexane	
Methyl acrylate	9	76.8	lc	18.7 ± 0.2	IV, 44	18.5[d]
	3	20	ss	20.2 ± 1.0	DVC, 14, in ethanol	
	3	74.5	lc	18.8 ± 0.2	IV, 48	
	5	74.5	ss	19.4 ± 0.2	IV, 52, in hexane	
	5	25	ss[g]	18.58 ± 0.05	DMC, 18	
Ethyl acrylate	4	74.5	lc	18.6 ± 0.2	IV, 52	18.4[d]
	5	25	ss[g]	18.79 ± 0.04	DMC, 18	
n-Butyl acrylate	8	74.5	lc	18.5 ± 0.3	IV, 52	
	5	25	ss[g]	19.07 ± 0.05	DMC, 18	
Methacrylic acid	8	20	ss[g]	15.8 ± 0.2	DVC, 14, in water	13.6[d]
	6	74.5	lc	10.1 ± 0.2	IV, 50	
	10	74.5	ulc[h]	13.6	IV, 50, in methanol	
	6	25	ss[g]	13.46 ± 0.07	DMC, 18	
Methacrolein	3	74.5	lc	15.6 ± 0.3	IV, 50	
Methacrylonitrile		130	ss	15.3 ± 1.0	TE, 59, in benzonitrile	13.2[d]
	7	74.5	lc	13.5 ± 0.2	IV, 50	
Methacrylamide	2	74.5	ss	13.9 ± 0.2	IV, 47, in water	
	4	74.5	ss	8.4 ± 0.2	IV, 47, in benzene	
Methyl methacrylate	8	20	ss[g]	12.9 ± 1.1	DVC, 14	13.2[d]
	5	76.8	lc	13.0 ± 0.2	IV, 39	
	16	76.8	lc	13.9 ± 0.3	IV, 46, corrected for residual monomer	
	5	125	lc	13.4 ± 0.5	TE, 57	
	5	125	ss	12.9	TE, 57, in o-dichlorobenzene	
	15	120	lc	13.4	TE, 58	
	2	24	ls	13.1	TTD, 33	
	4	26.9	ls	13.8 ± 0.2	IF, 35	
	12	74.5	lc	13.3 ± 0.2	IV, 47	
	8	74.5	ss	14.0 ± 0.1	IV, 52, in benzene or acetonitrile	
	21	25	ss[g]	13.57 ± 0.06	DMC, 18	

TABLE 8-2 (continued)

Compound	No. of expts.[a]	Temp., °C	Phys. states xy	$-\Delta H_{xy}$, kcal/mole	Method, ref., and notes[b]	Selected value of $-\Delta H_{lc}$ at 25°C
Ethyl methacrylate	20	120	lc	14.4 ± 0.6	TE, 60	13.8[d]
	4	26.9	ls	13.8 ± 0.2	IF, 35	
	5	74.5	lc	14.2	IV, 52	
	9	25	ss[g]	13.78 ± 0.05	DMC, 18	
n-Propyl methacrylate	6	74.5	lc	13.7 ± 0.2	IV, 52	
Isopropyl methacrylate	7	74.5	lc	14.3 ± 0.2	IV, 52	
n-Butyl methacrylate	9	76.8	lc	13.5 ± 0.2	IV, 42	13.9[d]
	4	26.9	ls	14.3 ± 0.3	IF, 35	
	5	74.5	lc	13.7	IV, 52	
Isobutyl methacrylate	12	25	ss[g]	13.86 ± 0.11	DMC, 18	
	5	74.5	lc	14.3 ± 0.2	IV, 52	
t-Butyl methacrylate	3	26.9	ls	13.0 ± 0.1	IF, 35	
β-Ethoxyethyl methacrylate	4	26.9	ls	14.8 ± 0.4	IF, 35	
	5	74.5	lc	13.7 ± 0.3	IV, 52	
n-Hexyl methacrylate	4	26.9	ls	14.4 ± 0.3	IF, 35	
Cyclohexyl methacrylate	6	25	ss[g]	14.00 ± 0.08	DMC, 18	12.5[d]
	4	76.8	lc	12.2 ± 0.2	IV, 42	
	3	26.9	ls	12.7 ± 0.3	IF, 35	
Phenyl methacrylate	2	76.8	lc	12.3 ± 0.2	IV, 42	
Benzyl methacrylate	5	76.8	lc	13.4 ± 0.2	IV, 42	
β-Hydroxyethyl methacrylate	5	25	ss[g]	11.94 ± 0.08	DMC, 18	
β-Hydroxypropyl methacrylate	7	25	ss[g]	12.10 ± 0.07	DMC, 18	
Dimethyl itaconate	7	26.9	ss	14.5 ± 0.3	IF, 35, in o-dichlorobenzene	
Vinyl acetate	7	76.8	lc	21.3 ± 0.2	IV, 44	21.2[d]
	11	25	ls	20.0 ± 1.0	TTD, 30	
	20	25	ls	21.4	TTD, 31	

Vinyl acetate	2	24	ls	21.6	TTD, 33
	6	74.5	lc	21.0 ± 0.5	IV, 47
Vinyl propionate	3	74.5	lc	20.5 ± 0.2	IV, 47
Vinyl β-ethyl hexoate	5	74.5	lc	21.0 ± 0.3	IV, 52
Vinyl benzoate	5	74.5	lc	20.2 ± 0.3	IV, 52
Allyl chloride	9	74.5	ls	18.5^f ± 0.3	IV, 50
Maleic anhydride	6	74.5	ls	14.0^f ± 2	IV, 49
Maleimide	6	74.5	ss	21.4 ± 0.3	IV, 51, in dioxane
	7	74.5	ss	21.2 ± 0.3	IV, 51, in acetonitrile
	9	74.5	ss	20.9 ± 0.5	IV, 51, in dimethyl formamide
Acenaphthylene	12	26.9	ss	23.8 ± 0.4	IF, 36, in o-dichlorobenzene
		26.9	cc	19.6 ± 0.4	Corrected for heats of solution
	5	74.5	ss	17.6 ± 0.4	IV, 50, in benzene
	4	74.5	ss	16.9 ± 0.4	IV, 50, in o-dichlorobenzene
		74.5	ss	15.8^f	IV, 50
N-Vinyl carbazole	4	74.5	ss	15.2 ± 0.3	IV, 50, in hexane
2-Vinyl pyridine	3	74.5	ls	18.0 ± 0.2	IV, 50
	3	74.5	lc	17.1 ± 0.1	IV, 50
	4	25	ls	17.3	TTD, 32
4-Vinyl pyridine	8	74.5	ss	18.7 ± 0.3	IV, 47, in nonpolar diluents
Formaldehyde	8	75	gc	12.24 ± 0.08	TE, 55
		25	gc	13 ± 1	DC, 55
	−10^e	25	gc	13.23 ± 0.1	DC, 56
Ethylene oxide		25	lc	22.6	DC, 4
		25	gg	24.9	DC, 4
Trimethylene oxide (oxacyclobutane)	4	−9	ss	19.2 ± 0.2	IV, 94, in mixture of MeCl and EtCl
3,3-Dimethyl-1-oxacyclobutane	4	−9	ss	16.0 ± 0.2	IV, 94, in mixture of MeCl and EtCl
3,3-Di(chloromethyl)-1-oxacyclobutane		26.9	lc	20.2 ± 0.2	IF, 35
3,3-Di(phenoxymethyl)-1-oxacyclobutane	10	26.9	ss	19.8 ± 0.3	IF, 35

7.4^a

TABLE 8-2 (continued)

Compound	No. of expts.[a]	Temp., °C	Phys. states xy	$-\Delta H_{xy}$, kcal/mole	Method, ref, and notes[b]	Selected value of $-\Delta H_{lc}$ at 25°C
Tetrahydrofuran	6	60	ls	4.3	TE, 66	
	8	40	ls	5.3 ± 1.0	TE, 65	
1:1 Copolymerization of M₁ + M₂						
Sulfur dioxide (M₁):						
+ Propylene		26.9	sc	10.1 ± 0.05	IF, 34	
+ Butene-1		26.9	ss	10.6 ± 0.05	IF, 34	10.0[d]
+ *cis*-Butene-2	-7[e]	25	lc	10.00 ± 0.5	DC, 95	8.9[d]
		26.9	ss	10.07 ± 0.05	IF, 34	
	-5[e]	25	lc	8.93	DC,95	
+ *trans*-Butene-2		26.9	ss	9.35 ± 0.05	IF, 34	8.4[d]
	-5[e]	25	lc	8.43	DC, 95	
+ Isobutene	-4[e]	25	lc	7.41 ± 0.05	DC, 95	7.4[d]
Maleic anhydride (M₁):						
+ Vinyl acetate	4	76.8	lc	20.2 ± 0.4	IV, 45, excess M₂	
+ Isopropenyl acetate	12	76.8	lc	17.8 ± 0.4	IV, 45, excess M₂	
+ Styrene	6	74.5	ss	19.3 ± 0.2	IV, 52, in benzene	
	6	74.5	ss	19.7 ± 0.2	IV, 52, in acetonitrile	
+ α-Methyl styrene	7	74.5	ls	17.3 ± 0.8	IV, 52, excess M₂	
+ Allyl chloride	9	74.5	ls	17.7 ± 0.2	IV, 52	
+ Vinyl *n*-butyl ether	4	74.5	ss	21.5 ± 0.2	IV, 52, in benzene	
Maleimide (M₁):						
+ Styrene	5	74.5	ss	20.9 ± 0.3	IV, 52, in acetonitrile	
+ α-Methyl styrene	5	74.5	ss	17.2 ± 0.3	IV, 52, in acetonitrile	
Fumaryl chloride (M₁):						
+ Styrene	5	74.5	ss	19.1 ± 0.3	IV, 52, in hexane	
+ α-methyl styrene	4	74.5	ss	17.1 ± 0.2	IV, 52, excess M₂	

B. Isothermal Methods

In the isothermal calorimetry the exothermic reaction is not allowed to change the temperature of the calorimetric system. Instead, the heat liberated is exchanged with another substance (heat-exchange medium), so as to cause an equivalent, endothermic physical change (such as fusion or vaporization) to be brought about isothermally, which is then measured in place of the temperature rise. For the calorimeters there are preset working temperatures, which may be fixed by the choice of the heat-exchange medium and the phase change. The choice is, however, limited, because for a good sensitivity of the calorimeter the working substance should be such that a small amount of heat should bring about a large phase change associated with a large change in the physical property, which is ultimately measured. So far two calorimetric substances have been much used for polymerization studies, and the calorimeters employ the isothermal fusion of diphenyl ether at 26.9°C in one (34) and the isothermal vaporization of carbon tetrachloride at about 74 to 76°C in the other (42–53). The fusion of diphenyl ether for measuring the heat of reaction involves a relatively low (4.11 kcal/mole) heat of fusion and a high volume change (about 16 ml/mole). The vaporization of carbon tetrachloride is similar in these respects, with a low heat of vaporization and high density, which render the calorimeter sensitive to a gravimetric procedure. Both these phase-change methods have a common limitation of accuracy due to the heat losses caused by superheating. This drawback is more serious in the vaporization calorimeter than in the fusion apparatus, but inadequate thermal contact between a poorly formed diphenyl ether solid mantle and the walls of the reaction well may form a serious source of heat leak in the latter apparatus.

1. ISOTHERMAL FUSION CALORIMETER

The diphenyl ether fusion calorimeter was first constructed by Dainton et al. (34,35) to measure heats of polymerization, although similar calorimeters had been described earlier by Giguere et al. (36) and Jessup (37) for

---

[a] Where two figures are given, the first is for monomer and the second for polymer.

[b] DC = differential combustion, IV = isothermal vaporization, DVC = Dewar-vessel calorimeter, LTA = low-temperature adiabatic calorimeter, TTD = thermocouple-thermistor and dilatometer method, IF = isothermal fusion (diphenyl ether) calorimeter, TE = thermodynamic equilibrium method, DMC = differential microcalorimeter.

[c] Number of monomer samples burnt.

[d] Values for "lc" states, based on judgement of present writers; see text, end of Section 8-3-D.

[e] Number of polymer samples burnt.

[f] Values extrapolated to zero catalyst concentration.

[g] Emulsion systems.

[h] Monomer as unassociated liquid (ul), a condition at infinite dilution in a polar solvent such as methanol.

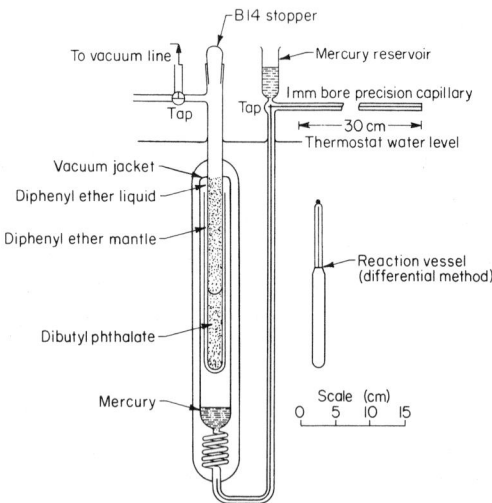

Fig. 8-2. Diphenyl ether fusion calorimeter and dilatometric polymerization vessel.

other purposes. Mention may also be made of a sensitive Bunsen ice calorimeter, constructed by Tamplin (*38*), which may be used for some polymerizations at 0°C. Dainton's apparatus (shown in Fig. 8-2) consists of a tubular container of diphenyl ether, connected to a precision bore capillary through a pool of mercury introduced at the bottom, and the volume change due to fusion is read from the movement of the mercury thread in the capillary. The diphenyl ether chamber has an outer jacket that can be evacuated so as to isolate the chamber thermally when it has attained the equilibrium temperature of the thermostat. In the center of the diphenyl ether chamber is a long, concentric, tubular well, holding in a pool of some thermal-contact liquid a sealed reaction dilatometer in which polymerization is carried out; the rate of polymerization is followed separately from volume contraction. The diphenyl ether is highly purified through several crystallizations and vacuum distillation, and no grease joints are used in any portion of the apparatus coming in contact with the ether or its vapor. A reasonably uniform and firm solid mantle of the ether around the well is achieved by chilling the side wall with an acetone–CO_2 cold "pencil" and repeatedly melting the mantle partially and then rebuilding. The maintenance of the thermostat at a very constant temperature of the fusion equilibrium is absolutely necessary for the effective mean temperature in the calorimeter to be kept constant to within one tenth of a millidegree. Under these conditions alone the background drift rate of the system is kept within a reproducibility of ± 0.002 cal/min and easily corrected for. Only then can slow polymerizations, lasting for some hours, be performed so as to give heat values within an uncertainty of ± 0.06 cal. The total measuring capacity of the calorimeter with a size permissible for an unsupported mantle is about 30 cal, so that the over-all precision of the calorimetric measurements on this apparatus remains about 0.2%. The measuring capacity can be increased to as high as 300 cal, as in Giguere's apparatus (36), the supporting studs being introduced on the outer side of the well and so preventing mantle detachment. It is, however, normally unnecessary to increase the total heat effect when the precision of a microcalorimeter (± 0.06 cal) is readily attained.

The relatively low operating temperature of this calorimeter would normally produce rather low rates of polymerization of most monomers. Only with the high sensitivity of this apparatus (similar to that of Laidler's differential microcalorimeter, described above) is it possible to measure the heats of polymerization in the vicinity of the standard temperature of 25°C. Three different procedures of working the calorimeter have been developed (35). These are the integral method, the differential method, and the extrapolation method. In the first method the total heat evolved and the weight of the polymer produced during a polymerization completed in the calorimeter are measured, the ratio of the two being the integral heat of polymerization. In the second the two rates, that of heat generation and that of polymerization, are measured when a steady reaction is in progress, and the respective ratio of the two rates is calculated. When the rate of polymerization cannot be measured with sufficient accuracy, owing to low molar volume change, or when the polymerization is very slow and never complete at the end of the reaction, then the third method is employed, in which the heat evolved to infinite time is calculated by graphical extrapolation and attributed to the weight of monomer initially taken for polymerization. The heats of alternating copolymerization of sulfur dioxide with several α olefins forming polysulphones (34) were measured with the calorimeter in a "ceiling temperature" study. The polymerization enthalpies of nineteen monomers consisting of cyclic and ethylenic compounds were determined with an average precision of $+0.3$ kcal/mole by these pioneering workers (35). An interesting observation was made regarding the unusually large heat of polymerization of acenaphthylene; it was attributed to the steric strain in the monomer ring that is partially relieved on polymerization.

2. ISOTHERMAL VAPORIZATION CALORIMETER

Tong and Kenyon (39) constructed the important calorimeter, the isothermal vaporization calorimeter, for polymerization. It was their original extension of the earlier heat of vaporization apparatus (40). A recent paper (41), however, mentions that such an apparatus was first applied by Khokhlovkin and others for measuring the heat of reaction. The essential parts of this all-glass apparatus are (a) a boiler flask, a reflux condenser, and an isothermal tubular chamber maintained by the vapor bath of the heat-exchange liquid, and (b) a suspended Dewar bucket with lid, containing the freshly distilled calorimetric liquid and an inner reaction tube, all attached to a weighing balance. The method consists of measuring the loss in weight of the calorimetric liquid (held in equilibrium with its vapor at the boiling point) resulting from evaporation due to the heat of reaction. The polymeriza-tion tube, about 5 to 6 cm long, is made from 8-mm glass tubing, and its surface is made irregular by being depressed, when hot, while fine capillaries are driven into its wall without its being punctured. Heat transfer is thereby improved, promoting smooth ebullition with less superheating. The tube is filled with weighed amounts of monomer and catalyst, flushed with nitrogen, and sealed. Before the reaction is started, the tube must be brought to the equilibrium temperature and then introduced into the Dewar bucket containing the working fluid at this temperature. During this warming-up period no polymerization must occur, and this is achieved either through the natural induction period associated with ordinary polymerization or by deliberate addition of traces of an inhibitor. In the work of Tong and Kenyon carbon tetrachloride, b.p. 76.8°C, was mostly used as the working substance, and the concurrence of results with other, higher-boiling, heat-exchange liquids, such as toluene, is rather fortuitous, the results, perhaps, being mutually compensated for by opposing factors. Higher working tempera-tures are not ordinarily suitable for this type of calorimeter, because appre-ciable polymerization is likely to occur during the warm-up period. The apparatus had a background drift (weight change in the Dewar bucket) that depended upon the boiling rate of the working liquid maintaining the vapor bath. This drift was kept constant by keeping to a certain height the extent of vapor bath in the open tube above the isothermal chamber and correcting for it. In their first measurements with alkyl methacrylates Tong and Kenyon assumed the polymerization to have proceeded to completion, and the values reported were therefore somewhat low. In the latter work, with substituted styrenes, they estimated the unreacted monomer by bromi-nation and also introduced the photographic weight-recording device, which gave automatic and continuous polymerization curves showing certain special kinetic features, such as the well-known autoacceleration, or "gel effect," in the polymerization of styrenes, methacrylates, and other vinyl monomers, at definite stages of conversion. The apparent heat of polymeriza-tion of styrene was found to increase by as much as 5%, somewhat linearly with the catalyst concentration. This was ascribed to oxidative side reactions of the peroxide and was corrected for by extrapolating to zero catalyst concentration. Eckegren et al. (46) used an almost similar apparatus with photographic weight-recording and obtained values for the heat of polymerization of methyl methacrylate, corrected for incomplete polymerization, and of chloroprene.

Joshi (47) incorporated a few modifications in this calorimeter, which considerably improved the reproducibility and ease of operation. The precision was brought to an average standard deviation of less than ± 0.3 kcal/mole, and the systematic drift was practically eliminated. Some of these new features of the modified Tong and Kenyon calorimeter are depicted in Fig. 8-3. The electronic weight-recording system consists of a spring-balance suspension holding the Dewar bucket on an adjustable micrometer screw-block and running through an inductive type of displacement trans-ducer. The signal due to core displacement of the transducer upon a weight change is amplified and fed to a pen recorder. Automatic polymerization curves are obtained or, alternatively (and with higher resolution and sen-sitivity), the amplified signal is fed to a null detector, the null position being kept adjusted with the micrometer screw. A metallic thermal damper, a tubular jacket whose solid leg is immersed in the boiler flask, was introduced in the isothermal chamber, to enclave the Dewar bucket, and this device has presumably eliminated the drift of the earlier apparatus, which was due to

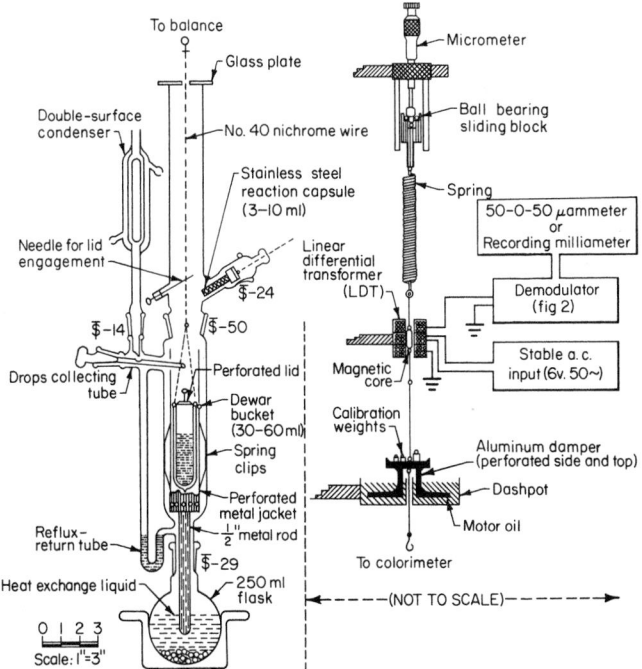

Fig. 8-3. Isothermal vaporization calorimeter with electronic weight-recording system.

the changes in the boiling rate. Still another modification was the use of
pressure-tight stainless-steel reaction capsules in place of the capillary-
studded glass ampules. The metal surface promoted ebullition without
superheating and with reduced heat losses. The better heat transfer due to
the metal reduced the thermal lag between polymerization and ebullition.
In addition, the metal capsules permitted the use of higher catalyst concentrations without the hazard of an explosion, enabling polymerizations to be
carried out to completion (95% and above) within the calorimeter. Full
details of the mode of introducing the reaction tube "isothermally" into the
Dewar bucket without disturbing thermal equilibrium have been provided.
Reliable data on a considerable number of monomers have been obtained
(presented in Table 8-2), and some new features affecting the heat of polymerization, such as the influence of hydrogen bonding (48,50), the effect
of strain energies (51) and resonance energies in the monomer and polymer,
and the effects of electrophilic substitutions (53), have been reported. The
heats of copolymerization of several systems of maleic anhydride and allied
compounds with vinyl monomers, forming essentially the 1:1 alternating
copolymers, have been measured (52). Owing to the improved consistency
in measurements it was possible to follow the reaction rates and elementary
kinetics of the maleic anhydride homopolymerization (49), an extremely
sluggish reaction.

C. Thermodynamic Equilibrium Method

The heat (and entropy) of polymerization are derivable from studies of
the reversible nature of this reaction. It has been shown by Dainton and
Ivin (54) that there should exist for every polymerization system that is
exothermic a "ceiling" temperature (T_c), above which the monomer is in the
thermodynamically stable state and undergoes no polymerization leading
to high-molecular-weight polymer. At this temperature the negative enthalpy
($-\Delta H$) is exactly counteracted by the entropy contribution ($T_c\Delta S$), so that
the Gibbs energy of polymerization (ΔG) is zero. The situation is identical
with liquid–vapor equilibrium and, like it, can be treated by application of
the reaction isochore $d \ln (M)/dT = -\Delta H_x^\circ/RT^2$, where (M) is the equilibrium monomer concentration (activity). Thus, with a long-chain polymer
there is always associated an equilibrium monomer concentration (activity)
at all temperatures below T_c. Measurements of monomer activity at different
temperatures (at least two) permit evaluation of ΔH and ΔS from the slope
and intercept, respectively, of the plot of $\ln (M)$ versus $1/T$ as related by the
integral equation

$$\ln (M)_{\text{equi}} = \frac{1}{T} \frac{\Delta H}{R} - \frac{\Delta S}{R} \tag{8-1}$$

The equilibrium between formaldehyde (gaseous) and polyoxymethylene (solid) was studied by Dainton et al. (55), and values of $\Delta H_{gc} = 12.2\,\text{kcal/mole}$ and $\Delta S_{gc} = 30.6\,\text{eu}$ were derived for the first time by this method. This value of the heat of polymerization is in fairly good agreement with the one from recent combustion data (56) on Delrin. Better establishment of the equilibrium is attained in a homogeneous solution of monomer and polymer, provided the active propagating centers are constantly replenished, because they mutually terminate rapidly, becoming dead polymer, especially at elevated equilibrium temperatures. Such an equilibrium in solution, between monomer and polymer with free-radical intermediates, was studied in the case of methyl methacrylate (57,58), methacrylonitrile (59), ethyl methacrylate (60), and the 1 : 1 copolymerization of sulfur dioxide and several olefins (61) with high-temperature free-radical sources, such as photodecomposition of benzoin or ultraviolet irradiation, and valuable data were obtained on the heats and, particularly, the entropies of polymerization.

Anionic polymerization, in which little or no termination occurs ("living" polymers), offers a unique opportunity for studying the equilibrium in solution, which is rapidly established at all temperatures and can be quenched instantaneously simply by the admission of air or moisture. The concentration of monomer (or polymer) is then readily estimated by analytical or physical methods. Worsfold and Bywater (64b) employed an anionic polymerization technique (sodium naphthenide in tetrahydrofuran), originated by Szwarc et al. (63) for the equilibrium polymerization of α-methyl styrene below $0°C$, and obtained values for heat ($\Delta H = -8.1\,\text{kcal/mole}$) and entropy ($\Delta S = -27.5\,\text{eu}$) in excellent agreement with those established by other methods (92). McCormick's independent work (64a) on the same system gave somewhat lower values for both ΔH and ΔS. The equilibrium method has recently been applied to the polymerization of tetrahydrofuran (65) (ring opening) by means of a novel cationic initiating system (triphenyl methyl or tropylium carbonium ion), which can also be described as containing "living" polymers. The equilibrium was followed in the temperature range 25 to 70°C by measuring the weight of polymer recovered after quenching of the system. The heat and entropy data are in good agreement with the similar work of Sims (66), who used PF_5 as initiator. For both these monomers because of the low heat of polymerization the equilibrium was substantially shifted towards monomer in the convenient temperature range of the experimental work. If it is desired, however, to apply this method to other monomers with higher ΔH_p (such as styrene, for which the equilibrium concentration would be about $10^{-7}\,M$ at $0°C$), more extraordinary and sensitive methods, such as the ^{14}C tracer technique, for assaying monomer concentrations of this low order may have to be attempted. An alternative solution would be to work the equilibrium in a higher temperature range, so that the monomer concentration is brought up within the reach of spectrophoto-metric methods, say 10^{-4} to 10^{-3} M, but then the propagating anionic species would be likely to undergo side reactions such as isomerization at the high temperature and complicate the equilibrium. Bywater and Worsfold successfully established the equilibrium anionic polymerization of styrene (67) in the temperature range 100 to 150°C, which is well above that normally considered suitable for anionic polymerization. Butyllithium was used as initiator, when the propagating polystyryl anion suffered no detectable isomerization. The monomer concentration was followed spectroscopically in the region of the 245-, 283-, and 292-mμ absorption bands of styrene. The final values of ΔH_{1c} and ΔS_{1c} (the former corrected for the heats of solution of monomer and polymer in the solvent employed) are -17.4 kcal/mole and -24.8 eu, respectively, at 400°K and show a unique agreement with the combustion data and many other calorimetric estimations. Equilibrium monomer concentrations at 25°C and the ceiling temperatures of several other systems have been calculated by Dainton and Ivin (54). These served also as a useful index of the relative thermal stability of the polymers studied by Wall (68).

The reaction calorimetry offers the advantage of simultaneously following the polymerization reaction kinetically and adding valuable information regarding the mechanism, but it is suited only for specific types of polymeriza-tion and, furthermore, the experimenter does not have much choice about the starting conditions or the end products, once the particular method and apparatus has been selected. The isothermal vaporization calorimetry is thus more suited to free-radical polymerizations, which work at a reasonably fast rate at the temperature (between 40 and 100°C) fixed by the choice of the working substance. The isothermal fusion calorimeter with diphenyl ether has the advantage that the measured values are directly obtained almost at the standard thermodynamic temperature (298.15°K), and no correction in this respect is necessary. The polymerizing substance and its initiating system, however, must be chosen for a reasonably fast rate of reaction at 26.9°C but not so fast as to upset the isothermal conditions. Because of these restrictions the polymers are sometimes of too low molecular weight [e.g., acenaphthylene (356)] and the side reactions of these low-temperature initiating systems are appreciable, causing dependence of the apparent heats of polymerization on the initiator concentration. The same features are characteristic of the thermocouple-thermistor method and of the differential microcalorimeter of Laidler, if worked at the standard temperature. Poly-merizations by ionic mechanism are very fast, almost instantaneous, and the calorimeter for such reactions must be provided with a device for adding the catalyst in situ, such as the magnetic breaker in the low-temperature calori-meter of Biddulph and Plesch (27). The thermodynamic equilibrium method is faced with the difficulties of radical initiation at higher temperature, above 100°C, although the technique of producing living polymers has considerably expanded the scope of this method. The polymer from these reaction calorimeters is structurally ill defined, of varying degrees of polymerization, amorphous or partly crystalline, and often in the solvated state or dissolved in monomer or solvent. None of the methods of reaction calorimetry can be applied at will to any particular polymerization system, but the method and the system must suit each other.

It has now become well understood that the energy difference between the two stereoisomeric forms of a vinyl-type polymer is of the order of 1 to 2 kcal/mole (69,70) and is not a negligible quantity in the 5 to 25 kcal range of the polymerization enthalpy if such data are to be utilized for a subtle study of the effects of substituents or other structural features. It is not, therefore, adequate to obtain or reduce the enthalpy data merely to the physical states connoted by the subscript "lc" or "lc'," where "c" or "c'" represent the condensed state. The degree of crystallinity (c') is yet another factor, which does not necessarily go with the degree of tacticity. A highly isotactic or syndiotactic polymer can be made to exist in an essentially amorphous state (supercooled liquid) or in the maximal crystalline state by quenching and annealing techniques, and the two states are clearly recognized by specific heat studies, as is shown by Karasz and O'Reilly (71). Other factors affecting the heat content of a polymer, such as degree of polymerization, extent of branching, molecular-weight distribution, and nature of end groups, have been discussed semiquantitatively (4) and found to introduce an uncertainty as great as 0.5 to 1.5 kcal/mole in the heat of polymerization data obtained from reaction calorimetry. Moreover, the heat of mixing of monomer and polymer, either alone or with the solvent employed, can affect the data by as much as 4 kcal/mole, as is seen in the case of acenaphthylene (55), and may become still more serious in the case of polar compounds.

D. Differential Combustion Calorimetry

In order to obtain enthalpy data in well-defined states of monomer and polymer, so that a close, unambiguous comparison of the different systems and structures becomes possible, one has to adopt the more sophisticated and versatile technique of combustion calorimetry and deduce the definitive thermodynamic property of a chemical substance, namely the heat of formation ΔH_f°. The potential of combustion calorimetry for highly accurate work, which was earlier limited to compounds containing carbon, hydrogen, oxygen, and nitrogen only, has now been so well developed as to cover sulfur, fluorine, chlorine, bromine, phosphorus, and metal or metaloid through the relatively new techniques of moving-bomb calorimetry (72) and also through the use of gases other than oxygen in the bomb for oxidation or reduction (73) of the combustion specimen. Outstanding examples are fluorine bomb calorimetry (74) and the novel use of carbon monoxide gas for "burning" tetranitromethane (7). Use of the bomb calorimeter for combustion measurements of gaseous substances, such as the lower fluorocarbons, by Skuratov and co-workers (16) is a striking new phase [originated by Neugebauer and Margrave (75)] of the combustion calorimetry of explosive gaseous mixtures. Suitable flame calorimeters for gaseous compounds or very volatile liquids have been described, and the technique of flame calorimetry is being extended to combustion in fluorine gas by Armstrong and collaborators (74), although its accuracy is still much lower (0.3 %) than that attained in the oxygen flame calorimetry. Nevertheless, the extraordinary oxidizing vigor of the fluorine gas literally leaves no compound unburnt and inaccessible, and use of fluorine as the oxidant in a bomb calorimeter has also now attained a fairly high precision, 0.05 %. The use of digital computers (73,74) for reducing the combustion data to standard state (such as the Shomate data reduction program) adds superior accuracy and reliability and eliminates the tedium of manual calculations.

In the experimental arrangement of the bomb calorimeter the noteworthy developments are as follows. A tenfold-increased precision in the platinum-resistance thermometry has been achieved through use of the G-3 G-4 Mueller bridge, the smallest step, 10 μohms, corresponding to a tenth of a millidegree. An automatic balancing and digital readout circuitry, fabricated at the National Bureau of Standards (77), has been added. The classical technique of immersing the bomb in a liquid (usually water) within an isothermal jacket is being shifted to "dry calorimetry," in which technique the bomb is embedded in a solid metallic matrix, again within an isothermal jacket. The low heat capacity of the metal enhances the sensitivity of the calorimeter by a factor of 10 or so, and much smaller samples (10 to 20 mg) are adequate for combustion in the semimicrocombustion or microcombustion calorimeters of aneroid type, described by Mackle and O'Hare (76), Calvet (74e), and others. The determination of the ignition energy (which becomes a significant fraction in semimicrocombustion or microcombustion) has received considerable attention in recent years, and methods employing electronic current integrators have been developed by many workers (76,78). The combustion bomb with a transparent window or the microcalorimeter completely made of glass, both of which permit visual inspection and even moving photography of the combustion (and so ensure its proper conduct), have been developed (73).

With these vast improvements in the technique every monomer and polymer system can be profitably restudied in definite physical states by combustion calorimetry, and standard data can be obtained, not only on the heats of formation and of polymerization (by difference), but also on the small energy changes associated with structural isomerism and phase transitions in polymers (164). Surprisingly, even the former data are very meager at present (all available data are given in Tables 8-1 and 8-2), in contrast to the considerable amount of data yielded by reaction calorimetry. In the combustion of organic compounds the highest precision so far attained in many standard laboratories in which certified benzoic acid is prepared is ± 1 cal in 10,000 cal, or 0.01 %. A precision of 0.03 to 0.05 % is, however, more common and only rarely falls to 0.1 %, doing so chiefly because of impure samples. A detailed procedure of conducting bomb calorimetry with a precision of 0.05 % has been described in a monograph by Jessup (79) and is believed to be adequate for much of the future work in the polymer field. The standard heats of combustion (ΔH_c°) for most organic compounds generally lie in the range of 300 to 1100 kcal/mole, and the heats of polymerization of vinyl and related monomers are in the range of 5 to 25 kcal/mole. The standard deviation of $+0.05 \%$ in the former data, which is 10 to 100 times larger, would introduce an uncertainty factor of 0.5 to 5 % in the values of heats of polymerization obtained by the energy difference ($\Delta\Delta H_c^\circ$) between monomer and polymer. The maximal error of 5 % in the extreme cases can be reduced to less than 2 % by increasing the usual quantity (about 1 g) of the sample taken for combustion to 2 or 3 g, so as to produce a net heat effect of 10,000 cal in the calorimeter, uniformly for all compounds of interest. The highest precision attained so far in the various reaction calorimeters (1 to 2 %) can thus be easily attained by the differential combustion method of ordinary precision. However, for evaluating the subtle energy differences (0.5 to 2 kcal/mole) due to stereoisomerism in polymer chains every advancement in the combustion calorimetry (0.01 % or better) must be invoked to give even the low precision of 10 % in the former.

Details of combustion methods have been fully treated in two volumes on experimental thermochemistry (74) and elsewhere, and only comments specific to the work on monomers and polymer need be made here. Traces of inhibitors usually found in the monomer as supplied may either be eliminated by purification immediately prior to combustion or be accurately assayed and corrected for. Certain vinyl monomers have a small thermal rate of polymerization, especially in the extremely pure state ($> 99.9 \%$), which is required for combustion calorimetry. Therefore, care must be taken to allow a minimal stay-on period and to avoid the application of heat to any portion of the monomer or its vapor during the filling and sealing of ampules. A special procedure for this operation with the monomers has been laid down (80). Some monomers are hygroscopic and some others may be susceptible to slow oxidation at 25°C in the high-pressure oxygen atmosphere and may require preliminary testing for whether such a reaction with oxygen occurs under the bomb conditions before ignition. During combustion a part of the monomer may polymerize in the vapor phase and escape combustion, remaining as a tarry deposit on the colder parts of the bomb. As a check of this situation, which may become serious in the combustion of polymer itself, particularly with certain high-temperature-resistant polymers, an accurate analytical assay of the products of combustion (mostly as CO_2 absorbed on ascarite or Indicarb in special absorption tubes and weighed) is necessary, to determine the amount of combustion that has actually taken place in the bomb. An analytical train, therefore, becomes an essential part of the combustion calorimetry of monomers and polymers. Polymers must be made scrupulously free from traces of residual monomer, catalyst, and organic solvents and precipitants used for their purification, because these are known (81) to adhere tenaciously in the polymer matrix. The polymers taken for combustion should be characterized at least approximately as to molecular weight, molecular-weight distribution, and branching and as accurately as possible as to degree of tacticity, in the way indicated by the method of preparation. Either a completely amorphous (glassy, liquid, or rubbery) state or, in the case of stereospecific polymers, a maximal and definite degree of crystallinity should be developed by special heat treatment, and the thermal history should be recorded.

The monomers and polymers subjected to combustion calorimetry are very few so far; they are listed in Tables 8-1 and 8-2. A broad program of such studies on both the experimental and theoretical levels is under way (164), at the Thermodynamics Research Center, Texas A & M University, College Station, Texas. In both tables the physical states of the monomers and polymers are given in the notation of Dainton and Ivin (4b), except for the omission of the symbol "c'," for lack of any well-defined crystallinity in polymers. Recent studies have shown (71) that many stereospecific "crystalline" polymers are only 30 to 50% crystalline from the thermodynamic point of view and that some enthalpy is always associated with the so-called "amorphous" glassy state of the atactic polymers, unless they are specially prepared by a particular heat treatment. The degree of tacticity is also always partial. In the Table 8-2 the monomers have been grouped roughly according to industrial development and usage. The second column gives the actual number of experiments, to help the reader to judge the quantity of work performed. The copolymerization systems selected are only those whose yielding of strictly alternating, equimolar sequences in the polymer chains has been established. The single figures in the last column are based on the concurrence of more than one method, the quality and quantity of work performed under a particular method, the inherent limitations of accuracy associated with it, and such other factors. Being uniformly for the "lc" states, they are corrected with the best known heats of vaporization of monomer or its structural analogue, the heat of fusion, and the degree of crystallinity in the polymer, if known to be stereospecific, and these are considered accurate within ± 0.5 kcal/mole. The structural and mechanistic interpretations of the heat of polymerization are founded mainly on these selected values for the specific change of state, either "lc" or "gg."

8-4. STRUCTURAL INFLUENCES IN POLYMERIZATION ENTHALPY

By far the largest body of the experimental data in Tables 8-1 and 8-2 pertains to ethylene derivatives; the rest pertains to the ring compounds polymerizing either through ring opening or through the unsaturation embodied in the ring without opening of the ring. It is possible to relate the heat of polymerization of the ethylenic monomers to substitution effects; that of the cyclic compounds, to ring size and strain energies. Since the heat of polymerization necessarily gives only a *difference* between the bonding energy in the monomer and the polymer, viz., the heat of (bond) formation, ΔH_f°, it represents the net result of the two individual substitution effects, which are sometimes additive and at other times opposite to each other. Each monomer–polymer system therefore needs individual consideration. The ethylenic monomers for which a good amount of data are now available for comparative study contain one or more of the following classic substituents: electron-withdrawing (rendering the double bond electron-deficient), $-F$, $-Cl$, $-NO_2$, $-C=O \cdot OH$, $-C=ONH_2$, $-C\equiv N$, $-C=OOR$, $-C=OR$, etc., and electron-donating, $-CH_3$, $-C_6H_5$, $-OR$, $-OC=OR$, $-CH=CH_2$, $-CH_2Cl$, $-C_6H_4Cl$, $-C_5H_4N$, etc. Except for the very strong electronegative substituents, such as fluorine or chlorine, the heat of self-polymerization is not influenced much, at least detectably (over other major factors) by the polar character of the group, although the heat of alternating copolymerization is substantially governed by the polarity factor of the comonomers. The substitution may either be of a single group (monosubstitution) or of a 1:1 or 1:2 disubstitution, and the effects of these are typically different.

For ethylene derivatives the $-\Delta H_{lc}$ vary over a considerable range, from a minimum of about 8 kcal (α-methyl styrene) to about 23 kcal (vinyl chloride) and to the exceptionally high values for the difluoro and tetrafluoroethylenes. These variations in ΔH arise mainly from the following causes:

1. Energy differences in monomer and polymer on account of either resonance stabilization (delocalization) due to conjugation-hyperconjugation or change of bond type (hybridization).

2. Steric strain (or, very rarely, strain relief) in the polymer as a result of bond-stretching, bond angle deformation, or interaction between nonbonded

atoms (usually repulsive, tending to make the ΔH_f° of the polymer less negative).

3. Steric strain in the monomer (which makes the ΔH_f° of the monomer less negative).

4. The (energy) difference in the extent of hydrogen bonding (and perhaps also of strong dipole interactions) in monomer and polymer.

A. Resonance Stabilization

The basic magnitude of the energy change due to the primary-bond changes associated with a vinyl polymerization may be taken as (a) the value for ethylene, $-\Delta H_{lc} = 21.2$ kcal/mole, which is derived from the most recent experimental value (56), $-\Delta H_{gc} = 25.88$, as (b) the value of the heat of vaporization of ethylene monomer at boiling point, $\Delta H_v = 3.2$, and as (c) the value of the heat of fusion of the 98 % crystalline Marlex (Phillip's) polyethylene, $\Delta H_m = 1.5$. Substitution of a methyl group lowers the $-\Delta H_{lc}$ of propylene by about 1.7 kcal, which is attributable to hyperconjugation [for propylene $-\Delta H_{lc} = 19.5$, based on the best value of ΔH_v, and $\Delta H_m = 1.0$ for the 64 % crystalline polypropylene used for combustion in a recent study (56)]. The heats of hydrogenation of these two olefins show a parallel effect but are slightly higher in magnitude. Hyperconjugation effects adequately explain small variations (about 1 and 2 kcal) in the heat of alternating copolymerization of different olefins with sulfur dioxide (61). They also appear to explain the slightly higher value of isoprene than of butadiene, since this may be looked upon as a reversed resonance effect of the hyperconjugation, namely the stabilization of the residual double bonds in polyisoprene, which is absent in polybutadiene. In a series of α-methyl-substituted monomers the contribution of hyperconjugation in stabilizing the monomer is apparent (50). The higher hyperconjugating action of the chloromethyl group is borne out by the value of allyl chloride (50), which is slightly lower than propylene.

The heats of polymerization of styrene and its ring-substituted derivatives are appreciably lowered by about 5 kcal owing to conjugation of the phenyl group with the double bond. Similar stabilization of the monomer state by conjugation is apparent in butadiene or isoprene (about 3 kcal), vinyl pyridines (2.5 to 4 kcal), N-vinyl carbazole, acenaphthylene, acrylonitrile, and others. Resonance stabilization in 2-vinyl pyridine clearly exceeds that of 4-vinyl isomer by about 1.5 kcal (50). Conjugation with a carboxyl or a carbonyl group in acrylic acid, acrylic esters, acrylamide, acrolein, and methyl vinyl ketone also seem to lower the ΔH_{lc} of these monomers. When the substituent is nonconjugating, as it is in vinyl acetate and higher vinyl esters, in nitroethylene, and in maleimide (in which the conjugation effect is prevented by symmetrical disubstitution), the basic value of 21 kcal remains practically unaltered.

B. Resonance-Induced Polymerization

Orr (*96*) recently discussed some very interesting features of resonance stabilization in polymer (which is nonexistent in monomer). It enhances the polymerizability, which Orr describes as "resonance-induced." Compounds containing a higher order or degree of unsaturation (e.g., a triple bond in acetylene, $C \equiv C$, or in a nitrile, $R-C \equiv N$) on polymerization yield linear polymers with a conjugated double-bond system. In acetylene the already favorable enthalpy change for such polymerization (a triple bond changing to a double bond and a single bond) is further augmented by the resonance energy, which is estimated to be about 10 kcal per unit in the resonance-stabilized long-chain polymer, $(CH=CH)_n$. The estimated $-\Delta H_{gg}^{\circ}$ of a nitrile polymerization (*96*), $n(R-C \equiv N) \rightarrow (R-C=N-)_n$, is about 10 kcal/mole, and it is 46 kcal/mole for acetylene. These polymerizations have recently materialized (*2,97,98*). Allene ($CH_2=C=CH_2$) has also been polymerized recently (*99*), and the polymer is found to contain three types of unsaturation, one of which would be a conjugated, alternant system, $(-C(CH_3)=CH-)_n$, formed by tautomeric shifting of the hydrogen atom. In Table 8-1 we have attempted to estimate $-\Delta H_{gg}^{\circ}$ for the polymerization of allene in the two modes of the polymer and also for a few other resonance-induced polymerizations. These estimates are based on the Cox scheme, which partially accounts for the resonance effects. The polymerization of any cyclic conjugated compound such as cyclooctatetraene, which is not resonance-stabilized, to a polymer that is so stabilized, is readily envisaged. The $-\Delta H_{gg}^{\circ}$ and the $-\Delta S_{gg}$ for cyclooctatetraene polymerization to $(CH=CH)_n$ are estimated by Orr (*96*) as 40 kcal/mole and 24 eu, respectively. Conceivably, cyclooctatetraene may be imagined to tautomerize to styrene monomer through the necessary hydrogen shifts in the diradical intermediate formed by opening of one of its single bonds, or directly to polystyrene. These reactions are energetically very favored, as may be seen from the data on heats of formation supplied in Table 8-1. The $-\Delta H_{gg}^{\circ}$ of the hypothetical polymerization of cyclooctatetraene to a polystyrene structure would be 56 kcal/mole.

It is rather difficult to account for the high polymerization enthalpies (exceeding that of ethylene itself) of the derivatives containing a strongly electronegative group, such as vinyl chloride ($-\Delta H_{lc} = 22.9$ kcal), nitroethylene ($-\Delta H_{lc} = 21.7$ kcal), vinylidene fluoride ($-\Delta H_{lc} = 31$ kcal), and tetrafluoroethylene ($-\Delta H_{lc} = 37$ kcal). An explanation, that the repulsive interactions between nonbonding electrons associated with the electronegative group may be reduced on polymerization, has been put forth by Mortimer (*100*). Flitcroft and Skinner observed that the heat of hydrogenation of vinyl chloride was higher than ethylene by about 2 kcal and explained (*101*) that the polar character of the $C-Cl$ bond in ethyl chloride led to a resonance effect between the ionic and covalent forms of the bond; the stabilizing energy in ethyl chloride thereby exceeds and offsets the resonance energy, owing to conjugation (or, rather, "hyperconjugation," in view of the mere 4% double-bond character of the C—Cl bond) in vinyl chloride. Heats of polymerization of these monomers may be explained in the same way, implying stronger bonds (pertaining to the electrophilic substitution) in polymer. Yet another explanation is possible. It is now recognized that the carbon atom can form weak hydrogen bonds (102) of the C—H$\cdots$Cl type. The hydrogen-bonding sites in adjacent polymer chains, more rigidly fixed than among free monomer molecules, would lead to higher inter-molecular association (the association energy) in the polymer, thus con-tributing to the heat of polymerization. Considerable intermolecular association in polyvinyl chloride and fluorocarbon polymers is a character-istic feature of these polymers and imparts crystallinity and valuable me-chanical properties. The heat of polymerization in such cases should be more temperature-dependent than would be expected from the specific-heat changes.

C. Steric Hindrance in Polymers, Steric Strain in Monomers

Steric hindrance is an important special feature of a polymer-forming process, governing largely the heats of polymerization, and is best understood from a study of the simplest case of isobutene polymers with only small methyl substituents. In monosubstituted polymer chains the steric hindrance, even from such sizable substituents as the phenyl ring in polystyrene, is minor compared with that which occurs when alternate carbon atoms of the chain bear two substituents. Not only are steric interferences in-tolerably severe in the fully extended, planar zigzag configuration, but they are usually impossible to eliminate altogether through any bond rotation. Even when substituents are no larger than methyl, as in the poly-isobutylene chain, and even when the strain is somewhat reduced by helix formation, the steric interference is so great as to preclude construction of a scale model with the usually accepted van der Waals radii and bond distances.

The case of isobutene polymerization both by cationic and free-radical mechanism was earlier worked out in full detail by Evans and Polanyi (103). The heats of reaction (considering no steric hindrance) for the *first* addition of an isobutene unit to a growing carbonium ion end were cal-culated from the proton affinity or carbonium ion affinity of isobutene; to a growing radical end, from "atom affinity." These are shown in the follow-ing table:

	Heat of reaction ΔH_{gg}, kcal/mole	
Mode	Free radical	Carbonium ion
Head to tail	−19.5	−19.5
Head to head	−12	+ (slightly endothermic)
Tail to tail	−27	−40

Although the tail-to-tail mode of addition is energetically the most favorable, it must necessarily accompany the head-to-head, which is not only less favorable than the *normal* head-to-tail but even slightly endothermic in the carbonium-ion chain propagation. The net result is that (considering no steric influences) the two modes of addition polymerization by both ionic and free-radical mechanisms are energetically almost equal or, perhaps, only slightly in favor of head-to-tail by about 1 kcal or so. The propagating species, however, is always a "head," represented by $\cdots CH_2—C^*(XY)$ or $\cdots CH_2—C^+(XY)$, which is, in both free-radical and cationic mechanisms of initiation, stabilized by the resonance and inductive effects of the substituents X and Y. Therefore it follows that, once the "head" chain starts or preponderates, it will essentially lead to a head-to-tail type of addition with a constant heat of reaction of 19.5 kcal at each step. The experimental heat of dimerization of isobutylene is in conformity with this value, but the addition of a third unit (and subsequent units), leading to a longer polyisobutylene chain, entirely changes the picture. The middle segment, which is now sandwiched between the two others, loses its earlier full freedom to rotate and to take up configuration of minimal nonbonding interaction with respect to both its neighboring segments. The steric strain in the polymer is thus built up progressively, lowers the heat of polymerization of isobutene per double bond consumed, and ultimately falls to the value of 12.9 kcal/mole, which is the recent accurate value (28) for high-molecular-weight cationic polymerization. This pattern of the diminishing of ΔH_p with the chain length may be empirically fitted to the equation

$$-\Delta H = 19.5 - 6.6(1 - 1/n^2)\,\text{kcal/mole} \qquad (\text{for } n \geq 1)$$

where n is the number of hindered (sandwiched) dimethyl segments. The validity of the proposed empirical equation must await the experimental value of the heat of formation (combustion) of at least the trimer olefin, 2,4,4,6,6-pentamethyl-2-heptene ($C_{12}H_{24}$) and, preferably, the tetramer, 2,4,4,6,6,8,8-heptamethyl-2-nonene ($C_{16}H_{32}$), for which the predicted heats of formation, $\Delta H_f^\circ(g)$, would be −46.0 and −63.7 kcal/mole, respectively.

This is based on the heat of reaction of dimer → trimer (14.6 kcal) and trimer → tetramer (13.7 kcal), and so on. Evans and Polanyi give an experimental estimate of about 14 kcal for the dimerization of diisobutene (9) (dimer → tetramer), and this value has primarily been used in proposing the general equation for the long-chain olefins of this type.

A somewhat more precise idea of the trend of growing steric hindrance in the polyisobutylene chain may be gained by calculating the nonbonding interaction energies between polymer segments with the method that was outlined by Ferstandig and Goodrich (104) in connection with the stereospecific polymerization of propylene. Employing methods developed by Mason (105), they calculated the total nonbonded interaction energies arising from all combinations between the interacting groups of an approaching monomer and a growing chain end at various distances and rotation angles around the line of approach. At a distance of 2.6 A the energy was minimum (at an angle of 40°), but it was as high as 7 to 9 kcal and would be enormously high at the normal C—C bond distance of 1.5 A. Bawn et al. (70) applied similar calculations to methyl methacrylate, a 1 : 1 disubstituted ethylene, and found that the interaction energy between the terminal and the penultimate unit (both conformed in a chain with normal bond distances) was at the minimum about 5 kcal and that the complete rotation was hindered by a barrier (a maximum) greater than 20 kcal. The major portion of these repulsive interactions is already implied in the normal bond energies and has been taken care of in the normal heats of formation of the unhindered polymer chain. Only a fraction of these net repulsive energies (varying between 5 and 20 kcal) that arises from a departure from the minimal energy position due to the imposed constraint in chain formation contributes to the reduction in the heat of polymerization. When a new monomer unit adds to a growing chain, the terminal unit must rotate about the penultimate unit through a certain angle, so as to take up its new minimum (allowable) energy position, consistent with statutory conformation of the chain. In turn, the penultimate unit and, perhaps, a few units beyond may also be required to rotate around various C—C bonds, and these rotational barriers should exert substantial influence on the propagation step both with respect to the enthalpy and the activation energy. It is here, we feel, that the hypothesis of the penultimate-unit effect (106) finds a sounder theoretical basis than do other premises, e.g., distant electrostatic repulsion. Even the semiquantitative calculations of the rotational barriers around a few critical C—C bonds in different types of polymer chain would be a new and interesting approach to the understanding of steric hindrance and of the penultimate-unit effect.

In α-methyl styrene ($-\Delta H_{lc} = 8.4$ kcal) all the structural factors lowering the ΔH have combined : namely, the resonance of the benzene ring, the $-CH_3$

hyperconjugation stabilizing the monomer, and the 1:1 disubstitution destabilizing the polymer. The same is true of methacrylic acid and all its derivatives ($-\Delta H_{lc}$ ranging between 13 and 14 kcal) and of vinylidene chloride ($-\Delta H_{lc} = 18.0$ kcal). In the latter case the electronegativity of the chlorine substitution has caused the compensating effect of raising the value, since otherwise chlorine substituent, being almost the same size as the methyl, should have lowered the ΔH_p to ≈ 13 kcal as for the isobutylene. A few other 1:1 disubstituted monomers, which readily polymerize to high-molecular-weight polymers (in spite of steric hindrance) but have received little attention in thermochemical study, are methyl α-cyanoacrylates (107), α-chloro-acrylates (108), and α-chloroacrylonitrile (108).

The oldest observation regarding the 1:2 disubstituted ethylenes is their usual reluctance to self-polymerize, which has exerted a somewhat restrictive influence on their study except as comonomers (109). The synthesis of some new monomers in this class and the application of new initiation techniques, such as high-energy irradiation (110) and high pressure (111), has shown that homopolymerization can occur and lead to at least a low-molecular-weight polymer of 10 to 1000 units. Thus, diethyl ester of fumaric acid (110) and trans-dichloroethylene (112) have been polymerized through ^{60}Co gamma irradiation, generally a free-radical initiation. The polymerizations of α-chlorovinyl ethers (113), alkenyl ethers (1), β-nitrostyrene (114), 1-nitro-propene (115), and tert-butyl crotonate (116) have been recently achieved through ionic or ionic-coordination catalysts (117). By applying high pressures (10,000 atm) Holmes–Walker and Weale (111) examined the polymerization of a number of these monomers essentially through free-radical initiation, and Weale (111) successfully obtained a solid polymer of 1,2-dichloroethylene. The attempts at polymerizing 2-butene, isopentene, 2,3-dimethyl-2-butene, and tri- and tetrachloroethylenes at high pressures, up to 30,000 atm, made by Gonikberg and others, had either failed or resulted in, at most, a pentamer. This failure was perhaps due more to the simultaneously applied high temperature (300°C) than to the lack of polymerizability, as was explained by Ivin (118). Steric hindrance, however, in the polymers of these 1,2 disubstituted olefins is not a factor in the sluggishness of their polymerization, and has been discussed in full detail in many texts (10,109). The only monomer in this class for which ΔH_p has been measured is tetrafluoroethylene, but in this case, because of the small size of the fluorine atom and its extreme electronegativity, forming exceptionally strong bonds, no steric hindrance is traceable.

The construction of scale models of 1,2 disubstituted ethylene polymers, such as poly(butene-2) is easier than the construction of scale models of polymers with two substituents alternating on the same carbon as in polyisobutylene. The hypothetical polymer poly(butene-2) must have two modes of conformation, the isotactic and the syndiotactic, because every carbon in the chain $-C^*(CH_3)H-$ is asymmetric. The isotactic chain is rather strained and difficult to construct even in the helical configuration, but the syndiotactic is almost completely strain-free, and the rotational barriers around the skeletal C—C bond also appear to be small. The study of models shows that syndiotactic polymers, once formed, should be sterically as little hindered as the monosubstituted ethylene polymers (polypropylene), and the heat of their polymerization should show no large departure from the basic value of about 20 kcal, unlike the case of polyisobutylene. The steric hindrance perhaps plays a more prominent role in the transition state than in the final state of the polymer, although the 1,2 disubstituted ethylene is thermodynamically as potentially polymerizable as the mono-substituted one. A recently achieved polymerization of tert-butyl crotonate (116), $HC(CH_3)=HC(COOR)$-tert, through lithium alkyls to high-molecu-lar-weight polymer (50,000) contributes to the same inference. This polymer–monomer system offers a unique opportunity to evaluate the heat of poly-merization from a comparison of its differential combustion with that of tert-butyl methacrylate $(-\Delta H_{1s} = 13.0 \text{ kcal})$ (34). Such a study would decisively show whether the polymerization of 1,2 disubstituted ethylenes, like that of the cycloalkanes, is hindered more by lack of a mechanism of low activation energy than by lack of intrinsic polymerizability.

Ring compounds embodying a double bond, which polymerize without ring opening, may be considered 1,2 disubstituted ethylenes. These deriva-tives are more readily polymerized for one or more of the following reasons. Both substituents are rigidly held in the ring in a particular orientation that may render the double bond more vulnerable to a radical or ion attack. The stabilizing influences due to conjugation or inductive effects cancel out by virtue of the symmetrical nature of the disubstitution; this applies also to open olefins, such as the 2-butenes (cis-trans), and makes these derivatives potentially as reactive as ethylene itself, which has hydrogens as the sym-metrical substituents. The rings are generally strained more or less, depend-ing upon the size of the ring and the nature and hybridization of the atoms contained. The strain energy elevates the potential energy of the monomer, and in the process of polymerization part of the strain is relieved. According to the internal-strain concept of Brown et al. (119), for all chemical reactions of a ring compound a change in the coordination number (hybridization) of a ring atom through which the reaction is likely to pass in the transition state, or which occurs in the final product, causes a change in the internal strain of the ring and contributes to the activation energy and the heat of reaction, respectively. An interesting account of the 1,2 disubstituted ethenoid rings, which have been polymerized in recent years, is given by Schuerch (120). Some experimental ΔH_p data available for a few of these are given:

acenaphthylene, $-\Delta H_{cc} = 19.6$ kcal ($34,50$); maleic anhydride, $-\Delta H_{ls} \geq$ 14 kcal (49); maleimide, $-\Delta H_{ss} = 21.0$ kcal (51). The contribution of strain energy to the heat of polymerization is apparent, especially in the case of maleimide (51). Cyclopropene represents a highly strained, three-membered ring with two trigonal carbon atoms which change to the tetrahydral symmetry on polymerization, forming a chain containing cyclopropane rings, presumably δ-*trans*-oriented. A reliable estimate of ΔH_p can be made from the experimental heat of formation of cyclopropene (121) and from that of its polymer, calculated on the basis of the Cox scheme (see Table 8-1) by means of a group contribution value for cyclopropane, which is also a strained unit. The predicted value is about 41 kcal/mole, which involves a strain energy of about 27 kcal [Wiberg and Bartley's estimate (121) of the strain energy in cyclopropene in excess of that in cyclopropane, made from heats of hydrogenation] contributed by the strain relief on polymerization.

In the other class of (saturated) ring compounds polymerization takes place through opening of the ring, and the linear polymers so formed are virtually free from strain, because the substituent groups become widely spaced in the polymer. The heat of polymerization therefore provides a direct measure of the strain energy in the monomer ring. By using the heats of formation and other precise thermodynamic data available on the series of cycloalkanes and their methyl and 1,1-dimethyl derivatives Dainton et al. (122) calculated the heat, entropy, and free-energy changes in the hypothetical polymerization. A few typical values of $-\Delta H_{lc}$ of unsubstituted cycloalkanes have been included in Table 8-1. The ring strain in three- and four-membered carbon systems is very high, decreases to a minimum for cyclohexane (with sign reversal, indicating endothermicity of polymerization), and then increases with further increase in the ring. This pattern of the strain energy appears to remain unaltered when a small heteroatom, such as nitrogen or oxygen, replaces a carbon atom, but the strain is considerably reduced by introduction of the larger sulfur or silicon atom. Comparing the data on alkylene oxides in Table 8-2 with those on the cycloalkanes, one finds that the trend of ΔH_p in the series ethylene, cyclopropane, cyclobutane, and cyclopentane is exactly repeated by the corresponding alkylene oxides: formaldehyde (regarded here as methylene oxide, i.e., a two-membered heterocyclic ring), $-\Delta H_{lc} \approx 7.4$ kcal; ethylene oxide, 22.6 kcal; oxacyclobutane, 19.2 kcal; and tetrahydrofuran, 5 kcal.

D. Hydrogen-Bonding Influences

Hydrogen bonding (123) in lower fatty acids or their amides leads to complete dimerization of the molecules, even in the gaseous phase, and involves association energies as high as 4 to 7 kcal/mole per bond of the type O—H $\cdots$ O or N—H $\cdots$ O. The detailed molecular structures of acrylic and methacrylic acids have been determined by Ukaji (*124*) from electron diffraction measurements and show complete dimerization of these monomers in the solid state. It should also be appreciable in liquid or gaseous states, as in the well-confirmed instances of formic and acetic acids. In the process of polymer formation these hydrogen bonds must be broken first (an endothermic process), although they are re-formed in the polymer. The steric constraints in the polymer chain would, however, preclude the ready accessibility of the polar substituents for both inter- and intramolecular association, and the number of hydrogen bonds per mole in the polymer would generally be less than in the monomer in the case of strong hydrogen-bonding sites. This situation may be reversed sometimes for feeble hydrogen bonds, as we have postulated in case of the $C-H \cdots Cl$ type of interchain bonding in polyvinyl chloride. The monomer state (pure liquid state or in nonpolar medium) is thus more stabilized on account of this secondary bonding energy than the polymer state, and this is clearly reflected in the lowering of the heats of polymerization, as shown by Joshi (*48*) in his experimental study of these monomeric acids and their amides. The ΔH_p values in the liquid state or in nonpolar media for acrylic acid ($-\Delta H_{lc} = 16.0$ kcal), methacrylic acid ($-\Delta H_{lc} = 10.1$ kcal), acrylamide ($-\Delta H_{ss} = 14.4$ kcal in benzene and 13.8 kcal in hexane), and methacrylamide ($-\Delta H_{ss} = 8.4$ kcal in benzene), are all considerably lower than what the monomer structure would suggest. If, however, polymerization is carried out in water (or other polar media), the intermolecular association in both monomer and polymer, i.e. monomer–monomer and polymer–polymer contacts, is replaced with co-association, i.e. by monomer–water or polymer–water contacts. If a sufficiently dilute aqueous or alcoholic solution of a monomer is polymerized in the calorimeter, the differential effect of association may be appreciably reduced or eliminated almost completely. The ΔH_{ss} (water or methanol) for all these hydrogen-bonded monomers have been found *normal* in relation to structure and were uniformly higher by about 3 to 5 kcal than those of the associated liquid state.

E. Copolymerization

Monomer units that experience steric hindrance in the chain on account of their 1,1 or 1,2 disubstitution may be linked easily into a polymer chain through copolymerization. Not only is the steric strain due to the consecutive placement of three or more similar units completely relieved in the copolymer with an alternative ($M_1 M_2 M_1 M_2 M_1 M_2$) or a semialternative ($M_1 M_1 M_2 M_1 M_1 M_2$ or $M_1 M_2 M_2 M_1 M_2 M_2$) arrangement of the two monomer segments M_1 and M_2, but certain $C-C$ linkages in the chain backbone, particularly those joining two dissimilar units, presumably become strengthened if the natures of the substitutions in the two species

are complementary to each other. Such copolymerizations are more exothermic than either of the two self-polymerizations, if the latter occurs at all.
Thus, maleic anhydride with electron-withdrawing (positive) carbonyl
substitution copolymerizes readily with the electronegative styrene or
α-methyl styrene (electron-donating $-C_6H_5$ or $-CH_3$ or both), the heat
of copolymerization exceeding that of either homopolymerization (see
Table 8-2 for experimental values). The Alfrey–Price Q–e scheme ($109,125$)
provides an excellent semiquantitative index of the electrical character of
the substituents, and the copolymerization enthalpy is much guided by the
e factor. Alfrey and Lewis (126) developed a mathematical treatment relating
the over-all heat of copolymerization (per mixed mole) with the composition
of the copolymer in terms of the molar enthalpies of the four basic propaga-
tion steps ΔH_{11}, ΔH_{12}, ΔH_{21}, and ΔH_{22} and the monomer reactivity ratios
$r_1 = k_{11}/k_{12}$ and $r_2 = k_{22}/k_{21}$, the latter governing the probability of
occurrence of the steps and, hence, the copolymer composition. Suzuki
et al. (33) investigated two copolymerization systems of 1,1 disubstituted
methyl methacrylate with styrene and vinyl acetate and found the heat of
cross-propagation, $\Delta H_{12} + \Delta H_{21}$, to be larger than $\Delta H_{11} + \Delta H_{22}$ by 2 or
3 kcal/mole as a result of the relief of strain provided by the $M_1 M_2$ structural
sequences. Complete thermochemical aspects of butadiene–styrene copolymerization have been worked out by Orr (127) on the basis of the
Alfrey–Lewis treatment of the heats of copolymerization, including a
calculation of the residual entropy of copolymers from heat-capacity data.
He concluded that the contribution to the entropy at 0°K made by the glassy
state was negligible and that the contribution of the growing polymer chain
to entropy and enthalpy changes was determined chiefly by the nature of the
terminal unit. Some of the new significant experimental data (52) on heats of
alternating copolymerization recently obtained are the systems of maleic
anhydride with styrene (19.5 kcal), α-methyl styrene (17.3 kcal), allyl chloride
(17.7 kcal), and vinyl-n-butyl ether (21.5 kcal). More recently a theoretical
treatment of the heat of copolymerization based on probabilities of the four
propagation steps has appeared (128), which essentially leads to the Alfrey–
Lewis expression with the function $r_1 r_2$ replaced with a parameter Ω,
representing the enthalpy difference between self- and cross-propagations.
This treatment, which is based on four *types of bond* rather vaguely defined
only as A—A, A—B, B—A, and B—B (except, perhaps, that they are of the
head-to-tail type), is inadequate to resolve the heat of copolymerization in
terms of the primary C—C covalent bonds in the thermochemical sense.
Each monomer A or B contains two such primary C—C bonds, whose
strengths, as in the homopolymer, would differ appreciably in the copolymer
owing to strain relief and inductive effects. In the copolymerization of two
dissimilar monomers it is possible that a strong head-to-head C—C bond

between two "heads" of opposite polar character can be formed, notwith-standing the higher energy of formation of a "tail" type (H_2C*) of propagating species, which must ensue from such head–head interaction. Recent evidence (*129*) concerning poly(vinylidene fluoride) containing 10% head-to-head placements shows that the head-to-head or tail-to-tail mode of propagation is not completely ruled out in free-radical polymerization and may be quite easily effected in a copolymerization involving strongly polar substituents. The transition state of such alternating copolymerizations has already been recognized as potentially *ionic* because of electron transfer from the donor substrate (*130*), and in an anionic polymerization the unsubstituted carbon is invariably the propagating carbanion. In a comprehensive analysis of the heat of copolymerization the penultimate units need to be distinguished, pri-marily to resolve steric factors on the basis of rotational barriers between the penultimate and the terminal unit, as mentioned before, and head-to-head and tail-to-tail modes of addition also need to be taken into account, to resolve the inductive influences of polar substituents. When these additional propagation steps are incorporated, the absolute analytical expression for the heat of copolymerization becomes intractable.

8-5. MECHANISTIC IMPLICATIONS OF THE HEAT OF POLYMERIZATION

For a polymerization reaction to occur the monomer's change of state must pass two tests, the thermodynamic test and the kinetic test. Failure in the first makes *direct* polymerization impossible forever, while failure in the second makes polymerization impossible until a suitable mechanism is found.

A. Thermodynamics of Equilibrium

The quantity ΔH_p° (heat of polymerization), which we have hitherto dis-cussed, is only part of the thermodynamic test; the equally important counterpart is the entropy of polymerization, ΔS_p°. These are related, as in any chemical or physical change by the equation $\Delta G^\circ = \Delta H^\circ - T\Delta S^\circ = -RT \ln K_e$, where K_e is the equilibrium constant of the propagation step. Dainton and Ivin (*4*) have established a complete thermodynamic analysis of addition polymerization taking place through opening of either a higher-order chemical bond (C=O, C=C, etc.) or a ring. Addition polymerization (propagation) proceeds according to the equation

$$M_n^* + M_1 \underset{k_d}{\overset{k_p}{\rightleftharpoons}} M_{n+1}^* \tag{8-2}$$

in which the rates of propagation and depropagation are given by $k_p[M^*][M_1]$ and $k_d[M^*]$. With the assumption fairly well established that the reactivity of a propagating active center does not *ordinarily* depend upon the chain length or "history" the species M_n^* and M_{n+1}^* become indistinguishable and are represented simply by $[M^*]$, the concentration of the active species. Here $[M_1]$ is the monomer concentration, and k_p and k_d are the rate constants related to the equilibrium constant K_e in the equations above by $K_e = k_p/k_d$. Under the equilibrium conditions the rates of forward and reverse reactions occurring at all active centers M_n^*, M_{n+1}^*, etc., may be equated:

$$k_p \sum_n^\infty [M_n^*][M]_e = k_d \sum_{n+1}^\infty [M_n^*] \qquad (8\text{-}3)$$

For a high-molecular-weight polymer

$$\sum_n^\infty [M_n^*] = \sum_{n+1}^\infty [M_n^*]$$

For a high-molecular-weight polymer $\sum_n^\infty [M_n^*] = \sum_{n+1}^\infty [M_n^*]$ and, hence, $k_p/k_d = K_e = [M]_e^{-1}$, where $[M]_e$ is the equilibrium monomer concentration. The equilibrium condition may be established at any temperature T_e, so that

$$\Delta G° = -RT \ln K_e = RT \ln [M]_e = \Delta H_p° - T_e \Delta S_p°$$

$$T_e = \Delta H_p°/(\Delta S_p° + R \ln [M]_e) \qquad (8\text{-}4)$$

where $\Delta S_p°$ is the entropy change for $[M]_e = 1$ mole liter^{-1}. The ceiling temperature T_c of a polymerizing system has been *defined* as the temperature at which the Gibbs energy of propagation changes from a negative to a positive value (through zero) as the temperature is varied. The ceiling temperature in a particular system with unit monomer concentration (or, conversely, the temperature at which the monomer concentration in equilibrium with long-chain polymer becomes unity) is given by $T_c = \Delta H_p°/\Delta S_p°$ and is somewhat better defined by this condition.

In comparison to the substantial amount of data on ΔH_p in Tables 8-1 and 8-2 the entropy data are meager. The entropy of polymerization is obtainable either by direct equilibrium-polymerization study based on Eq. (8-4) or as the difference between the third-law entropies $\int C_p/T \, dT$ of monomer and polymer, obtained separately from the experimental relationship between their specific heats and temperatures. It may also be calculated as $\Delta S°$ of monomer minus $\Delta S°$ of polymer by means of semiempirical group-contribution methods, such as that of Anderson, Beyer, and Watson or of Benson and Buss and others, which have been reviewed and compiled by Janz (*134*). The calculated entropies of polymerization show better agreement with the experimentally found values than do the predicted heats of polymerization listed in Table 8-1, because the entropy change in polymerization is not as sensitive to monomer structure. The calculated entropies may therefore be safely taken in calculations of Gibbs energy, for which reliable enthalpy data are available. In Table 8-3 we give all available experimental data on ΔS_p together with our selected values of ΔH_{1c} and ΔS_{1c}, the calculated

TABLE 8-3

Standard Entropy and Gibbs Energy Changes and Equilibrium Constants (at 25°C) for Polymerization

Monomer	$-\Delta S_{xy}$ (exptl.), cal deg^{-1} mole^{-1}, with ref.[a]	$-\Delta S_{lc}^\circ$ (selected)	$-\Delta H_{lc}^\circ$, kcal/mole	$-\Delta G_{lc}$ at 25°C ([M] = 1)	$-\Delta G_{lc}$ at 25°C (liq.)	K_e at 25°C, liter mole^{-1}
Tetrafluoroethylene	gc' = 47.13, 4a	47.13	41.5	27		
	lc = 26.76	26.8	37	29	30.5	3.0×10^{22}
Ethylene	gc' = 41.5, 131	41.5, gc	25.88, gc	13.51	15.6	2.7×10^{11}
	gc = 37.7, 131	24,[c] lc	21.2,[c] lc	14.0	15.5	2.3×10^{11}
	gg = 34.0,[b] 54					
3,3-Dichloromethyl 1-oxacyclobutane	lc = 19.85, 131	19.85	20.2	14.3		
Vinyl acetate	ls = 26.2, 54	26.2	21.2	13.4	14.8	7.1×10^{10}
Butadiene	lc = 21.2, 4a	20.5	17.6	11.5	12.9	2.9×10^{9}
	lc = 20.1, 131					
Propylene	gc' = 49.0, 131	49.0	24.89	10.3		
	gc = 44.2, 131					
	gg = 39.9[b]					
Butene-1	lc = 27.8, 4a	27.8	19.5		12.7	2.0×10^{9}
	gc = 45.4, 131					
	gc' = 52.3, 131					
	gg = 39.8,[b] 131					
Isoprene	lc = 26.8	26.8	19.0	10.7	12.4	1.3×10^{9}
Styrene	lc = 24.2, 4a	24.2	17.9		12.1	7.5×10^{8}
	gg = 35.5,[b] 54					
	lc = 25.8, 54					
	lc = 26.7, 132					
	lc = 24.9, 4a					
	lc = 27.7, 4a					
	lc = 26.2, 131					

Styrene	lc = 25.2, 131	25.0	16.7	9.2	10.5	5.0×10^7
Methyl methacrylate	ls = 28.9, 54					
	lc = 28.0, 58	28.0	13.2	4.8	6.2	3.5×10^4
	ss = 29.5, 57					
Ethyl methacrylate	lc = 29.7, 60	29.7	13.8	4.9	6.2	3.5×10^4
Isobutylene	gg = 41.0,[b] 4a					
	lc = 28.8	28.8	12.9	4.3	6.0	5.0×10^4
Formaldehyde	gc' = 30.66, 55					
	gc' = 41.65, 131	41.8	13.2	0.77		
	gc' = 41.99, 131					
	gc' = 43.1, 131					4.3×10^2
α-methyl styrene	lc = 26, 54					
	lc = 26.3, 4a					
	lc = 24.8, 64	19-1c	7.4	1.7	3.6	
Tetrahydrofuran	ls = ≈18, 65	24.8	8.4	1.0	2.2	4.1×10
Sulfur	ls = −4.63, 133	18	5.3	0.0	1.4	1.0×10
			−3.17	−1.8		4.8×10^{-2}
Selenium	cs = −5.47, 133		−2.27	−1.5		8.0×10^{-2}
Cyclopropane		16.5	27.0		22.1	
Cyclobutane		13.2	25.1		21.5	
Cyclopentane		10.2	5.2		2.2	
Cyclohexane		−2.5	−0.7		−1.4	
Cyclooctane		−8.9	8.3		11.0	

[a] The symbol c' represents the partly crystalline state of the polymer.
[b] Calculated values.
[c] Liquid-state hypothetical above critical temperature; value derived by extrapolation for comparative purposes.

ΔG_{lc} at 25°C and unit monomer concentration, and the equilibrium constants. Some hypothetical (or as yet unachieved) polymerizations of significance have also been included for comparison.

In a comparison of the available data on the heats and entropies of polymerization of ethylenic monomers (Tables 8-2 and 8-3) it is observed that the $-\Delta H_{lc}$ values vary over a much wider range than do the $-\Delta S_{lc}$ values. Thus, the range of variation of $-\Delta H_{lc}$ is from 8.4 kcal/mole for α-methyl styrene to 22.9 kcal/mole for vinyl chloride and, still higher, to more than 30 kcal for the fluorocarbons and certain other monomers with strained rings and high-order unsaturation. On the other hand, the observed entropies vary within the narrow range† of 25 to 30 cal deg^{-1} mole^{-1}, neglecting the rather abnormally high value of 34 eu for methacrylonitrile (in solution), which needs confirmation. The entropy contribution to the Gibbs energy change at 25°C will therefore vary only within 7.4 to 9.0 kcal/mole. Structural influences on ΔG_{lc} thus operate mainly through the enthalpy term.

The relative constancy of the $-\Delta S_{lc}$ values has been analyzed by Dainton and Ivin (4a) for a few hydrocarbon systems in terms of the component monomer and polymer entropies, the contributions of translation, rotation, and vibration in monomer molecule and polymer segment being considered separately. The analysis of ΔS_{gg}° for ethylene, isobutylene, and styrene (see 4a, Table 6) in terms of the contributions made by various motions shows that the net entropy change due to polymerization stems chiefly from the loss of translational entropy (36 to 40 eu), the contribution of other motions (about 16 to 47 eu) remaining essentially unaltered in the polymer, although modes of rotation and vibration are slightly changed. On polymerization the loss of rotational entropy nearly balances the gain in vibrational and internal rotational entropy, so that $-\Delta S_{gg}^{\circ}$ has a value quite close to the monomer's translational entropy, and this is fairly insensitive to the molecular weight or structure of the monomer. The steric hindrance in the polymer, which markedly affects ΔH_{lc}, has comparatively little effect on the entropy of polymerization; a maximum of about 7 eu is shown in the typical case of isobutylene, which contributes only about 2 kcal/mole in the $-\Delta G_{lc}$ which is affected mainly by the low ΔH_{lc}. The loss of internal rotational entropy as a result of steric hindrance in this polymer and other 1,1 disubstituted ethylenes, such as methyl methacrylate, appears to be essentially outweighed by the gain in internal vibrational entropy, and the net entropy remains normal within the range 25 to 30 eu. The Gibbs energies and the

---

† We have observed that the variation of the polymerization entropy between 25 and 30 eu bears some relationship to the molar volume change of polymerization and may be *empirically* fitted to a linear relationship, approximately given by the equation $\Delta S_{xy} = 25 + \frac{1}{2}R \ln v_1/v_2$, where v_1 and v_2 are the unit volumes of monomer and polymer, respectively.

equilibrium constants (columns 5, 6, 7 of Table 8-3) are thus predominantly guided by the enthalpy of polymerization.

The theory of equilibrium polymerization has been extended by Tobolsky and Eisenberg (135), who showed that in certain cases, such as those of sulfur requiring no initiation and α-methyl styrene initiated by organo-metallics, in which the polymer is in equilibrium with its monomer at all temperatures, the transition (not restricted to a particular temperature region such as the ceiling temperature) is unusually sharp and can be expressed precisely in exact mathematical expressions for the degree of polymerization, size distribution, and equilibrium monomer concentration. Sulfur and selenium (133) present interesting instances of "inverted" ceiling-temperature ("floor" temperature) phenomena by the unusual endothermic and endoentropic nature of their polymerization. Elemental sulfur in its monomeric form exists essentially as eight-membered rings (S_8), the entropy change from which to an open chain on polymerization is positive, as it is in the case of the cyclooctane (C_8) ring. The enthalpy change is also positive in sulfur polymerization, because of the greater stabilization of the S—S bonds in the ring, due to resonance (136) and bond interactions, than in the open-chain polymer. The Gibbs energy of polymerization for sulfur and selenium passes from a positive to a negative value (due to favorable $T \Delta S$ contribution) as the temperature is raised. The floor temperatures ($\Delta G = 0$) are 159°C for liquid sulfur ($[M] = 3.90$) and 217°C for selenium ($[M] = 1$), below which polymerization is thermodynamically forbidden. It is interesting to note that, although ΔH and ΔS are positive, the volume change on polymerization ($-\Delta V = 6.15$ ml/mole) is negative, as in a vinyl polymerization.

B. Effect of Pressure on Polymerization Equilibrium

Pressure is potentially as significant a variable as temperature in polymerization reactions. Since polymerization is generally always accompanied by a diminution in volume ($\Delta V < 0$), an increase in pressure causes an increase (numerically) in free energy in favor of polymerization; this is given by the relationship $d(\Delta G)/dP = \Delta V$. An external pressure of 20,000 atm would bring about a Gibbs energy change of about 5 to 10 kcal/mole for a polymerization with a volume contraction of 10 to 20 ml/mole, assuming ΔV does not vary with pressure; this change is quite substantial compared to the magnitudes of the Gibbs energies of the reaction at 1 atm. The ceiling temperature T_c ($\Delta G = 0$) of a polymerizing system is thus raised by an increase in pressure, as also by an increase in monomer concentration, both of which cause a decrease in the numerical value of the entropy. In analogy (118) to a physical aggregation process, such as fusion, the variation in ceiling temperature with pressure is given by the Clapeyron–Clausius equation:

$$d(T_c)/dP = T_c(\Delta V/\Delta H)$$

$$\ln T_c = \ln T_c^\circ + P \,\Delta V/\Delta H \tag{8-5}$$

This relationship has been well established for polymerization in a ceiling-temperature study of α-methyl styrene made by Kilroe and Weale (137), who found a T_c° of 60 to 61°C (at $P = 0$) and a ΔV of -14.7 ml/mole, which are in good agreement with the well-confirmed ceiling temperature of this monomer at 1 atm, found in equilibrium studies, and with the volume contraction found by dilatometric and density measurements. Ivin (118) has calculated the pressure coefficients of $T_c(\Delta V/\Delta H)$ for some monomers and compared them with the melting point T_m. Since the variations of the Gibbs energy of polymerization with pressure and with temperature are in opposite directions, the need to repeat some earlier polymerization work (with high pressure aimed at enhancing the polymerization) with more appropriate conditions of temperature and pressure has been stressed, and the polymerization of certain monomers in the solid state for the purpose of achieving some gain in Gibbs energy through the lowered entropy of the solid monomer has also been suggested.

The equilibrium of nonolefinic monomers, such as aldehydes, ketones, nitriles, and even carbon disulfide, is substantially shifted in favor of poly-merization by the application of high pressure, and some extensive work on these "reluctant" monomers is being pursued at many laboratories (111). High pressure favors polymerization not only thermodynamically but also kinetically. The thermodynamic volume change (ΔV), which is the difference between the volume of activation of propagation and that of depropagation ($\Delta V_p^\ddagger - \Delta V_d^\ddagger$), essentially consists of $\Delta V_p^\ddagger$, of the forward reaction, because in the unimolecular reaction of depropagation a volume change is con-ceivably small, no larger than what would be caused by a 10% increase in bond length in the transition state of a depropagating species. Kinetically, therefore, the volumes of activation for polymerization are of the same order, namely 10 to 20 ml/mole, for vinyl compounds. Weale (111) has thoroughly reviewed the kinetic aspects of the high-pressure polymerization and co-polymerization of several ethylene derivatives and other compounds with a potentiality of yielding novel polymers. The recent interesting work of Walling and Tanner (138) on the radical polymerization of methyl methacryl-ate under pressures as great as 8000 kg/cm² shows that the stereochemistry of addition is influenced by pressure. Higher pressures decrease the amount of syndiotactic sequences significantly from 75 to 62% at 51°C, from which it was concluded that the transition state for syndiotactic addition is slightly larger, by about 5.5 ml/mole, than that for isotactic, in harmony with the fact that the syndiotactic polymer has the lower density.

C. Environmental Influences on Heat of Polymerization and Equilibrium

In Table 8-3 the monomers have been arranged in decreasing orders of "polymerizability" as judged by $-\Delta G_{lc}^{\circ}$ or the equilibrium constant at 25°C. Since the entropy and enthalpy data in most cases have been obtained by standard thermodynamic methods of specific heat and differential combustion, respectively, the calculated Gibbs energies and equilibrium constants are reliable measures of thermodynamic polymerizability. A review of the data of Table 8-2, which have been obtained through various other methods at differing temperatures, in solution, and with different states and phases of the monomer and polymer, however, points up an acute need for either reducing the data to standard state or reobtaining them through precise combustion calorimetry. In the former objective, correction factors arise from the following few variables and environmental conditions of polymerization, such as temperature and pressure. The heat of reaction from monomer to polymer consists mainly of the change in the internal energy due to changes in the bond type but is also associated to a minor extent with the difference in thermal energy (heat content: $H_T^{\circ} - H_0^{\circ} = \int_0^T C_p \, dT$) between monomer and polymer at a certain temperature. Although the internal-energy change remains essentially unaltered with temperature variation, the heat contents of monomer and polymer vary to different extents, depending upon the temperature coefficients of their specific heats. The temperature correction to the apparent heat of polymerization thus arises from the difference in the specific-heat increments or, in principle, from the different temperature–entropy behaviors of monomer and polymer. On an examination of the data on specific heats versus temperatures of some monomer–polymer systems recently studied (131) it is observed that the specific heat of monomer and, therefore, the heat content rise more rapidly with temperature than does that of the polymer. The apparent heat of polymerization, ΔH_{xy}^T, therefore becomes more negative with the higher temperature of measurement. The situation becomes involved if any phase transitions in the monomer, such as fusion, or in the polymer, such as the glass transition T_g, are incipient in the temperature range of ΔH_p measurements. The complete relationship of specific heat to temperature for both monomer and polymer, covering the range, which is usually 200 to 400°K, is required, to reduce most of the present data to standard temperature of 298.15°K. Such specific-heat data on monomer–polymer systems are at present hardly available, except for a few, such as styrene or methyl methacrylate (up to 300°K). Bywater (139) calculated the theoretical variation of ΔH_{lc} of styrene as a function of temperature with the help of the standard heat of polymerization (16.7 kcal/mole) at 25°C and the integrated specific-heat data on the styrene–polystyrene system. The range of temperature analyzed covers T_g, which is about 100°C. The temperature coefficient of ΔH_{lc} below T_g is somewhat large, about 1.4 kcal per 100°C, and above the glass temperature (which is the true "liquid" state of the polymer, implied in the subscript "c" of ΔH_{lc}) it is only about 0.37 kcal per 100°C. The magnitude of glass enthalpy (also dependent on temperature) was estimated to be 0.65 kcal/mole at 20°C, and this must also be taken into account if the ΔH_{lc} has been measured below the glass-transition temperature. In general, only a small correction, about 4 cal per degree, would be necessary for determinations made above T_g; this applies to most of the data obtained by the isothermal vaporization method (42–53) with CCl_4 as the heat exchanger. On the other hand, the data from low-temperature calorimetry with cationic initiators (27,28) and from anionic equilibrium measurements (62–64) appear to be several hundred calories removed from the standard value at 25°C. Some standard values corrected as described above are shown in the last column of Table 8-2 as "selected" values. Since all the data of reaction calorimetry are naturally at almost the standard pressure of 1 atm, and the combustion data are automatically corrected, no pressure correction need be considered. Moreover, the required enthalpy–pressure relationship is hardly ever encountered in the literature.

In reaction calorimetry or the equilibrium study of a monomer it becomes necessary to use a solvent to bring about homogeneity, a workable rate, a complete reaction, the elimination of association effects in polar monomers, etc., or to adjust the starting concentrations and provide an *inert* medium for the attainment of monomer–polymer equilibrium. In such cases the measured enthalpies of polymerization and the equilibrium are both appreciably shifted on account of the heats of solution (mixing) and the interaction parameters (the μ's of polymer solutions). It is necessary to convert the measured monomer equilibrium concentrations to the thermodynamic activities of monomer and polymer in equilibrium. Applying Scott's modification of the standard lattice theory of polymer solutions, Bywater (139) derived the necessary formulae to convert $-\Delta G_{ss}/RT$ to $-\Delta G_{lc}^\circ/RT$ at $[M] = 1$ in terms of the volume fractions of monomer, polymer, and solvent in equilibrium, of the three molar heats of mixing, and of the three interaction parameters of the combinations solvent–monomer, solvent–polymer, and monomer–polymer. He concluded that the derived formulae quantitatively explain the observed differences in the equilibrium concentration of styrene monomer in different solvents and the effects of solvent on the equilibrium polymerization of α-methyl styrene, which necessitate a correction of about 2 eu in all entropies of polymerization previously derived from equilibrium. The influence of solvent on equilibrium, though small (energically not more than 10%) must have a parallel effect on the kinetics, and much of the earlier kinetic data need revision similar to that outlined above.

D. Kinetic Aspects and Interrelation with Equilibrium

One of the oldest classical ideas, that the reaction rate should tend to parallel the equilibrium, is not quite correct as a general proposition, yet it would be a mistake to reject it altogether. In a series of organic reactions involving only a single reaction mechanism there is a distinct tendency of the rate constant to follow monotonically the equilibrium, and in some cases this trend even takes the form of an accurate linear relationship between $\Delta G°$ and $\Delta G^\ddagger$. Several such "extrathermodynamic" relationships, as $\Delta G°$ versus $\Delta G^\ddagger$, $\Delta H°$ versus $\Delta H^\ddagger$, $\Delta H°$ versus $\Delta S°$, and $\Delta H°$ versus $\Delta S^\ddagger$, are valid for closely related organic reactions and have been discussed by Leffler and Grunwald (140) in a recent volume. Many of these refer to the homolytic free-radical reactions, the Diels–Alder reaction, and association and complex formation, which in kinetic features resemble polymerization. The polymerization reaction, as measured kinetically from the over-all rate of polymerization, is a complex reaction involving at least three distinct mechanisms: initiation, propagation, and termination. In most cases the initiation is the slowest and is the rate-controlling step, which is generally endothermic. In a kinetic study, however, initiation can be measured and controlled precisely, independently of polymerization, so that propagation and termination become manifest in such composite parameters as $\delta = k_t^{1/2}/k_p$ or the average lifetime τ of a kinetic chain, representing k_p/k_t, derived from the steady-state and the non steady-state kinetics, respectively. The energetics of the termination step are relatively simple, at least in the free-radical mechanism, in which the interaction between two high-energy propagating radicals is a highly exothermic, rapid process, requiring little or no activation energy. Moreover, the frequency of occurrence of the propagation step compared with that of the termination or initiation step is so immensely large that one mechanism, i.e. propagation, entirely dominates the over-all energetics of the chain reaction. Since the equilibrium is mainly enthalpy-controlled, as stated before, it would be natural to expect a similar trend in the Gibbs energy of activation $\Delta G_p^\ddagger$ for the forward reaction, which again is the difference between $\Delta H^\ddagger$ and $T \Delta S^\ddagger$, expressed in terms of one of the two expressions for the specific rate constant:

$$k_p = PZ \exp(-E/RT) \tag{8-6}$$

$$k_p = \frac{kT}{h} \exp(-\Delta G_p^\ddagger/RT) = \frac{kT}{h} \exp(\Delta S^\ddagger/R) \exp(-\Delta H^\ddagger/RT) \tag{8-7}$$

In the second expression the transmission coefficient, $\varkappa$, is taken to be unity. The first expression follows from collision theory and the second from Eyring's activated-complex formulation with the kinetic parameters $\Delta H^\ddagger$,

$\Delta S^{\ddagger}$, PZ, and E, interrelated (140) approximately by

$$E = \Delta H^{\ddagger} + RT \quad \text{and} \quad \Delta S^{\ddagger} = 4.575 \log_{10}(PZ) - 60.53 \quad (8\text{-}8)$$

The pre-exponential factor (PZ factor, or A of the Arrhenius equation) in Eq. (8-6) for radical propagation generally has a value of about $10^{7 \pm 1}$ and does not vary more widely since the activated state of the polymer radical produced after the monomer addition differs only slightly from the final state, primarily involving a little greater rotational freedom of the added monomer unit in the polymer. The entropy of activation, $\Delta S^{\ddagger}$, thus differs from the entropy of polymerization, ΔS°, by a small amount only, certainly not more than 5 eu/mole. This small difference becomes manifest in the entropy of activation for depropagation, causing in the PZ factor for depropagation a small increase over 10^{13} sec^{-1}, which should be its *normal* value as a unimolecular decomposition or dissociation process. The entropy change ΔS° in polymerization varies between 25 and 30 eu/mole, which corresponds roughly to the same change in $\Delta S^{\ddagger}$, equivalent to a PZ factor of about $10^{7 \pm 1}$ liter mole^{-1} sec^{-1}. Allen and Patrick (141) have taken into consideration the small entropy component $R \ln V_m$ due to molar volume change V_m in polymerization in their calculations of the $\Delta S^{\ddagger}$ variations, which were found to be in agreement with the observed frequency factors for styrene and methyl methacrylate.

The major factor, however, in producing the wide range of rate constants for vinyl monomers is the Arrhenius activation energy E, or $\Delta H^{\ddagger}$. The available kinetic data on absolute rate constants, activation energies, and frequency factors in the propagation step of some ethylenic monomers are summarized in Table 8-4. Most of the driving energy required to open up an ethylenic double bond is supplied by the re-formation of partial bonds in the transition state. The propagation step is depicted in Fig. 8-4, in which the energy differences between various levels are shown by E_1, E_2, E_3, etc.

It may be recognized that E_2 and E_3 are the activation enthalpies, the $\Delta H^{\ddagger}$'s, for propagation and depropagation, respectively, and E_4 is the heat of polymerization, ΔH°. E_1 and $E_1 + \Delta H_p^{\circ}$ are the energies of initial and final states, respectively, of total bond dissociation into the hypothetical highest-energy state of the active propagating species (radical, ion, or coordinate complex + the Π bond in the triplet state). Empirical rules were proposed by Hirschfelder (142) for relating bond dissociation energies and enthalpies of activation. These rules predict that for the exothermic forward reaction of propagation the activation energy E_2 is given by $E_2 = 0.055E_1$ and for the endothermic depropagation process the activation energy E_3 is given by $E_3 = 0.055E_1 - \Delta H_p^{\circ}$.

At present there are no means of checking these predictions with vinyl monomers, for lack of spectroscopic data on the energies of the diradical,

TABLE 8-4

Absolute Rate Constants (at 25°C), Activation Energies, and PZ Factors for Propagation and Termination in Radical Polymerization

Monomer	Propagation			Termination			Ref.
	k_p, liter mole^{-1} sec^{-1}	E_p, kcal mole^{-1}	$PZ \times 10^{-7}$, liter mole^{-1} sec^{-1}	$k_t \times 10^{-7}$, liter mole^{-1} sec^{-1}	E_t, kcal mole^{-1}	$PZ \times 10^{-9}$, liter mole^{-1} sec^{-1}	
Ethylene	470 (83°C)	6		100 (83°C)			156
Styrene	50	6.4	0.45	0.23	1.9	0.06	148
Methyl methacrylate	269	4.7	0.09	1.5	1.2	0.11	148
Vinyl acetate	980	5.0	3.2	2.0	3.2	3.7	148
Vinyl chloride	6200	3.7	0.33	1200	4.2		148
Methyl acrylate	720	7.1	10				148
Vinylidene chloride	8.6			0.02	1.1		148
tert-Butyl methacrylate	350	4.4		1.4			149
Acrylonitrile	1450	4.1	3	200	5.4	3300	150
	52			0.5			157
Acrylamide	18,000			1.45			151
Butadiene	20	9	12				148
Isoprene	10	10	12				148
2-Vinyl pyridine	96	8		0.89	5		32
4-Vinyl pyridine	12						148
Nitroethylene	14,000	≈5					15

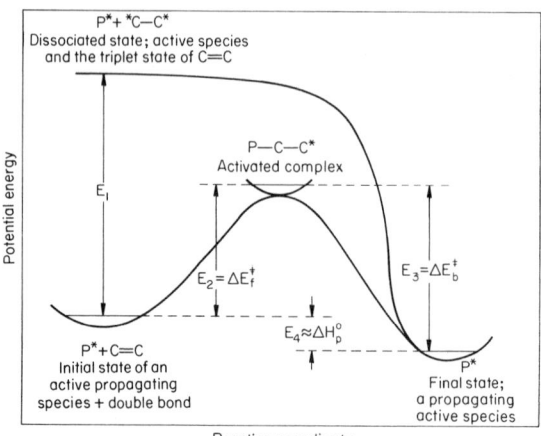

Fig. 8-4.

triplet states and for lack of sufficiently accurate experimental activation energies (E_2) for these processes.

Another important theoretical exposition has been developed by Evans et al. (143) to describe the activation energies of some of the basic kinetic steps in radical polymerization in terms of bond energies and of repulsion energies between reacting centers. In a number of simple prototype reactions involving radicals or atoms and ethylenic bonds it was found that the heat of reaction is a most important factor governing the activation energies of reactions of a wide variety of substituted radicals and monomers. The variations in the heats ($\Delta\Delta H°$) of such radical–molecule reactions were attributable to the resonance energies of the reacting radicals and molecules and to the repulsion energy, the latter being affected by (a) charge distribution on the reacting centers and coulombic interaction and by (b) steric effects, or the non bonding, van der Waals type of repulsive interaction of substituent groups. In an analysis of these factors by molecular-orbital method and other quantum-mechanical techniques approximate potential energy surfaces and contours of attraction and repulsion were drawn in terms of internuclear distances in a model transition state, which assumed that the double-bond distance remained practically unaltered in the transition state on account of its much greater force constant. The heights of intersections of these curves represented the activation energies for a series of vinyl compounds and were altered distinctly by the shapes of the potential-energy curves, which also defined simultaneously the heats of polymerization. Hence, the two quantities E (or $\Delta H^{\ddagger}$) and $\Delta H_p°$ become directly interrelated, but in an inverse manner, so that for a series of similar reactions we have

$$\Delta E^{\ddagger} = \alpha(\Delta\Delta H^{\circ}) = \alpha(R_x + R_m - R_y) \tag{8-9}$$

Thus, the largest amount of heat of polymerization accompanies the lowest activation energy. The factor α has a value less than unity, best judged from the shapes of some of these potential-energy curves to be 0.4, and R_x, R_m, and R_y are the respective resonance energies of the initial radical, the monomer, and the radical formed after addition of the monomer. This is an important and, perhaps, the only well-founded linear relationship between thermodynamic and kinetic enthalpies of polymerization, but it is somewhat limited to resonance-energy considerations.

The linear relationship between $\Delta H^{\ddagger}$ and ΔH°, given above, has been used in a few instances for interpreting the observed marked effect of the polymerization temperature on the tacticity of the polymer in the radical polymerization of vinyl chloride (69), vinyl acetate (144), and methyl methacrylate (145). The two stereochemical modes of addition, the isotactic and the syndiotactic, differ energically by a small magnitude lying between 0.5 and 2 kcal/mole, and their forward rate constants of propagation are given by the equations

$$k_i = \left(\frac{kT}{h}\right) \exp\left[(\Delta S_i^{\ddagger}/R) - (\Delta H_i^{\ddagger}/RT)\right] \tag{8-10}$$

$$k_s = \left(\frac{kT}{h}\right) \exp\left[(\Delta S_s^{\ddagger}/R) - (\Delta H_s^{\ddagger}/RT)\right] \tag{8-11}$$

Similar equations with the thermodynamic quantities ΔH_i°, ΔH_s°, ΔS_i°, etc. hold for the two propagation equilibria, the subscripts "i" and "s" denoting the thermodynamic and kinetic quantities for isotactic and syndiotactic propagation, respectively. The length of a particular sequence of units in a polymer chain (and, hence, the mole fraction or percentage tacticity) depends upon the relative probabilities of occurrence of these two kinetic steps. The parameter σ, first defined clearly by Bovey and Tiers (145) as a measure of microscopic tacticity, represents the probability that a polymer chain will add a monomer unit to give the same configuration as that of the last unit at its growing end; it is given by

$$\sigma = k_i/(k_i + k_s) \tag{8-12}$$

The quantity σ is experimentally measurable for polymers through nuclear magnetic resonance spectroscopy, as it is for methyl methacrylate with α-methyl hydrogens, through quantitative x-ray analysis of the crystallinity, as it is in the case of vinyl chloride, and through chemical analysis of polymers, as it is for vinyl acetate. It varies significantly with the temperature of polymerization. By plotting $\sigma/(1 - \sigma)$, which is equal to k_i/k_s, against the reciprocal temperature the difference between $\Delta\Delta H^{\ddagger}$ and $\Delta\Delta S^{\ddagger}$ of the activation enthalpies and entropies in respect of the two kinetic modes of addition can be obtained in the usual manner. It was shown by Bovey (146) in a nuclear magnetic resonance analysis of polymethyl methacrylates made at four different temperatures in the range -78 to $100°$C that the $\Delta\Delta H^{\ddagger}$ was 0.78 ± 0.08 kcal/mole and the $\Delta\Delta S^{\ddagger}$ was 0.0 ± 0.1 eu/mole. The stereospecificity of radical polymerization is thus essentially enthalpy-controlled, the lower temperatures favoring syndiotacticity. It would be interesting to inquire further whether any correspondence really exists between such kinetic $\Delta\Delta H^{\ddagger}$ and the $\Delta\Delta H°$, that is, the differences in the heats of polymerization. The latter quantity is clearly the difference between the heats of formation of the isotactic and syndiotactic polymers, obtainable experimentally from measurements of the heats of combustion as also from calculations of the energy difference of the rotational isomerism (rotational barriers) in small, model compounds resembling a polymer segment. No data exist at present on the heats of combustion of such stereopolymers of methyl methacrylate or of any other such polymer.† Using Eq. (8-9) with $\alpha = 0.4$ and the above-given value of $\Delta\Delta H^{\ddagger}$, one may expect a thermodynamic energy difference of about 1.9 ± 0.2 kcal/mole between the heats of formation of the two stereopolymers of methyl methacrylate.

Fordham et al. (144) calculated the potential-energy difference between isotactic and syndiotactic polyvinylchlorides as about 1.4 to 1.9 kcal/mole, considering both steric and electrostatic factors in the most probable conformational arrangements of the two isomeric segments, and showed that the actual activation-energy difference between isotactic and syndiotactic propagation, obtained from the Arrhenius plot of the infrared absorption ratio of the two polymers, was about 0.6 kcal/mole. This would give a reasonably agreeing value of about 0.4 for α in Eq. (8-9). The temperature dependence of the stereospecific radical propagation for vinyl chloride has been confirmed in a recent similar work (147) based on the infrared absorbance of polymer, which gave an activation-energy difference of the same order, 0.3 to 0.74 kcal/mole. In a comparison of kinetic parameters involving primarily the propagation step, such as $1/\delta = k_p/k_t^{1/2}$ or the copolymerization parameter $r_1 = k_{11}/k_{12}$, of a series of methacrylic esters and their respective heats of polymerization a close parallelism between k_p and $\Delta H_{lc}°$ was observed (52).

The kinetics of anionic polymerization initiated with metal alkyls and without a termination step has been the subject of a large amount of study in recent years, and an excellent review (152) has just appeared. The capillary fast-flow technique (153) is a noteworthy development in the investigation

† The most recent data on polystyrenes may be found in (164).

of specific rate constants in the anionic polymerization of substituted styrenes and a few other monomers polymerizable anionically. The propagation constant k_p (at 25°C) varies from 2.5 to 7300 liter mole^{-1} sec^{-1} for different monomers in the same range (152) as the radical reaction, and both the entropy of activation and the energy of activation have been shown to be low (more negative); in particular, the entropy of activation for styrene polymerization was lower by about 14 eu than in the free-radical polymerization. In further contrast, such external factors as the dielectric constant of the medium and the nature of the metal counterion appear to be very dominant in the anionic polymerization, more so than the structural variations of the monomer. The penultimate unit of the growing end also seems to influence (154) the velocity coefficients of anionic propagation. The kinetics of anionic polymerization with alkali metals and of the very similar Ziegler–Natta catalysis (155) with organometallic complexes are still in a stage of development, the extent of which is limited to only a few monomers, mostly hydrocarbons, and very meager data are available on the absolute activation energies and entropies of propagation. In these heterolytic polymerizations the equilibrium and kinetics may not show any mutual correspondence, because of the very specific and individual nature of the transition state with partial metal–carbon bonds (158) of the counterion, and the entropy factor may have an equally significant role in these polymerizations.

ACKNOWLEDGMENTS

This work was supported through The Robert A. Welch Foundation, Houston, Texas. One of the authors (R.M.J.) wishes to express his thanks to the Thermodynamics Research Center for use of its facilities.

REFERENCES

1. G. Natta, *Science*, **147**, 261 (1965); C. E. H. Bawn and A. Ledwith, *Quart. Rev. (London)*, **16**, 361 (1962); J. Furukawa and T. Saegusa, *Polymerization of Aldehydes and Oxides*, Wiley, New York, 1963.
2. (a) Kargin et al., *Dokl. Akad. Nauk SSSR*, **134**, 1098 (1960); **139**, 605 (1961); *CA*, **54**, 6280b (1960); **55**, 8282h (1961);
   (b) J. Furukawa et al., *Makromolekul. Chem.*, **52**, 230 (1962); W. Kawai, *Bull. Chem. Soc. Japan*, **35**, 516 (1962);
   (c) P. Kovacic, *J. Polymer Sci.*, **A2**, 1193 (1964); *Tetrahedron Letters*, **1962**, 467;
   (d) E. Whalley, *Can. J. Chem.*, **38**, 2105 (1960).
3. W. M. D. Bryant, *J. Polymer Sci.*, **A2**, 4643 (1964).
4. (a) F. S. Dainton and K. J. Ivin, *Quart. Rev. (London)*, **12**, 61 (1958);
   (b) F. S. Dainton et al., *Trans. Faraday Soc.*, **51**, 1710 (1955);
   (c) F. S. Dainton and K. J. Ivin in *Experimental Thermochemistry*, Vol. II (H. A. Skinner, ed.), Wiley (Interscience), New York, 1962, Chap. 12.
5. (a) H. A. Skinner and G. Pilcher, *Quart. Rev. (London)*, **17**, 264 (1963); *Trans. Faraday Soc.*, **61**, 75 (1965);

(*b*) G. R. Somayajula, A. P. Kudchadker, and B. J. Zwolinski, *Ann. Rev. Phys. Chem.*, **16**, 213 (1965).

6. J. D. Cox, *Tetrahedron*, **18**, 1337 (1962); **19**, 1175 (1963).
7. H. A. Skinner, *Ann. Rev. Phys. Chem.*, **15**, 449 (1964).
8. S. W. Benson and J. H. Buss, *J. Chem. Phys.*, **29**, 546 (1958).
9. A. G. Evans and M. Polanyi, *Nature*, **152**, 738 (1943).
10. P. J. Flory, *Principles of Polymer Chemistry*, Cornell Univ. Press, Ithaca, N.Y., 1953, pp. 246–256.
11. D. E. Roberts, *J. Res. Natl. Bur. Std.*, **44**, 221 (1950).
12. G. Goldfinger, D. Josefowitz, and H. Mark, *J. Am. Chem. Soc.*, **65**, 1432 (1943).
13. M. F. Shostakowski and I. F. Bogdanov, see Ref. *11*.
14. A. G. Evans and E. Tyrrall, *J. Polymer Sci.*, **2**, 387 (1947).
15. J. Grodzinski, A. Katchalski, and D. Vofsi, *Makromolekul Chem.*, **44–46**, 594 (1961).
16. S. M. Skuratov and co-workers, *CA*, **46**, 8506c (1952); *Kolloidn. Zh.*, **14**, 185 (1952).
17. E. G. Lovering and K. J. Laidler, *Can. J. Chem.*, **40**, 26 (1962).
18. K. G. McCurdy and K. J. Laidler, *Can. J. Chem.*, **41**, 1867 (1963); **42**, 818 (1964).
19. J. M. Corkill, J. F. Goodman, and J. R. Tate, *Trans. Faraday Soc.*, **60**, 996 (1964).
20. B. Ke, ed., *Newer Methods of Polymer Characterization, Polymer Reviews No. 6*, Wiley (Interscience), New York, 1964, Chap. IX.
21. B. H. Clampitt, D. E. German, and J. R. Galli, *J. Polymer Sci.*, **27**, 515 (1958).
22. C. H. Klute and W. Viehmann, *CA*, **55**, 15988c (1961); **55**, 26507f (1961).
23. M. L. Bhaumik, A. K. Sircar, and D. Banerjee, *J. Appl. Polymer Sci.*, **4**, 366 (1960).
24. L. Hock and G. Schröter, *Kolloid-Z.*, **152**, 98 (1957).
25. B. Ke, *J. Polymer Sci.*, **42**, 15 (1960).
26. Perkin-Elmer Corporation, *Bulletin DSC-1* (1965).
27. R. H. Biddulph and P. H. Plesch, *Chem. & Ind.* (*London*), **1959**, 1482.
28. R. H. Biddulph, W. R. Longworth, J. Penfold, and P. H. Plesch, *Polymer*, **1**, 521 (1960).
29. W. I. Bengough and H. W. Melville, *Proc. Roy. Soc.* (*London*), **A225**, 330 (1954).
30. W. I. Bengough, *Trans. Faraday Soc.*, **54**, 54 (1958).
31. W. I. Bengough, *Trans. Faraday Soc.*, **54**, 1560 (1958).
32. W. I. Bengough and W. Henderson, *Trans. Faraday Soc.*, **61**, 141 (1965).
33. H. Miyama, *Bull. Chem. Soc. Japan*, **29**, 711 (1956); M. Suzuki, H. Miyama, and S. Fujimoto, *J. Polymer Sci.*, **31**, 212 (1958).
34. F. S. Dainton, J. Diaper, K. J. Ivin, and D. R. Sheard, *Trans. Faraday Soc.*, **53**, 1269 (1957).
35. F. S. Dainton, K. J. Ivin, and D. A. G. Walmsley, *Trans. Faraday Soc.*, **56**, 1784 (1960).
36. P. A. Giguere, B. G. Morissette, and A. W. Olmos, *Can. J. Chem.*, **33**, 657 (1955).
37. R. S. Jessup, *J. Res. Natl. Bur. Std.*, **55**, 317 (1955).
38. W. S. Tamplin, *Anal. Chem.*, **24**, 941 (1952).
39. L. K. J. Tong and W. O. Kenyon, *J. Am. Chem. Soc.*, **67**, 1278 (1945).
40. J. H. Mathews, *J. Am. Chem. Soc.*, **48**, 565 (1926); **53**, 3212 (1931).
41. A. A. Korotkov and E. N. Marandzheva, *Russ. J. Phys. Chem. English Transl.*, **37**, 135 (1963); *CA*, **58**, 14264a (1963).
42. L. K. J. Tong and W. O. Kenyon, *J. Am. Chem. Soc.*, **68**, 1355 (1946).
43. L. K. J. Tong and W. O. Kenyon, *J. Am. Chem. Soc.*, **69**, 1402 (1947).
44. L. K. J. Tong and W. O. Kenyon, *J. Am. Chem. Soc.*, **69**, 2245 (1947).
45. L. K. J. Tong and W. O. Kenyon, *J. Am. Chem. Soc.*, **71**, 1925 (1949).
46. S. O. Eckegren, K. Ohrn, K. Granath, and P. O. Kinell, *Acta Chem. Scand.*, **4**, 126 (1950).
47. R. M. Joshi, *J. Polymer Sci.*, **56**, 313 (1962).
48. R. M. Joshi, *J. Polymer Sci.*, **60**, S56 (1962).
49. R. M. Joshi, *Makromolekul. Chem.*, **53**, 33 (1962).

50. R. M. Joshi, *Makromolekul. Chem.*, **55**, 35 (1962).

51. R. M. Joshi, *Makromolekul. Chem.*, **62**, 140 (1963).

52. R. M. Joshi, *Makromolekul. Chem.*, **66**, 114 (1963).

53. R. M. Joshi, *Indian J. Chem.*, **2**, 125 (1964).

54. F. S. Dainton and K. J. Ivin, *Trans. Faraday Soc.*, **46**, 331 (1950).

55. F. S. Dainton, K. J. Ivin, and D. A. G. Walmsley, *Trans. Faraday Soc.*, **55**, 61 (1959).

56. G. S. Parks and H. P. Mosher, *J. Polymer Sci.*, **A1**, 1979 (1963).

57. S. Bywater, *Trans. Faraday Soc.*, **51**, 1267 (1955).

58. K. J. Ivin, *Trans. Faraday Soc.*, **51**, 1273 (1955).

59. S. Bywater, *Can. J. Chem.*, **35**, 552 (1957).

60. R. E. Cook and K. J. Ivin, *Trans. Faraday Soc.*, **53**, 1132 (1957).

61. R. E. Cook, F. S. Dainton, and K. J. Ivin, *J. Polymer Sci.*, **26**, 351 (1957).

62. R. E. Cook, F. S. Dainton, and K. J. Ivin, *J. Polymer Sci.*, **29**, 549 (1958).

63. M. Szwarc, M. Levy, and R. Milkovich, *J. Am. Chem. Soc.*, **78**, 2656 (1956).

64. (*a*) H. W. McCormick, *J. Polymer Sci.*, **25**, 488 (1957);
    (*b*) D. J. Worsfold and S. Bywater, *J. Polymer Sci.*, **26**, 299 (1957).

65. C. E. H. Bawn, R. M. Bell, and A. Ledwith, *Polymer*, **6**, 95 (1965).

66. D. Sims, *J. Chem. Soc.*, **1964**, 864.

67. S. Bywater and D. J. Worsfold, *J. Polymer Sci.*, **58**, 571 (1962).

68. L. A. Wall, *SPE J.*, **16**, 810 (1960).

69. J. W. L. Fordham, *J. Polymer Sci.*, **39**, 321 (1959).

70. C. E. H. Bawn, W. A. Janes, and A. M. North, *J. Polymer Sci.*, **C1**, 427 (1963).

71. F. E. Karasz and J. M. O'Reilly, *Abstract of ACS Meeting-148*, (1964); *Bull. Am. Phys. Soc.*, **10**(3), 327 (1965).

72. H. A. Skinner, *Roy. Inst. Chem.* (*London*), *Lectures, Monographs, Rept.*, **1958**(3).

73. *Thermodynamics and Thermochemistry*, Plenary Lectures, Lund, Sweden, IUCAP, Butterworth, London, 1964.

74. *Experimental Thermochemistry*, Vol. II (H. A. Skinner, ed.), Wiley (Interscience), New York, 1962.
    (*a*) W. N. Hubbard, *ibid.*, Chap. VI;
    (*b*) G. T. Armstrong, *ibid.*, Chap. VII;
    (*c*) H. A. Skinner, *ibid.*, Chaps. VIII, IX;
    (*d*) F. S. Dainton and K. J. Ivin, *ibid.*, Chap. XII;
    (*e*) E. Calvet, *ibid.*, Chap. XVII.

75. C. A. Neugebauer and J. L. Margrave, *J. Phys. Chem.*, **60**, 1318 (1956).

76. H. Mackle and P. A. G. O'Hare, *Trans. Faraday Soc.*, **59**, 2693 (1963).

77. A. J. Williams and G. C. Mergner, *Instr. Soc. Am. Conf. Preprint, 12, 19th Ann. ISA*, (1964); also Leeds & Northrup Cat. 8071.

78. G. Pilcher and L. E. Sutton, *Phil. Trans. Roy. Soc. London*, **A248**, 23 (1955).

79. R. S. Jessup, *Natl. Bur. Std. U.S. Monograph*, **7** (1960).

80. W. D. Good, Bureau of Mines, Bartlesville, Okla., private communication, 1965.

81. N. Grassie, *J. Polymer Sci.*, **6**, 643 (1951).

82. R. S. Jessup, *J. Chem. Phys.*, **16**, 661 (1948).

83. G. S. Parks and J. R. Mosley, *J. Chem. Phys.*, **17**, 691 (1949).

84. C. M. Fontana and G. A. Kidder, *J. Am. Chem. Soc.*, **70**, 3745 (1948).

85. G. C. Sinke and D. R. Stull, *J. Phys. Chem.*, **62**, 397 (1958).

86. (*a*) W. D. Good, J. L. Lacina, B. L. DePrater, and J. P. McCullough, *J. Phys. Chem.*, **68**, 579 (1964);
    (*b*) V. P. Kolesov, A. M. Martynov, S. M. Shtekher, and S. M. Skuratov, *Russ. J. Phys. Chem., English Transl.*, **36**, 1118 (1962); *CA*, **58**, 2909e (1963).

87. D. W. Scott, W. D. Good, and G. Waddington, *J. Am. Chem. Soc.*, **77**, 245 (1955).

88. R. A. Nelson, R. S. Jessup, and D. E. Roberts, *J. Res. Natl. Bur. Std.*, **48**, 275 (1952).

89. R. S. Jessup and A. D. Cummings, *J. Res. Natl. Bur. Std.*, **13**, 357 (1934); **20**, 589 (1938).

90. D. Vofsi, the Weizmann Institute of Science, Israel, private communication, 1965.

91. D. E. Roberts, W. W. Walton, and R. S. Jessup, *J. Res. Natl. Bur. Std.*, **38**, 627 (1947).

92. D. E. Roberts and R. S. Jessup, *J. Res. Natl. Bur. Std.*, **46**, 11 (1951).

93. J. H. Baxendale and G. W. Madaras, *J. Polymer Sci.*, **19**, 171 (1956).

94. J. B. Rose, *J. Chem. Soc.*, **1956**, 546.

95. K. J. Ivin, W. A. Keith, and H. Mackle, *Trans. Faraday Soc.*, **55**, 262 (1959).

96. R. J. Orr, *Polymer*, **4**, 187 (1963).

97. M. L. H. Green, M. Nehme, and G. Wilkinson, *Chem. & Ind. (London)*, **1960**, 1135; C. E. H. Bawn, B. E. Lee, and A. M. North, *J. Polymer Sci.*, **B2**, 263 (1963); R. J. Fredericks, D. G. Lynch, and W. E. Daniels, *ibid.*, **2**, 803 (1963).

98. L. B. Luttinger, *Chem. & Ind. (London)*, **1960**, 1135; *J. Org. Chem.*, **27**, 1951, 3752 (1962).

99. W. R. Baker, Jr., *J. Polymer Sci.* **A1**, 655 (1963).

100. C. T. Mortimer, *Reaction Heats and Bond Strengths*, Pergamon, London, 1962.

101. T. L. Flitcroft and H. A. Skinner, *Trans. Faraday Soc.*, **54**, 47 (1958).

102. L. L. Ferstandig, *J. Am. Chem. Soc.*, **84**, 1323, 3553 (1962).

103. A. G. Evans and M. Polanyi, *J. Chem. Soc.*, **1947**, 252.

104. L. L. Ferstandig and F. C. Goodrich, *J. Polymer Sci.*, **43**, 373 (1960).

105. E. A. Mason, *J. Chem. Phys.*, **22**, 169 (1954); *J. Am. Chem. Soc.*, **77**, 5808 (1955).

106. W. G. Barb, *J. Polymer Sci.*, **11**, 117 (1953); G. E. Ham, ed., *Copolymerization, High Polymers*, Vol. XVIII, Wiley (Interscience), New York, 1964, Chap. I.

107. A. J. Canale, W. E. Goode, J. R. Panchak, R. L. Kelso, and R. K. Graham, *J. Appl. Polymer Sci.*, **4**, 231 (1960).

108. C. E. Schildknecht, *Vinyl and Related Polymers*, Wiley, New York, 1952.

109. T. Alfrey, Jr., J. J. Bohrer, and H. Mark, *Copolymerization*, Wiley (Interscience), New York, 1952.

110. R. H. Wiley and D. J. Parish, *J. Polymer Sci.*, **45**, 503 (1960).

111. K. E. Weale, *Quart. Rev. (London)*, **16**, 267 (1962).

112. J. H. Futrell, *CA*, **53**, 1930 (1959).

113. G. Natta, M. Farina, M. Peraldo, and G. Bressan, *Makromolekul. Chem.*, **55**, 139 (1962).

114. O. C. Bochman and C. Schuerch, *J. Polymer Sci.*, **B1**, 145 (1963).

115. A. V. Topchiev, V. P. Aliniya, and Z. A. Makarova, *Dokl. Akad. Nauk SSSR*, **131**, 1359 (1960); *CA*, **54**, 20839a (1960).

116. M. L. Miller and J. Skogman, *J. Polymer Sci.*, **A2**, 4551 (1964).

117. G. Natta, *Science*, **147**, 261 (1965).

118. K. J. Ivin, *Makromolecular Chemistry*, Butterworth, London, 1962, p. 271.

119. H. C. Brown and co-workers, *J. Am. Chem. Soc.*, **73**, 212 (1951); **74**, 1896 (1952); **76**, 467 (1954).

120. C. Schuerch, *Ann. Rev. Phys. Chem.*, **13**, 195 (1962).

121. K. B. Wiberg and W. J. Bartley, *J. Am. Chem. Soc.*, **84**, 3980 (1962).

122. F. S. Dainton, T. R. E. Delvin, and P. A. Small, *Trans. Faraday Soc.*, **51**, 1710 (1955); P. A. Small, *ibid.*, **51**, 1717 (1953).

123. G. C. Pimentel and A. L. McClellan, *The Hydrogen Bond*, Reinhold, New York, 1960.

124. T. Ukaji, *Bull. Chem. Soc. Japan*, **32**, 1266 (1959).

125. T. C. Schwan and C. C. Price, *J. Polymer Sci.*, **40**, 457 (1959).

126. T. Alfrey and C. Lewis, *J. Polymer Sci.*, **4**, 221 (1949).

127. R. J. Orr, *Polymer*, **2**, 74 (1961).

128. H. Sawada, *J. Polymer Sci.*, **A2**, 3095 (1964).

129. R. E. Naylor and S. W. Lasoski, *J. Polymer Sci.*, **44**, 1 (1960); C. W. Wilson, *ibid.*, **A1**, 1305 (1963).
130. C. Walling, *Free Radicals in Solution*, Wiley, New York, 1957.
131. F. S. Dainton and collaborators, *Polymer*, **3**, 263 (1962).
132. R. W. Warfield and M. C. Petree, *J. Polymer Sci.*, **55**, 497 (1961).
133. A. Eisenberg and A. V. Tobolsky, *J. Polymer Sci.*, **46**, 19 (1960).
134. G. J. Janz, *Estimation of Thermodynamic Properties of Organic Compounds*, Academic, New York, 1958.
135. A. V. Tobolsky and A. Eisenberg, *J. Colloid Sci.*, **17**, 49 (1962).
136. G. Gee, *Trans. Faraday Soc.*, **48**, 515 (1952).
137. J. G. Kilroe and K. E. Weale, *J. Chem. Soc.*, **1960**, 3849.
138. C. Walling and D. D. Tanner, *J. Polymer Sci.* **A1**, 2271 (1963).
139. S. Bywater, *Makromolekul. Chem.*, **52**, 120 (1962).
140. J. E. Leffler and E. Grunwald, *Rates and Equilibria of Organic Reactions*, Wiley, New York, 1963.
141. P. E. M. Allen and C. R. Patrick, *Makromolekul. Chem.*, **39**, 246 (1960).
142. J. Hirschfelder, *J. Chem. Phys.*, **9**, 645 (1941).
143. M. G. Evans, J. Gergely, and E. C. Seaman, *J. Polymer Sci.*, **3**, 866 (1948).
144. J. W. L. Fordham, D. H. Burleigh, and C. L. Strum, *J. Polymer Sci.*, **39**, 335 (1959); **41**, 73 (1959).
145. F. A. Bovey and G. V. D. Tiers, *J. Polymer Sci.*, **44**, 173 (1960).
146. F. A. Bovey, *J. Polymer Sci.*, **46**, 59 (1960).
147. M. Takeda and K. Imura, *J. Polymer Sci.*, **57**, 383 (1962).
148. (a) C. Walling, *Free Radicals in Solution*, Wiley, New York, 1957, p. 95;
     (b) H. W. Melville and G. M. Burnett, *J. Polymer Sci.*, **13**, 417 (1954).
149. D. H. Grant and N. Grassie, *Trans. Faraday Soc.*, **55**, 1042 (1959).
150. F. S. Dainton and D. G. L. James, *J. Polymer Sci.*, **39**, 299 (1959); F. S. Dainton and R. S. Eaton, *ibid.*, **39**, 313 (1959).
151. F. S. Dainton and M. Tordorff, *Trans. Faraday Soc.*, **53**, 499 (1957).
152. M. Szwarc and J. Smid, *Progress in Reaction Kinetics*, Vol. II (G. Porter, ed.), Pergamon, London, 1964.
153. G. Geacintov, J. Smid, and M. Szwarc, *J. Am. Chem. Soc.*, **84**, 2508 (1962).
154. C. L. Lee, J. Smid, and M. Szwarc, *J. Am. Chem. Soc.*, **85**, 912 (1963).
155. G. Natta, G. Mazzanti, A. Valvassori, G. Sartory, and A. Barbagallo, *J. Polymer Sci.*, **58**, 843 (1962).
156. Z. Laita and Z. Machacek, *J. Polymer Sci.*, **38**, 459 (1959).
157. W. I. Bengough, *Proc. Roy. Soc.* (*London*), **A260**, 205 (1961).
158. R. J. Orr, *J. Polymer Sci.*, **58**, 843 (1962).
159. (a) F. D. Rossini, D. D. Wagman, W. H. Evans, S. Levine, and I. Jaffe, *Natl. Bur. Std. U.S. Circ.*, **500**, (1952);
     (b) R. R. Dreisbach, *Physical Properties of Chemical Compounds, Advances in Chemistry Series 15*, American Chemical Society, Washington, D.C., 1955; 22, 1959; 29, 1961.
160. Commercial literature and data sheets from Manufacturing Chemists' Association.
161. W. S. Holmes, *Trans. Faraday Soc.*, **58**, 1916 (1962).
162. R. C. Wilhoit and D. Shiao, *J. Chem. Eng. Data*, **9**, 595 (1964); [ΔH(fusion) = 3.3 kcal/mole] (*160*).
163. J. H. S. Green, *Quart. Rev.* (*London*), **15**, 125 (1962).
164. R. M. Joshi and B. J. Zwolinski, Paper (V-166) presented at the *152nd National Meeting of the American Chemical Society*, New York, Sept. 1966; see Abstracts.

Author Index

Numbers in parentheses are reference numbers and indicate that an author's work is referred to although his name is not cited in the text. Numbers in italics give the page on which the complete reference is listed.

A

Subject Index